PLANTS AND ISLANDS

Plants and Islands

Edited by

D. BRAMWELL

Jardín Botánico, "Viera y Clavijo"
del Excmo. Cabildo Insular de Gran Canaria

ACADEMIC PRESS · 1979
A Subsidiary of Harcourt Brace Jovanovich, Publishers
London · New York · Toronto · Sydney · San Francisco

ACADEMIC PRESS INC. (LONDON) LTD
24/28 Oval Road
London NW1 7DX

United States Edition published by
ACADEMIC PRESS INC.
111 Fifth Avenue
New York, New York 10003

British Library Cataloguing in Publication Data

Plants and Islands (*Conference*),
Las Palmas de Gran Canaria, 1977
Plants and islands.
1. Island flora—Congresses
I. Title II. Bramwell, David
581.9′1   QK101   79–50299
ISBN 0–12–125460–7

Printed in Great Britain by Willmer Brothers Ltd., Birkenhead, Merseyside

LIST OF CONTRIBUTORS

ANGELA E. ALDRIDGE Jardín Botánico "Viera y Clavijo", Aptdo. 14, Tafira Alta, Las Palmas de Gran Canaria, Canary Islands, Spain

LIV BORGEN Botanical Garden and Museum, University of Oslo, Oslo 5, Norway

D. BRAMWELL Jardín Botánico "Viera y Clavijo", Aptdo. 14, Tafira Alta, Las Palmas de Gran Canaria, Canary Islands, Spain

M. A. CARDONA Departamento de Botánica, Facultad de Biología, Universidad de Barcelona, Barcelona, Spain

J. CONTANDRIOPOULOS Université de Provence, Centre de St. Charles, Cytotaxinomie végétale, 13331 Marseille Cedex 3, France

F. EHRENDORFER Botanisches Institut und Botanischer Garten der Universität Wien, Rennweg 14, A-1030 Wien, Austria

D. J. GALLOWAY Botany Division, DSIR, Private Bag, Christchurch, New Zealand

MARY GIBBY Department of Botany, The British Museum (Natural History), Cromwell Road, London SW7 5BD, England

P. S. GREEN Royal Botanic Gardens, Kew, Richmond, Surrey TW9 3AE, England

WERNER GREUTER Botanischer Garten und Botanisches Museum, Berlin-Dahlem, 1000 Berlin 33, Königin-Luise Strasse 6–8, Germany

MICHEL GUÉDÈS Laboratoire de Phytomorphologie (E.P.H.E.), Muséum d'Histoire Naturelle (Phanérogamie), Rue Buffon, Paris V, France

V. H. HEYWOOD Department of Botany, Plant Science Laboratories, The University of Reading, Whiteknights, Reading RG6 2AS, England

C. J. HUMPHRIES Department of Botany, The British Museum (Natural History), Cromwell Road, London SW7 5BD, England

G. Ll. LUCAS Royal Botanic Gardens, Kew, Richmond, Surrey TW9 3AE, England

D. J. MABBERLEY Wadham College, Oxford OX1 3PN, England

R. MELVILLE   Royal Botanic Gardens, Kew, Richmond, Surrey TW9 3AE, England

D. M. MOORE   Department of Botany, Plant Science Laboratories, The University of Reading, Whiteknights, Reading RG6 2AS, England

DUNCAN M. PORTER   Department of Biology, Virginia Polytechnic Institute and State University, Blacksburg, Virginia 24061, U.S.A.

WERNER RAUH   Institut für Systematische Botanik und Pflanzengeographie, 6900 Heidelberg, Im Neuenheimer Feld 280, Germany

S. A. RENVOIZE   Royal Botanic Gardens, Kew, Richmond, Surrey TW9 3AE, England

PER SUNDING   Botanical Garden and Museum, University of Oslo, Trondheimsveien 25B, Oslo 5, Norway

A. H. M. SYNGE IUCN Threatened Plants Committee, c/o The Herbarium, Royal Botanic Gardens, Kew, Richmond, Surrey, England

ROLLA TRYON   Gray Herbarium, Harvard University, 22 Divinity Avenue, Cambridge, Massachusetts 02138, U.S.A.

H. VAN DER WERFF   Institut voor Systematische Plantkunde, Rijksuniversiteit Utrecht, Heidelberglaan 2, Utrecht, 2506, Holland

PREFACE

In April 1977 an international symposium on *Plants and Islands* was held in Las Palmas de Gran Canaria to celebrate the 25th aniversary of the foundation of the Jardín Botánico "Viera y Clavijo", and this volume is based on the papers presented at the meeting.

The subject of island biology is an intriguing one which has occupied the minds of many great naturalists and scientists but innumerable problems and puzzles remain to be solved.

Oceanic islands and their organisms are outstanding subjects for studies of colonisation, evolution, adaptive radiation and, indeed, extinction. The vast majority of island biota are, however, at the present time under serious pressure from the activities and influence of Man who is destroying their natural ecosystems at an alarming rate. It is extremely doubtful if we will even arrive at an alpha-taxonomy state of knowledge of some insular floras before catastrophic numbers of endemic island plants (and animals) become extinct.

This then was the background against which the symposium was arranged: the need to examine our present state of knowledge of insular floras and their biology, outline progress in research, formulate possible future fields of investigation and, above all, emphasise the need for drastic measures to be taken on an international scale for the conservation of our remaining insular biotopes.

The contributed papers were organised in four main groups. Those of Sunding, Moore, Green, Renvoize, Tryon, and Greuter, were all concerned with the origins of insular floras, whilst the papers presented by Humphries, Cardona and Contandriopoulos, Galloway, and Porter dealt with evolution and endemism in island plants. The third section with outstanding papers from Ehrendorfer, Mabberley, Aldridge, Gibby, and Borgen covered special topics on island biology. The perhaps controversial paper by Guédès was unfortunately not read at the meeting but is included in the publication as it was listed in the original programme and is a stimulating new contribution on a difficult subject.

The final session of the symposium was devoted to the problems of conservation on islands, the papers of Rauh, van der Werff, and Melville outlining some of the problems and those of Synge, and Lucas indicating

possible solutions to some of them. The last paper, a summing up of the
meeting by Heywood, leaves us rightly pessimistic about the future of
insular organisms and communities and I hope that the publication of
this volume will go some way towards drawing attention to the serious
situation of island conservation.

About 80 participants from 15 countries attended the symposium and
many people helped to make it successful. I would personally like to
thank the President and Consejeros of the Excmo. Cabildo Insular de
Gran Canaria and the Excma. Mancomunidad de Cabildos de la
Provincia de Las Palmas de Gran Canaria for financial and other
support. The staff of the Jardín Botánico "Viera y Clavijo" worked
tremendously hard in preparing for the meeting and I am extremely
grateful to all of them and to many other helpers too numerous to
mention.

Finally I should like to thank Academic Press for their outstanding
help in taking on the publication of the papers presented at the meeting
and for their cooperation in the preparation of the book for the press.

AUGUST 1979   DAVID BRAMWELL

CONTENTS

A*

12 Pachycaul Plants and Islands   259
    D. J. MABBERLEY
13 Evolution Within a Single Genus: *Sonchus* in Macaronesia   279
    ANGELA E. ALDRIDGE
14 Reproductive Biology in Island Plants   293
    F. EHRENDORFER
15 Magnolioid Island Plants and Angiosperm Evolution   307
    MICHEL GUÉDÈS
16 Karyology of the Canarian Flora   329
    LIV BORGEN
17 Palaeoendemism and Evolution in Macaronesian *Dryopteris*   347
    MARY GIBBY

SECTION 4 *Conservation*

18 Endangered Island Floras   361
    R. MELVILLE
19 Botanic Gardens and Island Plant Conservation   379
    A. H. M. SYNGE
20 Conservation and Vegetation of the Galapagos Islands   391
    H. VAN DER WERFF
21 Problems of Biological Conservation in Madagascar   405
    WERNER RAUH
22 The Threatened Plants Committee of IUCN and Island Floras   423
    G. LL. LUCAS
23 The Future of Island Floras   431
    V. H. HEYWOOD

    Subject Index   443

    Index of Organisms   447

1 Introduction

D. BRAMWELL   *Jardín Botánico, "Viera y Clavijo", Las Palmas de Gran Canaria, Spain*

Los organismos de las islas han jugado un importante papel en el desarrollo de la biología moderna y pensamiento biológico, especialmente en el desarrollo de la taxonomía de plantas durante la primera parte del siglo XIX ("la era Banksiana") y la formulación de la teoría evolutiva de Darwin y Wallace. La visita de Darwin a las islas Galapagos durante el viaje del Beagle le permitió enfocar los factores implicados en los cambios evolutivos en una pequeña escala y así reconocer el significado de la adaptación y presiones selectivas en la supervivencia de los organismos.

Durante los siglos XIX y XX, la mayoría de las islas del mundo fueron, por lo menos, superficialmente exploradas y descubiertos muchos problemas científicamente importantes y fascinantes. Todavía muchos de estos están por resolver a pesar de la gran contribución por parte de Carlquist, McArthur y Wilson etc. Parece dudoso que sea posible estudiar y resolver estos problemas y comprender completamente los recursos naturales de la isla antes de que muchas plantas y animales o todos los ecosistemas de las islas llegen a extingirse. Medidas internacionales, incluso financiar estudios científicos intensificados y el establecimiento de reservas, son urgentes antes de que sea demasiado tarde para salvar incluso pequenos ejemplares representantes de los biotopos de las islas.

The interrelationships between plants and islands do not seem to have been the subject of a previous meeting on an international scale. The theme is very appropriate in view of the importance of island organisms in the development of modern biology and biological thought and the absolute and urgent necessity for us to take action at an international level for the conservation of insular plants, animals and, indeed, entire island ecosystems. By just simply flicking through the IUCN Red Data Books we can see that a disproportionately large number of the world's endangered species are insular endemics. As MacArthur and Wilson (1967) have pointed out the smaller the land area the higher the rate of natural extinction, but the endangered species and probable extinctions that must really concern us are those whose survival would not be in doubt if it were not for the influence and activities of Man. Our island organisms with their small populations and genetic depletion are in trouble from all sides and we must attempt to save at least some of them. Scientifically, of course, that corner-stone of contemporary biology, the Darwin and Wallace theory of evolution by natural selection, gives island organisms priority of place in recent biological history, how can we

1

consider allowing the destruction of such organisms to take place
unchecked when our knowledge of so many of them is still at the level of a
fairly primitive alpha-taxonomy?

Some historical land-marks in island botany

Historically island plants have played an important part in the
development of taxonomy and evolutionary science.

One of the most important pre-Linnaean works on island organisms
was Sloane's *Natural History of Jamaica* (1707) a book which seems to have
been an important factor in the bargaining between Burmann and
Clifford which eventually took Linnaeus to Clifford's Garden at the
Hartekamp. Linnaeus himself had little opportunity in his early days to
study plants from islands of the world. The islands of the major oceans,
the Pacific, Atlantic and Indian oceans were still almost completely
unexplored and Linnaeus' experience of island plants was largely
confined to a few Macaronesian species, some from Mediterranean
islands and collections from the Dutch East Indies, Ceylon and the West
Indies made by explorers and employees of the Dutch East India
Company. They were, for Linnaeus, his first encounter with tropical
plants and must have had a considerable influence on the development of
his ideas on his natural system of classification. Linnaeus also published
his first island Flora, *Flora Zeylanica* in 1747.

The immediate impact of the Linnaean system on biology led to a
major phase of exploration which involved many of Linnaeus' own
former pupils, Loefling, Forsskål, Sparrman, Thunberg, Osbeck,
Solander etc. Of these, Sparrman, and especially Solander, were to be of
primary importance in island discovery and exploration.

Perhaps the central figure in this mid-to-late eighteenth century phase
of expansion was the British naturalist Sir Joseph Banks, described by
Stafleu (1971) as "traveller, collector, practical idealist, philanthropist
and long-time president of the Royal Society". Such was his influence on
exploration and systematic botany during the latter part of the 18th
century that Stafleu aptly terms his period the "Banksian Era".

The age was one of imperial expansion stimulated by the competition
between several nations for the establishment of colonial empires. While
Spain concentrated her efforts on the American continent resulting in the
botanical exploration by Mutis in C. and S. America, Ruiz, Pavon and
Dombey in Peru and Chile etc., the British and French were attempting
to expand their own empires by exploring the South Pacific in the
search for the *Terra Australis Incognita*.

In 1768 Captain James Cook set off on a three-year voyage round the world which was to set a pattern for future exploration. His ship, the *Endeavour* carried, almost entirely at Joseph Banks' personal expense, a complement of naturalists and biological draftsmen, and the scientific success of the voyage paved the way for two more led by Cook and, of course, for the later nineteenth century voyages of Hooker with the ships *Erebus* and *Terror* and, from our point of view, more significantly, that of Charles Darwin and the *Beagle*.

The voyage of the *Endeavour* was undertaken at the initiative of the Royal Society who wanted an expedition to the island of Tahiti in the Pacific to make astronomical observations on the transit of the planet Venus, but Banks was able to add a complement of naturalists including himself, Solander and Sporing. The list of islands visited and explored during the voyage is impressive indeed and plant specimens were obtained from places such as Madeira, Staten Island, Tahiti, the Society Islands, New Zealand, Australia where Botany Bay with its wealth of new plants was discovered in April 1770, New Guinea, Princes Island, St. Helena, Java, the Friendly Islands (the Tonga group) and so on.

Surprisingly, the biological results of this voyage were never published. Banks left in Solander's hands the classification and description of the material collected and though Solander prepared numerous manuscripts using the Linnaean System (Krok in 1925 listed some 64 items) only four relatively insignificant publications appeared in his lifetime and his accounts of the botany of the *Endeavour* though unpublished were obviously a major source of material for his contemporaries such as Dryander and Aiton, who referred to them extensively in the preparation of *Hortus Kewensis* (1789), L'Héritier and Gaertner.

Cook made two further voyages to the South Seas, one with Masson, Sparrman and the Forsters as naturalists and the other with David Nelson which was the one during which Cook met his death at the hands of the natives of Hawaii on the 11th of February 1779. These voyages greatly enriched the collections of Banks and of Kew Gardens and made both key centres for botanical research at the time.

Nelson eventually sailed again as naturalist on the ill-fated *Bounty* expedition to take the bread-fruit from Tahiti to the West Indies and, after being cast adrift with Bligh as a result of the mutiny, died at Timor when they had almost reached safety.

The nineteenth century was an epoch of great botanical activity, travel became much easier and with colonisation and settlement many islands were at least initially explored. In the Macaronesian region, first the Norwegian Christen Smith and later Webb and Berthelot, explored the Canary Islands and Richard Thomas Lowe, Madeira. I feel it is a sad comment that both the *Phytographia Canariensis* of Webb and Berthelot, completed in 1850 and Lowe's incomplete *Manual Flora of Madeira* dating from 1868, are still the basic descriptive reference works for these two groups of islands.

Authors of other important island floras during the nineteenth century include Hillebrand on Hawaii, Blanco and Vidal y Soler on the Philippines, Baker on Mauritius and the Seychelles, Melliss on St. Helena, the various works by Hooker (1844, 1867) on insular floras around the Antarctic region and the monumental studies of insular floras by Hemsley (1885) as a result of the H.M.S. *Challenger* expedition.

Charles Darwin and the voyage of the Beagle

All this nineteenth century activity is, however, completely overshadowed by a single name and a single event. On 17 December 1831 began a voyage which was to lead to the formation of, to use Loren Eiseley's words, "a theory that would shake the foundations of scientific thought in all countries of the world" (Eiseley, 1956). The voyage of course, was that of H.M.S. *Beagle* captained by Robert Fitzroy and carrying on board a young English naturalist by the name of Charles Darwin. Never has a scientific theory had such wide acceptance and yet been surrounded by so much controversy and criticism as Darwin's theory of evolution by natural selection. So much has already been written on this subject that it would be pointless for me to mention more than that which to us is probably the most interesting feature in the theory, the central rôle played by oceanic island fauna and flora in its conception.

The great "Man descended from Monkeys" controversy was the one which aroused public interest at the time but in fact it was in the Galapagos Islands, "One of the most marvellous evolutionary laboratories on the planet" is how Eiseley describes them, that Darwin was able to envisage the transmutation of species. As he himself noted in *A Naturalists Voyage Round the World*, "One might really fancy that, from an original paucity of birds one species had been taken and modified for different ends" – obviously the first glimmerings of the idea of adaptive radiation!

The small size of the islands and the disharmonic nature of the flora and fauna enabled Darwin to visualise a miniature insular world where relatively simple evolutionary change and adaptation took place continuously and allowed him to escape from the difficulties imposed by the sheer magnitude of continental systems. Geologists and palaeontologists of the time could not supply Darwin with his missing links but islands were able to indicate to him how the missing links arose and why some survived and others did not. As Eiseley comments "Darwin's recognition of the significance of this miniature world where the forces operating to create new beings could be plainly seen, was indispensable to his discovery of the origin of species; the islands reduced the confusion of continental life to more simple proportions; one could separate the factors involved with greater success".

The embryonic theory of evolution so slightly hinted at in the *Voyage* was developed by Darwin and independently at the same time by that somewhat neglected personality Alfred Russel Wallace and was introduced to the world in a joint paper before the Linnean Society of London on July 1st 1858, presented by Hooker and Lyell, neither of the authors being present!

Wallace arrived at his conclusions on how changes of species could be brought about while, to use his own words "Suffering from a rather severe attack of intermittent fever at Ternate in the Moluccas" and an important piece in this puzzle was also an inspiration to Darwin. This was an *Essay on Population* published by Thomas Malthus, the key by which both Darwin and Wallace were able to understand natural selection, "the survival of the fittest".

The affinity between the Edinburgh and Cambridge educated gentleman Charles Darwin, who circumnavigated the world, and Wallace who was without formal university education but was an excellent young observer, was perhaps that they both had the opportunity to work on islands, and it was certainly Wallace who, by sending Darwin a copy of his own manuscript on evolution, precipitated the publication of Darwin's *magnum opus*, *Origin of Species* (1859). The publication of this work not only revolutionised the biological sciences to an extent which could not have been appreciated at the time, but also by being so utterly opposed to current theological and scientific thought changed the whole outlook of Western philosophy.

The criticisms and opposition to "Darwinism" at the time were due to its controversial nature and were largely based on theological and philosophical premises.

Modern critics have objected on the basis of a supposed lack of scientific method and thought in Darwin's reasoning. Himmelfarb (1959) seems to consider him a congenital idiot and Leon Croizat (1962) would have us believe that Darwin was "an impostor" and "definitely not a thinker". As Julian Huxley (1942), however, admirably pointed out, it was precisely Darwin's use of a blend of induction and deduction in the true scientific manner which made him so successful.

Before leaving Darwin and Wallace I must add a little more about Alfred Russel Wallace who, as well as being so closely associated with evolutionary theory, was also, in his own right, an eminent biogeographer and island biologist This is demonstrated by his two essays on *Natural Selection and Tropical Nature* (1891) and by his book *Island Life* (1880) in which he was the first to bring together many of the principles and concepts of distribution and dispersal of island organisms. He also appreciated the fundamental differences between continental and oceanic islands and I feel that, due to his association with the Darwinian era, this aspect of his scientific work has been rather neglected.

The early and mid-twentieth century produced a further series of island biologists of considerable repute and many of these have been particularly prominent in studies of the Pacific Ocean region. Probably the most important of these has been the Swedish botanist Carl Skottsberg who was the creator and first director of the Gothenburg Botanical Garden. Between the years 1907 and 1909 he paid his first visits to the Falkland Islands and the Juan Fernández Islands. By 1908 Skottsberg had already become interested in the flora of the Juan Fernández Islands and the phytogeographical problems surrounding this flora. He also warned of the probability of its destruction even at this early stage. The Juan Fernández Islands were declared a National Park by the Chilean government largely due to the efforts of Carl Skottsberg who produced a monumental series of publications on the natural history of Juan Fernández and Easter Island (1956).

Intrigued by the possible relationships between the Juan Fernández flora and that of the Hawaiian Islands, Skottsberg also made four trips to Hawaii and as a result published a number of important contributions to the plant geography of the Pacific region.

The Pacific area has also been the subject of extensive studies by Fosberg, A. C. Smith and Merrill, whose studies of the Philippines and unrivalled bibliographical researches have been a major contribution to Pacific botany. The Hawaiian Islands have also been fortunate to have had such eminent students as Rock, St. John, the Degeners, and Sherwin Carlquist. In our own region, the Canary Islands were the subject of floristic studies by Pitard and Proust, Burchard, Ceballos and Ortuño, and above all E. R. Sventenius.

As general background works we have had several major contributions to plant geography which are of fundamental importance in island studies. For example we have seen Willis' theory of "Age and Area." come and go (Willis, 1922). There has been the remarkable work on dispersal by Ridley (1930) and more recently the excellent compilations on insular floras by van Balgooy (1969). The very diversely scattered literature on island organisms and island biology which has been accumulating for almost 200 years, has been admirably drawn together and summarised by Carlquist in his books *Island Life* published in 1965 and *Island Biology* in 1974. In these two accounts, Carlquist envisages what he terms an "Island Syndrome", a series of phenomena intimately connnected with islands and island-like conditions and the result of disharmonic colonisation of islands and subsequent evolution in isolation.

In *Island Biology* he sets out 24 principles for dispersal and evolution of island organisms which will be commented on at some length by other contributors to this volume. Here I would just like to mention a few of them such as long-distance dispersal about which Carlquist (1974) comments "positive adaptations to long-distance dispersal are the key to disharmony". Can we consider dispersal and establishment ability separately?

A further question meriting our attention is that of relict plants and insular floras. I mention *Degeneria, Lactoris* and the primitive survivors on New Caledonia. At the same time, what is the significance of insular woodiness? Are woody insular endemics relicts or modern giants derived from weedy herbaceous ancestors? The concept of paedomorphosis elaborated in the 1960s seems to have been placed in doubt in the 1970s. The loss of dispersability in island plants has also been the subject of some controversy. Successful dispersal is surely that which allows the maximum number of propagules to contribute to the next generation. Thus a change from a wider dispersal to a narrower one in an organism which successfully finds an ecological niche in which it can survive on an island would seem to be a fairly immediate advantage. Perhaps we should consider this to be a positive change in dispersal strategy rather than negatively a loss of ability to disperse.

The importance of outcrossing, hybridisation etc. in the building-up of the depleted gene-pools of small populations of successful island colonisers seems to be opposed to the advantages of self-compatibility in post-colonisation establishment in the probable absence of pollen-vectors. This poses the question of just how do our successful island populations pass through Mayr's genetic "bottleneck" of reduced variability? (Mayr, 1954).

Though I find myself at times disagreeing with Carlquist's opinions on many of these subjects it is his painstaking research on islands plants and his willingness to express his views in his publications which have provided a major stimulus to the study of island biota and which have drawn our attention to the wealth of unsolved problems that exist on islands throughout the world.

Many theoretical aspects of our subject have been studied by means of mathematical models such as those presented by MacArthur and Wilson (1967). The fact that many of these models have been subjected to considerable criticism and frequent modification when applied to particular individual cases simply demonstrates the complications which are to be found when applying such models and extrapolating from one situation to another and indicates the multiplicity of factors involved in island colonisation and evolution.

As I mentioned at the beginning of this chapter the conservation of island organisms and ecosystems is a subject with which we must all be preoccupied. How many island species have already become extinct as a result of Man's activities and how many are in danger of becoming so in the immediate future? We as scientists are faced with the difficult situation of having to bring our influence to bear on governments and international organisations in order to save even representative samples of island life. Many islands of subtropical and tropical regions of the world have as their only natural resources their plants and vegetation which may contain much untapped, potentially useful material. On Madagascar, Rauh has noted that less than 20 per cent of the original primary ecosystems still remain and in the Canary Islands very little of the primary laurel forest vegetation has escaped the ravages of five centuries of exploitation. On the other hand, the brilliant research carried out by González and his team on chemical products from endemic Canarian plants (González, 1976) has shown us the enormous potential value that many of these species have. I know of no other group of island plants which has been subjected to such intensive study. The recent discovery of a primitive diploid *Avena* species in the Canary Islands (Baum *et al.*, 1973) and the limited potential for the use of modern agricultural practises in island regions suggest that many primitive cultivars and crop precursers may still be found today. These plants are potentially a wealth of genetic resources of the sort that our international agencies are now taking such pains to preserve. As Frankel (1970) has stated "the task of preserving genetic resources is one which concerns the whole of mankind and the responsibility is not confined towards those now living, nor can it be discharged by any one nation".

In many cases small islands are in the economically paradoxical situation where they cannot afford to finance the effort and personnel needed to conserve their natural resources but by not conserving they are further endangering their local economies. Raven (1976) poignantly brings the point home when he says "Billions of dollars have been spent on the exploration of the Moon and we now know more about the surface of the Moon than we do about the tropical forests of, say, Western Colombia". I am sure we could substitute for Colombia any of the major islands groups of the world. The ecosystems of many small islands are, because of the pressures of population and the demands of modern society, in even greater danger than tropical forests and I am firmly convinced that even small representative samples can only be saved by a massive international effort.

The initiative for both the creation of reserves and the scientific study of island organisms must be taken at an international level and probably initially financed to a major extent by such organisations. Small island economies may eventually be considerably aided by the promotion of conservation as a stimulus to tourism, but unfortunately few island communities are, at the present time, in an economic position to be able to go in for conservation and the necessary and closely interconnected scientific study of their ecosystems on anything other than a fairly modest scale.

As island plants may, in the future, be a source of new plants of agricultural and horticultural value, a reserve of primitive germplasm of crop plants and of chemical products some with a potential value we have not yet even begun to understand, perhaps we, as island biologists, who are directly aware, because of our field experience, of the seriousness of the need for conservation, should be thinking in terms of some sort of island resources research centre on an international scale. Such a centre integrating exploration, resource research and screening, conservation projects and advisory service, propagation of endangered species, long-term seed storage facilities and so on could be a major stimulus to conservation in many subtropical and tropical island areas. The practical problems would, of course, be many. The assembled material would have to be effectively preserved and used and I am sure such a project would have to operate at the level of an international agency in order to make it successful.

This idea, has been seeded by the frustration of seeing so much written about conservation but so little effective conservation taking place where it really matters, that is where there are very high concentrations of endangered species about which we know, at present, very little, and I hope perhaps at least some aspects of it might become a reality in the future.

REFERENCES

Aiton, W. (1789). *Hortus Kewensis*. Longman, Hurst *et al.*, London
Baker, J. G. (1877). *Flora of Mauritius and the Seychelles*. Reeve & Co., London
Baum, B. R., Rajhathy, T. and Sampson, D. R. (1973). An important new diploid Avena species discovered on the Canary Islands. *Canad. J. Bot.* **51**, 759–762
Carlquist, S. (1965). *Island Life*. Natural History Press, New York
— (1974). *Island Biology*. Columbia University Press, New York and London
Croizat, L. (1962). *Space, Time, Form: The Biological Synthesis*. L. Croizat, Caracas

Darwin, C. (1839). *Journal of Researches into the Geology and Natural History of the Various Countries visited by H.M.S. Beagle*. Murray, London.

— (1859). *On the Origin of Species by means of Natural Selection*. Murray, London

Eiseley, L. C. (1956). *Charles Darwin*. (Reprinted from Scientific American, Feb. 1956), California

Frankel, O. H. (1970). Genetic Conservation in Perspective. In *Genetic Resources in Plants* (O. H. Frankel and E. Bennett, eds.). I.B.P. Handbook No. 11, Oxford and Edinburgh

González y González, A. (1976). Natural Products Isolated from Plants of the Canary Islands. In *Biogeography and Ecology of the Canary Islands* (G. Kunkel, ed.), 297–326. Junk, The Hague

Hemsley, W. B. (1885). Report on the Present State of Knowledge of Various Insular Floras. *Rep. Sci. Results voyage H.M.S. Challenger. Bot.* Vol. 1, 1–75

Hillebrand, W. (1888). *Flora of the Hawaiian Islands*. Williams & Norgate, London

Himmelfarb, G. (1959). *Darwin and the Darwinian Revolution*. Garden City, New York

Hooker, J. D. (1844–7). *Flora Antarctica*. Reeve Bros., London

— (1867). Lecture on Insular Floras. *Gardener's Chronicle*. 6–7, 27, 50–51, 75–76

Huxley, J. (1942). *Evolution the Modern Synthesis*. George Allen & Unwin, London

Krok, T. O. B. N. (1925). *Bibliotheca Botanica Suecana*. Private publication, Uppsala

Linnaeus, C. (1747). *Flora Zeylanica*. Private publication, Stockholm

Lowe, R. T. (1868). *A Manual Flora of Madeira*, J. van Voorst, London

Malthus, T. B. (1798). *First Essay on Population*. Reprint, Macmillan, London (1926)

McArthur, R. H. and Wilson, E. O. (1967). *The Theory of Island Biogeography*. Princetown University Press, N.J.

Mayr, E. (1954). Change of Genetic Environment and Evolution. In J. S. Huxley, A. C. Hardy, and E. B. Ford, *Evolution as a Process*. George Allen & Unwin, London

Raven, P. H. (1976). The destruction of the tropics. *Frontiers* **40**, 22–23.

Ridley, N. (1930). *The Dispersal of Plants Throughout the World*. Reeve & Co., London

Skottsberg, C. (1922). The phanerogams of the Juan Fernández Islands. *Nat. Hist. Juan Fernández Easter Island* **2**, 503–47

— (1956). Derivation of the flora and fauna of Juan Fernández and Easter Island. *Nat. Hist. Juan Fernández Easter Island* **11**, 193–438

Sloane, H. (1707–25). *A voyage to the Islands: Madeira, Barbados, Nieves, St Christophers and Jamaica*. Private publication, London

Stafleu, F. (1971). *Linnaeus and the Linnaeans*. Regn. Veg. 79. Utrecht

Van Balgooy, M. M. J. (1969). A study on the diversity of island floras. *Blumea* **17**, 139–178

Wallace, A. R. (1880). *Island Life*. Macmillan & Co., London

— (1891). *Natural Selection and Tropical Nature*. Macmillan & Co., London

Webb, P. B. and Berthelot, S. (1836–50). *Histoire Naturelle des Iles Canaries*. Tome III Botanique, Paris

Willis, J. C. (1922). *Age and Area*. Cambridge University Press

SECTION ONE
Origins

2 Origins of the Macaronesian Flora

PER SUNDING *Botanical Garden and Museum, University of Oslo, Norway*

La región biogeográfica de Macaronesia (Azores, Madeira, islas Salvajes, islas Canarias y Cabo Verde), puede ser subdividida en dos subregiones con un origen parcialmente diferente de sus floras, a saber, los cuatro archipiélagos del Norte por una parte y las islas de Cabo Verde por la otra. El grupo de islas del Norte comparten una alta proporción de sus especies de plantas y animales, tanto en número total de especies como entre los elementos "macaronésicos" en la flora y fauna, mientras que el archipiélago de Cabo Verde es más variado y tiene un espectro biogeográfico diferente.

Generalmente se ha convenido que las islas Canarias orientales son de naturaleza continental y estuvieron probablemente conectadas al continente africano en el Cretaceo, es decir, en la época en que Africa estaba todavía más o menos conectada a Sur América. Las islas Canarias centrales y occidentales, más jóvenes, parecen ser auténticas islas oceánicas. La evidencia geológica indica que también las Azores y Madeira son de naturaleza oceánica, aunque esto haga la explicación de la llegada de su biota de alguna forma complicada.

La flora actual de los cuatro Archipiélagos macaronésicos del Norte pueden dividielo en una serie de elementos floristicos (geoelementos), de los cuales la mayor proporción entre las no endémicas cae en el elemento mediterraneo, y tambien entre las endémicas, el grupo de especies más grande es aquella con afinidades a la flora del Mediterraneo. Existen numerosas disyunciones de larga distancia (al Este y Sur de Africa, Este de Asia, y Norte y Sur de América), que han sido explicadas en principio como el resultado de un resquebrajamiento de áreas de distribución más amplias y no a través de dispersión a larga distancia. Se ha demostrado que una gran parte del elemento endémico macaronésico constituye un relicto de la flora tetiana del terciario del Sur de Europa-Norte de Africa de la que se conocen fósiles de un número de localidades en los paises del Mediterráneo. A través de los grandes cambios climáticos en el último periodo terciario y cuaternario, esta flora tropical/subtropical con pocas excepciones llegó a extinguirse en Europa y además en áreas tropicales más al Este. Sobrevivieron en refugios donde las condiciones eran más favorables, como por ejemplo en las islas macaronésicas. El elemento americano en la flora macaronésica debe ser considerado muy antiguo y posiblemente date del periodo Cretaceo, cuando las masas de tierra alrededor del Atlántico estaban aún conectadas o por lo menos cerca la una de la otra, y cuando la flora de los (ahora) dos continentes era muy semejante.

Que una alta proporción de la flora vascular macaronésica es de gran antigüedad se demuestra por las reglas de distribución en hoy dia junto con características como la prevaleciente forma de vida leñosa de géneros en otras partes representados por hierbas, y en el bajo nivel de poliploidia.

Después del aislamiento del grupo de islas macaronésicas en el Atlántico, la flora relicta terciaria fue preservada debido a la gran variedad ecológica hallada en las islas. En muchos géneros (*Aeonium, Echium, Argyranthemum* etc.) la consecuencia de la radiación adaptativa y evolución vicariante ha dado un gran número de taxones endémicos en cada género.

Las islas de Cabo Verde, hoy situadas a unos 500 km del continente africano, han sido generalmente consideradas de origen oceánico. Sin embargo, las rocas más antiguas halladas en Macaronesia, a saber, rocas de edad jurásica, se ha demostrado que aparecen al Este de la isla Maio. Considerando los movimientos continentales en el Atlántico Sur y la naturaleza de la flora y fauna, un origen similar al dado para las Canarias orientales debe buscarse. Una parte de la flora y fauna endémica macaronésica de Cabo Verde puede haber llegado del mismo área de procedencia que la de los otros archipiélagos macaronésicos, es decir, desde el continente durante la migración hacia el Sur de la flora tetiana del terciario. La flora de Cabo Verde que posee una gran proporción de especies tropicales (54% endemismos de afinidades tropicales) que deben haber llegado en parte del Palaeotrópico en épocas históricas, traida por el hombre, parcialmente puede ser explicado como un antiguo elemento relicto del Periodo Cretaceo, probablemente dimanado desde el entonces conectado África y Sur América.

Introduction

The name Macaronesia will be sought in vain in ordinary topographical maps or atlases. Nevertheless, the word is frequently used among biologists to designate an area of natural delimitation as regards its plant and animal life. The Macaronesia concept was introduced by the botanist Philip Barker Webb about 120 years ago, to include the five archipelagos of the Azores, Madeira, the Salvage Islands, the Canary Islands, and the Cape Verde Islands. Grisebach, Engler and other famous phytogeographers were among the users of the term, and contributed to its acceptance among biologists. Recently it has also been adopted in the above-mentioned meaning for the *Flora of Macaronesia Project* (Bramwell, 1972a).

From a biogeographical point of view it should also be stressed that an area on the African mainland – in South Morocco and Spanish West Africa – has a natural relationship with Macaronesia, as a "Macaronesian Enclave" on the mainland (Fig. 1). A great number of plant taxa within this mainland area show greater affinity to taxa in the Macaronesian islands than to taxa on the mainland outside the enclave; the same appears to be the case within the animal kingdom (Evers, 1964). The present account will, however, primarily deal with the island groups, to which the term is normally restricted.

For a discussion of the origin of the Macaronesian flora, let us first

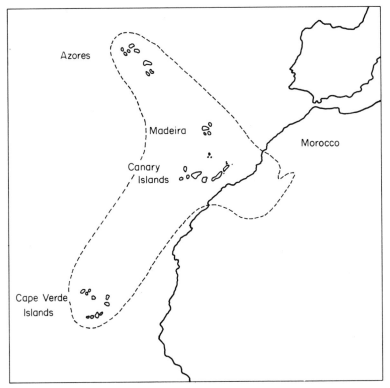

Fig. 1   The biogeographical region of Macaronesia

consider what we know about the place where the plants grow today, the islands themselves. The five Macaronesian archipelagos are situated in the Atlantic Ocean, stretching over a considerable area, from about 39°N to about 15°N, and at distances from the European or African continents varying from 115 to 1600 km. Their areas and highest elevation likewise vary considerably, from the small group of the Salvage Islands with a land area of less than 15 km² and highest elevation at 183 m, to the Canary Islands with an area of more than 7000 km² and the impressive Pico de Teide rising to more than 3700 metres above sea level. Large areas and high elevation are features indicating ecological diversity and thus certainly have great influence upon the species number found within each of the Macaronesian archipelagos. Thus the richest vascular flora by far and the highest percentage of endemics are found in the Canary Islands. These and other features shown in Table 1 will be further commented upon later.

TABLE 1 Physical data and number of vascular plants and endemics of the Macaronesian archipelagos

	Number of Islands	Area (km²)	Highest altitude (m)	Origin	Oldest rocks	Distance (km) to mainland	Distance (km) to nearest other Macar. archipelago	Species number (vascular)	Number of endemics	Percentage of endemics
Azores	9	2304	2351	Ocean.	Tertiary (?Cretaceous)	1600	900	843	44	5
Madeira	3	728	1861	Ocean.	Tertiary	600	260	1141	120	11
Salvage I.	2	<15	183	Ocean.	Tertiary	360	170	87	1	1
Canary I.	7	7273	3718	Ocean./Cont.	Cretaceous	115	170	1860	520	28
Cape Verde I.	10	4033	2829	Ocean.	Jurassic	500	1400	650	92	14

Floristic comparison of the Macaronesian archipelagos

When discussing the origin of the Macaronesian flora it is important to stress the fact that we are dealing with five individual archipelagos, each with its own distinctive features. Although they certainly have common "Macaronesian" features as regards plant and animal life, different

TABLE 2 Number of species of vascular plants in common between the individual Macaronesian archipelagos (lower left half) and degree of floristic similarity expressed in terms of the Sørensen's index of similarity (upper right half)

		Azores	Madeira	Salvage I.	Canary I.	Cape Verde I.
Azores	(843 spp.)	—	56	10	37	17
Madeira	(1141 spp.)	551	—	11	49	20
Salvage I.	(87 spp.)	44	70	—	8	9
Canary I.	(1860 spp.)	499	735	76	—	18
Cape Verde I.	(650 spp.)	124	181	33	229	—

explanations for the origin of the biota may be possible for individual parts of the area.

As a first step, let us make a rough comparison of the character of the flora of the individual Macaronesian archipelagos to see to what degree they are botanically alike, and to see if they might form separate groups that it would seem natural to deal with separately.

The checklist of Macaronesia by Eriksson *et al.* (1974) has been used as a basis for counting the number of plant taxa and calculating the degree of floristic similarity between the five island groups. With *species* used as the basic taxonomic unit – intraspecific variation not taken into account – the numbers of vascular plant species shared by pairs of archipelagos in the possible combinations are shown in the lower left half of Table 2.

Sørensen's index or quotient of similarity (Sørensen, 1948) was used to express degree of floristic similarity in a more comparable and easily readable form. The Sørensen index reads as follows:

$$K_s = \frac{2C}{A+B} \times 100$$

where A is the total number of species of the first, B the total number of species of the second unit to be compared, and C is the species number shared by the two. The Sørensen indices for the vascular flora of the five Macaronesian archipelagos are given in the upper right half of Table 2, and may also be illustrated through Fig. 2.

Both from the numbers of species shared and from the similarity indices it is directly evident that the Azores, Madeira, and the Canary Islands have fairly much in common in total vascular plant composition. Expressed in another way, 65% of the species of the Azores are also found in Madeira, and a similar percentage of Madeiran species is present in the Canary Islands. As will be shown, this total floristic similarity corresponds to the reciprocal occurrence of a considerable group of so-called Macaronesian plant taxa.

The figures given for the Salvage Islands in Fig. 2 are somewhat misleading. Because the species number of the small archipelago is so much lower than those of the neighbouring archipelagos with which it is compared, the resulting Sørensen indices are also low. Going back to the absolute species numbers in Table 2, it may be seen that of the Salvage Island's vascular flora as much as 87% is also present in the Canary Islands, and 80% in Madeira. The Salvage Islands are thus intermediate in their floristic character between the Canary Islands and Madeira, and in fact close to both. In conclusion one may state so far that

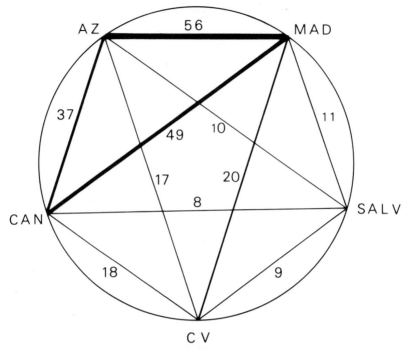

Fig. 2   Degree of floristic similarity between the five Macraronesian archipelagos, expressed in terms of Sørensen's index of similarity (see text for explanation)

all four northern archipelagos form a natural group that it might seem appropriate to discuss more or less in common.

The fifth and southernmost archipelago, *viz.* the Cape Verde Islands, has on the one hand a majority of Macaronesian taxa or taxa closely vicariant to those of the Canary Islands, that makes its inclusion in the Macaronesia area seem natural (Sunding, 1973). On the other hand, the total vascular flora and the phytogeographical spectrum show considerable differences from all other Macaronesian island groups. The origin of the Cape Verde Islands and of their flora and fauna will, therefore, be discussed separately later.

Origin of the Canary Islands, Salvage Islands, Madeira, and the Azores and their flora

Central to the question of origin of flora and fauna of the archipelagos is the problem of how the islands themselves originated. The shifting positions of land masses between Eurasia, Africa, and the Americas during the Mesozoic and Cainozoic and the emergence of archipelagos in what became the Atlantic Ocean pose a number of problems which one has just started to solve. Many different opinions have been held on the origin of the Macaronesian archipelagos, and they may be summarised by the following four hypotheses (Evers *et al.* 1970):

1. The islands must be regarded as remnants of a greater land mass situated between Africa and America, or possibly connecting the two continents ("Atlantis theory").

2. The islands are fragments of the Old World's continental edges, that either through disappearance of earlier land-bridges or in connection with the continental movements have been loosened from the continent.

3. The islands are products of oceanic vulcanism, results of at first submarine eruptions that have gradually built up land masses to above

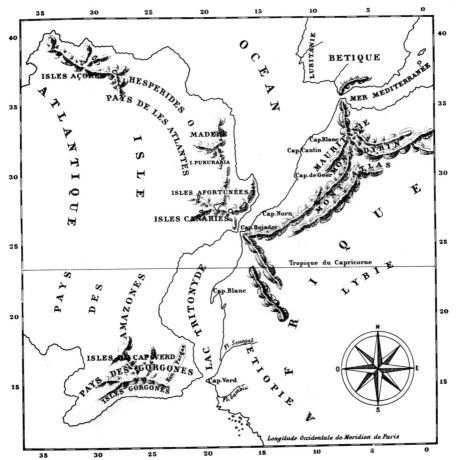

FIG. 3   The map of Bory de Saint Vincent (1802) showing his hypothetical Atlantis. Reproduced from Ceballos and Ortuño (1951)

sea level. No direct connections to the neighbouring continents have existed ("Oceanic Islands theory").

4. The islands are products of an oceanic vulcanism which in earlier periods has been much stronger than today. The islands therefore in earlier periods have been considerably larger than their present day size and have been more or less connected with each other or even with the mainland.

For all the Macaronesian archipelagos the Atlantis or sunken continent theory, so eagerly favoured in earlier times (cf. Fig. 3, and see Lundblad, 1947 for references), has been abandoned. Neither geological nor biogeographical evidence seem to give any reason for its maintenance.

The three remaining theories of origin of the Macaronesian archipelagos probably all express some truth, and the real answer seems to be a combination of them. Let us first consider the Canary Islands which is the island group closest to the continent and the one where research on this particular problem is most advanced.

Several features have been claimed to indicate close geological relationship between the Canary Islands and the African mainland, features like the situation of the archipelago in the continuation of the mountain chains of northwest Africa, similarities in rock types, considerable tectonic accordances with, among others, parallelism in direction of fractures and dike systems, etc. The weight of evidence of the features mentioned for such a relationship between the islands and the continent has, however, been questioned.

A bathymetric map (Fig. 4) shows that the ocean depths between the western Canary Islands are up to 3000 metres, whereas the sea floor between the eastern Islands on the one side and the African coast on the other lies at about one-third of this. During the last decade the nature of this sea floor has been studied by several scientists. Based on seismic and gravimetric investigations off the coast of northwest Africa and between the Canary Islands, Dash and Bosshard (1969) were able to show that the three western islands, La Palma, Hierro and Gomera, appear to lie over an oceanic crust, while the two eastern islands, Lanzarote and Fuerteventura, are underlain by continental crust. The crust beneath the central islands, Gran Canaria and Tenerife, is of intermediate character.

The oldest rocks found in the Canary Islands are sedimentary rocks in Fuerteventura shown to be of late Cretaceous age, about 80 million years old (m.y. BP) (Rothe, 1968), whereas vulcanism first seems to have started in the Miocene epoch, about 35 m.y. BP.

A further discussion of the many (and often contradictory) opinions on

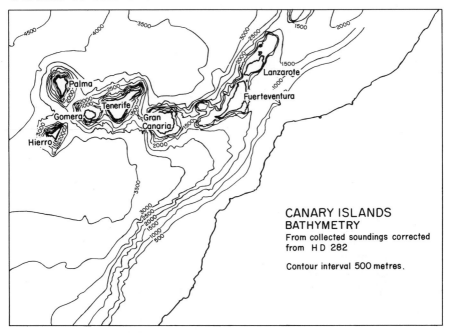

Fɪɢ. 4   Bathymetric map of the ocean areas around the Canary Islands. Reproduced from Dash and Bosshard (1969)

the geology of the Canary Islands and its meaning for the understanding of the origin of the archipelago lies outside the scope of the present review; the reader is referred to the thorough account by Schmincke (1976).

The geological evidence which indicates that the eastern Canary Islands are continental islands in the strict sense, and that there may for some time have existed a land connection to the mainland, is further supported by other biological or palaeontological evidence:

1. The striking floristic and faunistic similarity betweeen the Canary Islands and the "Macaronesian Enclave" on the African continent.

2. Finds of fossil ostrich eggs in deposits of Miocene age in Lanzarote (Rothe, 1964; Sauer and Rothe, 1972). Studies in progress (Evers *et al.*, 1970) seem to indicate the presence in the same deposits of a number of other kinds of birds not capable of flying.

3. Finds of fossils of terrestrial turtles in deposits of Pliocene/Pleistocene age in Tenerife (Burchard and Ahl, 1928; Mertens, 1942; Bravo, 1953).

In conclusion, it seems likely that Lanzarote and Fuerteventura are of true continental nature and that they were once connected mutually and to the mainland through a land bridge that could possibly form a migration route for plant and animal life. Raven and Axelrod (1974) assert that the eastern Canary Islands probably separated from the African continent at about the same time as separation between Africa and South America took place, i.e. in the Upper Cretaceous epoch, about 80–100 m.y. BP (see also Fig. 5). The central and western Canary Islands must be considered of oceanic nature (Rothe and Schmincke, 1968). Plant and animal migrations within the archipelago either must be explained through dispersal over the relatively short ocean distances now separating the islands, or through existence of earlier, now subsided land areas between the islands. Hausen (1958) and Fuster *et al.* (1968), through correlative stratigraphic studies within the archipelago, claim to be able to correlate certain volcanic horizons over large distances within the archipelago, i.e. that presumed identical strata may be followed from Lanzarote and Fuerteventura in the east to La Palma and Gomera in the west. These various authors also claimed that there is some evidence that those horizons must have been more or less continuous within the total area and have later been broken up.

Axelrod (1960) has used the term "composite islands" for islands which stand in an intermediate position between oceanic and true continental islands, and where their mode of origin must be expected to have followed a more complicated course. It seems appropriate to use the term "composite archipelagos" for island groups which like the Canaries have characteristic features from both oceanic and continental archipelagos.

About the other northern Macaronesian archipelagos, which also lie farther away from the mainland, we know far less than about the Canaries. The oldest rocks found in the Salvage Islands and in Madeira are of Tertiary age, whereas in the Azores they are of Tertiary or possibly late Cretaceous age. All geological evidence seems to indicate an oceanic origin of the three island groups, although depth contours in the North Atlantic Ocean indicate possibilities of a prehistoric land connection from Madeira to the Iberian peninsula. Central to this question stands the entire history of the North Atlantic during the various geological periods and the relative positions of the landmasses on both sides of what gradually became this ocean. The Atlantic Ocean began to open with the rotation of Africa and South America away from North America in the early Jurassic (180 m.y. BP). In mid-Cretaceous, Eurasia and North America were still rather close to each other, cf. Fig. 5 (Raven and Axelrod, 1974). It might be interesting to speculate about what positions the northernmost Macaronesian island groups may have had in the Atlantic rift during this period of continental movement in the Cretaceous and Tertiary periods. Judging from the great similarity in the

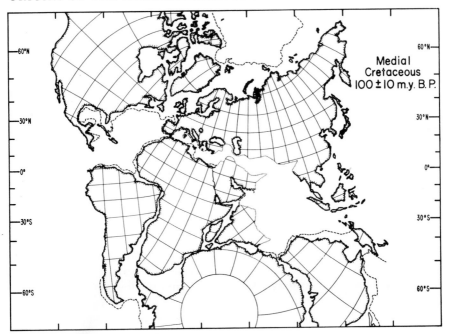

Fig. 5   Relative positions of the land masses in medial Cretaceous time (100 ± 10 m.y.
BP). From Raven and Axelrod (1974)

vascular flora between the Macaronesian archipelagos and the existence
in several of them of the same or closely related vicariant taxa, it would
seem tempting on a biological basis to postulate either land connections
or short dispersal distances from the Azores and Madeira to the Iberian
peninsula and to the Mediterranean, from where, as will be discussed
later, the Macaronesian floristic element originated. No geological evidence
has, however, yet been given to support such a connection to the
European mainland.

Van Balgooy (1969, p. 164), in a discussion on the diversity of island
floras, showed that the ratio plant genera/plant families in a particular
island or archipelago showed different values for areas of oceanic origin
(low ratio) or continental origin (high ratio). From the values calculated
for the five Macaronesian archipelagos (Table 3) it is evident that the
highest, or "most continental" genera/families ratio is found in the
Canary Islands, situated closest to the continent and in part probably of
continental nature, while the lowest values among the larger
archipelagos is the one given for the Azores, farthest away from the
continent. About the Azores van Balgooy (1969, p. 171) directly asserts
that access to this island group appears to have always been difficult.

B

TABLE 3 Number of plant genera and families within each of the Macaronesian archipelagos and the genera/families ratio (for Azores, Madeira and Canary Islands, from van Balgooy 1969)

	No. of genera	No. of families	Gen./fam. ratio
Azores	221	70	3.2
Madeira	290	71	4.1
Salvage I.	71	31	2.3
Canary I.	400	91	4.4
Cape Verde I.	391	112	3.5

From what has been stated so far, it is clear that the flora of the northern Macaronesian archipelagos during the Cretaceous, Tertiary and Quaternary periods arrived at the various areas via land bridges or by dispersal over ocean for shorter or longer distances. For the last mentioned period dispersal includes plants brought by Man. The present-day vascular flora of these island groups includes plants belonging to several distinct flora elements. A floristic element is here understood in its original and strict chorological sense ("geoelement" of Walter and Straka, 1970, p. 268), as a concept to include species of the same present-day distribution, or species of the same floristic region. Bramwell (1976) in a discussion of the Canary Islands' endemics, uses the concept in another and wider sense and includes in it aspects of history and origin ("Chronoelement" or "genoelement", Walter and Straka, 1970). The major flora elements of Macaronesia are the following (cf. Sunding 1970 for a more thorough discussion):

1. The Mediterranean element. A large group of species, for instance the classical example *Olea europaea* L. (Fig. 6).

2. The Atlantic element. The group especially includes pteridophytes (Fig. 7).

3. The Saharo-Sindian element. As would be expected especially in the lower and arid parts of the Canaries (besides in the Cape Verde Islands); as examples may be given *Pteranthus dichotomus* Forssk. (Fig. 8) and *Launaea arborescens* (Batt.) Murb.

4. The tropical element. In the four northern archipelagos represented by only few species. Also some ferns, represented by some species of anthropochorous nature.

5. The cosmopolitan element.

6. The endemic element, which includes partly endemics of a larger part of the Macaronesia area, partly endemics of single archipelagos or single islands. The endemic group of vascular plant species, which in the four northern archipelagos comprises about 685 species, may be further

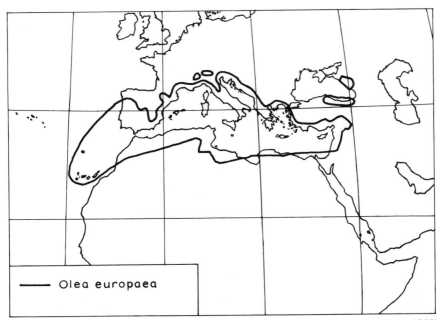

Fig. 6   Distribution of *Olea europeaea* L. (Figures 6–15 reproduced from Sunding, 1970)

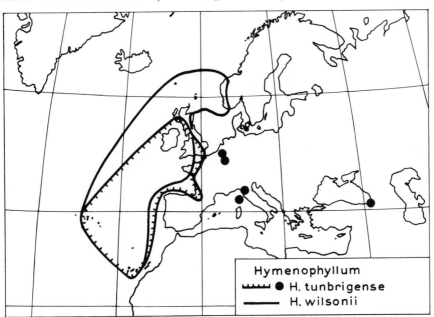

Fig. 7   Distribution of *Hymenophyllum tunbrigense* and *H. wilsonii* in Europe and Macaronesia

25

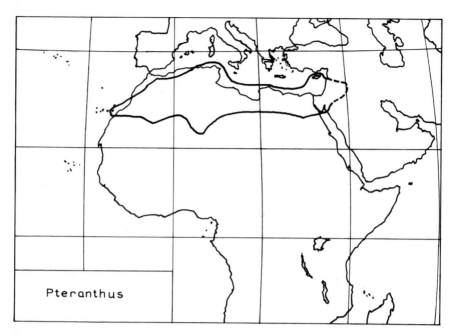

Fig. 8   Distribution of the Saharo-Sindian genus *Pteranthus*

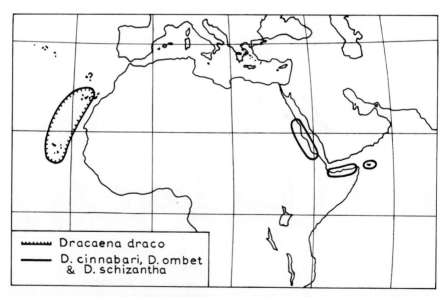

Fig. 9   Distribution of the Macaronesian *Dracaena draco* L. (Canary Islands, Cape Verde Islands) and its closest relatives

26

subdivided, according to their present-day relations to the flora of other parts of the world:

(*a*) Endemics of Mediterranean affinity. Here belongs a greater part of the endemic flora of Madeira and the Canary Islands, a relatively smaller part of the Azorean endemics. Examples: *Echium* spp. and *Sonchus* spp. of the subgenus *Dendrosonchus*. For some of the taxa within this group their closest relatives are today found in the east Mediterranean: *Sideritis* spp. and *Erysimum* spp. (Bramwell and Richardson, 1973; Bramwell, 1976).

(*b*) Endemics of Atlantic affinity. Hygrophilous ferns and forest plants. Relatively few species in the Canaries, several in the northern Macaronesian archipelagos.

(*c*) Endemics of Saharo-Sindian affinity. Predominantly in the lower, arid zones of the Canary Islands (and in the Cape Verde Islands), for instance *Forsskaolea* spp., *Kickxia* spp., and *Zygophyllum* spp.

(*d*) Endemics of East African affinity. A phytogeographically interesting group of the flora, showing a present-day disjunction from Macaronesia to East Africa. A well-known example constitutes the genus *Dracaena*, with the species most closely related to the Macaronesian *D. draco* L. found around the Red Sea and on Socotra (Fig. 9).

(*e*) Endemics of South African affinity; examples are found for instance within the genus *Phyllis* (Rubiaceae), with its closest relative *Galopina* (Fig. 10) and in *Bencomia* and *Argyranthemum*.

(*f*) Endemics of Afromontane affinity, as exemplified by the Canaries' "National Flower" *Canarina canariensis* (L.) Vatke, and by the section *Afrosciadium* of the genus *Cryptotaenia* (Umbelliferae) (Fig. 11).

(*g*) Endemics of East Asian (-Australian) affinity. Here belong some of the Macaronesian endemics which apparently have the least possibility of long distance dispersal, among others two Macaronesian *Apollonias* species of the Lauraceae (Fig. 12), and *Picconia azorica* (Tutin) Knobl. and *P. excelsa* (Ait.) DC. (Oleaceae), the latter two with their closest relatives in eastern Australia about 19 000 km away from Macaronesia (Fig. 13).

(*h*) Endemics of American affinity. To this group of species representatives are found in all the large Macaronesian island groups. As examples may be given the *Bystropogon* species (5 spp.) of Madeira and the Canary Islands (Fig. 14).

The largest group of species among the ones cited above are the Mediterranean species among the non-endemics, and species with a Mediterranean affinity among the endemics. This at once indicates a close relationship between the Macaronesian and the Mediterranean floras, and phytogeographically the Macaronesian floristic region has

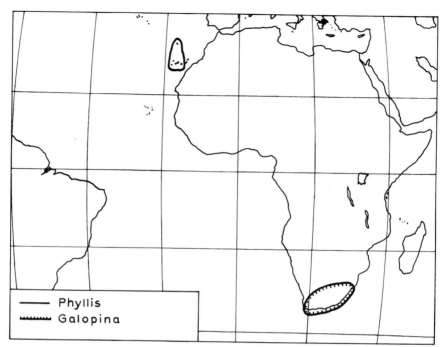

Fig. 10 Distribution of the rubiaceous genus *Phyllis* (Madeira, Canaries) and its closest relative *Galopina* in South Africa

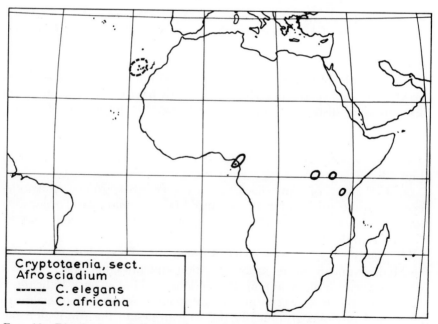

Fig. 11 Distribution of *Cryptotaenia*, section *Afrosciadium* as an example of the Macaronesia-Afromontane floristic connections

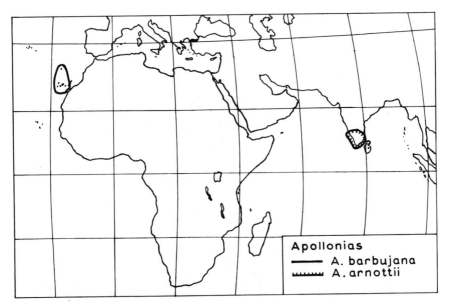

FIG. 12 World distribution of the genus *Apollonias* (Lauraceae)

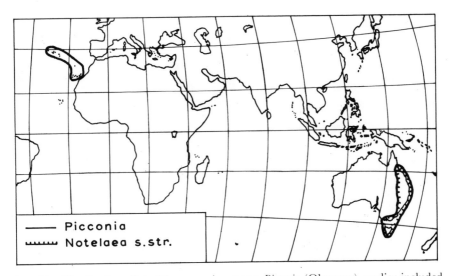

FIG. 13 Distribution of the Macaronesian genus *Picconia* (Oleaceae), earlier included within *Notelaea*, and of *Notelaea* sens. str.

29

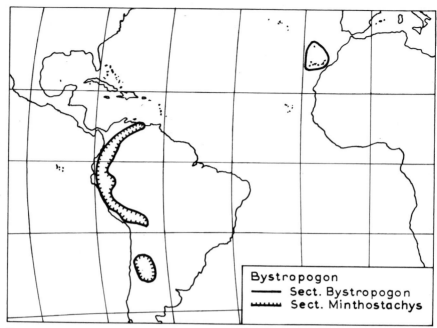

FIG. 14   Distribution of the genus *Bystropogon* sens. lat. (Labiatae), with one section in Madeira and the Canary Islands and the second in South America.

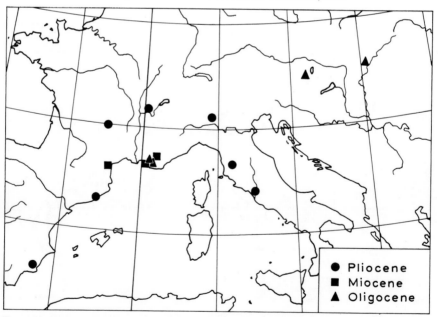

FIG. 15   Central and South European localities where fossils have been found of plants that are today Macaronesian.

often been considered a subregion under the Mediterranean. But also groups of endemic species of more distant present-day relations are of a considerable size as regards species number, as for instance those with affinities to the East Africa taxa (91 species within the Canaries alone, Sunding, 1970). Large disjunctions may always give rise to unlimited speculation, and much has been written and many different opinions given to explain such disjunctions from Macaronesia to far away places.

As discussed by many workers, in later years among others Ciferri (1962), Meusel (1965), Tahktajan (1969), Sunding (1970, 1972), and Bramwell (1972b, 1976), but in fact already demonstrated by Engler (1879), a greater part of the Macaronesian endemic element, irrespective of its present-day affinities to different regions, must be considered a relict flora of once wider distribution, *viz.* of the humid subtropical flora which until the Late Tertiary (Miocene and Pliocene) was distributed in Europe and partly in North Africa. The Tertiary (Oligocene, Miocene, and Pliocene) flora of South Europe and North Africa has been studied in great detail by, among others, Saporta (1865-1873, 1873, 1889), Schimper and Schenk (1890), Schenck (1907), Depape (1922), and Andréanszky (1968). In a number of localities in Spain, France, Italy, Austria, and Hungary (Fig. 15) plant fossils have been found that may look familiar to a botanist who has worked in Macaronesia, especially in Madeira or the Canary Islands (cf. also Sunding, 1970; Bramwell, 1976):

Fossil taxon	Corresponding Macaronesian taxon, if different from the fossil
Adiantum reniforme	
Apollonias aquensis	*A. barbujana, A. ceballosi*
Asplenium hemionitis	
Clethra berendtii	*C. arborea*
Dracaena brogniartii,	*D. draco*
D. narbonensis	
Ilex canariensis	
Laurus azorica	
Maytenus canariensis	
(Catha cassinoides)	
Myrsine spp.	
Ocotea heerii	*O. foetens*
Persea indica	
Phoenix sp.	*P. canariensis*
Picconia excelsa	
Pinus consimilis, P. resurgens	*P. canariensis*
Smilax targionii	*S. canariensis*
Viburnum pseudotinus	*V. tinus* ssp. *rigidum*
Woodwardia radicans	

One may note that all the four lauraceous genera of the Macaronesian Laurisilva were represented in the Tertiary flora of the Mediterranean by taxa identical or related to those of the present-day Macaronesian flora. For those and several others of the list above, long-distance dispersal of their diaspores seems very unlikely. Already in the Cretaceous or in the early Tertiary this flora therefore ought to have been present in the northernmost archipelagos, when land connections – if such ever existed – were still established or, at least, before distances to the continents became too great.

During the Tertiary the climate gradually became cooler. The climatic zones in Europe – and thereby also the vegetation zones – were pressed southwards towards the Tethys, later the Mediterranean Ocean, and further southwards over three occasional land connections, i.e. by the Strait of Gibraltar, via East Mediterranean – Sicily – Tunisia, and via the Near East – Arabia – East Africa respectively (Brinkmann, 1960). The climate also became generally drier and the large desert areas of North Africa and West Asia formed. Through this displacement of vegetation zones and because of the gradually more arid character of North Africa, the earlier continuous distribution areas for many taxa were split up and several plant species disappeared totally within this part of the world, or they found a possibility of continued existence in the most favourable places like the Macaronesian islands, in East and South Africa, or farther east in Asia. The reason why so great a part of the flora of the Tethys countries has survived in the Macaronesian islands may be found partly in the buffering effect of the ocean, partly in the fact that they offer a wide series of ecological niches, and also in that their mostly high elevations make survival during changing climatic conditions easier. It should, however, also be emphasised that a still larger portion of the Tethys subtropical and tropical flora did *not* survive in Macaronesia.

Some species of the South European Tertiary flora, like *Davallia canariensis* (L.) J.E.Sm. *Culcita macrocarpa* C. Presl., *Myrica faya* Ait. and *Umbilicus heylandianus* Webb & Berth., besides occurring in Macaronesia, are still found in certain suitable places in the southwest of the Iberian peninsula.

Davis and Hedge (1971) and Bramwell (1976) discuss separately the East Mediterranean element in the Macaronesian flora and suggest that this had a relatively later arrival in the Macaronesian area, notably in the Late Tertiary or in the pre-Pleistocene, at a time when the east Mediterranean region was probably linked to North Africa via Sicily. Against this it may be argued that several of the actual taxa (*Erysimum* spp.,

Ranunculus cortusifolius Willd.) are also present in Madeira and the Azores. It is hard to understand how all archipelagos may share species of this kind if they did not arrive there at an earlier time; besides, they have, after all, also had time enough to evolve several endemic taxa.

Also the American element in the flora and fauna of Macaronesia and, in a broader sense, in Africa, has caused much discussion. For this disjunct element in the Canary Islands' flora Lems (1960a, p. 77) claimed that the actual taxa had arrived by long-distance dispersal. As stated by Bramwell (1972b, 1976) long-distance dispersal in general appears to have played a minor role in the establishment of the Macaronesian disjunct flora, and also for the American–Macaronesian connections other explanations ought to be sought. This element in all likelihood is very old and may be dated back to the Cretaceous. At that time and even in the early Tertiary the floras of South America and Africa were much more alike than today, the African flora later being impoverished by the climatic catastrophes. As discussed by Raven and Axelrod (1974) the floristic similarities between the two sides of the Atlantic Ocean and between Macaronesia and America are then best explained in terms of continental movements (Axelrod 1970; Raven and Axelrod 1974). Separation between Africa and South America took place about 100 m.y. BP, whereas the two continents in the early Palaeocene were still only about 800 km apart.

After isolation of the Macaronesian islands and their biota in the Atlantic Ocean, evolution of plant and animal life took place through adaptive radiation and vicariant evolution (Bramwell, 1972b) in accordance with the great ecological diversity. In several genera this has led to a wide range of endemic species, each often endemic to a single island. Examples of genera where such an evolution has taken place are *Aeonium* with 37 endemic species in Macaronesia (Lems, 1960b), *Echium* with 28 species (Bramwell, 1972c), *Sonchus* of the subgenus *Dendrosonchus*, with 19 species (Boulos, 1972–1974), and *Argyranthemum* with 22 species (Humphries, 1976).

This mode of evolution is pronounced in Madeira and the Canary Islands, contrary to the case in the Azores. The low rate of adaptive radiation in the Azorean flora has its counterpart in the evolution of the fauna in this archipelago (Evers *et al.*, 1973).

That a large proportion of the Macaronesian vascular flora is of a great age is shown, not only by its present-day distribution patterns with often large distribution gaps to the nearest related taxa, but also by features like the prevailing woody life-form in genera elsewhere represented by herbs (*Echium, Sonchus, Limonium, Plantago, Sanguisorba* etc.) (cf. Meusel, 1952, 1965), and a low level of polyploidy (Borgen, 1969, 1979).

The non-endemic Mediterranean element in Macaronesia constitutes a large group, in the Canaries about 56% of the total vascular flora (Sunding, 1970). Although they have not differentiated into endemic Macaronesian taxa, it would seem that a greater part of this group of species ought to be considered a *native* part of the flora. It seems that too much weight has been put on Man as a dispersal agent and that too large a percentage of the Macaronesian flora has been considered "introduced" just because it is not endemic (Kunkel, 1972, 1976).

So far, mainly vascular plants have been considered in this discussion of the Macaronesian flora, naturally enough since this is the best known part of the flora. From what we know about mosses, lichens and fungi of the archipelago, it seems that the same floristic elements and the same relative distribution will occur, with the Mediterranean element prominent, but the difference from the vascular flora is that endemics are fewer and cosmopolitans a larger group. An element to which there is evidently no direct parallel in the vascular flora is the mosses (*Antitrichia californica* Sull., *Tortula bolanderi* (Lesq. & Jam.) Howe, *Trichostomopsis brevifolia* Bartr. etc.) and lichens (*Dimelaena radiata* (Tuck.) Hale & Culb., *Parmelia subolivacea* Nyl.) disjunct from Macaronesia (-Spain) to western North America (Størmer, 1960a, b; Sunding, 1967; Llimona and Werner, 1975; Østhagen and Krog, 1976). The existence of such an element probably has its explanation in the climatic similarity between the two areas and the easy mode of dispersal typical of the mosses.

Origin of the Cape Verde Islands and their flora

The vascular flora of the Cape Verde Islands in its total composition shows a marked difference to that of the northern island groups and the phytogeographical spectrum is likewise quite different. As much as 54% of the species belong to tropical flora elements, with a significant part being of neo-tropical character (Sunding, 1973). In addition several of the endemics have tropical affinities.

Situated at about 500 km distance from the African continent and rising from ocean depths to more than 4000 metres, the Cape Verde Islands have generally been considered of oceanic nature. However, both the age of the oldest rock material found within the archipelago, the presence of Macaronesian flora and fauna elements, and the nature of the tropical elements in the Cape Verdes, make one feel that a similar origin as given for the eastern Canary Islands may also be sought:

1. In Maio, situated in the eastern part of the archipelago, limestone

rocks of Jurassic age have been shown to occur (Krejci-Graf, 1961; Klerkx and De Paepe, 1971), these being the oldest rocks found within Macaronesia. The time of deposition of this rock material coincides more or less with the opening of the South Atlantic and may point towards a continental nature of the eastern Cape Verde Islands (Rothe, 1968).

2. A great number of Macaronesian plant species identical to or related to those of the Canaries or Madeira are found; *Dracaena draco*, *Sideroxylon marmulano* Lowe, and species of the genera *Aeonium*, *Echium*, *Asteriscus*, *Sonchus*, *Campylanthus* etc. The Canaries are situated 1400 km away to the north, and it is impossible to imagine a way by dispersal alone that the Cape Verde Islands could have achieved such a considerable addition to its flora (69 of its 650 species, or 11%) Also as regards animal life of the Cape Verde Islands a great similarity to that of the Canary Islands has been demonstrated.

It seems that this part of the flora and fauna of the Cape Verde archipelago must have arrived either via a land connection (many plant species with poor adaptations to dispersal, and the parallel offered by wingless insects) or over short ocean distances, from the same source areas as for the other Macaronesian island groups, i.e. from the mainland during the southwards migration of the Tethyan-Tertiary flora.

3. The tropical element in the Cape Verde flora partly includes species of palaeotropical or pantropical distribution which may have had the same way of arrival as the Macaronesian element, or in part may have been introduced by the native population originating from the African mainland. The neotropical element, including the endemics of such an affinity, may – at least for the endemics – be an old relict element within the flora, probably of Cretaceous age and originating from the then connected Africa and South America.

Concluding remarks

A discussion of the origins of the Macaronesian flora ends up with many suggestions, hypotheses and "ifs", which also concern the important question of the origin of the islands themselves. Our knowledge of the great tectonic changes in the North and South Atlantic and the relative positions of landmasses in Mesozoic and Cainozoic is still incomplete (Table 4). This is especially so regarding the island groups and in particular the Azores, Madeira and the Cape Verde Islands. Old sedimentary rocks are found in several of the archipelagos, of Cretaceous (?) age in the Azores and of Jurassic age in the Cape Verde Islands. It should, however, be remembered that we do not always know whether

TABLE 4 Geological time scale with important events in the Macaronesia area

Years (m.y. BP)	Era	Period	Epoch	Age (m.y. BP)	Major geological events	What happened in Macaronesia?
0	CAINOZOIC	QUAT.	Pleistocene	1.5		Land turtles in Tenerife
		TERTIARY	Pliocene	7		Cooling of climate, "Macar". spp.
20			Miocene		Connection re-establ. Africa-Eurasia	become extinct in Europe. Gran Canaria forested
				26		Ostriches in the eastern Canaries
40			Oligocene	38		Vulcanism starting in the Canaries. Oldest rocks Madeira
			Eocene		Separation Eurasia -N. America	? Last possibility for direct migration of Mediterranean biota to Azores
60			Palaeo-cene	54	Finish of possibility for migration	
				65	Africa- S. America	? Oldest rocks Azores
80	MESOZOIC	CRETACEOUS	Upper		Africa-SW Europe connected	Oldest rocks Canary Is
100				100	Separation Africa – S. America starting	? Separation eastern Canaries – Africa
120			Lower			
				136		
140		JURASSIC	Upper			
				154	Africa separated from Eurasia	Oldest rocks Cape Verde I.
160			Lower			

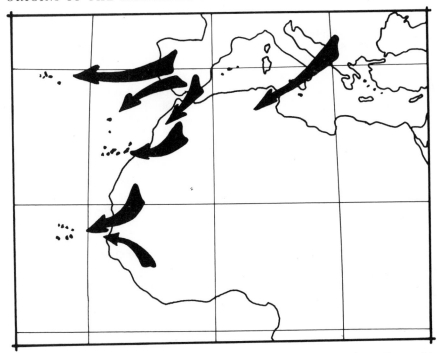

FIG. 16   Various migration routes for plants and animals to Macaronesia, as discussed in the text.

these undoubtedly old rocks were deposited above sea level or were submarine.

It is only too easy to put arrows of possible migration routes on a map with the present-day land contours (Fig. 16). As stated by Carlquist (1965) in his *Island Life*: "getting there is half the problem". It seems that we end up with the fact that has become familiar from other such situations – that geologists deny the landbridges which the biologists so gladly would have seen.

REFERENCES

Andréanszky, G. (1968). Neue und interessante tertiäre Pflanzenarten aus Ungarn. *Acta Bot. Acad. Scient. Hung.* **14**, 219–242

Axelrod, D. I. (1960). The evolution of flowering plants. In *Evolution after Darwin*, **1** (S. Tax, ed.), 227–307. Univ. Chicago Press, Illinois

Balgooy, M. M. J. van (1969). A study of the diversity of island floras. *Blumea* **17**, 139–178

Borgen, L. (1969). Chromosome numbers of vascular plants from the Canary Islands, with special reference to the occurrence of polyploidy. *Nytt. Mag. Bot.* **16**, 81–121

Borgen, L. (1979). Karyology of the Canarian Flora. This volume, pp. 329–346.

Bory de Saint Vincent, J. B. M. (1802). *Essais sur les Îles Fortunées et l'antique Atlantide*. Paris

Boulos, L. (1972–74). Révision systématique du genre *Sonchus* L. s.l. I–VI. *Bot. Notiser* **125**, 287–319; **126**, 155–196; **127**, 7–37, 402–451

Bramwell, D. (1972a). Flora of Macaronesia Project. *Taxon* **21**, 730–731

— (1972b). Endemism in the flora of the Canary Islands. In *Taxonomy, Phytogeography and Evolution* (D. H. Valentine, ed.), 141–159. Academic Press, London and New York

— (1972c). A revision of the genus *Echium* in Macaronesia. *Lagascalia* **2**, 37–115

— (1976). The endemic flora of the Canary Islands. In *Biogeography and Ecology in the Canary Islands* (G. Kunkel, ed.), 207–240. *Monogr. Biol.* **30**. Junk, The Hague

— and Richardson, I. B. K. (1973). Floristic connections between Macaronesia and the East Mediterranean region. *Monogr. Biol. Canar.* **4**, 118–125

Bravo, T. (1953). *Lacerta maxima* n. sp. de la fauna continental extinguida en el Pleistoceno de las Islas Canarias. *Estud. Geol. Inst. Invest. Geol. 'Lucas Mallada'* **9**, 7–34

Brinkmann, R. (1960). *Geologic Evolution of Europe*. Enke, Stuttgart

Burchard, O. and Ahl, E. (1928). Neue Funde von Riesen-Landschildkröten auf Teneriffa. *Z. Dtsch. Geol. Ges.* **79**, 439–444.

Carlquist, S. (1965). *Island Life. A Natural History of the Islands of the World*. Natural History Press, New York

Ceballos Fernández de Córdoba, L. and Ortuño Medina, F. (1951). *Estudio sobre la vegetación y la flora forestal de las Canarias occidentales*. Inst. forestal invest. exper., Madrid

Ciferri, R. (1962). La Laurisilva canaria: una paleoflora vivente. *Ricercha Scient.* **32** (1), 111–134

Dash, B. P. and Bosshard, E. (1969). Seismic and gravity investigations around the western Canary Islands. *Earth Planet. Sci. Lett.* **7**, 169–177

Davis, P. H. and Hedge, I. C. (1971). Floristic links between N.W. Africa and S.W. Asia. *Ann. Naturhist. Mus. Wien* **75**, 43–57

Depape, G. (1922). Recherches sur la flore pliocène de la Vallée du Rhône. *Ann. Sci. Nat., Bot.* ser. 10, vol. 4, 73–265.

Engler, A. (1879). *Versuch einer Entwicklungsgeschichte der Pflanzenwelt, insbesondere der Florengebiete seit der Tertiärperiode. I. Die extratropischen Gebiete der nördlichen Hemisphäre*. Wilh. Engelmann Verlag, Leipzig

Eriksson, O., Hansen, A. and Sunding, P. (1974). *Flora of Macaronesia. Check-list of Vascular Plants 1974*. University of Umeå

Evers, A. (1964). Das Entstehungsproblem der makaronesischen Inseln und dessen Bedeutung für die Artentstehung. *Entomol. Blätt.* **60**, 81–87

— Klemmer, K., Müller-Liebenau, I., Ohm, P., Remane, P., Strassen, R. zur and Sturhan, D. (1970). Erforschung der mittelatlantischen Inseln. *Umsch. Wissensch. Techn.* **70**, 170–176

Evers, A., Ohm, P. and Remane, R. (1973). Allgemeine Gesichtspunkte zur Biogeographie der Azoren. *Bol. Mus. Munic. Funchal* **27**, (115), 5–17

Fuster, J. M., Cendreo, A., Gastesi, P., Ibarrola, E. and Lopez Ruíz, J. (1968). *Geología y volcanología de las Islas Canarias. Fuerteventura.* Intern. Symp. Volcanol. Can. Isl. 1968. Inst. 'Lucas Mallada', Madrid

Hausen, H. (1958). On the geology of Fuerteventura (Canary Islands). *Soc. Scient. Fenn., Comm. Phys.-Math.* **22**, (1)

Humphries, C. J. (1976). A revision of the Macaronesian genus *Argyranthemum* Webb ex Schultz Bip. (Compositae – Anthemideae). *Bull. Brit. Mus. (Nat. Hist.), Bot.* **5**, 145–240

Klerkx, J. and De Paepe, P. (1971). Cape Verde Islands: Evidence for a Mesozoic oceanic ridge. *Nature, Lond.* **233**, 117–118

Krejci-Graf, K. (1961). Vertikal-Bewegungen der Makaronesen. *Geol. Rundschau* **51**, 73–122

Kunkel, G. (1972). Über einige Unkräuter auf Gran Canaria (Kanarische Inseln) und deren Verbreitung. *Vegetatio* **24**, 177–191

— (1976). Notes on the introduced elements in the Canary Islands' flora. In *Biogeography and Ecology in the Canary Islands* (G. Kunkel, ed.), 249–266 *Monogr. Biol.* **30**. Junk, The Hague

Lems, K. (1960a). Floristic botany of the Canary Islands. *Sarracenia* **5**, 1–94

— (1960b). Botanical notes on the Canary Islands. II. The evolution of plant forms in the islands: *Aeonium. Ecology* **41**, 1–17

Llimona, X. and Werner, R. G. (1975). Quelques lichens nouveaux ou interessants de la Sierra de Gata. *Acta Phytotax. Barcinon.* **16**, 1–32

Lundblad, O. (1947). Makaronesien und Atlantis. Eine historisch-biogeographische Übersicht. *Zool. Bidr. Uppsala* **25**, 201–323

Mertens, R. (1942). *Lacerta goliath* n. sp., eine ausgestorbene Rieseneidechse von den Kanaren. *Senckenbergiana* **25**, 330–339

Meusel, H. (1952). Über Wuchsformen, Verbreitung und Phylogenie einiger mediterran-mitteleuropäischer Angiospermen-Gattungen. *Flora* **139**, 333–393

— (1965). Die Reliktvegetation der Kanarischen Inseln in ihren Beziehungen zur süd- und mitteleuropäischen Flora. In *Gesammelte Vorträge über moderne Probleme der Abstammungslehre 1* (M. Gersch, ed.), 117–136. Jena

Østhagen, H. and Krog, H. (1976). Contribution to the lichen flora of the Canary Islands. *Norw. J. Bot.* **23**, 221–242

Raven, P. H. and Axelrod, D. I. (1974). Angiosperm biogeography and past continental movements. *Ann. Mo. Bot. Gard.* **61**, 539–673

Rothe, P. (1964). Fossile Strausseneier auf Lanzarote. *Natur u. Museum* **94**, 175–178

— (1968). Mesozoische Flysch-Ablagerungen auf der Kanareninsel Fuerteventura. *Geol. Rundschau* **58**, 314–332

— and Schmincke, H.-U. (1968). Contrasting origins of the eastern and western islands of the Canarian archipelago. *Nature, Lond.* **218**, 1152–1154

Saporta, G. de (1865–1873). Études sur la végétation du sud-est de la France à l'époque tertiaire. *Ann. Sci. Nat., Bot.* ser. 5, vol. 4, 5–264; vol. 17, 5–44

Saporta, G. de (1873). Fôrets ansevelies sous les cendres éruptives de l'ancien volcan de Cantal. Ibid. ser. 5, vol. 17, 402–406

— (1889). Dernières adjonctions à la flore fossile d'Aix-en-Provence. Ibid. ser 7, vol. 10, 1–192

Sauer, E. G. F. and Rothe, P. (1972). Ratite eggshells from Lanzarote, Canary Islands. *Science* **176**, 43–45

Schenck, H. (1907). *Beiträge zur Kenntnis der Vegetation der Canarischen Inseln. Mit Einfügung hinterlassener Schriften A. F. W. Schimpers.* Wiss. Ergebn. Deutsch. Tiefsee-Exped. 'Valdivia' 1898–1899, Bd. 2, Teil 1, Nr. 3. Gustav Fischer Verlag, Jena

Schimper, W. P. and Schenk, A. (1890). *Handbuch der Palaeontologie. II. Palaeophytologie.* R. Oldenburg Verlag, München and Leipzig

Schmincke, H.-U. (1976). The geology of the Canary Islands. In *Biogeography and Ecology in the Canary Islands.* (G. Kunkel, ed.), 67–184. *Monogr. Biol.* **30**. Junk, The Hague

Sørensen, T. (1948). A method of establishing groups of equal amplitude in plant sociology based on similarity of species content and its application to analyses of the vegetation on Danish commons. *Biol. Skr. Dan. Vid. Selsk.* **5**, No. 4

Størmer, P. (1960a). A contribution to the bryology of the Canary Islands. Mosses, chiefly collected by Johannes Lid. *Skr. Norske Vid. Akad. Oslo. I. Matem.-naturv. Kl.* 1959, No. 5, 1–90

— (1960b). *Antitrichia californica* in the Canary Islands. *Rev. Bryol. Lichénol.* **29**, 254–255

Sunding, P. (1967). Studies in the distribution and ecology of the bryophytes of Gran Canaria. *Nytt. Mag. Bot.* **14**, 44–67

— (1970). Elementer i Kanariøyenes flora, og teorier til forklaring av floraens opprinnelse. *Blyttia* **28**, 229–259

— (1972). The Vegetation of Gran Canaria. *Skr. Norske Vid. Akad. Oslo. I. Matem.-naturv. Kl.* n.s. **29**, 1–186

— (1973). Endemism in the flora of the Cape Verde Islands, with special emphasis on the Macaronesian flora element. *Monogr. Biol. Canar.* **4**, 112–117

Takhtajan, A. (1969). *Flowering Plants; Origin and Dispersal.* Edinburgh. English translation (by C. Jeffrey) of *Poriskhozhdenie polrytosemennykh rastenii.* Smithsonian Inst. Press, Washington D.C.

Walter, H. and Straka, H. (1970). *Arealkunde. Floristisch-historische Geobotanik 2.* Aufl. Eugen Ulmer Verlag, Stuttgart

3 Observations on the Phytogeography of the New Hebrides, Lord Howe Island and Norfolk Island

P. S. GREEN   *Royal Botanic Gardens, Kew, England*

Las relaciones fitogeográficas de las Nuevas Hebridas, islas de Lord Howe e isla Norfolk, son discutidas. Una reciente exploración en el área ha mejorado el conocimiento ya existente de la región y varios problemas fitogeográficos han sido resueltos.

El parentesco entre las Nuevas Hebridas y Nueva Caledonia, Fiji y Nueva Zelanda ha sido tanteado y varios casos de taxonomía incorrecta, conduciendo a una equivocada interpretación fitogeográfica han sido ya informados. La especiación activa en la región S. Pacifico en el género *Cyrtandra* (Gesneriaceae) con 11 especies en las Nuevas Hebridas, 35 en Fiji y 24 de las islas Salomón está demostrada. Otros centros insulares de diversidad en el mismo género aparecen en Hawaii y Nueva Guinea. La dispersión en el género parece ser por pájaros.

Se discuten varias formas de distribución disyunta con otras islas, S. y Central América y Australia. Las posibilidades de estas disyunciones, que son debido a dispersión de larga distancia, o por el contrario a residuos relictuales de distribuciones alguna vez más extensas, se consideran y se dan ejemplos de ambos.

El género *Bubbia* (Winteraceae) parece ser un buen ejemplo de una distribución relictual, estando representado en Madagascar, Australia, Nueva Caledonia e isla de Lord Howe.

Varias especies endémicas locales en peligro de extinción son mencionadas, *Hibiscus insularis* (3–4 plantas sobrevivientes) y *Arucaria heterophylla*, ambas son de la isla Philip.

Finalmente, el autor comenta brevemente el factor de que en edades geológicas pasadas, la distribución de muchas de estas disyunciones de taxones relictos insulares, puede haber sido más extensa a través de lo que ahora está cubierto por los hielos del Oeste de la Antártida.

The relationships of the floras of individual islands in the Pacific have long interested botanists. Van Balgooy (1971) has analysed very thoroughly the Spermatophyte flora of the whole Pacific basin. Just previous to his analysis the large Solomon Islands archipelago had been very little explored but collections stimulated by T. C. Whitmore, or made by him and by the Royal Society Expedition to the Solomon Isles in 1965, arrived just in time to provide important data that filled what would otherwise have been a considerable phytogeographic gap. In contrast, at the time of the analysis the smaller New Hebridean archipelago was still little known – since then, however, another Royal Society Expedition has taken place, this time to the New Hebrides in 1971. It fell to my lot to name most of the collections made on this expedition and it became apparent that many new records and range extensions had been added. Some 50 or more genera, for example, are now known from these islands for the first time. Despite this, however (and despite the continuing need for more collections from the New Hebrides, especially the northern islands, including the Banks Group), van Balgooy's general conclusions have not been upset, and the only changes called for are ones of detail. It is still true that the New Hebridean flora is an extension of that of Malesia, through Bougainville and the Solomon Islands, to Fiji, and beyond to Samoa and Tonga – in terms of taxa the richness gradually becoming less and less, except for a slight upsurge of endemism in Fiji (where, for example, one meets the ancient, endemic family Degeneriaceae). However, it is perhaps not surprising that the flora of the New Hebrides should be somewhat depauperate, when one considers their relatively recent geological history and the relatively small size of the islands – the vegetation is rich and lush, as one might expect in the humid tropics but poor in terms of diversity of species – and there are no endemic genera.

Although the nearest land to the New Hebrides is that of New Caledonia the affinity between the floras of the two areas is contrastingly weak. New Caledonia is an old land mass originally part of Gondwanaland and now lying at the end of the submerged Norfolk Island Ridge, with a deep trough between it and New Hebrides (I am no geomorphologist but I interpret this trough as representing the front of the drifting tectonic plate). As we shall see shortly the affinity of the New Caledonian flora is rather in the opposite direction, with Australia, Norfolk Island and Lord Howe Island and even with New Zealand, although this last is subtropical only in its northernmost parts.

Relatively few species are found only in the New Hebrides and New Caledonia. This cannot be entirely due to the fact that, in contrast to the former, large areas of New Caledonia are covered by inhospitable ultrabasic rocks, for in the North East there is rainforest on a gneissic substrate. To the few species they have in common may now be added *Haloragis prostrata* J. R. & G. Forst., a species otherwise previously known only from New Caledonia which was collected for the first time in the New Hebrides, on Erromanga, by the Royal Society expedition. It was collected on the coast in the upper zones – on coral limestone just above the *Pemphis* zone – and one wonders whether it could have been a relatively recent arrival by sea.

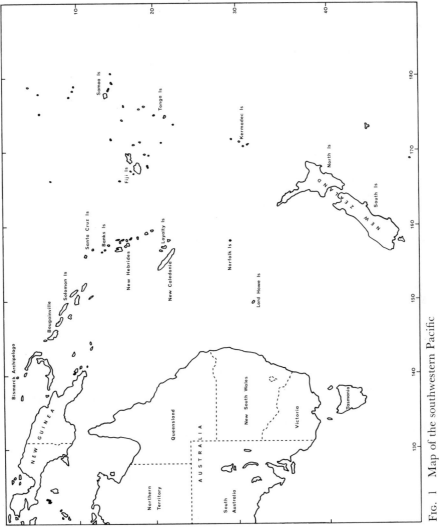

Fig. 1   Map of the southwestern Pacific

Another strand plant with this distribution, although one wonders why it is so limited in its distribution, is *Trachymene cussonii* (Montr.) B.L. Burtt – known from New Caledonia and the New Hebrides only. There is a specimen in the Herbarium at Kew bearing an old label that indicates that it came from Fiji, but the collector also collected in New Caledonia and, as it has never been found in Fiji since, it is my belief that this is almost certainly a case of mislabelling.

An epiphytic liliaceous plant was collected in the mountains of the New Hebridean islands Aneityum, Tanna and Espiritu Santo. In the field one was immediately reminded of *Astelia* and thus of a New Caledonian connection through *Astelia neo-caledonica* Schltr., but on closer examination the plant has been found to be *Collospermum montanum* (Seem.) Skottsb., known before only from Fiji and a member of a small, related genus previously thought to be confined to Fiji and New Zealand. The moral is that inaccurate identification can give a misleading idea of phytogeographical connections.

The genus *Piliocalyx* in the Myrtaceae was known from New Caledonia and Fiji only, with seven or eight species in the former and one in the latter. It has now been collected from the New Hebrides where the representation turns out to be the Fijian species, *P. concinnus* A.C. Sm., and not any of those from New Caledonia.

In fact the collections that have accumulated during the last half-a-dozen years have strengthened the realisation of the closeness of the floristic affinities between the New Hebrides and Fiji. Some dozen or so species, from almost as many families, which had previously been thought to be endemic to Fiji are now recorded from the New Hebrides as well. I will not tabulate them but confine myself to an example which shows this Fijian connection with, in addition, other links in the Pacific, yet missing out New Caledonia altogether. *Melicytus ramiflorus* J.R. & G. Forst. (Violaceae) exists as four subspecies. The type from New Zealand, one from Norfolk Island, one from Samoa, and one from Fiji, ssp. *fascigera* (Gillespie) P.S. Green (Green, 1969, 1970). This last has now been collected from three of the New Hebridean islands.

This same floristic affinity between the New Hebrides and Fiji has also been revealed by careful taxonomic examination of some of the so-called New Hebridean endemics which have now been identified with species from Fiji. Many of these New Hebridean "endemics" were described by Guillaumin and it is clear that when describing them he failed to compare them with the then known Fijian species, presumably either because, being himself the authority on the New Caledonian flora he thought only of the plants of that country, or because he had an inadequate representation of the Fijian flora at hand for comparative purposes. For example, when he described *Melodinus neo-ebudicus* as a new New Hebridean species he compared it with the New Caledonian *M. buxifolius* Baill. and *M. celastroides* Baill. (which are now considered to be conspecific anyway) and quite failed to mention the Fijian *M. glaber* Turrill with which it is actually conspecific and into the synonymy of which it falls. Another good example of bad taxonomy is provided by the case of *Ligustrum neo-ebudicum*, also described by Guillaumin. Critical examination of the type material shows that it is in fact the widespread *Olea paniculata* R. Br., known also from Australia, Lord Howe Island, New Caledonia, Solomon Islands, Malesia and India (but not in this case from Fiji).

That there are good species endemic to the New Hebrides is borne out by, for example, the recent description of *Ophiorrhiza brachyantha* by S. P. Darwin (1976a, p. 63) who has been working on the Pacific Rubiaceae. The New Hebrides has several endemics in those genera which seem to be undergoing active speciation, for example *Cyrtandra* (Gesneriaceae) in which collections on the Royal Society Expedition led to the recognition by the late George W. Gillett of six new species (Gillett, 1973, 1974). For some of these the affinity is said to lie with Fiji and for others even with New Guinea or Australia. In this genus Gillett recognised eleven species from the New Hebrides, and one, *C. mareënsis* Däniker, from the small island of Maré, one of the Loyalty Islands, just off the NE coast of New Caledonia and lying between there and the New Hebrides. Thirty-five species were recognised from Fiji, 24 from the Solomon Isles, while it was suggested that there are about 100 from New Guinea and not fewer than 40 in Hawaii (although St. John (1966) maintains over 130 from the island of Oahu alone). In this genus the fruit is characteristically a fleshy white berry and the seeds are small, which indicates that dispersal is probably by birds which eat the berries. Once they have dispersed them to new islands, isolated differentiation could give rise to a multiplicity of species. One speculates as to whether *C. mareënsis*, the only New Caledonian species, as mentioned, has arrived on the outlying Loyalty Islands by dispersal from the New Hebrides and then differentiated – giving a floristic link between the New Hebrides and New Caledonia which has been established relatively recently.

Possibly older links concern species whose distribution extends to Fiji as well as to New Caledonia, for example, *Styphelia cymbalae* (Labill.) Spreng., in the Southern Hemisphere family Epacridaceae, or the Sapindaceous, *Elattostachys falcata* (A. Gray) Radlk., known since the Royal Society expedition from the New Hebrides, as well as Fiji, Samoa, Tonga and Niue, and also recorded from New Caledonia – although I have not seen material from there myself.

The expedition also extended the recorded range of Solomon Islands species, quite a number of which do not reach Fiji (nor New Caledonia), for example *Cominsia gigantea* (Scheff.) K. Schum. (Marantaceae), known previously from the Solomon Islands, New Guinea and the Moluccas, or *Gunnera macrophylla* Bl. collected on the mountains on Tanna and Espiritu Santo, and also known from the Solomons and Malesia. Another interesting extension of range, which also poses a question of considerable disjunction which may or may not be real, was the collection on Tanna of *Vaccinium whiteanum* Sleum. previously known only from Bougainville. Likewise the discovery of the small saprophyte *Burmannia lutescens* Becc. on Aneityum, the southernmost island in the archipelago. In order to find such saprophytes, including for example members of the Triuridaceae, I recommend that one slips face forward as one mounts a hillside in dense tropical forest, for that is exactly how I became aware of the rather insignificant, creamy white and pale blue *Burmannia* which was the first record for the Burmanniaceae from the New Hebrides. The nearest other locality known for this species and family is in New Ireland (it is also known from New Guinea and Malaysia). Clearly with such an easily overlooked and fairly ephemeral plant it may well turn up in one of the intermediate areas and fill in what at present is almost certainly a false disjunction.

Whilst on the subject of disjunctions, it may not be out of place to consider the interesting case of *Lindenia* in the Rubiaceae, even though this example does not actually involve the New Hebrides, but New Caledonia and Fiji. S. P. Darwin has published a revision of the genus in which he recognised three species (Darwin 1976b): *Lindenia austro-caledonica* Brongn. from New Caledonia, *L. vitiensis* Seem. from Fiji and *L. rivalis* Benth. from Central America. I remember collecting the New Caledonian plant in 1963 and have looked out the specimens in the Herbarium at Kew and it is clear, as Darwin states, that the two Pacific plants are very similar – in fact I would have been inclined to treat them as one species with two subspecies. The Central American plant is clearly of the same genus, although placed by Darwin in a separate section. *Lindenia* belongs to the tribe *Rondeletieae* and it is in fact the only member of the tribe represented in the Pacific, so the main affinity is clearly with America. Darwin, after considering the matter, concludes that the Pacific plants have not arrived there recently – there is little evidence of transpacific dispersal (the seeds are against it, there would be need for an association with a long-tongued insect, and the genus does not occur in any geographically intermediate localities). He has concluded that *Lindenia* used to occupy a wide, more continuous range, including South America, Western Antarctica and New Zealand – that is around the southern Pacific.

This transpacific disjunction is paralleled by *Epistephium* in the Orchidaceae. *E. smilacifolium* Rchb. occurs in New Caledonia and is quite distinct from the other 17 or so species, all of which are found in central or tropical South America (Garay, 1961). Or, yet again, in *Stillingia* of the Euphorbiaceae which has 30 or more species in the warm parts of America, and one on the other side of the world – *S. lineata*, with ssp. *lineata* in the Mascarenes and ssp. *pacifica* in Timor and adjacent islands, and in Fiji (van Steenis, 1966).

These disjunctions may be true ones and not reflect a lack of collections from intermediate areas. There are relatively few regions of the world now where no collections have ever been made but certain groups or forms, even of vascular plants, are still often overlooked or rarely collected. Aquatic plants fall into this category. On the New Hebrides expedition we were able to add two genera of seagrasses (Cymodoceaceae) to the recorded flora, *Syringodium* and *Thalassodendron*. While on the island of Aneityum and waiting for the boat to call to transport us to Tanna a low tide almost uncovered a wide, underwater meadow consisting of plants of these two genera. Freshwater aquatics are often overlooked and under-collected too. *Potamogeton* specimens were collected, but the most remarkable such collection was a *Ceratophyllum* collected by H. S. McKee (*McKee* in RSNH 24308) in a very good fruiting condition (so much material of the genus in herbaria is without fruits). In this collection the fruits, as well as bearing a characteristic large apical spine bore a crest round the edge with numerous smaller spines. Clearly this was not either of the two common species of *Ceratophyllum* and on looking through all the collections at Kew I have only been able to match it with one other made during the last century in Brazil (*Spruce*, 1883) which is the type of *C. demersum* L. var. *cristata* K. Schum. Does this plant occur anywhere else? As I say, the genus is under-collected, especially in fruit. From the description in the literature I suspect that this may also be the same as *C. echinatum* A. Gray from Eastern North America, but I have seen no authentic material of this last with fruit.

Returning to New Hebridean plants, a more common pattern of distribution is that linking the New Hebrides, not just with New Caledonia alone – which is rare – but stretching beyond that country to Australia and often to Lord Howe Island and Norfolk Island too. The genus *Bauerella* (Rutaceae), split off *Acronychia*, has recently been revived by Hartley (1975). There are two species, one endemic to New Caledonia, and the other occurring as three subspecies. The type, *Bauerella simplicifolia* (Endl.) Hartley ssp. *simplicifolia* comes from eastern tropical Australia, Lord Howe and Norfolk Islands, another, ssp. *petiolaris* (A. Gray) Hartley, from Fiji and the third, ssp. *neo-scotica* (P. S. Green) Hartley, is so called because it comes from New Caledonia and the New

Hebrides. This type of distribution is well-known and paralleled by that monogeneric family the *Balanopaceae*, a small, systematically isolated and probably ancient group of uncertain affinity. Two species are found in Queensland, one in Fiji, six or seven in New Caledonia and one in the New Hebrides (I suspect the distinctness of the last, but the genus is in need of a modern revision).

Amongst the New Hebridean Expedition collections there was material which matched *Polyscias neo-ebudarum* (Guillaum.) B. C. Stone (Araliaceae) but on examination it also matched *P. monticola* Harms from New Caledonia and *P. cissodendron* (Moore & F. Muell.) Harms from Lord Howe Island – and this last is the earliest name. This was a case where three species which were each thought to be endemic to their own island groups were found instead to be conspecific and to strengthen the floristic affinity not only between Lord Howe and New Caledonia but with the New Hebrides too. Other links from the New Hebrides to Eastern Australia via New Caledonia are found in the so-called Australian Chestnut, *Castanospermum australe* A. Cunn. & Fraser, a monotypic leguminous genus. There is also *Halfordia kendack* (Montr.) Guillaum. (Rutaceae). But several such cases could be cited.

This link with Australia may also extend to Malesia – for example *Passiflora aurantia* Forst. f., one of the relatively few species of Passion Flower native outside the New World, is known from the New Hebrides, New Caledonia and Australia, also from New Guinea in one direction and from Norfolk Island and Fiji, in the other. There are some ten or more synonymous epithets (Green, 1972). Such a distribution may not extend to Fiji and may miss out New Caledonia, for example *Eurycles amboinensis* Loud. (Amaryllidaceae) is known for Malesia and New Guinea, from Australia and New Hebrides.

As may be seen from the underwater contours, Lord Howe Island and Norfolk Island lie on submarine ridges which stretch out in a northerly direction from the area of New Zealand. The Lord Howe Rise being the most westerly, with a relatively deep trough between it and the east coast of Australia, except opposite the northern half of Queensland. Next to this is the Norfolk Island Ridge which extends to New Caledonia, and most easterly the Kermadec Ridge which connects with Fiji. Much speculation has taken place on the significance of these marine contours but with recent theories it is becoming apparent that they represent the remains of more extensive land in the past which has foundered, leaving only small areas of Lord Howe, Norfolk Island and the Kermadecs. On these islands exist very disharmonious floras with numerous endemics, some of which may well represent evolutionary differentiation from plants that have arrived there by dispersal, but others almost certainly represent ancient stock, the remains of a once more extensive and diverse flora which is now extinct, except for the few species which found refuge and survived on the island. Endemic genera, sometimes without obvious affinities, for example *Ungeria* (of the Sterculiaceae) from Norfolk Island, clearly represent the remnants of an ancient flora, but so do many endemic species. From Norfolk Island also comes the endemic leguminous genus *Streblorrhiza*, or rather came, for it is now extinct. It presents an example of how very restricted these relict species and genera can be, for it was known only from Philip Island, an island barely 2 km by 2 km close to and just to the south of Norfolk Island.

Lord Howe Island has four endemic genera. *Negria*, an absorescent gesneriad and the palm genera *Howea* (two species), *Hedyscepe* and *Lepidorrhachis*, the last two monotypic. These palms have palaeotropical affinities but *Negria* is allied to *Depanthus* (two species from New Caledonia) and *Rhabdothamnus* (one species from New Zealand). Together with *Coronanthera* (eleven species in New Caledonia and the Solomons) they constitute the Tribe *Coronantherae* of the Gesneriaceae which, with the E. Australian *Fieldia* in another tribe, happen to be the only Old World members of the large and otherwise New World subfamily, the Gesnerioideae. *Negria rhabdothamnoides* forms a stout tree up to six or even more metres tall – a good example perhaps of island gigantism (Green, 1973).

Colmeiroa was described as a monotypic genus endemic to Lord Howe Island but it has now been shown that the species really belongs to *Corokia* (Escalloniaceae) and as such its affinities lie with northern New South Wales (one species), New Zealand (three species) and far away Rapa (one species) (L. S. Smith, 1958).

Representative of an old relictual distribution is the Lord Howe Island *Bubbia howeana* (F. Muell.) van Teigh. (of the Winteraceae). This ancient, primitive genus has a present distribution of Madagascar, Queensland and New Caledonia, as well as Lord Howe. Its link is with Gondwanaland, the ancient, southern landmass (and it is perhaps significant that this archaic family, and others like it, is not represented in the flora of the relatively recent islands that make up the New Hebrides).

For both Lord Howe and Norfolk Islands the floristic affinities lie with New Zealand in the south, New Caledonia in the north, and, to a slightly less extent but more strongly in the case of Lord Howe than Norfolk Island, with Australia to the west, especially with Queensland and northernmost New South Wales. Between the two islands there is a close affinity, *Lagunaria patersonia* (Andr.) G. Don, in the Malvaceae near to *Hibiscus*, is confined to them but for the little known and presumably rare var. *bracteata* Benth. in eastern Australia.

In *Macropiper excelsum* (Forst. f.) Miq. two forms have recently been recognized (A. C. Smith, 1975), f. *psittacorum* (Endl.) A.C. Sm. being confined to the two islands and to the Kermadecs and islands off the coast of North Island New Zealand, while the type form is known only from New Zealand and Chatham Island. This link with New Zealand is also shown on Lord Howe by the endemic *Carmichaelia exsul* F. Muell., the only species of this genus known from outside New Zealand. A new subspecies of the New Zealand grass *Chionochloa conspicua* (Forst. f.) Zotov has recently been found and collected on the steep, hazardous flanks of Mt. Lidgbird, a member of a genus known only from New Zealand but for one species in Australia. While the two endemic species of *Olearia* on Lord Howe are related more to the New Zealand species than the Australian representative of this genus.

The connection with New Zealand is perhaps even stronger in the case of Norfolk Island. Here at generic level we have the palm genus *Rhopalostylis* which contains three species. *R. baueri* (Hook. f.) Wendl. & Drude from Norfolk Island, one from New Zealand and Chatham Island, and one from the Kermadecs. In other cases the link is at subspecific level – *Freycinetia baueriana* Endl. ssp. *baueriana* (in the Pandanaceae) is the Norfolk Island plant, while ssp. *banksia* (A. Cunn.) B. C. Stone occurs in New Zealand (Stone, 1973). In yet other plants the taxonomic similarity is even closer. There is some undescribed differentiation which needs investigation in *Phormium tenax* J. R. & G. Forst., the New Zealand flax, which on Norfolk Island is confined to damp areas on cliffs and by the sea. *Ileostylis micranthus* (Hook. f.) van Teigh. (Loranthaceae), a monotypic genus previously endemic to New Zealand, is now known from Norfolk Island. I collected it there in 1963. Could it have arrived by bird transport in the last half century? I think it must have done so for it is a very distinct and conspicuous parasite yet not included by Laing in his list of the island's flora (1915), even though there is an undated specimen in his herbarium, presumably collected after his list was published. *Nestegis apetala* (Vahl.) L. Johnson occurs in the northernmost parts of New Zealand and on Norfolk Island (while three of the other four species are also found in New Zealand (Green, 1963) and one in Hawaii).

The genus *Dracophyllum* (Epacridaceae) links Lord Howe Island with both New Zealand and New Caledonia, as well as, but not so closely, with Australia, *D. fitzgeraldii* Moore & F. Muell. being endemic and a characteristic part of the vegetation on the upper parts of the Lord Howe mountains. Similarly, *Nicotiana debneyi* Domin links Lord Howe with eastern Australia and New Caledonia, the three areas constituting its total distribution. Likewise, *Acronychia laevis* J. R. & G. Forst. (Rutaceae) is also known from the same three areas, and in his revision of this genus, Hartley (1974, p. 505) has suggested that this species has arrived relatively recently from Australia by long-distance dispersal because the New Caledonian population differs only slightly from the Australian and is more homogeneous. There is lack of differentiation between the two areas and a lack of variation in the New Caledonian plant.

The Norfolk Island species of the genus *Exocarpus* (Santalaceae), *E. phyllanthoides* Endl., is known from New Caledonia and constitutes the mono-specific subgenus *Phyllodanthos*. Lord Howe Island also possesses an endemic member of this genus, *E. homocladus* Moore & F. Muell., in this case related on the one hand to a species from E. Australia and on the other to one from Rapa, far out in SE Polynesia. At one time there was confusion over the Norfolk Island endemic species of *Euphorbia*, *E. norfolkiana* Boiss. A suffrutescent species, it was suggested by Laing (1915; p. 29), who had visited the island but not seen it there, that it was not native but had been introduced from the New Hebrides and was really *E. tannensis* (there had been a very strong missionary link between the two areas, Norfolk Island having been the headquarters of the Melanesian Mission). But while *E. tannensis* Spreng. is known from New Caledonia, where it was called *E. vieillardii* Baill., the Norfolk Island plant is undoubtedly distinct. Its affinities lie closer to *E. fidjiana* Boiss., which is endemic to Fiji.

As an example of a plant which may be overlooked easily and has only recently been found on Norfolk Island (by R. D. Hoogland) one may cite a minute, leafless orchid in the genus *Taeniophyllum*. It has been found to be *T. muelleri* Benth., otherwise known from southeastern Queensland and northeastern New South Wales. Further search has been made for it and one can say with assurance that it is rare on Norfolk Island as well as being inconspicuous, yet one cannot help wondering how long it has been there or whether it may be found in the forests on Lord Howe Island, which lies mid-way between Norfolk Island and Australia.

One endemic Norfolk Island plant I wish to mention because of the conservational significance of its present status is *Hibiscus insularis* Endl., known only from Philip Island, the same small island already mentioned in connection with the extinct genus *Streblorrhiza*. This *Hibiscus* exists today in the wild only as three or four bushes and at present is not regenerating. This island presents us with a first-rate example of what man, by means of goats and pigs and finally by rabbits, can do to exterminate a flora. The famous botanical explorer, Alan Cunningham, who was marooned on the island for a few days by escaping convicts in 1836, wrote (Heward, 1842, pp. 114–116) that the island was more or less covered with vegetation like the adjacent Norfolk Island, but today this has practically all disappeared. The surface is nearly all eroded subsoil and only rabbit-resistant plants, which are almost without exception introduced weeds, grow there, except for the remnants of the older trees and bushes which, as I say, are not regenerating. A few trees of the Norfolk Island Pine, *Araucaria heterophylla* (Salisb.) Franco, survive, all top soil having been washed away from around the upper parts of their roots. Fortunately, the Pine survives on the adjacent Norfolk Island – at present very unhappily, but that is another story. My main theme in this paper is geographic affinity and in this connection the distribution of *Araucaria* is well known and documented, but incidentally the nearest relative to *A. heterophylla*, the Norfolk Island species, is *A. columnaris* (Forst. f.) Hook. from lowland New Caledonia.

Finally, one may perhaps consider two very different but interesting distributions relating to Lord Howe plants. Section *Edwardsia* of *Sophora* (Leguminosae) has a strong southern connection (Green, 1970; pp. 204–5); from Réunion comes *S. denudata* Bory, from Lord Howe Island *S. howinsula* (W. R. B. Oliver) P. S. Green, from New Zealand two species, *S. microphylla* Ait. and *S. tetraptera* J. Mill., from Hawaii *S. chrysophylla* (Salisb.) Seem., from Easter Island *S. toromiro* (Phil.) Skotsb., three species from Juan Fernandez and from Chile *S. macrocarpa* and *S. microphylla* ssp. *macnabiana* (R. Graham) Yakovlev (and one wonders whether this last is more worthy of specific rank like the other taxa in this section). The other remarkable disjunct distribution connected with the flora of Lord Howe Island is exhibited by the genus *Dietes* in the Iridaceae. In this genus there are three species in South Africa but otherwise there is only the distinct. *D. robinsoniana* (F. Muell.) Klatt on Lord Howe Island. It has been suggested by Paramanov (1958) that it might have been introduced from South Africa – perhaps by a whaling ship, they used to call in at Lord Howe – but this cannot be for it is quite distinct from each of the other species and is undoubtedly a *Dietes*. Disjunct South African and Australian distributions are well known at the family level, for example the Restionaceae, but at the level of genus it is rare. Today we see only the existing distributions, yet, in my opinion, in such cases one is looking at the remnants of what, in past geological ages, was a much more continuous and complete distribution, when plants grew on land which is now under ice, in western Antarctica, or under the sea, in the foundered ridges of the SW Pacific.

No single factor may explain present-day, disjunct distribution patterns. In some cases dispersal, even long distant dispersal, may be the explanation, in others the disappearance of land once available for plant growth and in yet others extinction from intermediate areas.

REFERENCES

Balgooy, M. M. J. van (1971). Plant Geography of the Pacific. *Blumea* Suppl. VI, 222

Darwin, S. P. (1976a). The Pacific species of *Ophiorrhiza* L. (Rubiaceae). *Lyonia* **1**, 47–102

— (1976b). The genus *Lindenia* (Rubiaceae). *J. Arn. Arb.* **57**, 426–449

Garay, L. (1961). Notes on the genus *Epistephium*. *Amer. Orchid Soc. Bull.* **30**, 496–500

Gillett, G. W. (1973). The genus *Cyrtandra* (Gesneriaceae) in the South Pacific. *Univ. Calif. Publ. Bot.* **66**, 1–59

— (1974). New records for *Cyrtandra* (*Gesneriaceae*) in the New Hebrides. *Kew Bull.* **29**, 699–709

Green, P. S. (1963). The genus *Nestegis* from New Zealand. *J. Arn. Arb.* **44**, 377–389

— (1969). Notes on Melanesian plants: I. *Kew Bull.* **23**, 337–346

— (1970). Notes relating to the floras of Norfolk and Lord Howe Islands, I. *J. Arn. Arb.* **51**, 204–220

— (1972). *Passiflora* in Australia and the Pacific. *Kew Bull.* **26**, 539–558

— (1973). *Negria rhabdothamnoides. Curtis's Bot. Mag.* **179**, t.N.S. 659

Hartley, T. G. (1974). A revision of the genus *Acronychia* (Rutaceae). *J. Arn. Arb.* **55**, 469–567

— (1975). The taxonomic status of the genus *Bauerella* (Rutaceae). *J. Arn. Arb.* **56**, 164–170

Heward, R. (1842). Biographical sketch of the late Allen Cunningham Esq., F.L.S., M.R.G.S., etc., etc. *Hooker's Lond. J. Bot.* **1**, 107–128

Laing, R. M. (1915). A revised list of the Norfolk Island flora, with some notes on the species. *Trans. & Proc. N. Z. Inst.* **47**, 1–39

Pavamanov, S. J. (1958). Lord Howe Island, a riddle of the Pacific, part 1. *Pacific Sci.* **12**, 89

Smith, A. C. (1975). The genus *Macropiper* (Piperaceae). *Bot. J. Linn. Soc.* **71**, 1–38

Smith L. S. (1958). *Corokia* A. Cunn. – an addition to the Australian genera of Saxifragaceae. *Proc. Roy. Soc. Queensl.* **69**, 53–55

Steenis, C. G. G. J. van (1966). *Stillingia lineata*. In, Pacific Plant Areas, 2. *Blumea* Suppl. V, 302–3

Stone, B. C. (1973). Materials for a monograph of *Freycinetia* Gaudich. XIV. On the relation between *F. banksii* A. Cunn. of New Zealand and *F. baueriana* Endl. of Norfolk Island, with notes on the structure of the seeds. *N. Z. J. Bot.* **11**, 241–246

St. John, H. (1966). Monograph of *Cyrtandra* (Gesneriaceae) on Oahu, Hawaiian Islands. *Bull. Bishop Mus.* **229**, 1–465

4 Biogeography of the Antillean Fern Flora

ROLLA TRYON   *Gray Herbarium, Harvard University, U.S.A.*

Entre las islas del Caribe consideraremos el centro biogeográfico de mayor interés las Antillas Mayores y Menores. Las cuatro Antillas Mayores: Cuba, Jamaica, Española y Puerto Rico, son islas bastante grandes, con una extensa área de altas montañas. La más baja, Puerto Rico, tiene una altitud de 1350 m y la más alta, Española, una altitud de 3100m. Las islas son antiguas, datan desde el Cretaceo o quizás antes. En comparación, las Antillas Menores, todas de origen volcánico, se alzaron durante el Oligoceno o Plioceno. Son pequeñas y tienen áreas montañosas relativamente limitadas. Solo siete de las 21 islas con una flora de helechos tienen una altitud que supera los 1000 m., siendo la más alta Guadalupe, con 1500 m.

Existen cinco características principales biogeográficas de los helechos antillanos: 1. Tienen un caracter continental en lugar de insular. 2. Las Antillas Mayores tienen 98 géneros de Pteridofitos, siendo cinco de ellos endémicos. Las Antillas Menores tienen 68 géneros y ninguno endémico. 3. Las Antillas Mayores tienen 1100 especies, aproximadamente 500 son endemismos y 175 de estas son endemismos exlcusivos de una sola isla. Las Antillas Menores poseen 325 especies, incluyendo 40 endemismos con siete de ellos de una sola isla. 4. Los helechos de las dos Antillas difieren significativamente, no solo en sus especies endémicas, sino también en las no endémicas. 360 de las últimas aparecen en las Mayores, pero no en las Menores, y 65 aparecen en las Menores pero no en las Mayores. 5. Alrededor del 40% de las especies de Mexico y América Central también existen en las Antillas Mayores y un 15% de las especies del norte de Sur América tambíen aparecen en las Antillas Menores.

Las dos Antillas difieren mucho en su diversidad de características biogeográfica, especies endémicas y especies comunes en otras áreas. Estas diferencias se relacionan con la gran diversidad ecológica de las Antillas Mayores y la relativamente baja diversidad de las Antillas Menores. La diferente antiguedad de las islas y la gran cantidad de espacios variados, no parecen ser significativo para su biogeografía presente. El área y altitud de las islas, relacionan, sin embargo, a su biogeografía en que ambos reflejan la extensa diversidad ecológica.

El número de especies en un área depende de la migración de especies en una especiación dentro de un área. La diversidad ecológica mantendrá un fuerte control sobre la migración entre áreas, la especiación en un área y la evolución de endemismos locales. La gran diversidad ecológica suministra la base para una rica flora, teniendo en cuenta las oportunidades de un amplio espectro de migrantes y establecimiento de endemismos locales.

c

Introduction

An analysis of the fern floras *(Filicopsida)* of the islands of the Antilles indicates that while they do not reflect characteristics of insularity, they do illustrate basic problems of plant geography in an especially diagrammatic way. Data on the ferns of the Antilles have been obtained from Duek (1971) for Cuba, Proctor (1953) for Jamaica, Christensen (1937) for Hispaniola, Maxon (1926) for Puerto Rico, and Proctor (1977) for the Lesser Antilles. These primary sources have been augmented by data from recent monographic treatments, other modern literature, and the collections in the herbaria of the Arnold Arboretum and the Gray Herbarium.

Fern biogeography

Ferns are an ideal group for biogeographic studies because nearly all species are homosporous with small spores readily dispersed by wind, and have a potentially hermaphrodite gametophyte. A single spore has the potential to establish a species at a new site, and spores are frequently dispersed for distances of several hundred kilometers and may reach to distances of 3200 km (A. Tryon, 1966; R. Tryon, 1970). Because of this high dispersal capacity, the distribution of a species should correspond closely to the geographic distribution of its ecology. Since the dispersal capacity will allow frequent testing of areas for suitable habitats, a species may be expected to achieve its maximum distribution within a relatively short time. In contrast, among the flowering plants, low dispersibility, dioecism, self-incompatibility and pollination vectors, for example, may severely limit the capacity of a species to occupy all of the geographic area where suitable habitats occur.

Related to the high dispersal capacity of ferns is an insensitivity to degrees of geographic isolation that are of significance in many groups of flowering plants. Only the fern floras of the most isolated of oceanic islands have the attributes of true insularity derived from migration by very rare dispersal events: a few species representing a random selection from source areas, a low species to genus ratio, and high endemism derived from geographic isolation. Data are presented in Table 1 to illustrate the essentially continental character of the fern floras of the Antilles. All of the islands are too close to other islands and continental areas for their fern floras to reflect strong geographic isolation.

The important feature of fern biogeography in an archipelago is that migration between islands must be by separate dispersal-migration events across a water barrier. The general biogeographic basis for the

TABLE 1 Selected islands and continental areas compared with respect to the insularity of their fern floras

Island or area	Size (km²)	No. of species	No. of genera	Species/ genus ratio	% species endemism	Index of insularity*
Barro Colorado†	15	89	37	2.4	0	0.4
Honduras	112 000	325	65	5.0	0	0.2
Peru	1 250 000	750	95	7.9	11	1.5
St. Kitts	180	117	32	3.7	0	0.3
Guadeloupe	1550	252	57	4.4	2	0.4
Puerto Rico	8800	277	64	4.3	4	1.2
Hispaniola	74 000	660	87	7.6	11	1.6
Easter	116	15	12	1.2	37	31.7
Tristan da Cunha archipelago	260	30	16	1.9	27	14.7
Society Islands	1700	150	52	2.9	30	10.3

* The index of insularity is % species endemism + 1/species/genus ratio. In order to accommodate cases in which there is no endemism, 1 is added to the numerator. The characteristic low number of species on isolated islands is not included directly, it is represented in the species/genus ratio. The effect of size of continental areas is essentially eliminated by this formula: the small number of species on Barro Colorado, for example, is offset by the lack of endemism, while the moderately high endemism of Peru is offset by the high species/genus ratio.

†Now an island in the Canal Zone, Panama, formerly a hilltop prior to the creation of Gatun Lake.

occurrence of a species on an island will be migration to an environmental area similar to that of the source and (usually) initially small populations. On continents, in comparison, the basis for an isolated occurrence of a species is often obscure because of the uncertain history of present barriers, because large populations may be involved in migration, and because species may have the opportunity to adapt gradually to new environments.

Biogeographic features of the Antillean fern flora

The biogeographic features of species diversity and species endemism in the Antillean fern flora are presented in Table 2. The Greater Antilles have high diversity with 1000 species and high endemism of 45%. The diversity is highest in Hispaniola and lowest in Puerto Rico. Endemism is low to moderate on individual islands, ranging from 4% in Puerto Rico to

TABLE 2   Biogeographic data on the fern floras of the islands of the Antilles. The 11 islands of the Lesser Antilles with 1 to 36 species are not included

Island	Size (km²)	Maximum altitude (m)	No. of genera	No. of species*	No. of endemic species	Endemism (%)
Hispaniola	74 000	3100	87	660	70	11
Jamaica	10 880	2250	78	520	52	10
Cuba	113 950	2000	85	466	28	6
Puerto Rico	8800	1350	64	277	11	4
Greater Antilles			93	1000	450	45
Guadeloupe	1550	1500	57	252	5	2
Martinique	1100	1350	54	204	0	0
Dominica	780	1600	51	177	2	1
St. Vincent	340	1250	47	149	0	0
Grenada	310	850	43	143	0	0
St. Kitts	180	1150	32	117	0	0
Montserrat	100	900	40	110	0	0
St. Lucia	600	1000	40	104	0	0
Nevis	130	1100	23	74	1	1
Saba	13	850	21	62	0	0
Lesser Antilles			65	300	35	12

* Subspecies and major geographic varieties have been counted as species.

11% in Hispaniola. About 65% of the endemics of the Greater Antilles occur on two to four islands, while 35% are single-island endemics. The Lesser Antilles have low diversity with 300 species and moderate endemism of 12%. Diversity is highest on Guadeloupe with 252 species. Endemism is very low on individual islands; it is 1% or 2% on three islands and absent on the others. About 77% of the endemics of the Lesser Antilles occur on two or more islands, while 23% are single-island endemics.

The fern flora of the Greater Antilles is quite distinctive, of the 1000 species 780 do not occur in the Lesser Antilles. Among the remaining species, about 185 are rather widely distributed in tropical America, or at least in the circum-Caribbean region, and 30 are endemic to the whole Antillean area. The distinctiveness is reinforced by four endemic genera – *Adenoderris*, *Camptodium*, *Atalopteris* and *Faydenia*. The Greater Antilles have a rather large representation of species that also occur in mesic Mexico and Central America, and northern South America. These three regions share 520 species, including 335 that do not occur in the Lesser Antilles.

Fig. 1 Map of the Antilles, scale: 1 cm = 240 km. Greater Antilles: 1-Cuba, 2-Jamaica, 3-Hispaniola, 4-Puerto Rico. Lesser Antilles: 5-Saba, 6-St. Kitts, 7-Nevis, 8-Montserrat, 9-Guadeloupe, 10-Dominica, 11-Martinique, 12-St. Lucia, 13-St. Vincent, 14-Grenada

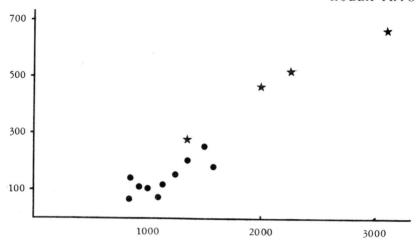

F<small>IG</small>. 2   Relation of maximum altitude of islands (abscissa in m) and number of fern species (ordinate) in   the Greater Antilles (★) and in 10 of the Lesser Antilles (●) listed in Table 2

The fern flora of the Lesser Antilles is less distinctive, for only 28% of the 300 species do not occur in the Greater Antilles. They have a rather poor representation of the species of northern South America. The two regions share 235 species, including only 50 that are not also in the Great Antilles. The remainder are members of the widely distributed element mentioned above.

The two Antillean island groups (Fig. 1) have had different geological histories. The Greater Antilles are large islands of Cretaceous age or somewhat older while the Lesser Antilles are small, most of them forming classical examples of volcanic arcs of about Oligocene age or younger. The length of time that the present environments have been in existence is difficult to assess because of the complex history of orogeny and vulcanism in the Antilles. Present environments may extend from the Miocene or earlier in the Greater Antilles, and from the Pliocene or later in the Lesser Antilles. The Greater Antilles are composed of a great variety of sedimentary, igneous and metamorphic rocks and most of them have rather extensive regions of high elevation. Puerto Rico has a less complex geology than the other islands and it is lower, with relatively small areas at the higher elevations. The Lesser Antilles are composed largely of limestone and volcanic rocks. Guadeloupe, Dominica, Martinique and St. Vincent have altitudes that are comparable to, or somewhat higher than, Puerto Rico; the other islands are significantly lower. The areas of high altitude are usually small, the largest being on Guadeloupe (Basse-Terre) and Dominica.

The striking differences in fern biogeography of the two archipelagoes is undoubtedly based on the high ecological diversity of the Greater Antilles and the lower ecological diversity of the Lesser Antilles. The diversity of habitats within the montane forest is of special importance because it is the vegetational zone where tropical ferns are always best developed. The role of ecological diversity and of montane forest in controlling the number of ferns in a region can be seen by a comparison of the Andes from Colombia to Bolivia with Brazilian Amazonia. The former region has at least 2500 species and 500 endemics while the larger, but low, Amazonian region has only 280 species and few or no endemics. (Tryon and Conant, 1975). In Jamaica, the three Parishes of Portland, St. Thomas and St. Andrew, that contain the Grand Range of the Blue Mountains (maximum elevation 2250 m) occupy an area of 2100 km². These Parishes have a total of 443 species, 85% of those known in Jamaica, while the remainder of the island with an area of 9300 km² has 223 species.

Other features of the Greater and Lesser Antilles that might have a biogeographic role such as their different ages and different distances from continental source areas, do not seem to be of significance. The high dispersibility of ferns undoubtedly rapidly obscures original floristic differences due to age or to distance from a source area. For example, the numbers of species and endemics are rather similar on the older island of Puerto Rico and the younger Guadeloupe (Basse-Terre). The Lesser Antilles with the richer fern floras are Guadeloupe, Dominica and Martinique, rather than those closest to Trinidad and Venezuela. Maximum altitude (Fig. 2) and size of an island correlate with species diversity, but in the Antilles these clearly reflect the more basic feature of ecological diversity.

Biogeographic processes

The biogeographic features of species diversity, species endemism, and floristic affinity of an area are the result of the processes of environmental adaptation, migration, and speciation. These processes operate in a species according to the opportunities available in the geography of the environment. The optimal geography will be one of high ecological diversity and nearly duplicate environments in partially isolated areas. This pattern of environment is one that supports the largest number of species and at the same time promotes the geographic-evolutionary processes that increase species diversity and endemism.

Environmental adaptation may occur especially when the process of speciation involves small populations. A new adaptation may be broader or narrower than that of the parent species and the change may result in different distributions. Adaptation of a new species to a broad ecology promotes migration and a considerable distribution. Adaptation of a new species to a narrow ecology promotes a limited distribution or the maintenance of the new species as a local endemic. The geographic consequences of different breadths of adaptation are illustrated by two species of Cyatheaceae (Conant, 1976).

Cyathea arborea (L.) Sm. is a species of lower to mid-elevations that becomes established especially in landslide areas where it forms handsome colonies as the slide area becomes revegetated. The plants grow to about 10 m tall but have a relatively short life of about 35 years. The species is not able to reproduce in stabilised conditions in and near the colony; it must re-establish itself each generation by dispersal to another site. In this case a relatively broad ecological adaptation is advantageous since it will increase the number of places where the species can grow. The development of a good capacity for migration, even for rather short distances on one island, would also endow the species with the capacity for long-distance migration because of the high dispersibility of the spores. The broad adaptation of *Cyathea arborea* has led to its present wide distribution (Fig. 3) throughout the Antilles from Cuba to Grenada.

Alsophila bryophila Tryon is a species of cloud forest at the higher elevations of Puerto Rico. The plants are mostly 4 m (to rarely 7 m) tall, they have a relatively long life of at least 130 years, and they reproduce in the same habitat. *Alsophila bryophila* has a relatively narrow ecological adaptation, which is maintained by local reproduction. Selection appears to favour the plants that grow best in the one community. The ecological specialisation of *Alsophila bryophila* has resulted in its distribution being limited to the mountain ranges of Puerto Rico.

In the Lesser Antilles there are also examples of endemics that are ecologically specialised and of limited distribution (Fig. 4). *Diplazium godmanii* (Baker) C.Chr. grows in wet glades at high altitudes on Guadeloupe, Martinique and St. Vincent; *Gleichenia farinosa* (Kaulf.) Hook. is a species of exposed mossy lava of volcano summits on St. Kitts, Guadeloupe and Martinique; and *Thelypteris cooleyi* Proctor grows on scree slopes at high altitudes on St. Vincent.

The migration of species into a region can be a major source of species diversity. It also provides the basis for floristic affinity between the source and receptor areas. It is difficult to assess the rôles of the Greater Antilles mesic Mexico and Central America, and northern South America as sources from which species have migrated to the other floras. There has undoubtedly been movement in different directions, but it is difficult clearly to identify species with their source areas. However, there are

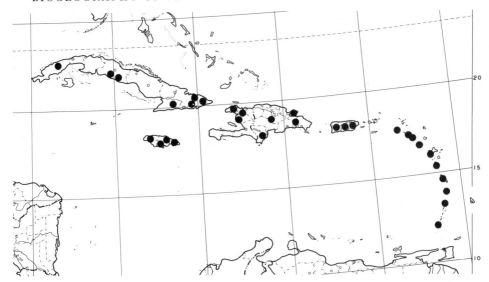

F<small>IG</small>. 3   Distribution of *Cyathea arborea* (L.) Sm

some clear examples of migration to the Greater Antilles among members of the rich Mexican xeric flora which is very poorly represented in the Greater Antilles. For example, *Pellaea ternifolia* (Cav.) Link var. *ternifolia*, *Notholaena sinuata* (Sw.) Kaulf. var. *sinuata*, *N. incana* Presl, and *N. schaffneri* (Fourn.) Davenp. each occur in one or two localities in Jamaica or Hispaniola.

The opportunities for the migration of the rich flora of northern South America into the Lesser Antilles have been limited. Some examples (Fig. 5) are *Dicranoglossum desvauxii* (Kl.) Proctor, *Elaphoglossum schomburgkii* (Fée) Moore, *Polypodium glaucophyllum Kze*.

Migration increases the opportunities for geographic speciation. Examples of geographic speciation within the Greater Antilles are provided by two genera of tree ferns (Cyatheaceae). In both *Nephelea* (Gastony, 1973) and in *Alsophila* (Conant, 1976), species of the Greater Antilles are more closely related than they are to species of other areas of tropical America. In *Nephelea* (Fig. 6) there are eight species, one with three varieties, and all but one of the taxa are confined to a single island. In *Alsophila* (Fig. 7), there are eight species, six of them on a single island. This strong pattern of species radiation on the four islands of the Greater Antilles illustrates the operation of migration within an ecogeographic context that is evidently optimal for the process of speciation.

In some cases the Lesser Antilles have been a route of migration involving speciation, from northern South America to the Greater

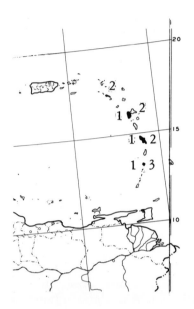

FIG. 4 (*above left*)   Endemics of the Lesser Antilles. 1-*Diplazium godmanii* (Baker) C.Chr., 2-*Gleichenia farinosa* (Kaulf.) Hook., 3-*Thelypteris cooleyi* Proctor.

FIG. 5 (*above right*)   South American taxa in the Lesser Antilles. 1-*Elaphoglossum schomburgkii* (Fée) Moore, 2-*Polypodium glaucophyllum* Kze., 3-*Dicranoglossum desvauxii* (Kl.) Proctor. All species are in Venezuela (ellipse) and elsewhere in South America

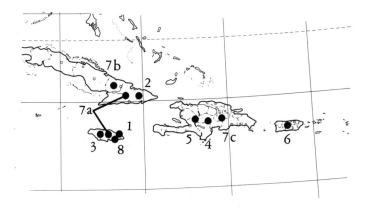

FIG. 6   The occurrence of taxa of *Nephelea* on the islands of the Greater Antilles. A dot represents the occurrence of one taxon on an island, placed within its range. 1-*N. pubescens* (Kuhn) Tryon, 2-*N. balanocarpa* (D. C. Eaton) Tryon, 3-*N. grevilleana* (Mart.) Tryon, 4-*N. crassa* (Maxon) Tryon, 5-*N. fulgens* (C.Chr.) Gastony, 6-*N. portoricensis* (Kuhn) Tryon, 7a-*N. woodwardioides* (Kaulf.) Gastony var. *woodwardioides*, 7b-var. *cubensis* (Maxon) Gastony, 7c-var. *hieronymi* (Brause) Gastony, 8-*N. tussacii* (Desv.) Tryon

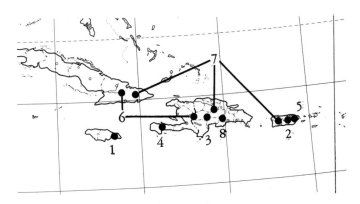

FIG. 7   The occurrence of species of *Alsophila* on islands of the Greater Antilles. A dot represents the occurrence of a species on an island within its range. 1-*A. Nockii* (Jenm.) Tryon, 2-*A. dryopteroides* (Maxon) Tryon, 3-*A. abbottii* (Maxon) Tryon, 4-*A. hotteana* (C. Chr. & Ekman) Tryon, 5-*A. bryophila* Tryon, 6-*A. minor* (D. C. Eaton) Tryon, 7-*A. brooksii* (Maxon) Tryon, 8-*A. urbanii* (Brause) Tryon

65

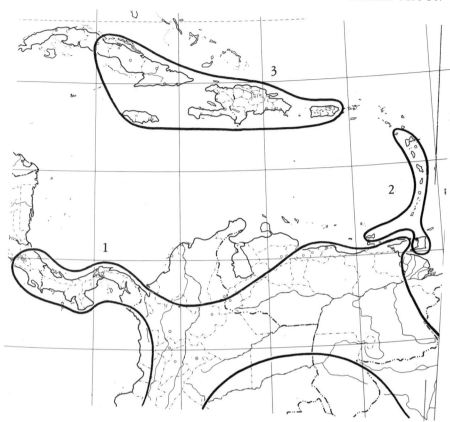

Fɪɢ. 8   Three related species of *Cyathea*. 1-*C. delgadii* Sternb. (also south to Argentina, Paraguay and southeastern Brazil), 2-*C. tenera* (Hook.) Moore, 3-*C. furfuracea* Baker

Antilles. For example, *Doryopteris pedata* (L.) Fée var. *multipartita* (Fée) Tryon occurs in northern South America (also disjunct southward), while the derived var. *pedata* occurs in the Greater Antilles, St. Thomas, Antigua and Montserrat. Intermediates between the two varieties are in Martinique and Guadeloupe. In the tree ferns there are also three closely related species of *Cyathea* distributed along the same migration route (Fig. 8). *Cyathea delgadii* Sternb. is in northern South America (also general to the south and in Costa Rica), *C. tenera* (Hook.) Moore occurs on Isla Margarita, Trinidad and in the Lesser Antilles, and *C. furfuracea* Baker is on all of the Greater Antilles.

The role of alloploidy in the development of the Antillean fern flora is difficult to assess since the only available cytotaxonomic survey is that of T. Walker (1966, 1973) for Jamaica. Examples of alloploidy are found in groups such as the *Anemia adiantifolia* (L.) Sw. complex, *Trichomanes*, and the *Blechnum occidentale* L. complex. Walker's data indicate that about 60% of the taxa studied are polyploid. However, among the endemic taxa only 33% are polyploid. The implication is that ". . . the majority of the endemics have arisen by genetical means. . ." (Walker, 1966). The origin of most of the polyploids can be understood only through further cytotaxonomic studies of a broad geographic scope in tropical America.

Summary

The fern floras of the islands of the Antilles have an essentially continental rather than an insular character due to the high dispersal capacity of ferns and the biogeographic proximity of the islands to each other and to continental areas of tropical America. The Greater Antilles have high species diversity, high species endemism and a rich representation of species also in adjacent regions of tropical America. These features have developed as a result of the high ecological diversity in this archipelago. The Lesser Antilles have low species diversity, low endemism, and a rather poor representation of species in northern South America. These biogeographic features are a consequence of the relatively low ecological diversity of the Lesser Antilles. Ecogeographic speciation has been an important mode of speciation, especially in the Greater Antilles. This has resulted in many ecologically specialised species that are limited in their distribution to one or more islands of an archipelago.

REFERENCES

Christensen, C. (1936). The collection of Pteridophyta made in Hispaniola by E. L. Ekman, 1917 and 1924–30. *Svenska Vetensk. Handl.* **16** (2), 1–93
Conant, D. S. (1976). Ecogeographic and systematic studies in American Cytheaceae. Ph.D. Thesis, Harvard University.
Duek, J. J. (1971). Lista de las especies cubanas de Lycopodiophyta, Psilophyta, Equisetophyta y Polypodiophyta (Pteridophyta). *Adansonia ser. 2*, **11**, 559–578, 717–731
Gastony, G. J. (1973). A revision of the fern genus *Nephelea*. *Contr. Gray Herb.* **203**, 81–148
Maxon, W. R. (1926). Pteridophyta of Porto Rico and the Virgin Islands. *Sci. Survey P.R. and V.I.* **6**, 373–521
Proctor, G. R. (1953). A preliminary checklist of Jamaican Pteridophytes. *Bull. Inst. Jam., Sci. Ser.* **5**, 1–89
— (1977). Pteridophyta. In *Flora of the Lesser Antilles* (R. A. Howard), vol. 2. Arnold Arboretum, Harvard University
Tryon, A. (1966). Origin of the fern flora of Tristan da Cunha. *Brit. Fern Gaz.* **9**, 1–8

Tryon, R. (1970). Developmental and evolution of fern floras of oceanic islands. *Biotropica* **2**, 76–84

— and Conant, D. S. (1975). The ferns of Brazilian Amazonia. *Acta Amazonica* **5**, 23–34

Walker, T. G. (1966). A cytotaxonomic survey of the Pteridophytes of Jamaica. *Trans. Roy. Soc. Edin.* **66**, 169 237

Walker, T. G. (1973). Additional cytotaxonomic notes on the Pteridophytes of Jamaica. *Trans. Roy. Soc. Edin.* **69**, 109–135

5 Origins of Temperate Island Floras

D. M. MOORE   *Department of Botany, University of Reading, England*

Las islas templadas son importantes cuando se consideran los orígenes de las floras isleñas porque producen evidencia relativa de los dos principales factores expuestos en discusiones concernientes a estos dos origenes: separación continental y dispersión a larga distancia. Nueva Zelanda, por ejemplo, que parece haber sido una isla separada del resto de Gondwana y con unas condiciones templadas en gran medida desde aproximadamente el último periodo Cretaceo (60–80 millones de años A.C.) es importante cuando se evalua el papel de placas tectónicas en la distribución de plantas en los tiempos actuales. Islas tales como las del grupo Tristan da Cunha, aisladas en mitad del Atlántico desde su origen, al parecer en la mitad del último periodo terciario (c. 20 millones A.C.) nos dá por otra parte, abundante evidencia de la restricción establecida en su flora, el origen de la cual depende de la capacidad de plantas para viajar largas distancias desde las zonas de procedencia. Además de la edad, el grado de aislamiento de una zona influye en el origen de la flora, reflejada en las actuales poblaciones de plantas y las islas templadas continentales y oceánicas aportan datos comparativos útiles.

La evolución ha demostrado estar estimulada por vicisitudes topográficas y climáticas, mientras que la estabilidad atmosférica ha sido importante permitiendo que la flora permanezca sin cambios durante largos periodos de tiempo. Debido a las influencias modificadoras de las masas de agua circundantes, la mayoría de las islas están en alguna medida, compensadas contra los extremos ambientales, proporcionando los ambientes templados refugio para la flora, o fragmentándola, lo que puede dar útiles indicaciones de su origen.

Por el contrario, la vida de las plantas en muchas islas templadas frías estuvieron sujetas a extinciones masivas durante las glaciaciones del Pleistoceno, y su flora actual proporciona pistas de las características necesarias para una recolonización desde condiciones periglaciales, como se ha visto hoy en Groenlandia, Islandia, Antártico y Georgia del Sur. En la mayoría de los casos el origen de algunas floras de islas debe ser sacadas de los estudios de las plantas actuales, ayudados algunas veces por información sacada de fósiles.

La violenta erupción volcánica de Krakatoa, en 1883, produjo una serie clásica de observaciones sobre la colonización de una isla tropical desvastada, pero el reciente surgimiento de la isla de Surtsey está proporcionando una oportunidad de presenciar en primera plana, los orígenes de la flora de una isla de clima templado fresco con todos los recursos disponibles para nosotros en la último parte del siglo XX.

Las islas no son necesariamente partes de tierra rodeadas de agua, ya que existen muchos ejemplos de islas templadas rodeadas por áreas de tierra no templada. Sorprendentes ejemplos de esto son las cumbres de las montañas en Sudamérica, Africa y Malasia, que son, efectivamente, islas templadas en un mar tropical. Estudios de estas floras a gran altitud muestran la importancia de su origen de inmigración desde regiones templadas más altas y la adaptación gradual de floras adyacentes no templadas.

Finalmente, muchas islas templadas han llegado a ser sujeto de la influencia humana en épocas históricas y proporciones significativas de su flora presente se han originado como una consecuencia directa de esta influencia. El estudio de la flora ajena de islas templadas dá información, no solamente de su proceso de colonización y adaptación, tan importante para los orígenes de la flora isleña, sino que también sirve como guía para los factores que deben considerar los programas de conservación.

Introduction

Temperate islands fall into two principal categories – pieces of land situated at temperate latitudes in one or other of the world's oceans, and the summits of mountains at low latitudes which, because of their altitude, lie above the tropical conditions prevalent at lower elevations that isolate them from other temperate areas. Since the former islands are much the most common, and since consideration of the origins of their floras encompasses virtually all of the problems associated with montane temperate islands, they will be the principal subject of this account. The origin of island floras, and their subsequent evolution, depend upon the age, isolation, environmental stability, habitat diversity and size of the islands. These factors are, of course, of similar importance in any flora but the clearer demarcation of islands, their frequently more restricted number of species, simpler ecosystems and the often reduced outside interference, make them ideal "natural laboratories" for examining the origins and evolution of floras – and temperate islands have proved particularly important in this respect.

Isolation and age

Continental and oceanic islands In considering the effects of isolation on their floras it is customary to distinguish continental ("chersogenous") and oceanic ("thalassogenous") islands. The former occurring adjacent to a continent, with which there is evidence of former, sometimes relatively recent, land connections, the latter being far distant from the continental shelf and without obvious evidence of former direct connections.

Island floras are derived, by some means, from the floras of continental areas – the source areas. Continental islands are sufficiently close to the source areas for there to be a reasonable flow of immigrants which can maintain their floristic diversity and their affinities with the continental flora, of which they often appear to be a somewhat impoverished fragment. The isolation of oceanic islands, on the other hand, results in greatly reduced numbers of immigrants so that inevitable losses are not readily made good. However, those plants which are present are able to evolve in isolation, free from a constant stream of competitors, so that they become increasingly different from their continental congeners. These effects of differing degrees of isolation are reflected in the size, diversity (indicated, for example, by the ratio between the number of families and genera – the higher the ratio the greater the floristic diversity) and distinctness (indicated by the number of endemics) of the floras of continental and oceanic islands (Van Balgooy, 1969). Thus, continental islands such as Tierra del Fuego (88 families: 213 genera – 2·4; 2% endemism) (Moore, 1974), separated from mainland South America by the narrow Strait of Magellan, the British Isles (133 families: 611 genera – 4·6; <1% endemism), 35 km distant from continental Europe, and the Falkland Islands (55 families: 115 genera – 2·4; 7·3% endemism) (Moore, 1968), 520 km from South America, have larger and more diverse floras, with lower endemism, than those of oceanic islands such as Tristan da Cunha (31 families: 51 genera – 1·6; 39% endemism) (Wace and Dickson, 1965), and Rapa (49 families: 90 genera – 1·8; 60% endemism) (Van Balgooy, 1971), isolated in the middle of the Atlantic and Pacific Oceans respectively.

Of course, the relationship between isolation and floristic richness is not always clear, because factors such as the size and topographic diversity of the islands are also important. In addition, the distinctiveness of an island's flora is not solely, or even principally, dependent upon its degree of isolation. It depends also on the effective age of the flora, and this correlation is of considerable importance in assessing the origins of the floras of oceanic islands since it raises the much-debated relative merits of long-distance dispersal and continental drift. The history of the flora of a continental island, on the other hand, is normally a reflection of the floristic history of the continent.

Long-distance dispersal and continental drift　Over the years discussions about the origins of the floras of oceanic islands have largely revolved around three possibilities:

(*i*) that seeds or spores have been dispersed from the source area(s) across the intervening ocean by some means, such as wind, water currents or migrating birds (long-distance dispersal);

(*ii*) that the island was formerly part of a continental mass from which it sundered by plate tectonics (continental drift); or

(*iii*) that it was formerly connected to a continent by a now submerged land-bridge.

Although there is overwhelming evidence that continental islands such as Britain and the Falkland Islands were connected to the adjacent continents in the relatively recent past, this is much more debatable for truly oceanic islands, for which continental drift and long-distance dispersal seem to offer the most likely explanations.

New Zealand, 1600 km from Australia and 2500 km from Antarctica, has been an island since it separated from the ancient "supercontinent" of Gondwanaland some 80 million years ago. At that time it lay at about lat. 60°–70°S. and, although it has been moving slowly northwards ever since, it has been in temperate latitudes since the late Cretaceous – the subtropical climate only appeared in the northern part of the North Island during the Miocene (Raven and Axelrod, 1972). The balanced flora of New Zealand, which has 10% of genera and 81% of species endemic (Godley, 1975), contains such groups as Proteaceae, Winteraceae and various austral gymnosperms (e.g. Podocarpaceae), generally considered to be relatively primitive and which, together with *Nothofagus*, are apparently unable to disperse across water gaps of any significant size (Fleming, 1963). The lowland flora of New Zealand thus has an ancient origin and is considered to be similar to that of temperate Gondwanaland 80 million years ago (Raven, 1972; Raven and Axelrod, 1972, 1974).

In contrast to the age of New Zealand, the Tristan da Cunha archipelago arose in the middle of the South Atlantic Ocean during the late Tertiary period (c. 20 million years ago) (Wace and Dickson, 1965). It has been isolated since its origin and its vascular flora is rather poor (70 species belonging to 31 families and 51 genera). Although 37% of flowering plants and 42% of Pteridophyta are endemic to the islands they are relatively new, neo-endemics, having rather close affinities with species in other areas. The greatest affinities of the flora, including the endemics, are with South America (3200 km away), although South Africa is closer (2800 km). The flora is unbalanced, comprising an unrelated group of plants which have in common a propensity for long-distance dispersal. Thus, the high proportion of ferns (54%, compared to 25% in a continental flora) reflects the easy wind-dispersal of their light spores, while similar considerations apply to the flowering plants, many of which have been shown to be well-suited to long-distance dispersal. Thus, Sykes and Godley (1968) have provided compelling evidence on the buoyancy of *Sophora* seeds which shows that they are perfectly capable

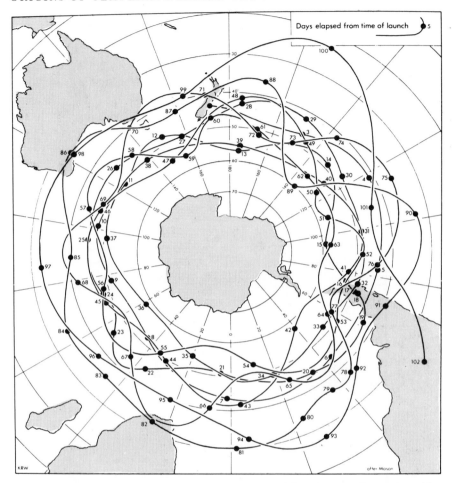

Fig. 1   Trajectories of a balloon released from Christchurch, New Zealand, making 8 circuits at about 12 000 m in 102 days (Mason, 1971; Raven and Raven, 1976)

of surviving in a viable state the journey between New Zealand, S. Chile and Tristan da Cunha (c. 13 000 km), since they remain viable after at least 3 years on seawater and the sea currents move around the southern oceans at a rate of some 18.5 km per day (Deacon, 1960), so that in 3 years they could be carried something over 20 000 km. Furthermore, whilst the Tristan da Cunha and S. Chilean populations have previously been referred to *S. macnabiana* Graham, distinct from the New Zealand species *S. microphylla* Aiton, recent detailed morphological and chemical studies have shown them to be conspecific (Sykes and Godley, 1968; Markham

and Godley, 1972). The circulation of the strong winds around the world
and in these latitudes is clockwise (Fig. 1), so that dispersal agents,
whether ocean currents, wind or "vehicles", such as birds (Falla, 1960),
borne by those winds, are carried in that direction – and South America,
with which the Tristan da Cunha flora has its closest affinities (Fig. 2), is
"upwind".

Even greater youth is shown by the floras of many sub-Antarctic
islands. Macquarie Island, for example, 960 km south of New Zealand,
was completely covered by the Pleistocene glaciations (Mawson, 1943) so
that its present scanty flora of some 36 species, 8·5% of which are neoendemic, has been derived since then. The absence of any connections to
source areas during that period re-emphasises the importance of long-
distance dispersal in the origins of the relatively recent floras of this and

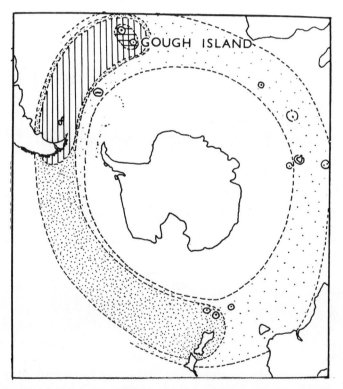

FIG. 2   "Contour map" showing the affinities of the flora of the oceanic Gough Island in
the Tristan da Cunha group to be closest with South America and New Zealand, lying to
windward (cf. Fig. 1) (Holdgate, 1960). Areas sharing: 20–25 species, cross hatch; 15–20
species, single hatching; 10–15 species, heavy stipple; 5–10 species, light stipple

other cool temperate oceanic islands (Barber *et al.*, 1959; Godley, 1967; Moore, 1964, 1972; Taylor, 1954, 1955).

Environmental Stability

As noted previously, the origins of the present floras of islands are a reflection not only of their age and isolation, but also of their environmental stability. Stebbins and Major (1965) have shown for the Californian flora that evolution is most rapid at the boundary between mesic and xeric zones where even small climatic shifts will change the conditions so that the plant populations are continually subjected to environmental instability. To some extent, of course, the conditions on all islands are buffered from climatic extremes by the surrounding water. Thus, the broadleaved forests in the humid zones of the Canary Islands are a relict of the extensive forests of the Mediterranean region which were destroyed by the climatic changes of the late Tertiary period, while Madagascar retains remnants of an earlier African flora decimated by the increased aridity of the continent (Raven and Axelrod, 1972, 1974), but the effects of environmental instability are evident in many island floras. The lowland floras of New Caledonia and New Zealand, for example, probably represent fragments of the ancient temperate flora of Gondwanaland but, whilst the former island appears to have had a relatively stable history since the Cretaceous, New Zealand was reduced to a rather small archipelago by the marine transgressions of the Oligocene period (c. 30 million years ago) and this was undoubtedly a significant factor in the extinction of many ancient groups still present in New Caledonia (Raven and Axelrod, 1972). Subsequently, during the late Pliocene period (c. 10 million years ago), there was considerable environmental change as the extensive mountain systems of New Zealand arose to provide new habitats which were colonised by such genera as *Celmisia*, *Epilobium* and *Hebe* arriving by long-distance dispersal from Australia and then undergoing rapid evolution to give the diversity of species known today (Raven, 1973).

In cool temperate islands the greatest environmental upset in relatively recent times was caused by the Pleistocene glaciations. As the glaciers advanced they "pushed' the plants before them, and the plants followed when the ice retreated. Montane plants were thus periodically forced together in ice-free lowland refugia, and isolated in mountain areas as the glaciers retreated. This "pump-action" of the glaciers has been shown to be a potent factor in the evolution of several plant groups (Simpson, 1973; Vuillemier, 1971). It probably accounts for the endemic species of *Nassauvia*, for example, in the mountains of the "continental"

Falkland Islands (*N. serpens* D'Urv.) and Tierra del Fuego (*N. latissima* Skottsb.), which diverged from their closest relatives in the southern Andes (*N. magellanica* J. F. Gmel.) following their retreat from the ice-free lowlands now occupied by the sea off the east coast of Patagonia (Moore, 1975).

In high latitude oceanic islands the glaciations caused massive extinction. The sporadic occurrence of the cold temperate family Hectorellaceae, with *Lyallia* in the sub-Antarctic Kerguelen Islands and *Hectorella* on the mountains of the South Island of New Zealand, suggests massive extinction of a pre-Pleistocene family having affinities with the Portulacaceae and, perhaps, the Caryophyllaceae (Skipworth, 1961; Philipson and Skipworth, 1961). The sporadic occurrence of distinctive broadleaved herbs in such genera as *Myosotidium*, *Pleurophyllum*, *Pringlea* and *Stilbocarpus* in the islands south of New Zealand (Fig. 3) may also reflect such extinctions (Godley, 1975). The impoverished floras of Britain and Iceland, for example, with their low levels of endemism, are a reflection of their recent return after the Pleistocene glaciers as well as, in the former, proximity to a continental source area. Greenland and, particularly, Antarctica are very large islands with fossil records showing extensive former floras. Both are only just emerging from the Pleistocene "deep-freeze" which largely or entirely obliterated their former plant life and their floras are now originating again *de novo*. Antarctica, for example, which once had temperate forests dominated by *Nothofagus* and other genera, now has only two native species of flowering plants (Skottsberg, 1954) – the herbs *Colobanthus quitensis* (Bartl.) H.B.K. and *Deschampsia antarctica* Desv., both relatively recent arrivals from South America. The dramatic environmental upheavals and recent recolonisation that have occurred on such large islands as these focus attention on direct observations on the origins of island floras.

Colonisation and establishment

As we have seen, the origins of island floras are generally inferred from the properties of the plants present today, sometimes aided by evidence from fossils. Direct observations are rarely available. The classical example of such observations involves the tropical continental island, Krakatoa, on which the plant and animal life was devastated by a volcanic eruption in 1883. Subsequent studies (e.g. Doctors van Leeuwen, 1936; Dammerman, 1948) showed a pattern of recolonisation which has been widely cited as an unique example in this field, although other relevant data in the tropics are now becoming available (e.g. Diamond, 1977). Recently, however, a new cool temperate island has provided an

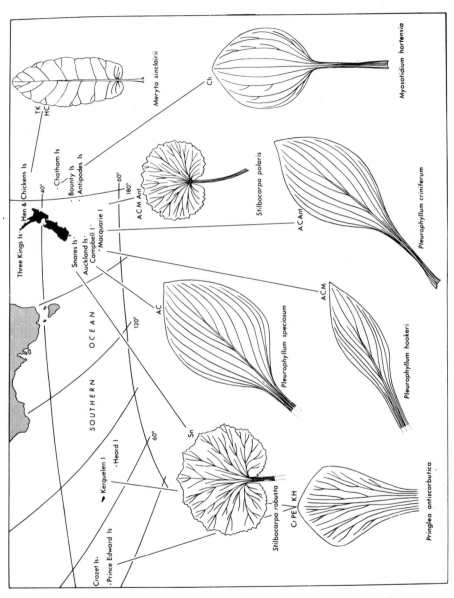

Fig. 3 Large-leaved plants on islands of the Southern Ocean which may represent the remnants of a more large-leaved preglacial flora (Godley, 1975). TK, Three Kings; HC, Hen and Chickens; Ch, Chathams; Sn, Snares; Ant, Antipodes; A, Auckland; C, Campbell; M, Macquarie; K, Kerguelen; H, Heard; Cr, Crozet; PE, Prince Edward

opportunity to study at first hand the processes of colonisation and establishment which are so important in the origin of a temperate island flora. In November 1963 the new island of Surtsey was formed by volcanic activity 40 km south of Iceland. By March 1964 it had reached an area of 1.15 sq km and an altitude of 173 m, and a month later it attained 2.45 sq km. By the middle of 1967, following further outpourings of lava and erosion by wind and sea, it stabilised at about 2.8 sq km and 169 metres above sea level. The island is readily accessible to botanists and has been under virtually constant surveillance since its origin and the positions of all plants and propagules have been carefully charted each year (e.g. Einarsson, 1968; Fridriksson, 1970, 1975).

The first arrivals on Surtsey, within 12 months of its formation, were sea-borne seeds of *Cakile edentula* (Bigelow) Hooker. The seeds showed 60% germination and probably gave rise to the seedlings found in the following year, 1965, which did not flower and were killed by the ash resulting from an eruption. During the first seven years of its existence a generally increasing number of species arrived on Surtsey but, as can be seen from Table 1, there was no gradual and inevitable build-up in the numbers of either species or individuals. These tremendous fluctuations show the uncertainty of colonisation once dispersal has been achieved – the plants arriving at Surtsey as viable fragments or as seeds brought by wind, water, trapped in floating "mermaids purses" (the egg capsule of the skate, *Raja batis*), or in the gizzards of birds such as the snow bunting (*Plectrophenaz nivalis*). Although mosses arrived later than the first flowering plants, after 3 years, they rapidly spread over the lava in the interior of Surtsey, the flowering plants are still mainly coastal. Lichens reached the island 8 years after it formation.

It is possible that the initial establishment of plants on Surtsey has now been effected, with small dunes formed by *Elymus arenarius* L. and a rudimentary vegetation of *Stellaria media* (L.) Vill. and *Cochlearia officinalis* L. on the steep coastal cliffs. The total number of plants is increasing, most dramatically between 1972 and 1973 when it rose from 119 to 1273 individuals, principally *Honkenya peploides* (L.) Ehrh. and *Cochlearia officinalis*. It would still be premature, however, to claim they will not suffer further vicissitudes before establishment is fully achieved.

The problems faced by the colonisers of Surtsey, only some 20–40 km from its source areas, serves to emphasise the difficulties encountered in the origins of the floras of isolated oceanic islands. Not only is the number of immigrants restricted to those capable of dispersing over large distances but, of these, many will not manage to establish themselves. In consequence there is lowered competition among the successful immigrants, which is reflected in their ecological amplitude, and,

TABLE 1 Case histories of the earliest flowering plants to reach Surtsey during the first ten years of its existence. (Data from Fridriksson, 1970, 1975)

Year	Cakile edentula	Elymus arenarius	Honkenya peploides	Mertensia maritima	Stellaria media	Festuca rubra	Cochlearia officinalis	Total plants
1964	Seeds drifted ashore—60% germination	—	—	—	—	—	—	—
1965	30 small plants from seed. Did not flower. Killed by ash	—	—	—	—	—	—	30
1966	1 seedling. Removed by heavy tide	4 seedlings. Removed by surf	—	—	—	—	—	5
1967	15 small plants—washed away after 1 month. 8 seedlings—1 flowered. 14 plants with flowers and fruit	1 small plant—washed away after 1 month. 4 plants—none flowered	25 small plants from seaborne seed—none flowered.	1 plant brought by sea	1 plant	—	—	52
1968	Seeds but no plants	6 plants—none flowered (1 overwintered from 1967)	103 plants—none flowered.	4 plants—non flowered	—	—	—	114
1969	Plants	Plants	Plants	—	—	—	Plants	63
1970	—	4 plants	63 plants (18 from 1969) (14 from 1967)	—	4 plants with flowers and fruits	—	30 plants —none flowered	101
1971	—	3 plants	50 plants	—	2 plants	—	21 plants	83
1972	1 plant	—	72 plants	15 plants	2 plants	—	97 plants	199
1973	33 plants	66 plants	548 plants	25 plants	1 plant	1 plant	586 plants	1273

79

therefore, it is frequently found that species on temperate oceanic islands tend to occupy a much wider range of habitats than in comparable continental areas.

It is in the processes of colonisation and establishment that temperate montane "islands" in tropical regions differ most significantly from islands surrounded by water, the comparison being most valid between montane and oceanic islands, since both are usually far-distant from source areas. Some of these tropicalpine species are identical with those occurring in temperate regions at high latitudes and dispersal must pose the same problems and constraints as for the floras of oceanic islands. However, significant portions of tropicalpine floras are derived from groups present in the surrounding tropical and subtropical regions (see, e.g. Smith, 1977) and there is thus a constant pressure from this source which must result in competition within the floras of montane islands much greater than is experienced by plants of oceanic islands. The origins of the floras of oceanic islands are not, of course, to be sought in their immediate surroundings, whilst for the floras of temperate montane islands they partly are.

Man and temperate island floras

Thus far this discussion of the origins of temperate island floras has generally involved interpreting events which occurred thousands or millions of years ago. However, significant proportions of the floras of many temperate island have reached them very much more recently through the influence of Man. Whilst this is almost certainly true of all islands where there has been any human impact, it becomes difficult to accurately assess the size of this anthropogenic element in the floras of islands such as Britain and Iceland, for example, which have a long history of human influence. However, the situation is much clearer for many islands, particularly in the southern cool temperate zone, which have become accessible to Europeans within the last one to four hundred years and many of which were apparently previously unvisited by Man.

As in other regions Man has, to a greater or lesser extent, disrupted the plant and animal communities on most southern temperate islands (Holdgate and Wace, 1961; Wace, 1966), particularly where permanent settlements have been established as, for example, in New Zealand, Tierra del Fuego, the Falkland Islands and Tristan da Cunha. The vegetation of oceanic islands, developed in the absence of herbivorous mammals, is particularly vulnerable to grazing by introduced animals such as cattle, sheep and rabbits (Holdgate, 1967) and the losses of many temperate island communities and endemic species have resulted from

TABLE 2 Sizes of native and alien floras of representative southern cool temperate islands with indication of aggressiveness (species in natural vegetation) and source of the aliens

Island	No. native species	No. alien species	% alien species in natural vegetation	% alien species from Old World	Reference
New Zealand	1200	1700	28.0	80	Godley, 1975
Tristan da Cunha	70	97	14.5	58	Wace, 1967; Wace and Holdgate, 1976
Falkland Islands	160	89	15.5	100	Moore and Sladen, 1965; Moore, 1968
Tierra del Fuego	430	129	15.2	100	Moore, 1974; Moore and Goodall, 1978

this. However, these factors also provide conditions suitable for alien plants introduced deliberately or unwittingly by Man. Most of the aliens come from continental areas, especially Europe (Table 2), where they have become adapted to continual human disturbance of their habitats, and consequently they tend to be associated with disturbed sites on the islands (Allan, 1936; Wace, 1967). However, there is clear evidence from several southern cool temperate islands that a significant proportion of the aliens have been able to invade native vegetation which has not been affected by Man or his animals (Table 2), although they frequently exploit naturally open or disturbed habitats such as beaches, river banks, land slips and the vicinity of seabird nesting sites, seal hauling out areas and the like. Interestingly, many of these successful invaders were amongst the earliest to arrive after the initial visits by Europeans and there is a remarkable similarity between widely separated southern temperate islands in the first alien species to reach them, of which the most ubiquitous include *Cerastium fontanum* Baumg., *Holcus lanatus* L., *Plantago major* L., *Poa annua* L., *Poa pratensis* L., *Rumex acetosella* L., *Sagina procumbens* L., *Sonchus oleraceus* L. and *Stellaria media* (L.) Vill. (Moore and Goodall, 1978; Ridley, 1930; Wace, 1967).

Although the all too frequently destructive effects of human influence on island plant life are rightly deplored by everyone concerned about conservation it cannot be overlooked that substantial proportions of many temperate island floras (Table 2) owe their origin to Man.

Furthermore, these aliens can provide useful information on the processes involved in the origins of the native species. Thus, whilst the vehicle of dispersal, Man, is scarcely relevant to this, studies of such factors as establishment and competition are equally as valid for aliens as for the new "natural" immigrants to, for example, Surtsey (p. 78). In addition, because of the economic importance of weeds, many of which are aliens in temperate islands, much effort has been devoted to elucidating their variation and biological properties, thus providing a firm basis for assessing the adaptation and differentiation of their island populations. For example, distinctive populations of *Poa annua* have evolved on Macquarie Island, between New Zealand and Antarctica, in the c. 160 years since that island was discovered in 1810 (Ellis *et al.*, 1971). Careful monitoring of aliens, as of native species, may be expected to provide further vital information on the processes involved in the origins and evolution of temperate island floras.

Summary

The origins of temperate island floras depend upon the age, isolation and environmental stability of the island. Continental islands have floras which are relatively unchanged fragments of the floras of the adjacent landmasses from which they originated and from which immigration continues. Some oceanic islands with relative environmental stability over geologically long periods have balanced floras whose origins must be partly sought in the floras of the super-continents which fragmented during the Cretaceous period. Geologically young oceanic islands, on the other hand, have unbalanced floras composed of those species able to disperse over large distances and establish themselves successfully. A combination of age and isolation is then important in determining the extent to which these oceanic island floras will preserve or evolve distinctive, endemic taxa. Environmentally unstable islands or parts of islands also provide conditions conducive to the evolution of new floras and the concomitant extinction of others. In many cool temperate islands such extinction has been complete in relatively recent times and the flora is originating *de novo* so that, in some cases, it is possible to make direct observations on the development of a flora rather than deducing its origins from often incomplete information. During the last 2000 years or so human influence on floras and vegetation has continually increased. The recent arrival of Man to some temperate islands has provided a clear picture of the important part played by him in the origin of an often substantial part of their present flora – the aliens, which can also provide information on factors such as establishment, competition and adaptation which are important in considering the origins of all floras, island or continental, temperate or tropical.

REFERENCES

Allan, H. H. (1936). Indigene versus alien in the New Zealand plant world. *Ecology* **17**, 187–193

Balgooy, M. M. J. van (1969). A study on the diversity of island floras. *Blumea* **17**, 139–178

— (1971). Plant geography of the Pacific. *Blumea* Suppl. **6**, 1–222

Barber, H. N., Dadswell, H. E. and Ingle, H. D. (1959). Transport of driftwood from South America to Tasmania and Macquarie Island. *Nature, Lond.* **184**, 203–204

Dammerman, K. W. (1948). The fauna of Krakatau 1883–1933. *Verhand. Konink. Ned. Akad. Wet. Afd. Natuurk. II* **44**, 1–594

Deacon, G. E. R. (1960). The southern cold temperate zone. *Proc. Roy. Soc. B.* **152**, 441–447

Diamond, J. M. (1977). Colonization of a volcano inside a volcano. *Nature, Lond.* **270**, 13–14

Doctors van Leeuwen, W. M. (1936). Krakatau, 1883 to 1933. *Ann. Jard. Bot. Buitenzorg* **56–57**, 1–506.

Einarsson, E. (1968). On dispersal of plants to Surtsey. *Surtsey Res. Progr. Rep.* **2**, 19–21

Ellis, W. M., Lee, B. T. O. and Calder, D. M. (1971). A biometric analysis of populations of *Poa annua* L. *Evolution* **25**, 29–37

Falla, R. A. (1960). Oceanic birds as dispersal agents. *Proc. Roy. Soc. B.* **152**, 655–659

Fleming, C. A. (1963). Paleontology and southern biogeography. In *Pacific Basin Biogeography* (J. L. Gressitt, ed.), 455–463. Bishop Museum Press, Honolulu, Hawaii

Fridriksson, S. (1970). Records of drifted plant parts on Surtsey in 1968. *Surtsey Res. Progr. Rep.* **5**, 15–18

— (1975). *Surtsey.* Butterworth, London

Godley, E. J. (1967). Widely distributed species, land bridges and continental drift. *Nature, Lond.* **214**, 74–75

— (1975). Flora and vegetation. In *Biogeography and Ecology in New Zealand* (G. Kuschel, ed.), 177–229. *Mongr. Biol.* **27**. Junk, The Hague

Holdgate, M. W. (1960). The Royal Society expedition to southern Chile. *Proc. Roy. Soc. B.* **152**, 434–441

— (1967). The influence of introduced species on the ecosystems of temperate oceanic islands. *Proc. IUCN 10th Tech. Meeting, IUCN Publs. New Ser.* **9**, 151–176

— and Wace, N. W. (1961). The influence of man on the floras and faunas of southern islands. *Polar Record* **10**, 475–493

Markham, K. R. and Godley, E. J. (1972). Chemotaxonomic studies in *Sophora*, 1. An evaluation of *Sophora microphylla* Ait. *N.Z. J. Bot.* **10**, 627–640

Mason, B. J. (1971). Global atmospheric research programme. *Nature, Lond.* **233**, 382–388

Mawson, D. (1943). Macquarie Island, its geography and geology. *Sci. Rep. Austral. Ant. Exped., 1911–14, Sec. A.* **5**, 1–194

Moore, D. M. (1964). Experimental taxonomic studies in Antarctic floras. In *Biologie Antarctique* (R. Carrick, M. W. Holdgate and J. Prévost, eds.), 195–202. Hermann, Paris

— (1968). The vascular flora of the Falkland Islands. *Brit. Antarct. Survey Sci. Rep.* **60**, 1–202

— (1972). Connections between cool temperate floras, with particular reference to southern South America. In *Taxonomy, Phytogeography and Evolution* (D. H. Valentine, ed.), 115–138. Academic Press, London and New York

— (1974). Catálogo de las plantas vasculares nativas de Tierra del Fuego. *Anal. Inst. Patagonia, Punta Arenas (Chile)* **5**, 105–121

— (1975). The alpine flora of Tierra de Fuego. *Anal. Inst. Bot. A. J. Cavanilles* **32**, 419–440

— and Goodall, R. N. P. (1978). La flora adventicia de Tierra del Fuego. *Anal. Inst. Patagonia, Punta Arenas (Chile)* **8**, 263–274

— and Sladen, W. J. L. (1965). Some recent records of native and alien flowering plants from the Falkland Islands. *Brit. Antarct. Survey Bull.* **7**, 29–35

Philipson, W. R. and Skipworth, J. P. (1961). Hetorellaceae: a new family of Dicotyledons. *Trans. Roy. Soc. N. Z., Bot.* **1**, 31

Raven, P. H. (1972). An introduction to continental drift. *Austral. Nat. Hist.* December, 245–248

— (1973. Evolution of subalpine and alpine plant groups in New Zealand. *N. Z. J. Bot.* **11**, 177–200

— and Axelrod, D. I. (1972). Plate tectonics and Australian paleo-biogeography. *Science* **176**, 1379–1386

— and Axelrod, D. I. (1974). Angiosperm biogeography and past continental movements. *Ann. Mo. Bot. Gard.* **61**, 539–673

— and Raven T. E. (1976). The Genus *Epilobium* (Onagraceae) in Australasia: A systematic and evolutionary study. *D.S.I.R. N.Z. Bull.* **216**, 1–321

Ridley, H. N. (1930). *The Dispersal of Plants Throughout the World.* Reeve, Ashford

Simpson, B. B. (1973). Contrasting modes of evolution in two groups of *Perezia* (Mutiseae: Compositae) of southern South America. *Taxon* **22**, 525–536

Skipworth, J. P. (1961). The taxonomic problem of *Hectorella caespitosa* Hook. f. *Trans. Roy. Soc. N.Z., Bot.* **1**, 17–30

Skottsberg, C. J. F. (1954). Antarctic flowering plants. *Bot. Tidsskr.* **51**, 330–338

Smith, J. M. B. (1977). Origins and ecology of the tropicalpine flora of Mt. Wilhelm, New Guinea. *Biol. J. Linn. Soc. Lond.* **9**, 87–131

Sykes, W. R. and Godley, E. J. (1968). Transoceanic dispersal in *Sophora* and other genera. *Nature, Lond.* **218**, 495–496

Taylor, B. W. (1954). An example of long-distance dispersal. *Ecology* **35**, 569–572

— (1955). The flora, vegetation and soils of Macquarie Island. *Rep. Austral. Nat. Antarct. Res. Exped., Ser. B.* **2**, 1–192

Vuillemier, B. S. (1971). Pleistocene changes in the fauna and flora of South America. *Science* **173**, 771–780

Wace, N. M. (1966). The last of the virgin islands. *Discovery* **27**, No. 2, 36–42

— (1967). Alien plants in the Tristan da Cunha islands. *Proc. IUCN 10th Tech. Meeting, IUCN Publs. New Ser.* **9**, 46–59

— and Dickson, J. (1965). The terrestrial botany of the Tristan da Cunha islands. *Phil. Trans. Roy. Soc. B.* **249**, 273–360

— and Holdgate, M. W. (1976). Man and nature in the Tristan da Cunha islands. *IUCN Monogr.* **6**, 1–114

6 The Origins and Evolution of Island Floras as Exemplified by the Aegean Archipelago

WERNER GREUTER   *Conservatoire Botanique de Génève, Switzerland*

En una aproximación global fitogeográfica al problema del origen de las floras isleñas, se tiene que distinguir entre islas quersogenas (desprendidas del continente) e islas talasogenas (emergidas del mar). En las últimas todos los taxones presents han llegado, o bien por dispersión natural de larga distancia, o mediante la acción humana (elementos telecoros y antropicos); en las primeras algunos pueden derivar de antecesores previos al hecho del aislamiento insular (elemento relíctico). Es necesario desechar el elemento antropico (el cual puede alcanzar casi un 50% de la flora total) cuando se consideren formas naturales fitogeográficas. También es importante señalar la contribución de las migraciones de largo-trayecto sobre el mar para la presente flora nativa. En terrenos teóricos, podría esperarse que en islas quersogenas con una flora relicta bien equilibrada, los establecimientos sucesivos por dispersión a gran distancia estén esencialmente limitados a unos taxones ecologicamente especializados, siendo sus más eficientes portadores los pájaros, seguidos por las corrientes marinas (solo halofitas), mientras que la dispersión a través del viento solo juega un papel menor. Los factores observados están de acuerdo con estas suposiciones. En las islas quersogenas, la antiguedad del elemento relíctico depende del momento en que el aislamiento por el mar llegó a ser efectivo, lo cual puede variar ampliamente: en la región Cardaegea el aislamiento retrocede a los principios del Plioceno (5 millones años A.C.), en las áreas marginales del mar Egeo, principalmente al final de la glaciación Würm (20 000 años A.C.). Si acceptamos esto, en Creta, casi el 50% de la flora vascular, pertenece al elemento relíctico (lo que es una suposición razonable, sobre la base de nuestras consideraciones en la efectividad de la migración de largo trayecto). Tenemos que señalar el factor de que los taxones no endémicos de este elemento, es decir, alrededor de 550 especies, no se han desarrollado apreciablemente durante el millón de años de aislamiento. Actualmente, los casos en donde la diferenciación de taxones sobre la isla pueda ser ampliamente demostrada son muy pocos y la mayoría de los endemismos pueden no haber evolucionado, in situ, después del aislamiento. Se debate que la evolución no se espera que tenga lugar bajo condiciones ambientales estables y que incluso los mayores trastornos climáticos no daran lugar necesariamente a cambios evolutivos, en tanto que la presión de selección, en un contexto estático de población, está principalmente reforzada por específicos desafios individuales. La evolución puede muy bien estar limitada a condiciones dinámicas excepionales como la expansión dentro de nuevos

D

territorios, cuando la media de población crezca incontenidamente y la presión de selección intraespecífica haya aflojado. La fase de colonización por dispersión a larga distancia, de islas recientemente emergidas, puede muy bien proporcionar condiciones apropiadas para un cambio evolutivo. Es altamente significativo que todos los ejemplos de pronunciada "explosión evolutiva" por radiación adaptativa, dentro de la flora insular, sean encontrados en las islas talasogenas como Hawai y las Canarias.

Introduction

Let me begin with an apologia of the subject. My job is systematic botany: a good, solid handicraft, dealing with facts one can see and measure, observations one can check, classifications one can verify. Unfortunately, the neater and less controversial are the results, the less are they suited as a subject of an essay.

The contrary is true with phytogeographical themes. On those you can build quite fascinating discussions, and can derive intellectual satisfaction from them: they deal with the causal analysis of the observed systematic and distributional facts as viewed in a four-dimensional frame of time and space. Less satisfactory are the scientific aspects: we are constantly dealing with clues not facts, and in the best of cases will end up with a sensible hypothesis, with rough and generalised pictures of potential states, events and relations.

May I stress the importance of the four-dimensional aspect of such considerations. The time factor has too often been neglected, which has led to mistaking chorology for phytogeography or, worse, to playing the game of differentiation and evolution of taxa on the chess-board of present-day geography, with the present climate and vegetation as corollaries. This doesn't make sense. It is hardly any better, though, to bypass the distributional problems and speak of the evolution of taxa without paying due consideration to their past and present range and environment.

What I am aiming at could be termed global phytogeography, stressing the attribute "global". We can only hope to succeed reconstituting, however roughly, the complex patterns and vicissitudes of past eras if we take into account data from every possible field of knowledge. Even so, the data will be few and scanty enough, and not all of them will be equally reliable. Interdisciplinary co-operation is absolutely essential in attempting to unearth, interpret and weigh the results of students in other scientific disciplines.

Insular floras are particularly well suited as a subject for global phytogeographic studies because of their clearcut geographical delimitation which remains constant over considerable periods of time, effectively inhibiting the migration of species. It is, alas, impossible to discuss fully the various aspects and problems of island floras in the limited framework of an essay. Rather than to restrict myself to a single facet which, anyway, could not be fully appreciated by itself, I prefer drawing a quick and rather superficial overall picture of the problems of insularity.

The origins of island floras

A biologist will start to distinguish (or try to distinguish) two categories of islands: the chersogenous type, which became detached from a continent, and the thalassogenous type which arose in isolation from the bottom of the sea.[1] Also he will make, theoretically at least, a distinction between three categories of organisms present on an island: those belonging to the relict element, the ancestors of which were already present in the pre-isolation phase; those of the telechorous element, descendants of individuals which have reached the island by way of natural long-distance transport over the sea; and those which are part of the anthropic element brought in by man. Obviously, only the two last-named are to be found on thalassogenous islands.

All Mediterranean islands of some size, and certainly all the major Aegean ones, are of the chersogenous type. I cannot speak authoritatively on the problems of thalassogenous islands since I don't know them from personal experience, and shall refer to them only marginally by way of contrast. I shall rely basically on observations made in my own research area, the Aegean Archipelago and principally Crete.

The anthropic element   For the phytogeographer, the anthropic element of a flora is essentially a distortional factor which one has to assess as accurately as possible in order to eliminate it. The importance of this factor can be exemplified by figures from the Aegean: approximately one third of the flora of Crete has reached that island thanks to human action (Greuter, 1971), and on Psara with its poor and monotonous plant cover almost 45% of the species are anthropophytes (Greuter, 1976).

There are several causes for this very conspicuous share of anthropophytes which is a general phenomenon at least in the Mediterranean region. To begin with the particularly long-lasting, intense human influence: forest destruction, grazing, and agriculture – which were not, of course, limited to islands. Also, the efficacy of Man as a vector for long-range dispersal exceeds by far that of any natural agent. This is due to the considerable quantities of diaspores he is able to

---

[1] I refrain from using the terms "continental" and "oceanic" islands, which are ambiguous owing to the general, old use of "continental" and "oceanic" to express climatic conditions.

transport, to the fact that many of them may be carried and deposited together at one time, and that they will usually reach suitable habitats which man has "cleaned" for them from the competing native species. Finally one has to consider that native island floras are relatively poor, competitively weak and therefore vulnerable, a consequence of the shield provided by isolation against newcomers spreading on the continents, which are better adapted to, and more competitive under, modified climatic and environmental conditions. As a result, anthropophytic species, especially those already introduced in prehistoric or early historic times, may be perfectly integrated into the native plant communities: it may be extremely difficult, or even impossible, to distinguish them from the truly native ones. As a rule, those species which are widespread both in Man-made and semi-natural vegetation types can be attributed only statistically, but not individually, to either floristic element.

The telechorous element   The influence of telechory on the composition of island floras is very controversial. Some would tend to explain every range disjunction by long-distance dispersal, while others would totally discard that possibility. Concrete observations in this field are still very inadequate, and we have to be content with some deductive, theoretical considerations and conclusions.

On the one hand there are hardly any limits to the long-distance transport of diaspores, given a sufficient period of time. It does not happen every day that a whirlwind or tornado transports a coconut, or a horse-chestnut, if you prefer, over great distances; but it certainly *will* happen once, or more than once, in a million years. The plant cover of newly emerged islands, as in the Åland Archipelago (Palmgren, 1922, 1925), and those on which the flora was partly or totally destroyed by volcanic eruptions, as Krakatoa (Ernst, 1934) and, in the Aegean, Nea Kaimeni near Thira (Cammerloher, 1935; Hansen, 1971), show clearly enough that recolonisation by diaspore transport over the sea takes place almost immediately.

But, on the other hand, long-distance transport of diaspores and long-range dispersal of taxa must not be equated. The establishment of newcomers may be an easy process on open, bare ground, but is far more problematical in the frame of a pre-existing plant community. It is, already, an exceptional event if a single diaspore, shed in a close vegetation cover, gives rise to a mature individual. But even then, as one can demonstrate mathematically with the reproductive drift model (Runemark, 1969), the chances of survival of the new colonist through successive generations tend toward zero if it is competitively equal or inferior to the taxa already present in large numbers. Only if it is a markedly superior competitor, or if the initial number of individuals is considerable, does it stand a chance of becoming definitely established.

Starting from these theoretical considerations we can, by inference, formulate some laws governing long-range dispersal that are in good agreement with the observed distributional patterns. We first conclude that different habitats will not be equally suited for colonisation by telechory:

Specialised habitats occurring sporadically and often arising anew, like swamps, pools, riversides, sea shores, alluvions, and landslides, provide suitable conditions for colonisation by pioneer species.

Habitats with a permanent, close vegetation of a climax or subclimax type, especially forest and scrub communities, are utterly unsuited for the establishment of newcomers; the same is true for specialist communities of a stable, conservative nature as found, e.g. in rock crevices.

In parallel, at species level, specialists will be favoured in the field of long-distance dispersal as long as they can find empty ecological niches where they meet no significant competition. This is particularly true for parasites like Orobanchaceae, or symbiotic plants like many Orchidaceae. If a plant community becomes extremely impoverished it may offer empty ecological niches even to less specialised species.

Finally we may draw some conclusions as to the effectiveness of the different agents of dispersal. Apart from Man whose influence has just been discussed, three natural vectors can ensure diaspore transport over the sea.

—Wind makes a very efficient transport agent as far as distance is concerned. But its efficacy for colonisation purposes is restricted to selected cases like the pioneer condition of open, newly created habitats. The problem, with wind dispersal, is that the diaspores become very much disseminated not only with respect to the mother plant, but also among themselves. In a reasonably natural model where the diaspores are regularly spread over the earth surface, the factor of dissemination will increase with the square of the distance of transport. This means that wind-borne diaspores carried farther than a few hundred metres will always arrive singly and be eliminated by reproductive drift from pre-existent plant communities.

—Transport by sea currents is necessarily restricted to salt-tolerant plants with buoyant diaspores. It is worthwhile noticing that the dissemination factor of drifting diaspores increases proportionally to the distance of transport, not to its square, since the diaspores are deposited along the shore line not scattered over the earth surface. Drift appears to be the normal way of dispersal of coastal halophytes, but has obvious

limitations as demonstrated by endemism and distributional gaps in
several littoral species.

—Birds might well be the most efficacious transport agent in our context.
Dispersal of hydro- and helophytes by waterfowl – both by exo- and
endo-ornithochory – is a well-known and rather generalised
phenomenon. Species with baccate fruits (in the biological, not
morphological sense of the term) might even be spread by birds, over
the sea, into existing native vegetation. The reason is that a bird may
transport quite a number of diaspores at one time, and evacuate them
simultaneously in an environment similar to the original one.
Especially with birds living in flocks, this may result in a relatively
frequent, concentrated and directed "infection" of insular biota with
foreign diaspores. The range of dispersal is of course limited by the
habits of the birds concerned and, especially, by their digestive period.

Excluding the specialist species in specialised habitats just mentioned, a
rich, well-balanced island flora is almost immune against contamination
by newcomers from outside. This is particularly true for chersogenous
islands since they possess such a "complete" flora from before the time of
their detachment from the mainland. If subsequently, during the
isolation phase, climatic changes or other factors lead to a drastic
reduction of the stock of relict species, "outsiders" may get a real chance
to get established and to compensate thereby some of the losses. Once the
impoverishment of the flora has reached a point where further extinctions
are completely balanced by new arrivals, the difference between relict
and telechorous element will become obsolete. It may then be difficult or
impossible, judging from the flora, to distinguish between chersogenous
and thalassogenous islands. This is the case with many of the smaller
islands and islets of the Aegean, and even of some medium-sized like
Psara (Greuter, 1976). On the other hand the largest of them, Crete, has
a very characteristic, rich relict flora to which 40–50% of the vascular
plant species belong.

The relict element

In order to give a sensible interpretation of the relict element on an island,
one needs a well-founded knowledge in the geohistorical context. Once
again I shall take the Aegean as an example and briefly outline what we
know of its past, summarising my previous reviews of the subject
(Greuter, 1970, 1975) as modified by the recent results of Hsü and others
(in Drooger, 1973).

—We start from the Oligocene-Miocene boundary, when in the general context of the Alpine orogenesis a new mountain area arose to the south of the old Cycladean Mass. It formed the southern limit of an extensive Aegean continent and linked the mountain ranges of the Balkans to those of South Anatolia. The climate was warmer than today, places suited for fossilisation were covered with mesophilous subtropical forest; the mountain areas, from where no fossil records are extant, may have housed sclerophyllous woodlands of a Mediterranean type.

—Tectonic processes led to the dismemberment of the South Aegean mountain ranges. Coming from the south, the sea reached the Ierapetra region in eastern Crete by the lower Tortonian. At the same time *Hipparion* faunas of a Vallesian type spread over the Aegean continent, pointing to a drier climate with predominant steppe vegetation. During the Tortonian the central portion of the South Aegean continent was gradually cut up to a group of islands.

—At the end of the Miocene an exceptional situation of great biogeographic relevance prevailed. During the 1.5 million years of the Messinian the entire Mediterranean Sea dried out repeatedly, being cut off from the Atlantic Ocean. At least in the lowlands subarid to arid conditions must then have prevailed. The former deep-sea basins were reduced to abiotic sebkhas, and on all the surrounding ridges there was ample opportunity for the establishment and migration of drought-resistant plant species.

—Five million years ago, the beginning of the Pliocene was marked by the sudden, permanent return of the sea, obviously due to the opening of the straits at Gibraltar. This resulted in the final separation of what have now become Crete and Karpathos from the continents. Somewhat later, during the Pliocene, the Cyclades were, in turn, isolated. Rhodes was apparently cut off from Anatolia in the early Pleistocene, when Crete was born as a result of the fusion of a group of Pliocene islands.

—Glacial-eustatic changes in sea level characterise the later part of the Pleistocene. During the ice ages huge quantities of water were accumulated on the continents in the form of glaciers, and the sea level was lowered accordingly. The strongest regressions took place during the Riss and Würm glaciations, when the sea level was lowered by at least 100 m and possibly up to 200 m. At that time most of the marginal Aegean islands were fused to the neighbouring continents, which was still the case 20 000 years ago (Fig. 1). During the ice ages, mean temperatures were lowered by 6–7°C in the mountains, resulting in a depression of the snow-line by c. 1000 m (Messerli, 1967), and by c. 4°C at sea level as shown by the summer temperatures of the surface water (Olausson, 1971). This has led to the extinction of some species and to the restriction of the distributional ranges of many others to refugial areas where they could survive, notably to the islands and sheltered peninsulas; elsewhere they were replaced by a flora of a temperate type which, being more competitive under cool climatic conditions, was then spreading all over the continents. The assumption that the whole Cardaegean region (Crete, Karpathos and the Cyclades; see Greuter, 1971a) remained insular throughout the Pleistocene is strongly supported by palaeontological data on mammalian faunas (Sondaar, 1971).

From the above survey we must accept fundamantal differences between the floras of the various Aegean islands with respect to their relict elements. On most of the marginal islands they are only c. 20 000 years old, on Rhodes possibly about one million years, on the Cyclades a few million years, while Crete and the Karpathos island group look back upon 5 million years of uninterrupted isolation. Indeed, the basic difference between the Cardaegean and the marginal Aegean lies in the age of the respective relict elements.

The Cardaegean islands share a number of floristic features: presence of endemics which have managed to survive only there, and absence of species which are widespread on the marginal islands. The Cardaegean distributional gap is a young type of area. Most of the species showing it belong to the submediterranean and temperate forest-belts which have spread during the Pleistocene in the regions surrounding the Mediterranean Sea, principally to the *Quercus pubescens* Willd. woods and to the montane Conifer forests with *Abies* and *Pinus nigra* Arnold.

Much older are those distribution ranges of relict species which cross the old lines of isolation around and within the Cardaegean, e.g. the particularly numerous ones that follow the old South Aegean mountain arch. We will have to give them some consideration now when we turn to the problems of evolution within island floras.

Evolution in island floras

A discussion of the relict hypothesis   I have stated above that almost one half of the flora of Crete, i.e., about 700 species, belongs to the relict element. One fifth of them, c. 130 species (and only one genus, *Petromarula*), are endemic to the island. Some of the remaining ones may be "crypto-endemics", showing a weak degree of differentiation with respect to the

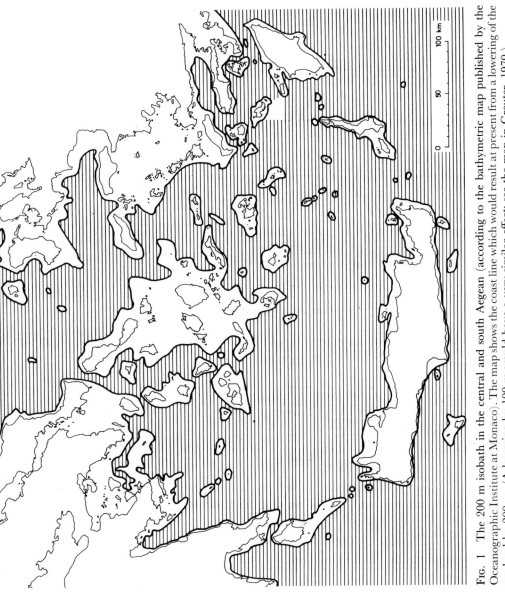

Fig. 1 The 200 m isobath in the central and south Aegean (according to the bathymetric map published by the Oceanographic Institute at Monaco). The map shows the coast line which would result at present from a lowering of the sea level by 200 m. (A lowering by 100 m would have a very similar effect: see the map in Greuter, 1970.)

D*

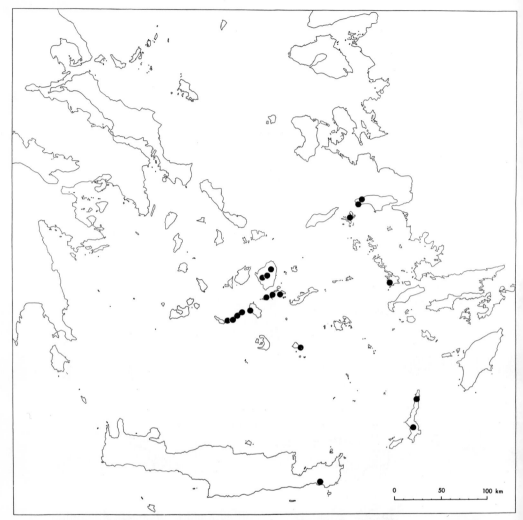

F<small>IG</small>. 2   The distributional range of *Tordylium hirtocarpum* Candargy, an annual relict species, transgresses several old lines of isolation between Crete, Karpathos, the Cyclades and the E. Aegean Islands. (From Runemark, 1968, completed.)

populations growing elsewhere, and might eventually be given taxonomic recognition, mostly at subspecies level. The majority, however, obviously transgress old isolation barriers without any significant differentiation (Fig. 2, showing the distribution of *Tordylium hirtocarpum*, is just one of many examples). This means that they have not undergone any appreciable evolutionary change subsequent to the onset of isolation.

If we accept the relict nature of these species, this deals a heavy blow to the reputation of islands as centres of differentiation and speciation. In the case of Crete the evolutionary standstill involves a period of 5 million years, which corresponds roughly to 3% of the whole span of existence of the Angiosperms, a time during which we would expect new genera or even new families to arise! This virtual fossilisation involves not only 80% of the surviving relict species, but probably many more, since some of the present endemics may have had wider areas originally but have now become extinct outside Crete, or else they may have been restricted to that portion of the Aegean Continent now corresponding to Crete, even before the cut-off date.

But is the relict hypothesis really sound? No doubt it will be challenged by many. Not so much the duration of insularity, which is now fairly safe thanks to recent geological findings, but the relict nature of the species involved is a subject open to discussion. Unfortunately fossil evidence for the age of the taxa concerned is conspicuously lacking, and at least on Crete itself there is little hope that this might ever change. It may be worth while pointing at the Miocene leaves described from Central Europe as *Liquidambar europaea* A. Br., since they do not appear to differ significantly from those of *L. styraciflua* L. still growing in Rhodes. Similarly, leaf fossils which can barely be distinguished from recent relict species growing in Crete (*Olea europaea*, L., *Phoenix theophrasti* Greuter, etc.) have been found now and again in Miocene layers of more northern countries.

The considerations on telechory just outlined are much in favour of the relict theory, but they are themselves hypothetical. In my opinion, the best support for the relict, as opposed to telechorous, nature of the bulk of the Cretan flora is provided by present distributional patterns. The following considerations may permit to appreciate this point:

—Telechory is an individual process and does not involve entire plant communities. Therefore, the association of species resulting from the random processes of long-distance dispersal must differ fundamentally from those of the neighbouring continents. Such "random communities" (Greuter, 1975a) are indeed found on some of the smaller islets in the area (Greuter, 1972; but see Greuter and Pieper, 1975), but not usually on Crete and most other Aegean islands. There, some vegetation units are lacking altogether, others are endemic but obviously well balanced (especially those of the high mountain and cliff habitats), still others, and notably the phrygana and scrub

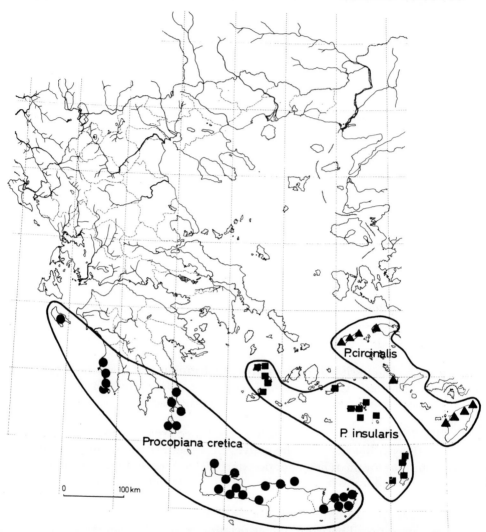

FIG. 3 The three species of the genus *Procopiana* show a coherent vicarious distribution suggestive of an old pre-isolation pattern. The range of two of them crosses old lines of isolation: in *P. cretica* (Willd.) Guşul. between Crete, Kithira and the Peloponnisos, in *P. insularis* Pawł. between Karpathos and the Cyclades; the third species, *P. circinalis* (Run.) Pawł., is restricted to the E. Aegaen Islands (Redrawn from Pawłowski, 1971.)

formations, are in good agreement with the corresponding ones on the mainland. Only one exception to this rule is known to me: the hydrophytic and wetland communities which, in good agreement with their supposed telechorous origin, are obviously of the random type (Gradstein and Smittenberg, 1968).

—Haphazard telechory cannot result in coherent, regular distributional areas. Nevertheless such areas are normally found in Aegean relict species. In particular, related and ecologically identical taxa which are mutually exclusive show, as a rule, neat vicariance of homogeneous ranges, and only exceptionally (as in *Phlomis* sect. *Dendrophlomis*) do we observe the interpenetrating mosaic distribution type which is to be expected if telechory plays the leading role. In many instances (as with *Procopiana*, Fig. 3, and *Ptilostemon gnaphaloides* (Cyr.) Soják, Fig. 4) the partial areas of coherent patterns of vicariance cross old isolation barriers, which is particularly suggestive of genuine relict status.

—In a few recently studied cases, old introgressional or transitional populations have maintained themselves on islands which are situated in-between the areas of two vicarious taxa. In *Centaurea raphanina* Sm. ssp. *raphanina* (S. Aegean) and ssp. *mixta* (DC.) Run. (Greek mainland) the Cyclades are such an old transitional field (Runemark, 1967, fig. 5).

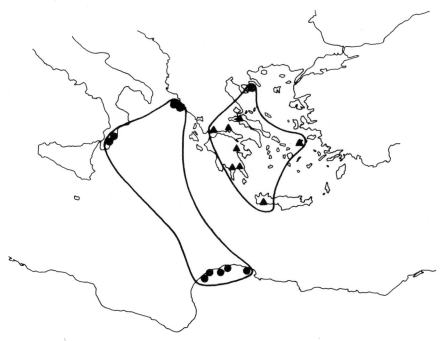

Fig. 4   The distributional ranges of *Ptilostemon gnaphaloides* (Cyr.)Soják ssp. *gnaphaloides* (●) and ssp. *pseudofruticosus* (Pamp.) Greuter (▲) are clearly vicarious, but show no correlation whatsoever with the post-Messiniano geography of the area.

(Compiled on the basis of detailed maps in Greuter, 1973.)

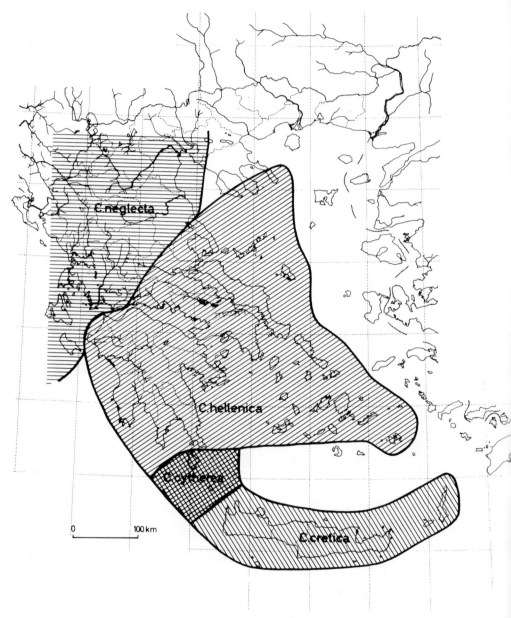

Fig. 5 The areas of Greek representatives of the *Crepis neglecta* group show the geographically intermediate position of *C. cytherea* Kam., presumably an old hybrid derivative from *C. hellenica* Kam. and *C. cretica* Boiss. (Redrawn from Kamarē, 1976.)

100

A taxon intermediate between *Crepis cretica* Boiss. (Crete and Karpathos) and *C. hellenica* Kam. (Greek mainland and Cyclades), which has the chromosome complement of the former and a morphology very similar to that of the latter, exists on the islands of Kithira and Andikithira (Fig. 5); it has been described as a hybrid *C* × *cytherea* Kam. and is obviously of old hybrid origin, although neither of the parents is now known to exist in that area (Kamarē, 1976). Transitional populations on Kithira and Andikithira are also known between the Cretan *Salvia pomifera* L. ssp. *pomifera* and its Greek vicariant subsp. *calycina* (Sm.) Hayek (Greuter and Rechinger, 1967). Such distributional patterns cannot be satisfactorily explained by long-distance dispersal, but only by the virtual fossilisation, through the ages, of situations which arose from a former direct contact. Ehrendorfer (1958) has long ago coined the term "fossil hybrid complexes" for similar patterns involving E. Mediterranean *Galium* taxa.

Evolution in the Cretan flora   We shall now turn to the question: can one observe patterns which are suggestive of differentiation processes which took place on Crete itself, during the isolation phase?

I have given extensive consideration to that question in an earlier paper (Greuter, 1972a) and need not repeat myself here. I have listed there two dozen cases where, in Crete, mountain taxa have evolved from lowland species, and one dozen littoral taxa corresponding to inland species. This is ecological differentiation, involving the colonisation of new habitats, with a very much impoverished flora, by plants from neighbouring stable habitats with a rich, well-balanced flora. In most cases the differentiation does not go beyond the infraspecific level, and some of the taxa involved are, indeed, still unnamed.

On the other hand, cases of apparent geographical differentiation without ecological change are frequent in the Aegean area. But there, surprisingly, no clear correlation can be established between the patterns of distribution of presumed old relict taxa and the past and present barriers of isolation. I have come to the conclusion that processes of geographical differentiation are quite unusual under the conditions of insularity and seem, as a rule, to have preceded the fragmentation of the area.

Plant evolution–some general considerations   I have tried, in my 1972a paper, to reconcile the prolonged evolutionary standstill which, as I hope to have plausibly demonstrated, affects the bulk of the Aegaen relict species, with the undisputed reality of Angiosperm evolution. I hope that my hypothesis, which I am going to outline again in a few words, has meanwhile been tested by others for other areas.

Evolution, according to my model, is an exceptional event linked to exceptional situations. Such short "dynamic phases", as I have termed them, would disrupt the natural equilibrium which I take to be the normal, stable condition. They would lead, in particular, to a rearrangement of distributional patterns, i.e. to the conquest of new habitats or areas by pioneer descendants of some of the old, stable populations. In every case, they require that new territories be created or that occupied areas or ecological niches be freed for new potential settlers following some change of the basic environmental, climatic or biological factors. They involve a sudden release of competitive pressure leading to an unrestrained increase of individual numbers and population size. As a corollary, we may imagine the repeated occurrence of a founder effect followed by the establishment of morphologically discrete populations, then again the meeting and interbreeding of such populations leading to a marked polymorphism and to numerous new gene combinations. We also expect that the criteria of selection will be radically different in the phase of expansion and in the subsequent process of stabilisation, when the pressure of competition gradually sets in again. Some of the characters eventually fixed in the restabilised population may have been adaptive with respect to the conditions of the "dynamic phase" and present no significant advantage under the "steady state" except the prospective one of being a pre-adaptation to dynamic conditions which may again occur in the future.

Until now, the beliefs of evolutionists were heavily influenced by facts and theories from the field of zoology. As botanists we have to be very careful and critical in this respect, since there are basic differences between plants and animals, affecting their evolutionary potentialities.

Owing to their parasitic, or at most symbiotic, way of life animals are extremely specialised, ecologically. Each species has its own ecological niche which it seldom shares with another species. Rather than being true competition, meaning struggle for the same niche, the antinomic relations between animal species are mostly of the predator-prey or parasite-host type. Furthermore, the intraspecific competition between individuals has in many cases been alleviated by mechanisms of social behaviour which are unknown in the plant kingdom. Animal species will react to any environmental change by adaptive processes at the genetic level, or else they will move away (mobility being another animal property uncommon in plants) or become extinct. There is of course a variety of unchanging, extremely stable habitats, as e.g. the deep-sea floor or karst cave systems, which may provide steady state conditions for given animal species. But as soon as the environment changes we expect an immediate response by adaptation through selection, at the genic level.

On the contrary, most plants have very wide ecological potentialities, often in striking contrast to a restricted ecological range in nature. The apparent exigencies of plant species with respect to the environment depend almost exclusively on the competition balance with other present species, not on physiological needs and limitations. The chances of success of an individual plant in surviving and seed-setting stand against the chances of other individuals, notably of the same species. The selective environment of a plant is its phytocoenosis and within that, particularly, the members of its conspecific population. To this coenotic context, exerting a tremendous selection pressure, each plant is genetically adapted, and is prevented by this pressure from any evolutionary change, notwithstanding the fact that other environmental factors less relevant to its survival, notably the climate, may be far from constant. The island condition, where the assemblage of species is kept relatively stable over long periods of time owing to the effective barriers against potential new immigrants, is particularly conservative in this respect.

The Mediterranean situation   In north and central Europe, the glaciations of the late Pleistocene period had marked consequences for the evolution of plants, leading to the differentiation of a great number of new taxa. It is my belief that the Messinian key period of Mediterranean biogeography has had parallel but far more important effects. Geologists have reasons to believe that the Mediterranean Sea, during the 1·5 million years of that era, dried out not once but dozens of times. We can easily imagine that each of these cycles involved extensive migrations of plants. Huge areas of land emerged and were colonised, to be flooded again after a while; recurrent changes of the climate, notably of aridity, must also be postulated. It is reasonable to assume that this long succession of "dynamic phases" was responsible for an almost explosive speciation and may account for the near totality of the diversity of non-arborescent Mediterranean genera. Their present remnants are of course only poor left-overs of the former wealth. The Messinian-type vegetation was suited to steppe and semi-desert conditions and was displaced almost immediately by forest vegetation at the onset of the Pliocene. It survived in specialised treeless habitats like cliffs, dunes and mountain tops, especially on the islands where it was protected against competition from the more northerly vegetation belts spreading on the mainlands during the Pleistocene. The relicts we find today have escaped the haphazards of extinction through reproductive drift, under gradually deteriorating climates, over 5 million years. The few that are widespread and common owe their present range to Man, i.e. to the destruction of the natural forest vegetation through human action.

Some thoughts on the thalassogenous islands   I have depicted the islands' role as repositories for old relicts, and denied their creative function in plant evolution. This may be a slightly provocative picture for many, and my aim is indeed to provoke criticism and contradiction. It would make the task of my detractors too easy, however, if I made no mention of those cases where speciation processes are known to have occurred on islands. The examples are well known, and many will be discussed in this volume. Consider the 22 species and 5 sections of *Argyranthemum*, a genus endemic to Macaronesia (Humphries, 1976). Also consider the 70 endemic Hawaiian species of *Pelea* (Stone, 1969).

My conservative model is that of a chersogenous island. It is obvious that, with thalassogenous islands, the initial colonisation process corresponds to a "dynamic phase" and may give rise to differentiation processes. Both Hawaii and the Canaries are volcanic island groups, and at least for the former we know that the individual islands arose in succession, through the ages, in a long line, so that colonisation and dynamism were repetitive events. Again, both Hawaii and the Canaries lie far off-shore, so that diaspore arrivals from the mainland must be rare events. This provides good opportunities, for the first settlers, to invade a variety of different, still unoccupied habitats, a process which will normally result in adaptive radiation. Indeed, Humphries (1976) estimates that 80% of the species differentiation in *Argyranthemum* was due to ecological adaptation processes.

As I have said before, I do not feel competent to judge the specific problems of thalassogenous islands. I would not be surprised, however, if there too the available data were compatible with, or would support, the hypothesis of a short initial "dynamic phase" involving differentiation, followed by a long-lasting static condition.

REFERENCES

Cammerloher, H. (1935). Ein Beitrag zur Flora von Kaimeni (Santorin). *Österr. Bot. Z.* **84**, 81–90
Drooger, C. W. (1973). Messinian Events in the Mediterranean. *Geodynamics Sci. Rep.* **7**
Ehrendorfer, F. (1958). Ein Variabilitätszentrum als "fossiler" Hybrid-Komplex: der ost-mediterrane *Galium graecum* L. *G. canum* Req.

Formenkreis. Eine Monographie. (Zur Phylogenie der Gattung *Galium*, VI.) *Österr. Bot. Z.* **105**, 229–279

Ernst, A. (1934). Das biologische Krakatauproblem. *Vierteljahrsschr. Naturf. Ges. Zürich* **79**, *Beibl.* **22**

Gradstein, S. R. and J. H. Smittenberg (1968). *Bron- beek- en moeras-vegetaties van west Kreta*. Thesis, Utrecht

Greuter, W. (1970). Zur Paläogeographie und Florengeschichte der südlichen Ägäis. *Feddes Repert.* **81**, 233–242

— (1971). L'apport de l'homme à la flore spontanée de la Crète. *Boissiera* **19**, 329–337

— (1971a). Betrachtungen zur Pflanzengeographie der Südägäis. *Opera Bot.* **30**, 49–64

— (1972). L'ecueil à *Silene holzmannii*, en Crète, et son peuplement végétal. *Saussurea* **3**, 157–166

— (1972a). The relict element of the flora of Crete and its evolutionary significance. In *Taxonomy, Phytogeography and Evolution* (D. H. Valentine, ed.), 161–177. Academic Press, London and New York

— (1973). Monographie der Gattung *Ptilostemon* (Compositae). *Boissiera* **22**

— (1975). Historical phytogeography of the southern half of the Aegean area. In *Problems of Balkan flora and vegetation. Proceedings of the first international symposium on Balkan flora and vegetation, Varna, June 7–14, 1973* (D. Jordanov, I. Bondev. S. Kožuharov, B. Kuzmanov, E. Palamarev and V. Velčev, eds.), 17–21. Sofia.

— (1975a). Die Insel Kreta – eine geobotanische Skizze. *Veröff. Geobot. Inst. ETH Stiftung Rübel Zürich* **55**, 141–197

— (1976). The flora of Psara (E. Aegean Islands, Greece.) *Candollea* **31**, 191–242

— and Pieper, H. (1975). Notiz zur Flora und Biogeographie der landfernen südägäischen Klippe Avgo. *Candollea* **30**, 7–11

— and Rechinger, K. H. (1967). Flora der Insel Kythera, gleichzeitig Beginn einer nomenklatorischen Überprüfung der griechischen Gefässpflanzenarten. *Boissiera* **13**

Hansen, A. (1971). Flora der Inselgruppe Santorin. *Candollea* **26**, 109–163.

Humphries, C. J. (1976). A revision of the Macaronesian genus *Argyranthemum* Webb ex Schultz Bip. (Compositae-Anthemideae). *Bull. Brit. Mus. (Nat. Hist.), Bot.* **5**, (4).

Kamarē, G. A. (1976). *Kuttarotaxonomikē meletē tēs omados Crepis neglecta L. en Elladi*, Thesis, Patrai

Messerli, B. (1967). Die eiszeitliche und die gegenwärtige Vergletscherung im Mittelmeerraum. *Georgr. Helv.* **22**, 105–228

Olausson, E. (1971). Tephrochronology and the late Pleistocene of the Aegean Sea. *Opera Bot.* **30**, 29–39

Palmgren, A. (1922). Über Artenzahl und Areal sowie über die Konstitution der Vegetation. Eine vegetationsstatistische Untersuchung. *Acta Forest. Fenn.* **22**[1]

— (1925). Die Artenzahl als pflanzengeographischer Charakter sowie der Zufall und die säkulare Landhebung als pflanzengeographische Faktoren. Ein pflanzengeographischer Entwurf, basiert auf Material aus dem Åländischen Schärenarchipel. *Fennia* **46** (2)

Pawłowski, B. (1971) De genere Procopiana Guşuleac – Rodzaj Procopiana Guşuleac. *Fragm. Florist. Geobot.* **17**, 39–58

Runemark, H. (1967). Studies in the Aegean flora XII. Cytologic and morphologic investigations in *Centaurea. Bot. Not.* **120**, 161–176, 486

— (1968). Studies in the Aegean flora XIII. Tordylium L. (Umbelliferae). *Bot. Not.* **121**, 233–258

— (1969). Reproductive drift, a neglected principle in reproductive biology. *Bot. Not.* **122**, 90–129

Sondaar, P. Y. (1971). Paleozoogeography of the Pleistocene mammals from the Aegean. *Opera Bot.* **30**, 65–70

Stone, B. C. (1969). The genus *Pelea* A. Gray (Rutaceae: Evodiinae). A taxonomic monograph. *Phanerog. Monogr.* **3**

7 The Origins of Indian Ocean Island Floras

S. A. RENVOIZE   *Royal Botanic Gardens, Kew, England*

La flora de las islas del Oceano Indico deriva de una gran variedad de procedencias, clasificándose desde muy cosmopolitas hasta extremadamente local. El número de regiones corológicas diferentes que deben contribuir a una flora es gobernado en gran medida por el ambiente del terreno adecuado para la colonización. A este respecto, las islas del Oceano Indico deben estár divididas en dos grandes categorías. 1. Las islas altas de Madagascar, Comoros, Mascarenas, Seychelles, Sri Lanka, Andamans y Nicobars, que ofrecen una amplia distribución de habitats. 2. Las islas bajas de coral tienen una selección de habitats muy restringida. La flora de las islas altas son más ricas que la flora de las islas bajas. La isla de Pascua y el grupo de islas de la Aldabra son más o menos intermedias entre estos dos extremos y aunque poseen un número considerable de especies pantropical y paleotropical, también tienen un elemento sustancial de su flora derivada de orígenes locales.

Un exacto análisis de los orígenes florísticos requiere una lista moderna y comprensible de las especies de cada isla. Desafortunadamente, estas listas no están disponibles para muchas de las islas altas y solamente puede darse un cálculo especulativo del origen de su flora. Por el contrario, para muchas de las islas coralinas bajas existen modernas listas pero estas floras se derivan casi enteramente de orígenes por esparcimiento, no ofreciendo las lista de especies ninguna información de importancia que sea comparable a la de las altas islas. La única isla que tiene una lista moderna y comprensible, con interesante información del origen de la flora es Aldabra.

Para las islas bajas, de muy reciente origen, los mecanismos de dispersión a largas distancias son los únicos medios para explicar la llegada de las especies de plantas que componen su flora. La dispersión a las islas altas que tienen ambientes terrestres de varios millones de años de antiguedad, pueden ser parcialmente explicados por medio de una separación continental.

Introduction

The flora of an island originates in many different ways and from a variety of regions, depending on its geological history and position in relation to possible sources of immigration. Usually an island which is a fragment of a continent will have a flora consisting mainly of species characeristic of the parent land mass. In contrast, an island which has emerged from the sea, remote from any continental connection, will have a flora consisting of species derived entirely from outside sources. Between

107

TABLE 1   Tropical islands and island groups in the Indian Ocean

High islands

Continental fragments
$$\begin{cases} \text{Madagascar} \\ \text{Seychelles} \\ \text{Andaman I.} \end{cases}$$

Volcanic
$$\begin{cases} \text{Comoros} \\ \text{Mauritius} \\ \text{Réunion} \\ \text{Rodriguez} \\ \text{Nicobar I.} \end{cases}$$

Elevated coral islands
Aldabra group
Christmas I.

Low islands

Sea level reefs or sand cays
$$\begin{cases} \text{Laccadive I.} \\ \text{Maldive I.} \\ \text{Minicoy} \\ \text{Addu Atoll} \\ \text{Chagos Archipelago} \\ \text{Cocos Keeling} \\ \text{Cargados Carajos} \\ \text{Tromelin} \\ \text{Agalega} \\ \text{Coetivy} \\ \text{Amirante Group} \\ \text{Alphonse} \\ \text{Gloriosa} \\ \text{Farquhar Group} \\ \text{Europa I.} \end{cases}$$

these two extremes however there are numerous intermediates. In addition, the composition of an island flora will be influenced not only by its sources but also by the size and structure of the island.

The islands in the Indian Ocean vary in size, geological history and structure; correspondingly their floras have originated in a variety of ways and from many different sources.

In this chapter only the isolated tropical islands of the Indian Ocean will be considered (see Table 1 and Fig. 1). Socotra is excluded, see Balfour (1888) for details of the flora. The African coastal islands of Zanzibar, Pemba and Mafia are excluded as they have a basically African flora and the islands of Kerguelen, Amsterdam and St. Paul are excluded as they have a specialised south-temperate flora.

One method of assessing the origins of an island flora is through a study of the geographical distribution of its constituent species. If each species is

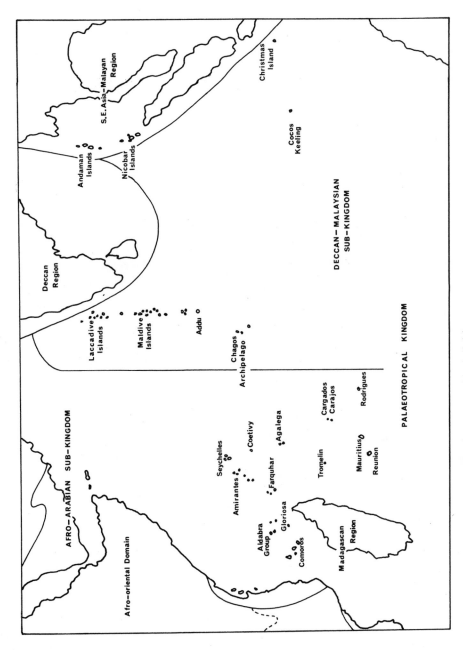

FIG. 1 Indian Ocean Islands and phytogeographical divisions

mapped, those with similar distribution patterns can be grouped and equated with known phytogeographical areas, thereby indicating the origins of the flora. This technique will also provide information for identifying the phytogeographical region to which an island belongs and correlating one island with another; island floras are not always derived solely from continental land masses and one island may be a source of species present on another, Clayton and Hepper (1974); Clayton and Panigrahi (1974); Renvoize (1975).

For such a study it is desirable to have a comprehensive list, using up-to-date taxonomy, of the species present on each island.

This is an ideal however which is seldom possible to achieve and for most of the Indian Ocean islands species lists are either not available or if a flora has been published it is usually out of date or incomplete. One notable exception is the Aldabra group for which a comprehensive flora list has recently been prepared.

Since it is not within the scope of this work to revise the taxonomy of species composing the floras of the Indian Ocean islands the ideas expressed here are based largely upon a review of the relevant literature.

In the Indian Ocean two broad categories of islands may be recognised on the basis of their geological structure: 1. High islands; these are either fragments of a continental land mass or the result of volcanic activity. As the term implies these islands generally reach hundreds or thousands of metres in height above sea level. 2. Low islands; these have usually evolved in isolation from a continent through a combination of volcanic activity, subsidence and coral growth. In contrast to the high islands these are only two or three metres above sea level. Intermediate between these two types are islands which, although the result of coral growth, have been elevated to tens or even hundreds of metres above sea level.

These differences in structure of the islands are important as they have profoundly influenced the composition of the floras.

On the basis of geological structure the islands of the Indian Ocean may be amalgamated into the groups shown in Table 1.

The origins of the floras of the high islands

Floristic accounts are available for many of the high islands but unfortunately the taxonomy used is often out-of-date and cannot be relied upon for a detailed comparative analysis.

In such instances, where accurate plant lists are absent, clues to the origins of the floras may be gained by considering the geological origin of the islands and their terrestrial environments.

Melville (1973) studied the distribution patterns of a few selected species, genera and families from which he developed a scheme for the geological evolution of the islands in the Indian Ocean, which he integrated with theories on continental drift. An understanding of continental drift in relation to the Indian Ocean is useful for explaining the possible origins of several island floras in this region.

When the great southern continent of Gondwanaland started to break up, in the early Triassic period 225 million years ago, the result was a drifting apart of large segments of the original land mass. These large segments now form the continents of Australia, India, Africa and Antarctica. The sea-space left between these continents now forms the Indian Ocean.

The break-up of Gondwanaland was not a neat affair and as the large segments drifted apart various fragments became isolated. Two of the largest fragments form the islands of Madagascar and Sri Lanka.

Madagascar This is one of the largest islands in the world. It has probably been isolated for a long time, at least since the Triassic, as evidenced by the high degree of endemism in the flora and fauna, especially at family and generic level. During the initial period of continental drift Madagascar remained close to India, which helps to explain why there are fewer genera in common between Madagascar and Africa than would be expected by their present proximity. In fact there are more endemic genera than there are genera in common with Africa.

The strong floristic links with India, Sri Lanka and Malaysia support the proposition that Madagascar became isolated from the east at a later date than from Africa. The Madagascar flora therefore is basically the Mesozoic flora of Gondwanaland which, through a long period of isolation has evolved a high degree of endemism at family, generic and species level.

The complete flora of Madagascar is not known and no reliable list has ever been published but an estimate would put the number of species between 8000 and 10 000 (Koechlin *et al.*, 1974; see also Rauh, chapter 21, this volume).

Seychelles These are granitic islands which appear to be isolated fragments of the original land mass of Gondwanaland. The flora of the Seychelles therefore is probably based on that of Gondwanaland but like Madagascar with a long period of isolation, has evolved many endemic species. The present flora of 233 indigenous species is very poor for a terrestrial area of 160 square miles and reaching elevations up to 1000 m. This poverty may be explained by the theory that the Seychelles terrestrial environment in earlier geological time was probably much larger than it is today and gradual submergence reduced the size of the land area and the variety of habitats. This in turn influenced the flora so that only a few remnants, of what was once a much larger flora, are extant today (Summerhayes, 1931).

Despite the relatively small number of species there is a high degree of endemism which supports the suggestion that the terrestrial environments of the isolated region are of great age.

The present flora, although small has, on evidence of geographical distribution, been derived from a wide variety of sources:

Introduced species
137 weeds
110 escapes from cultivation
Indigenous species
77   pantropical and palaeotropical
19   African/Mascarene
26   Asiatic/Mascarene
21   Mascarene
90   endemic, 31 of Asiatic affinities, 10 of African affinities,
     32 of Mascarene affinities and 17 others

Mascarenes and Comoros   The drift of the continents was not the placid process which the term implies. The earth movements which caused the drift were accompanied by volcanic activity along the mid-Indian Ocean Rise resulting in the establishment of the three Mascarene Islands, Mauritius, Réunion and Rodriguez and of the Comoro Islands.

During the period of emergence of the Comoros and Mascarenes, which possibly took place from the middle to the end of the Cretaceous period, the Mascarenes and Seychelles may have been interconnected and, with the Comoros, linked also to Madagascar and Sri Lanka. This would have permitted a limited amount of overland migration along the intervening land bridges.

Comoros   The only complete flora list for the Comoros is that of Voeltzkow (1917), who gives 935 species of which 416 are indigenous. A modern but incomplete account is included in the Flora of Madagascar and Comoros. The following analysis however is extracted from Voeltzkow (1917).

519 Introduced and pantropical
99   Africa, Madagascar and Mascarenes
96   Madagascar and Mascarenes
85   Madagascan
136 Endemic

Réunion   Cordemoy (1895), lists 1156 species but provides no analysis of their distribution.

Mauritius   Baker (1877), lists 869 species. This is combined with a flora of the Seychelles and no analysis is provided for Mauritius alone.

Rodriguez   Balfour (1879), lists 253 species which may be grouped as follows:

    108 *Introduced species*
    Indigenous species
    66   pantropical
    22   Old World
    8   African
    14   Asiatic
    35   endemic

Sri Lanka   Like Madagascar this island was isolated from the continental land mass very early in the period of continental drift, evidenced by its high degree of generic endemism. Trimen (1893), lists an estimated 3750 species but provides no analysis of the distribution of the species.

Although these analyses are reasonably reliable in the context of the islands for which they are provided it is unwise to use the plant lists for comparative analyses between the islands as the taxonomic concepts are likely to differ considerably according to the date of publication and the author.

To summarise, the Madagascar, Sri Lanka and Seychelles floras are probably based directly on the Mesozoic flora of Gondwanaland, much modified over a long period of time. The Mascarene and Comoro floras are probably based indirectly on the Gondwanaland flora, having been derived and filtered by migration from Madagascar and Ceylon and again modified over a long period of time.

Andaman and Nicobar Islands   These are the only other islands comparable geologically with those previously discussed.

The two groups form a chain running north-south, in the northeast Indian Ocean and are clearly fragments which have become isolated at the time of the drifting apart of the continents. Their floras are closely related to those of Burma and Malaya.

Andaman Islands   These consist of 204 islands, 253.4 km long, and 6331 km² in area. They are hilly islands covered with dense jungle, the highest point being 732 m. They form part of a submarine ridge which extends from Burma to the Moluccas. The older rocks are of early Tertiary or late Cretaceous period. Soils are soft, deep sandy loam, clay or sandy. These islands provide a wide range of habitats which support a rich and varied flora. No complete floristic account exists but Kurz (1870) estimates 1500–1800 species and Parkinson (1923) estimates 1000 species.

The flora is derived mainly from Burma but there are also links with Malaya, Sri Lanka and India. Thothathri (1962) supports Parkinson's estimate of 1000 species but publishes no complete list.

Nicobar Islands   These 22 islands cover an area of 1605 km² and consist of both flat and hilly islands. They are based on volcanic rocks, which have pierced through the stratified sea floor, and are of slightly younger origin than the Andamans. The soils are clay on calcareous sandstone and shales.

The vegetation is mostly scrub forest on the low flat islands of the north with no mangroves whereas the central and southern islands are more hilly and have coastal and inland forest and mangroves.

The flora of approximately 700 species is mostly related to Malaya, (Thothathri, 1962); no list is published.

The origins of the floras of the low islands

Whereas comprehensive flora lists are available for most of the high granitic and volcanic islands, albeit often rather out of date, the situation with the low, coral islands is slightly different. For many of the low islands recently published flora lists are available but although they incorporate modern taxonomic concepts they are in many instances the product of fleeting visits by collectors and are unlikely to be comprehensive. Once again one of the requirements for an accurate analysis cannot be fulfilled. However, sufficient data are available to permit a rough analysis of the origins of the floras for the low islands in the Indian Ocean.

Laccadive and Maldive Islands   These islands form a chain of huge atolls running north to south, off the west coast of India. They consist of islets, barely above sea level, composed of coral limestone rock, covered with sand.

The northerly group, the Laccadives, comprise 16 small islets. A detailed description of each islet is provided by Prain (1892) and a list of plant species for the whole group by Prain (1893).

For the Laccadives and Minikoi, Prain (1893) lists 121 species which may be grouped as follows:

34 cultivated
47 weeds
40 indigenous, pantropical and Indo-Pacific (25 of littoral habitats and 15 of inland habitats)

Some trees such as *Calophyllum inophyllum* L. and *Terminalia catappa* L., which occur naturally, have also been planted.

Minikoi, which lies between the Laccadives and the Maldives, is an isolated atoll 9·7 km in diameter. It consists of several islets of low lying reef rock covered with wind-blown sand. Although Prain (1893) included this island in his review of the Laccadive flora, Willis (1901) added further records to bring the total number of species for Minikoi alone to 134, of which 38 are introduced and 96 are indigenous.

The southerly group of islands, the Maldives consist of approximately 20 atolls or islet groups, including Addu in the south but excluding Minikoi. Willis and Gardiner (1901) list 284 plant species for these islands. Some of them have been visited by botanists recently and their floras are well known.

Malé, the capital of the Maldives has a long history of human occupation consequently there is little natural vegetation left. Most of the minor islets are dominated by coconut groves and marginal forest occurs only at the tops of beaches. Fosberg (1957) lists 260 species for this island, adding a further 29 records to the list of Willis and Gardiner. Approximately 50 of these species are cultivated.

Addu, in the extreme south, consists of three large islands and several smaller ones. Fosberg, Groves and Sigee in Stoddart (1966) record 142 species for this atoll, which may be grouped as follows:

Introduced species
57 weeds and exotics
33 cultivated
Indigenous species
52 pantropical and Indo-Pacific (32 of litoral habitats, 20 of inland habitats

Chagos Archipelago Directly south of the Maldives lies the Chagos Archipelago, of which the islands of Diego Garcia and Egmont are well known botanically. The vegetation consists of coconut groves, which dominate much of the atoll, *Casuarina* woodland, beach scrub and woodland and inland broadleaf woodland and areas of marsh. There is a notable lack of mangroves and *Pandanus* groves. For details of the vegetation see Stoddart and Taylor (1971).

The whole flora of Chagos includes approximately 150 species, (Fosberg and Bullock in Stoddart and Taylor, 1971; Renvoize, unpublished data) of which at least 50 are introduced. The 100 indigenous species are mostly of pantropical or Indo-Pacific distribution.

Cocos Keeling Islands   These two atolls lie in the eastern Indian Ocean. The larger is Cocos Island, the smaller Keeling Island; both are low reefs covered with sand. Wood-Jones (1912) recorded 57 species from these islands of which approximately 14 species are cultivated or introduced weeds and 43 are indigenous species of pantropical or Indo-Pacific distribution. He also provides a brief description of the vegetation of Keeling Island which is a horseshoe-shaped atoll 1·6 km long and 0·8 km wide, covered by a mixture of coconuts, *Pisonia grandis* R.Br. and *Cordia subcordata* Lam. Cocos Island is mainly covered with coconut plantations and no detailed information is provided on the natural vegetation.

Cargados Carajos   This group totals 48 km² in land area and consists of sand banks, shoals and islets. Although some islets are elevated to 6 m no species of strictly local distribution are present. The vegetation is mostly littoral scrub and herb mat, trees being more or less absent apart from a few stunted individuals. Staub and Gueho (1968) record 41 plant species which may be grouped as follows:

Introduced species
11 cultivated
13 weeds
Indigenous species
17 pantropical

Amirantes   This group of islands includes African Banks, Remire, Poivre, Desroches, Darros and Desnoefs, for which the total flora is 97 species (Gwynne and Wood (1969); Renvoize (1975), Renvoize unpublished data). Approximately 25 species are cultivated or introduced weeds and 72 are indigenous, of pantropical or Indo-Pacific origin.

Farquhar group   This includes the islands of Providence and St. Pierre for which the total flora is 59 species, (Gwynne and Wood, 1969; Renvoize, 1975). These may be grouped as follows:

Introduced species
13 cultivated
Indigenous species
23 pantropical
18 Indo-Pacific
5   African

The number of species recorded from each island is as follows:
Farquhar 44
St. Pierre 24
Providence 14

Coetivy This isolated island is 9·7 km long and 0·8 km wide. Hemsley (1919) states that 146 species grow there but this probably includes many cultivated plants. The recorded flora is 65 species, Gwynne and Wood (1969) Renvoize (1975) of which approximately 16 are cultivated or introduced weeds. Of the 49 indigenous species 46 are of pantropical and Indo-Pacific distribution and 3 are African.

Gloriosa Twenty species are recorded from this island by Hemsley (1919).

Agalega Six species are recorded from this island by Hemsley (1919) although a recent estimate (Procter, personal communication) suggests 60 species to be a more realistic number.

Tromelin Six species, all of pantropical or Indo-Pacific distribution, are recorded from this island (Staub in Stoddart, 1976).

Discussion of the high and low islands

A significant difference between high and low islands of the Indian Ocean is found in the range of sources which contribute to their floras. The high islands have derived their floras from a wide variety of phytogeographical regions whereas the floras of the low islands, with few exceptions, are composed solely of plants with pantropical or Indo-Pacific distributions.

This difference in floristic origins is largely due to profound differences in the range of habitats available for colonisation on each type of island. The high islands offer many more habitats than the low islands. The factors responsible for the diversity of habitats on these two categories of islands are tabulated below.

The greater range of temperature and wider rainfall range on high islands is a direct result of their mountainous topography and the richness and maturity of their soils may be attributed to the greater age of the islands and their frequent association with volcanism.

Another feature of high island floras, notably absent from those of low islands, is the evolution of endemic species, which can be attributed to the long period of genetic isolation and the selective pressures of the variety of

	High islands	Low islands
Size	Large	Small
Topography	Mountainous	Flat
Climate		
Rainfall variation	Wide range	Narrow range
Temperature variation	Wide range	Narrow range
Soils	Deep, mature soils	Thin, skeletal soils
Water resources	Fresh water streams and lakes	No permanent fresh water

habitats available. On low islands there are few areas beyond the influence of the sea and in the broadest sense all the habitats are coastal. Since the most constant agent of plant dispersal is the sea the coastal habitats will receive a steady flow of possible colonisers and therefore a steady flow of genes, which is not conducive to the evolution of new species. High islands do of course have coastal habitats but they do not dominate the islands and the characteristic coastal plants of widespread distribution do not therefore dominate the floras, as they do on the low islands.

Low islands, as the name implies, are coral reefs, seldom more than 1 or 2 metres high and usually covered by sand. Although scarcely beyond the influence of the sea at any point, and therefore consisting entirely of coastal vegetation types composed of pantropical or palaeotropical species, the following habitats may be present:

Shore
Subject to inundation, spray and wind.
Strand line
Beach crest communities
Sand dune vegetation
Inland
Sheltered from spray and wind, possibly subject to inundation.
Mixed scrub or forest
Plantations
Lagoon
Sheltered but subject to tidal inundation.
Brackish marsh
Mangroves

Some of these habitats will also be present on high islands.

So far only the high and low islands have been discussed, illustrating the two typical types of island floras. Two interesting examples of intermediates between these are provided by the islands of the Aldabra group and Christmas Island which, like the low islands, are composed of coral limestone rock. They differ however from the low islands in having a larger terrestrial area and in being higher in elevation. Although they do not reach the altitude of the high islands, they nevertheless offer a wide range of habitats which not only support species from a variety of phytogeographic regions but have also induced endemism.

The Aldabra group   Most coral islands have a complex history involving an initial growth of coral organisms on a submarine platform which has usually been the result of volcanic activity. With the emergence of the reef, due either to earth movements or changes in sea level, the coral organisms die and a terrestrial environment may develop. Subsequent submergence may occur resulting in a second period of coral growth until emergence occurs again and so on, thereby developing a series of coral growth phases.

The island of Aldabra last emerged during the mid-Pleistocene, approximately 80 000 years ago (Braithwaite *et al.*, 1973). By 27 000 years ago the whole area within the present reef was probably dry land, providing a terrestrial environment of 400 km². At that time the sea level had lowered considerably leaving the island 100 m above sea level. The sea level gradually rose again however and approximately 5000 years ago breached the outer rim of the island to flood the inner area and form the lagoon. At this point the land area was reduced by 60% to 155 km². Presumably the central part previously carried a mixed scrub type of vegetation. Many small islets which remain in the lagoon today usually have a variety of species on them which suggests that mixed scrub extended over a wide area of the central part of the island. After the formation of the lagoon the mangroves become established and where sea water permeated the coral rock *Pemphis* scrub developed.

Concurrent with the establishment of the present vegetation, or soon after, was the re-establishment of the major herbivore on Aldabra, the giant tortoise. Fossil evidence has shown that it arrived on Aldabra at least once before, during a previous period of terrestrial habitat development.

The four islands of the Aldabra group Aldabra, Assumption, Astove and Cosmoledo are exceptional amongst coral islands for the degree of elevation of the land surface as they now stand 8 m above sea level. This elevation has had a profound effect on the composition of the flora. Whereas the low lying coral islands previously discussed have indigenous floras composed almost entirely of pantropical or Indo-Pacific species, the flora of the Aldabra group includes not only pantropical and Indo-Pacific species but also African, Madagascan, Seychelles and endemic

E

species. The total flora, which numbers 257 taxa may be analysed as follows. (Renvoize and Fosberg, unpublished data.)

43 cultivated
55 pantropical
53 Indo-Pacific
36 African/Madagascan
28 Madagascan/Seychelles
42 endemic (34 species, 8 varieties)

Over half the flora is cultivated and of widespread origin but there is a considerable proportion of species from local sources (Renvoize, 1975).

The reason for the greater richness of the flora of the Aldabra group compared with the low islands would appear to be due to the greater variety of habitats available for plant colonisation. This variety is greatest on Aldabra itself where the following major habitats and corresponding vegetation types are present:

Lagoon mud and sand – mangroves
Deeply dissected, low level rock – *Pemphis* scrub
Flat, pavé rock above the marine watertable – mixed scrub
Rough rock near the coast – *Casuarina* woodland
Seaward intertidal zone, sand and mud – sea grasses
Seaward Sand dunes – coastal grassland
Sand beaches – beach communities
Sand inland of beaches – coconut groves and gardens

Christmas Island   Christmas Island consists mainly of a complex series of coral limestone rocks which have been elevated to a considerable extent and now form an island 19 km × 14 km, 135 km². The central plateau, is mostly 150 – 250 m above sea level but in parts reaches 361 m.

The base of the island is on a submarine volcanic peak and in a few places the limestone is interstratified with volcanic rocks, evidence of later volcanic activity after the growth of the coral. Phosphate rock, which occurs in large quantities, is probably derived from ancient guano deposits formed millions of years ago, possibly in the Pliocene.

The general aspect of the island is of coastal limestone cliffs 5 – 50 m high, rising to a shore terrace which extends to the first inland cliff, the ground then rises in a series of steep slopes, terraces and cliffs to the central plateau.

The vegetation on the plateau is forest which is supported mainly by the high rainfall of the wet season, which lasts from December to May. High humidity is maintained during the rest of the year by light rain, probably caused by cooling SE winds forced up over the island. The vegetation is also further encouraged by the fertile soil which has been enhanced by the phosphate deposits. Sadly much of the rainforest has been devastated in recent years as a result of phosphate mining.

Baker and Rendle in Andrews (1900) list 145 indigenous vascular plant species.

   31 pantropical
   21 palaeotropical
   76 tropical Asia (Madagascar to Polynesia and Australia)
   17 endemic

Since pantropical and palaeotropical species found on oceanic islands are usually of coastal habitats the somewhat reduced numerical status of these groups on Christmas Island, to a third of the indigenous flora, reflects the rather special habitats which this island offers. The rich well-drained soils well away from the direct influence of the sea have clearly favoured non-coastal species and this is shown in the composition of the flora.

The indication therefore is that Christmas Island has been colonised largely by plants from tropical Asia, which is hardly surprising in view of the close proximity of Indonesia.

Dispersal mechanisms

An outstanding problem in understanding the origin of floras and faunas on oceanic islands is that of dispersal; the mechanisms responsible for transporting disseminules from a source to the island destination.

The floras of the high islands can be accounted for largely on the basis of continental drift or land bridge theory, although long-distance dispersal should not be dismissed as a possible supplementary mechanism, responsible for adding further species to the original flora.

For the islands which have evolved in total isolation, new species could only arrive through long-distance dispersal by one of the following methods: 1. Wind, 2. Ocean currents, 3. Animal migration (mainly birds), and 4. Transport by Man.

Through these agencies species are carried between islands and between continents and islands, although different mechanisms may be responsible for long-distance transport to an archipelago and dispersal between the islands.

Each of these methods will be discussed very briefly, on a general basis in relation to the Indian Ocean and in detail in relation to the flora of Aldabra. For a detailed discussion and review of dispersal mechanisms see Carlquist (1974).

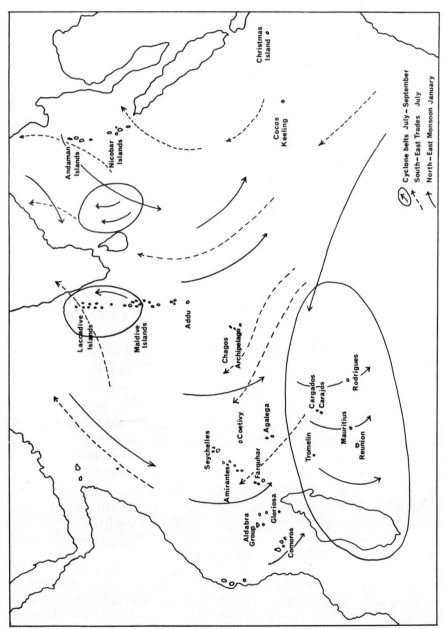

FIG. 2 Wind systems in the Indian Ocean

122

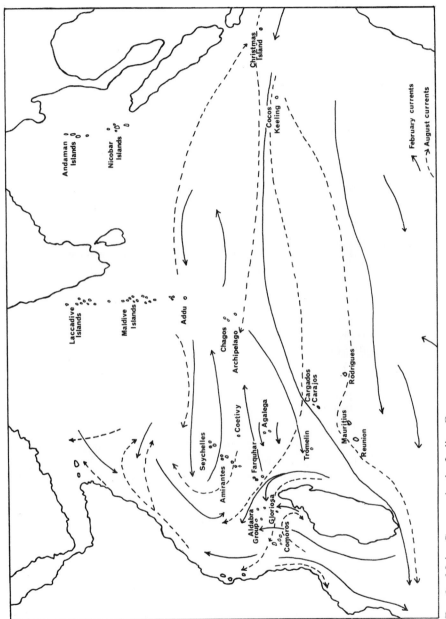

FIG. 3 Major Currents in the Indian Ocean

123

Dispersal to the Indian Ocean low islands

1 *Wind* It is difficult to be sure which species could be wind carried as most winds are of insufficient strength to carry many types of disseminules. Two families with seeds clearly adapted to wind dispersal are Asclepiadaceae and Compositae; however they may not travel far if the pappus gets damp, a situation which is highly likely over oceans. Furthermore in many island Compositae the pappus is reduced and adapted to dispersal by animals.

Cyclones are an important element when considering wind as a dispersal agent since much heavier disseminules could be carried than by ordinary winds. In the Indian Ocean there are three main cyclone areas one on either side of southern India, where they travel in a northerly direction, and one east of, and including most of Madagascar, where they travel in a southerly direction. In the Indian Ocean they are mostly likely to occur from July to September, the time of the SE trades and the summer monsoon in India.

Generally winds operate poorly over long distances and are unlikely to carry any disseminules other than fern spores or the very lightest seed (Fig. 2).

2 *Ocean currents and rafting* Most of the species of pantropical and Indo-Pacific distribution area associated with strand line or coastal habitats and many of them are clearly able to survive passage in sea water. Their typical habitat also allows for the disseminules to be carried away again by the sea. Ocean currents provide a very steady flow of introductions in contrast to the indirect mechanism of rafting which, although a means by which less adapted species can travel, is dependent on ocean currents and only provides an intermittent flow of possible introductions (Fig. 3).

3 *Animals (birds)* Birds are clearly an important agent of dispersal, especially the oceanic sea birds which may travel over long distances.

Unfortunately positive evidence of bird transport is severely lacking and most ideas are speculative. The concept of seeds travelling in the bird's gut or on muddy feet is hard to reconcile with the fact that birds usually clean their feet and bill before travelling and seldom travel with a full gut, although this mechanism may account for dispersal throughout an archipelago. The most likely method is by disseminules caught in the plumage but some seeds would clearly be too large for this.

4 *Transport by Man* Occupation by Man and passage by trading vessels between the islands, has been continuous throughout the Indian Ocean for at least 150 years. Many species have been introduced deliberately and cultivated in plantations or in gardens from which they

may have escaped. Along with the deliberate introductions are numerous weed species, probably also introduced by Man, although the status of weeds is often difficult to decide as some species of weedy habit may have arrived by long-distance dispersal.

Dispersal to Christmas Island

Although the prevailing winds for much of the year are SE trades the arrival of the Asiatic species is probably due to violent storms which blow from the north during the rainy season. More important than this however is the ocean current from the Timor Sea which carries rafts of vegetation and floating disseminules. Birds however are probably responsible for the majority of introductions.

Dispersal to Aldabra

The 4 islands of the Aldabra group – Aldabra, Assumption, Astove and Cosmoledo form a parallelogram 145 km – 40 km which could be regarded as the catchment area.

Aldabra is 620 km east of the African coast, 380 km NE of Grande Comore and 400 km NW of Cap d'Ambre (Madagascar)

Wind   The NW Monsoon, of light winds, blows from December to March and the SE Trades, which are steady winds, blow from May to September.

These winds are insufficient in strength to transport many disseminules from Africa or Madagascar although cyclones are a possible dispersal agency. 6–7 occur each year in the Madagascar area and may reach speeds of 100 km/h (see Fig. 2). Aldabra is north of the cyclone belt but occasionally it may experience a peripheral effect, which could bring in a few seeds or spores. Of the 11 possible wind dispersed species 2 are Compositae, 5 Aclepiadaceae, 2 Orchidaceae and 2 Polypodiaceae.

On Aldabra wind is probably the least effective dispersal mechanism.

Ocean currents   The introduction of most of the pantropical and Indian-Ocean species can be accounted for by sea currents. This is on the evidence of their disseminule type and habitat i.e. strand line or shore line, beach crest etc.

Currents of 3.5 km/h (2 knots) are recorded for the southern Indian Ocean and this would be adequate to carry disseminules from Africa and Madagascar to Aldabra in 7·5 and 5 days. A time which is sufficient for the transport of many species before they became water-logged and sink or became inviable.

The main currents around Aldabra are westward – the Equatorial current, northward – from the east coast of Madagascar and north east – from the coast of Africa.

Current speeds could of course be enhanced by strong winds.

One interesting aspect of drift propagules is that 50 species, all viable, have been recorded arriving at Aldabra but are not at the present time constituents of the flora (Hnatiuk, private communication). The reason for this is not clear but may be due to the inability of extra species to become established in the face of competition from the extant flora. It is a feature of Aldabra that the vegetation is comparatively stable and new habitat localities seldom become available for pioneer establishment by newly arriving disseminules.

Species of the strand line, both seaward and lagoon, which have small seeds could possibly be accounted for by rafting. The idea that a seed may remain lodged in a crevice on a log or piece of pumice throughout a long sea voyage seems unlikely, but being carried on a floating island of vegetation seems more feasible. Bamboo rafts have been recorded from Aldabra but unfortunately no-one has searched them for travellers.

Animals (birds)   Out of a total of 214 indigenous species 120 are adapted to bird introduction, either internally or externally. Suitable species either have fleshy fruits, small seeds or small, sticky fruits.

However, the present bird fauna of fruit eating and seed eating birds is mostly endemic and provides no obvious vectors for the introduction of these species.

Since the last emergence from the sea was 80 000 years ago, the introduction of 120 species would require a rate of 1 taxon/650 years at maximum exposure of the island. In view of the reduced size of the island 5000 years ago, when the lagoon was formed, the rate is more likely to be slightly faster, 1 taxon/400 years.

With a 1:1 million probability for the introduction of 120 species, at these rates a bird population of only 2500 individuals is required (Wickens, 1979).

A large bird dispersed flora with no obvious vectors can therefore be explained by a very slow rate of introduction.

The shortage of bird vectors has probably been the limiting factor in the rate of introduction for the inland flora. The present variety and quantity of plant food resources is far in excess of the requirements of the present bird population (Wickens, 1979).

At the present time there is no regular migration of fruit eating birds to and from Aldabra and bats, although present, are unlikely vectors as they have a restricted diet and do not normally travel beyond the island.

Man   Some species are assumed to be introduced by Man, especially where they are represented by single specimens (Renvoize,

1971). The following are some of the most obvious introductions:

Calophyllum inophyllum L. – takamaka, elsewhere this species occurs naturally

Erythrina variegata L.

Tamarindus indica L. – tamarind

Phoenix dactylifera L. – date palm

Most of the herb layer in coconut groves is of weedy species, of which the following are the most common:

Cleome strigosa Oliver

Stachytarpheta jamaicensis Vahl.

Tridax procumbens L.

Synedrella nodiflora Gaertn.

Catharanthus roseus G. Don.

Coconuts and *Casuarina* pose a problem. The earliest visits to the islands record the presence of these two species, which suggests that they arrived by natural means. The present-day distribution of them however is undoubtedly due to planting by Man. Wickens (1979) discuss this topic at some length.

Conclusions

From the evidence of floristic composition and species distributions it is apparent that the islands of the Indian Ocean have been populated by plants from a wide variety of phytogeographic areas.

The low islands have floras consisting almost entirely of species which are widespread throughout the old world tropics. These islands therefore may be considered to belong to the Palaeotropical Kingdom, Fig. 1. Designation to a smaller phytogeographic division is impossible because species with restricted distributions, indicative of regions or domains, are seldom present.

The high islands on the other hand, present an opposite situation since they possess species of both widespread and restricted distribution which have usually been derived from widely separated geographical areas. In addition the high islands all include endemic species in their floras and they may, therefore, be considered endemic centres.

On the basis of their largest or most significant geographical group of species the high islands may be assigned as follows. Sri Lanka is an endemic centre within the Deccan region. Madagascar, because of its size, is conferred with the status of region within the Afro-Arabian sub-Kingdom. The Seychelles, Mascarenes, Comoros and Aldabra group are endemic centres within the Afro-Arabian sub-Kingdom and possibly within the Madagascan region (Renvoize, 1975). The Andamans and

E*

Nicobars are within the SE Asia – Malayan region and Christmas Island is included as an endemic centre within the Deccan-Malaysian sub-Kingdom (Fig. 1).

This view however is an over simplification as it tends to detract from the fact that an island flora is usually composed of several chorological elements. Furthermore, several elements may contribute to a single vegetation type.

It is impossible therefore to say that an island belongs to one phytogeographical area and not another although there may be one element which is dominant over several minor elements. It is mainly on the basis of the dominant element that an island is identified with a specific phytogeographical area.

A preferable technique is that used by Clayton and Panigrahi (1974) in which chorological divisions are not plotted with single boundaries but with isochores representing the percentage of the total number of species in that division. This demonstrates not only that chorological elements tend to fade away at the edges but also that they often overlap.

The outstanding tasks which now lie ahead in plant studies of this region are firstly a comprehensive floristic survey of the area, to standardise the taxonomy of the species, and secondly, an analysis of the plant communities which, amongst other things, will contribute to a more thorough understanding of the origins of the Indian Ocean Island floras.

REFERENCES

Andrews, C. W. (1900). *Monograph of Christmas Island*. British Museum Publications, London

Baker, J. G. (1877). *Flora of Mauritius and the Seychelles*. L. Reeve and Co, London

Balfour, I. B. (1879). Botany of Rodriguez. *Phil. Trans. Roy. Soc.* **168**

— (1888). Botany of Socotra, *Trans. Roy. Soc. Edin.* **31**

Braithwaite, C., Taylor, J. and Kennedy, W. (1973). Evolution of an atoll. *Phil. Trans. Roy. Soc.* **266**, 307–340

Carlquist, S. (1974). *Island Biology*. Columbia University Press, New York

Clayton, W. D. and Hepper, F. N. (1974). Computer-aided chorology of W. African Grasses, *Kew Bull.* **29**, 213–234

— and Panigrahi, G. (1974). Computer-aided chorology of Indian Grasses. *Kew Bull.* **29**, 669–686

Cordemoy, J. E. (1895). *Flore de l'Ile de Réunion*. Paul Klincksieck, Paris

Fosberg, F. R. (1957). The Maldive Islands, Indian Ocean. *Atoll Res. Bull.* **58**

Gwynne, M. and Wood, D. (1969). Plants collected on islands in the Indian Ocean. *Atoll Res. Bull.* **134**

Hemsley, W. B. (1919). Flora of Aldabra and neighbouring islands. *Bull. Misc. Inf. Kew* **1919**, 108–153

Koechlin, J., Guillaumet, J.-L. and Morat, P. (1974). *Flora et Vegetation de Madagascar*. J. Cramer, Vaduz

Kurz, S. (1870). *The Vegetation of the Andaman Islands*. Government Printer, Calcutta

Melville, R. (1973). Continental drift and the distribution of the island floras of the Indian Ocean. *J. Mar. Biol. Assn. India* **15** (1), 236–241

Parkinson, C. E. (1923). *A Forest Flora of the Andaman Islands*. Government Central Press, Simla.

Prain, D. (1892). Botany of the Laccadives. *J. Bombay Nat. Hist. Soc.* **7**, 268–295.

— (1893). Loc. cit., 460–486

Renvoize, S. A. (1971). The origin and distribution of the flora of Aldabra. *Phil. Trans. Roy. Soc.* B **260**, 227–236

— (1975). A floristic analysis of the Western Indian Ocean Coral Islands. *Kew Bull.* **30**, 133–152

Staub, F. and Gueho, J. (1968). The Cargardos Carajos Shoals. *Proc. Roy. Soc. Arts Sci. Maurit.* **3** (1), 7–46

Stoddart, D. R. (1966). Reef studies at Addu Atoll, Maldive Islands. *Atoll Res. Bull.* **116**

— (1970). Coral Islands of the Western Indian Ocean. *Atoll Res. Bull.* **136**

— and Taylor, J. (1971). Geography and ecology of Diego Garcia Atoll, Chagos Archipelago. *Atoll Res. Bull.* **149**

Summerhayes, V. S. (1931). An enumeration of the Angiosperms of the Seychelles Archipelago. *Trans. Linn. Soc.* **19**, 261–299

Thothathri, K. (1962). Contributions to the flora of the Andaman and Nicobar Islands. *Bull. Bot. Survey India* **4**, 281–296

Trimen, H. (1893). *A Hand-Book to the flora of Ceylon*. Dulau and Co., London

Voeltzkow, A. (1917). Flora und Fauna der Comoren. Reise in Ostafrika 1903–1905. *Wiss. Ergeb.* Bd, 1, 1. Abt., 429–454

Wickens, G. (1979). Speculation on seed dispersal and the flora of the Aldabra archipelago. *Phil. Trans. Roy. Soc.* **B286**

Willis, J. C. (1901). Note on the flora of Minikoi. *Ann. Roy. Bot. Gard. Peradeniya* **1**, 39–43

— and Gardiner, J. S. (1901). Botany of the Maldive Islands. *Ann Roy. Bot. Gard. Peradeniya* **1**, 45–164

Wood-Jones, F. (1912). *Coral and Atolls*. L. Reeve and Co, London

Endemism and Evolution

8 Endemism and Evolution in the Islands of the Western Mediterranean

M. A. CARDONA   *Departamento de Botánica, Universidad de Barcelona, Spain*

J. CONTANDRIOPOULOS   *Laboratoire de Cytotaxinomie, Université de Provence, France*

El estudio de la flora endémica de las islas del Mediterráneo occidental pone en evidencia la importancia de este elemento el cual corresponde, approximadamente, a un 8% de la flora en Córcega y en Cerdeña y un 7% en las islas Baleares. Dicho estudio permite distinguir: – *endémicas tirrénicas* (Córcega, Cerdeña, Archipiélago Toscano), algunas de las cuales alcanzan a las Gimnesias (Baleares Orientales) (unas quince) y otras las islas de Hyères; – endémicas corsas (un centenar); – endémicas sardas (algo menos numerosas que en Córcega); – endémicas baleáricas (alrededor de 80) que se extienden por todo el archipiélago, o solo en las Gimnesias, o en las Pitiusas (Baleares occidentales) o, incluso, en una sola isla.

El análisis citotaxonómico de estos táxones endémicos permite distinguir el endemismo pasivo (paleo y patroendémicas) del endemismo activo (esquizo y apoendémicas). El endemismo pasivo y, en cierta medida, el esquizoendemismo están directamente asociados a factores de tipo histórico. Se trata, sobre todo, de un endemismo relictual consecuencia del aislamiento insular. El endemismo activo depende de la influencia del medio y de la selección, de las mutaciones, de los cruzamientos. Se forma por especiación gradual (esquizoendemismo) o por especiación brusca (apoendemismo) que engendra una poliploidía.

Las paleoendémicas, de las cuales no se conoce el origen, son tirrénicas, cirno-sardas o localizadas solamente en las Gimnesias.

Las patroendémicas pertenecen principalmente al elemento florístico mediterráneo (endémicas corsas, sardas, cirno-sardas, baleáricas.)

Las esquizoendémicas son las más numerosas. Se encuentran esencialmente en el elemento orófilo de las montañas del sur y centro de Europa. Su origen es muy antiguo. También se hallan en el elemento mediterráneo (origen antiguo, subreciente o reciente) y en el bóreo-meridional. La distribución de los esquizoendemismos (endémicas y táxones correspondientes) pone de manifiesto los territorios que tuvieron en común un stock de especies. Estas últimas, como consecuencia del aislamiento, se diferenciaron en las distintas partes del área primitiva. Cuando las esquizoendémicas y los táxones correspondientes son simpátridas, la diferenciación es reciente y depende del medio (nichos ecológicos).

Las apoendémicas son poco numerosas y pertenecen a los elementos bóreo-meridional y mediterráneo.

Los orígenes de las floras insulares endémicas en el Mediterráneo occidental son muy diversos. Se trata de una flora paleógena desarrollada "in situ" y que se ha enriquecido mediante aportaciones muy diversas como demuestran las afinidades de los táxones endémicos (elemento mediterráneo: del Mediterráneo occidental u oriental, elemento norte-africano, elemento bóreo-montano y bóreo-meridional).

La importancia de las paleoendémicas, la presencia de patroendémicas, la abundancia de esquizoendémicas reliictuales subrayan el caracter antiguo de la flora.

El endemismo por novación tampoco falta, pero es más difícil de detectar dado que la especiación es un fenómeno extremadamente lento y la diferenciación de los táxones nuevos es menos visible. Por ello debe prestarse la mayor atención a los micromorfismos.

Si la flora endémica de las islas tirrénicas y de las Baleares aparece, en su conjunto, como reliictual, no por ello es estática. El importante número de esquizoendémicas y de apoendémicas simpátridas, de endémicas muy polimorfas que no han perdido su potencial evolutivo constituyen la prueba. Puesto que las condiciones ecológicas no son invariables y que el endemismo activo a menudo está subordinado a la influencia del medio, se producen períodos de endemismo activo que suceden a períodos de endemismo pasivo en este movimiento de alternancia que rige los fenómenos biológicos.

Introduction

The importance of the endemic element is one of the most striking characteristics in the flora of the islands of the western Mediterranean. To investigate the endemics' origin and evolution poses problems whose solutions depend on historical factors associated with the palaeo-geography of the western Mediterranean and ecological factors which may have acted directly upon the genetic heritage.

Although we accept that endemism is a very general phenomenon in all territories which are geographically defined (islands, mountain chains etc.) or have specialised soils (serpentine, gypsaceous, dolomitic etc.) it is more difficult to find causes in the near or distant past. Studies of endemism require an understanding of geophysics, geology and genetics all subjects which depend upon technological progress and new methods of investigation. However, the present state of cytological and genetic discoveries allows us a better understanding of the processes of speciation. On the other hand, palaeoecological research on the western Mediterranean (Fig. 1), though progressing, presents hypotheses which are often contradictory because of the extreme complexity of the region under study, putting in question the ideas of classical geology and, as Blanc (1972) says "les résultats nouveaux affluent, rendant caduques les publications de synthèse dès leur parution".

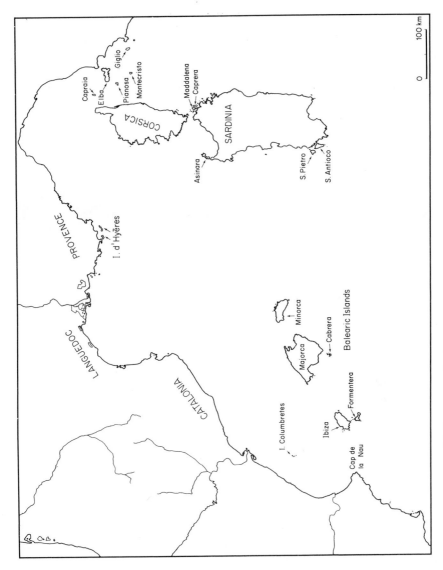

Fig. 1 The western Mediterranean basin

135

The Cyrno-Sardinian plate

The western Mediterranean, in the course of its history, has been
subjected to important tectonic movements which reached their height
during the Tertiary. The hypothesis of a rigid Tyrrhenian massif
supposedly existing in place of the Tyrrhenian sea, Corsica and Sardinia,
is today abandoned in favour of plate-tectonics. Nevertheless,
palaeogeographers remain very cautious as to their deductions. It seems
that the hypothesis of the derivation of the Cyrno-Sardinian plate at the
end of the Oligocene and early Miocene is generally accepted.
Furthermore, it has been demonstrated using geological and palaeomagnetic criteria (Alvarez, 1973; Westphal *et al.*, 1976) that the Cyrno-
Sardinian plate was once adjacent to the coasts of Provence and the
Languedoc, as well as those of NE Catalonia. It was part of a Hercynian
mountain arc which linked the massifs of the eastern Iberian Peninsula

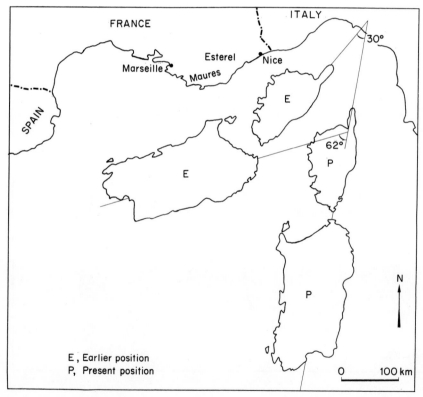

Fig. 2   Derivation of Corsica and Sardinia. E, earlier position; P, present position
(from Westphal *et al.*, 1976)

and the Pyrenees to the outer crystalline massifs of the Alps (Maures and Estérel), Fig. 2. To the south, this mountain arc could perhaps have included the primary cliffs of north and northeastern Minorca.

The Cyrno-Sardinian plate may well have started moving at the Oligocene-Miocene period, undergoing a rotation of 30° for Corsica and 62° for Sardinia relative to its initial position, about a point situated between Cap Corse and Genoa.

The timing of the complete isolation of the Cyrno-Sardinian plate is again a matter of controversy. Some palaeogeographers consider that from the start of the rotation of the Cyrno-Sardinian plate there was no further communication between Corsica and the European mainland and that since this period isolation has been complete. Other palaeogeographers think that at the beginning of the Miocene, when the Cyrno-Sardinian plate had started its rotation and was separated from continental Europe, an African peninsula might have been formed by the continental crust, emerging at the beginning of the Miocene between Sardinia and Africa (Thaler, 1973; Pecorini et al., 1974). It is by this route that an African fauna, such as the ctenodactylid rodents, would have appeared in Sardinia but was unable to reach Europe, the Cyrno-Sardinian massif being already cut off from Europe.

Finally, most palaeogeographers and geologists admit the existence of a Tuscan bridge between Corsica and Tuscany in the Quaternary at the time when sea levels were at their lowest (Würm). Among them, some estimate that even during the Tertiary there were numerous contacts between the Cyrno-Sardinian massif and Europe or Africa and summarise the biogeography of the Cyrno-Sardinian massif as follows: (cf. Pecorini et al., 1974.)

Oligo-Miocene phase: hypothetical population of European origin.

Lower Miocene phase: population of African origin, followed by isolation (Oschiri fauna).

Upper Miocene phase: African peninsularisation reaching Tuscany (*Oreopithecus* fauna of Monte Bamboli); followed by insularisation.

Messinian phase: European peninsularisation and renewal of the fauna (middle level between Alcoy and Hautemagne-Vendargues).

Pliocene phase: isolation and start of endemism (fauna of Mandriola, level of Hautemagne-Vendargues)'.

Pleistocene phase: penetration of Pithymys.

Recent phase: extinction of the endemic fauna and penetration of the present fauna.

As can be seen, the palaeogeographical history of the Cyrno-Sardinian massif is far from being completely resolved, and is differently interpreted by geologists, biologists and palaeontologists.

The palaeogeography of the Balearic Islands

The palaeogeography of the Balearics is likewise not easy to understand and opinions put forward by geologists and biologists also differ. From a study of the Balearics' flora and its endemic element, it appears that the islands form two different units: the western Balearics or Pithyusan Islands (Formentera and Ibiza) and the eastern Balearics or Gymnesian Islands (Majorca, Minorca and Cabrera). The former have Iberian and Ibero-Maghreb affinities, the latter Tyrrhenian affinities. Geologists, however, do not distinguish two such units in the same way.

In the opinion of Ríos (1975), the uplifting of the Balearics dates from alpine movements which were produced in the Oligo-Miocene and were a continuation of the Subbaetic chains. The Balearics would be supported by a submarine spur projecting from the continental shelf extending eastwards from the Iberian peninsula at the level of Cap de la Nau towards the Balearics. But Minorca, while situated on the axis of this spur, shows a different geological structure which may correspond with the remains of an ancient massif that might have existed during the Mesozoic and Eocene.

In the view of Obrador (1972–73) also, the Balearics are a continuation of the Subbaetic chain. At the end of the alpine orogenesis it formed at Minorca a system of NW–SE faults which delimited two blocks: the N–NE elevation, formed of Devonian and Triassic schists and sandstone, and which was not covered by Miocene deposits, and the S–SW–NW block, which was karstic, formed by Miocene deposits.

Finally Alvarez (1976) thinks that in the Oligocene there was a Hercynian "Protoligurian massif", formed by the NE of the Iberian Peninsula, part of Provence, the Cyrno-Sardinian block and the N–NE of Minorca. With the alpine orogenesis this massif broke up, forming the Balearics to which was added the primary part of the north of Minorca, while the Cyrno-Sardinian plate started its rotation (Fig. 3).

It seems that at the end of the Miocene to the Messinian, at the time when the sea level was at its lowest, some connections must have existed between the islands of the western Mediterranean and the continent. The isolation of the Pithyusan islands from the Iberian coast would date from the Upper Miocene, but it is possible that some connections may have existed during the Mindel glaciation.

The separation of the islands within the Balearic group also poses problems. According to Cuerda (1965, 1975), the Gymnesian Islands,

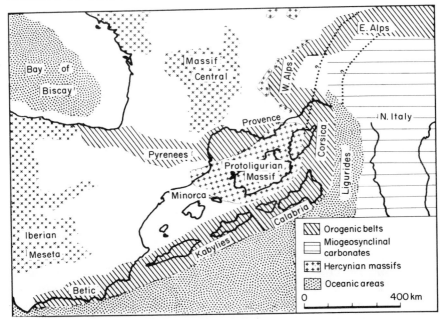

Fig. 3   Reconstructed Oligocene palaeogeography (from Alvarez, 1976)

which form a different unit from the Pithyusan group, would have been separated before the Villafrancian. Finally the isolation of Majorca and Minorca, which constituted on several occasions a single landmass, would be a recent event (Würm).

If our knowledge of the palaeogeography of the western Mediterranean remains fragmentary, sometimes even hypothetical, present research in biosystematics permits us to base on genetics and cytotaxonomy our studies of endemism on what appears to be a firm foundation, with few ambiguities. As Favarger (1962) wrote:

> . . . la biosystématique appliquée à la flore d'un territoire donné apporte 3 types d'informations:
> elle permet la mise en évidence de taxa nouveaux ou méconnus.
> elle approfondit et perfectionne les connaissances des taxa (surtout infraspécifiques) déjà reconnus par les systématiciens sur la base d'observations morphologiques et géographiques et permet de débrouiller la phylogénie de groupes complexes.
> elle fournit enfin des renseignements généraux sur l'origine, l'évolution et les migrations d'une flore, c'est-à-dire qu'elle apporte une contribution à la géographie botanique historique'.

Endemics

The study of endemics cannot be undertaken alone; it is inseparable, in our opinion, from that of corresponding taxa in order to detect relationships, which cytotaxonomic analysis can reveal, and understand their mode of formation. However these are precisely the relationships which serve as a basis for a biogeographical classification of endemics. The application of cytotaxonomic methods to the study of the endemics of a flora and their corresponding taxa permits one to establish the relationships between them by distinguishing passive endemism (palaeo- and patroendemics) from active endemism (schizo- and apoendemics) (Favarger and Contandriopoulos, 1961). Passive endemism and to a certain extent schizoendemism are directly associated with historical factors. One can speak of relictual endemism, of endemism by conservation. The interpretation of active endemism is not so easy:

> . . . l'isolement, l'influence du milieu et de la sélection, les mutations, les croisements sont les causes directes de l'endémisme actif. Celui-ci peut prendre naissance par spéciation graduelle (schizoendémisme) sans changement de nombre chromosomique avec dérive génique ou radiation adaptative ou bien par spéciation brutale (apoendémisme) qui implique une polyploidie. (Cardona and Contandriopoulos, 1977.)

The geographical distribution of endemics and of corresponding taxa indicates those areas which have had species in common, isolation being the principal factor in speciation. When vicariants are sympatric the phenomenon is recent or subrecent, and can continue today under the influence of their surroundings in ecological niches by adaptive radiation or by genetic drift. It would then be termed inchoative schizo-endemism. The same applies to apoendemism where abrupt speciation (auto- or allopolyploidy) is implied. When corresponding taxa are allopatric the phenomenon of speciation is older.

Finally, the allocation of endemics to given floristic elements, established from the present-day geographical distribution of corresponding taxa, allows us to understand the biogeographical side of ancient relationships which might have existed with insular floras, to interpret their colonisation and to determine their origin and evolution.

It is with the aid of these few data (cytotaxonomic analysis of the endemics and of corresponding taxa and their relationship with the existing floristic elements), and relying upon our present knowledge of the palaeogeography of the western Mediterranean, that we have undertaken this study of endemism.

The islands of the western Mediterranean are grouped in two principal sectors: the Tyrrhenian sector, containing, as well as the two principal islands of Corsica and Sardinia, the Tuscan archipelago (Elba, Giglio, Montecristo, Capraia, Giannuti, Gorgona etc.) and the Hyères Islands (Porquerolles, Port Cros and Levant Island). The Balearic sector comprises the eastern Balearics or Gymnesian islands (Majorca, Minorca, Cabrera etc.) and the western Balearics or Pithyusan islands (Formentera, Ibiza etc.).

The flora and vegetation of these islands is typically Mediterranean and is characterised by a quite remarkable endemism. The endemic element represents about 8% of the flora for Corsica and for Sardinia, and 7% for the Balearics. It is present, though to a lesser extent, also in the Tuscan archipelago and the Hyères Islands.

Distribution of endemics

If we study the distribution of endemics in the islands of the western Mediterranean it appears that there exist:

1 Endemics common to Corsica, Sardinia and the Balearics, some of whose geographical distributions extend to the Tuscan archipelago and the Hyères Islands. Some of these endemics are differentiated as schizoendemics or endemovicariants between the Balearics and Corsica/Sardinia. We have surveyed 18 such taxa:

Arum pictum L. (Corsica, Sardinia, Elba, Montecristo, Majorca, Minorca)

Orchis insularis Somm. (Corsica, Sardinia, Elba, Giglio, Majorca (?))

Soleirolia soleirolii (Req.) Dandy (Corsica, Sardinia, Majorca)

Arenaria balearica L. (Corsica, Sardinia, Montecristo, Majorca)

Delphinium pictum Willd. (Corsica, Sardinia, Hyères Islands, Majorca)

Cymbalaria aequitriloba (Viv.) Cheval. (Corsica, Sardinia, Capraia, Montecristo, Gorgona, Elba, Giglio, Majorca, Minorca, Cabrera)

Bellium bellidioides L. (Corsica, Sardinia, Balearics)

Cephalaria squamiflora (Sieber) Greuter ssp. *balearica* (Willd.) Greuter (Majorca, Corsica, Sardinia)

Helleborus trifolius Miller ssp. *corsicus* Briquet (Corsica, Sardinia) and ssp. *lividus* Schiff. (Majorca and Cabrera)

Erodium corsicum Lam. (Corsica, Sardinia) and *E. reichardii* DC. (Majorca, Minorca)

Pastinaca latifolia DC. (Corsica) and *P. lucida* L. (Majorca, Minorca)

Micromeria filiformis (Aiton) Bentham ssp. *filiformis* (Corsica, Balearics) and ssp. *cordata* (Moris ex Bertol.) Briquet (Sardinia)

Sesleria insularis Somm. ssp. *insularis* (Sardinia, Majorca) and ssp. *corsica* (Hackel) Ujh. (Corsica)

2 Cyrno-Sardinian endemics. We have enumerated about 40. Some of these also occur in the Tuscan archipelago (Arrigoni, 1975). Among the latter are, for example:

Pancratium illyricum L. (+ Capraia)
Romulea requienii Parl. var. *insularis* (Somm.) Rouy (+ Capraia)
Limonium articulatum L. (+ Capraia)
Borago pygmaea (DC.) Chater & Greuter (+ Capraia)
Stachys glutinosa L. (+ Capraia)
Crocus minimus DC. (+ Capraia)
Carduus pycnocephalus L. var. *sardous* (DC.) Fiori (+ Capraia)
Verbascum conocarpum Moris (+ Montecristo)
Scrophularia trifoliata L. (+ Elba)
Mentha requienii Bentham (+ Montecristo)
Carduus fasciculiflorus Viv. (+ Montecristo)
Hymenolobus procumbens (L). Nutt. ex Torrey & Gray var. *revelieri* Jordan (+ Pianosa and Giglio)

3 Tyrrhenian endemics whose area extends as far as Tuscany or Liguria:

Urtica atrovirens Req. ex Lois. (Corsica, Sardinia, Capraia, Pianosa, Gorgona, Elba and Tuscany near Campiglia). Note that in Minorca there is ssp. *bianori* (Knoche) Font Quer & Garcias
Crepis bellidifolia Lois. (Corsica, Sardinia, Capraia, Gorgona, Elba, Livourne mountains)

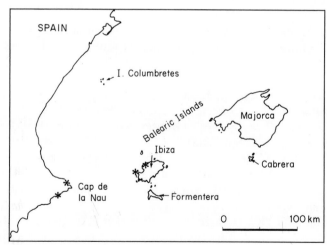

FIG. 4   Geographical distribution of *Silene hifacensis* (from Font Quer, 1927)

4 Corsican endemics. These are more numerous, numbering about 100 of various taxonomic ranks (from species to variety).

5 Sardinian endemics. This group is a little smaller than the Corsican endemics.

6 Endemics whose very restricted area is limited to 1 or 2 islands of the Tuscan archipelago or to Tuscany and the Tuscan archipelago (Arrigoni, 1975):

Carex grioletti Roem. (Giglio)

Crocus etruscus Parl. (Elba and Tuscan Maremma)

Limonium multiforme (Martelli) Pignatti (Tuscan Archipelago and Tyrrhenian coast at Gaeta near Livourne)

Silene salzmanni Bad. (Corsica, Elba, Gorgona, Capraia, Liguria)

Linaria capraia Moris & De Not. (Tuscan Archipelago). There are about 80 endemics of various taxonomic rank.

7 Balearic endemics. Given the complexity of the phytogeography of the Balearics it is not surprising to see that there are in fact few endemics common to all the islands of the group, but more often narrowly localised endemics on one island or another or exclusive either to the Gymnesian or Pithyusan islands.

8 Endemics common to the Pithyusan islands or to a number of them and to the Iberian Peninsula, for example *Genista hirsuta* Vahl (W. Spain, S. Portugal and Ibiza).

9 Similarly there are endemics common to the Pithyusan islands (principally Ibiza) and to the Valencian coast at Cap de la Nau: *Silene hifacensis* Rouy ex Willk. (Fig. 4), *Carduncellus dianius* Webb.

The geographical distribution of endemics, whether they are narrowly localised on one island or whether they inhabit territories which are now separated from one another, reflects the palaeogeography of the western Mediterranean. Moreover, the presence on Ibiza for example of about 60 Iberian species absent from the Gymnesian islands and conversely of Tyrrhenian species present in the eastern Balearics but absent from the Pithyusan islands illustrates the different origins of the Balearic assemblage. Indeed, it seems that the north of Minorca, which would belong according to Alvarez (1976) to the Protoligurian massif, possesses a Tyrrhenian flora. After the separation of the islands, some species were able to persist in Minorca and spread elsewhere to Majorca when the two islands were one. But these species were unable to reach the Pithyusan islands which were already separated from the Gymnesian islands.

The dominant character of the flora of the western Mediterranean islands is its antiquity: of Mediterranean origin, it has developed *in situ*. However, it has gradually accumulated various additions, coming mainly from Europe and to a lesser extent from North Africa. The flora of Corsica is perhaps the richest, with more than 2000 species. Sardinia numbers some 1200 species according to Moris (1837–59), but is in fact probably almost as rich as Corsica. Lastly, the Balearics have some 1500 species.

Cytotaxonomic analysis of numerous endemics collected in the different Mediterranean islands and of some of their corresponding taxa, permits us to group them into the 4 classes recognised by Favarger and Contandriopoulos (1961).

Palaeoendemics

Palaeoendemics are represented by monospecific genera: *Soleirolia soleirolii* (Req.) Dandy (Corsica, Sardinia, Capraia, Majorca), *Morisia monanthos* Gay (Corsica, Sardina), *Naufraga balearica* Const. & Cannon (Majorca), *Nananthea perpusilla* DC. (Corsica, Sardinia); and by morphologically isolated species without obvious affinities: *Arenaria balearica* L. (Majorca, Corsica, Sardinia, Montecristo), *Daphne rodriguezii* Tex. (Minorca), *Pimpinella bicknellii* Briq. (= *Sporoceratium bicknellii* (Briq.) Wolff (Majorca), *Ruta corsica* DC. (Corsica, Sardinia), *Hypericum balearicum* L. (Balearics), *Borago pygmàea* (DC.) Chater & Greuter

TABLE 1   Palaeoendemics.(Relict species with no corresponding taxa)

Palaeoendemics belonging to monospecific genera	
Soleirolia soleirolii (Req.) Dandy	Corsica, Sardinia, Capraia, Majorca
Morisia monanthos (Viv.) Asch.	Corsica, Sardinia
Naufraga balearica Const. & Cannon	Majorca
Nananthea perpusilla DC.	Corsica, Sardinia

Palaeoendemics which are morphologically very isolated species with no recognised affinities

Arenaria balearica L.	Majorca, Corsica, Sardinia, Montecristo
Daphne rodriguezii Tex.	Minorca
Pimpinella bicknellii Briq.	Marjorca
(= *Spiroceratium bicknellii* (Briq.) Wolff)	
Ruta corsica DC.	Corsica, Sardinia
Hypericum balearicum L.	Balearics
Borago pygmaea (DC.) Chater & Greuter	Corsica, Sardinia, Capraia
Stachys corsica Pers.	Corsica, Sardinia
Cymbalaria aequitriloba (Viv.) Cheval.	Majorca, Minorca, Cabrera, Corsica, Sardinia, Capraia, Montecristo, Gorgona, Elbe, Giglio
Helichrysum ambiguum (Pers.) C. Presl	Majorca, Minorca
(= *H. lamarckii* Camb.)	
Lotus tetraphyllus L.	Majorca, Minorca, Cabrera

(Corsica, Sardinia, Capraia), *Stachys corsica* Pers. (Corsica, Sardinia), *Cymbalaria aequitriloba* (Viv.) Cheval. (Majorca, Minorca, Cabrera, Corsica, Sardinia, Capraia, Montecristo, Gorgona, Elba, Giglio), *Helichrysum ambiguum* (Pers.) C. Presl. (= *H. lamarckii* Camb.) (Majorca, Minorca), *Lotus tetraphyllus* L. (Majorca, Minorca, Cabrera) (Cardona 1973, 1976, 1977, 1978; Contandriopoulos 1962, 1964).

None of these palaeoendemics is specific to Corsica or Sardinia. They are all present on both islands and often in the Tuscan archipelago, while palaeoendemics of very restricted area can be found in the Balearics.

When palaeoendemics are common to both the Mediterranean island groups, Tyrrhenian and Balearic, they are present only in the eastern Balearics, suggesting, as already mentioned, a different palaeogeography between the Gymnesian and Pithyusan islands.

Palaeoendemics, whose origin is obscure, are ancient taxa, showing little variation, and are sometimes on their way to extinction. Their present

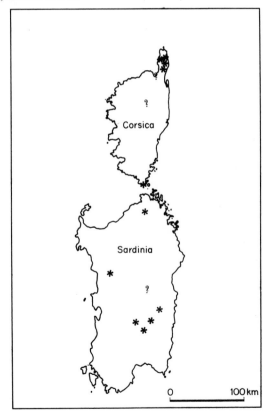

Fig. 5   Geographical distribution of *Morisia monanthos*

distribution, often of a relictual type, corresponds to the remains of a once larger area. This is illustrated by the disjunct distribution of certain palaoendemics. For example, *Morisia monanthos*, a Cyrno-Sardinian endemic, is on Corsica only found at the two extremities of the island: Cap Corse and around Bonifacio; and in Sardinia in the north of the island at Asfossado, in the centre at Campeda and Malcomer and in the southeast at Tonara (?), Tacco di Seuil, Gesturi, Nurri Mandas (Martinoli, 1949a) (Fig. 5); or again, *Nananthea perpusilla*, Corsica, on the Sanguinaires islands near Ajaccio and the Lavezzi islands near Bonifacio; in Sardinia on the islands of la Maddalena and Mortorio in the north and Piana and San Pietro in the south, as well as on the coast at Porto Scuso (Martinoli, 1940) (Fig. 6). Another example, here from the Gymnesian islands, is *Helichrysum ambiguum* (Fig. 7).

Not all the palaeoendemics which have been surveyed are, however, rare or locally restricted on these islands. Certain of them are quite

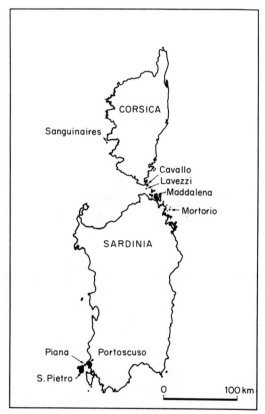

Fig. 6   Geographical distribution of *Nananthea perpusilla*

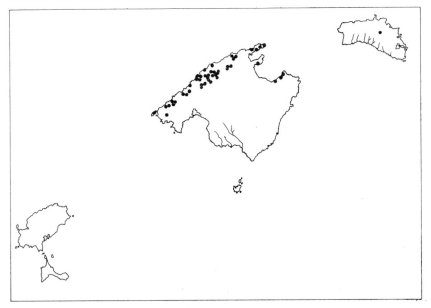

FIG. 7 Geographical distribution of *Helichrysum ambiguum*

widespread on the Tyrrhenian islands and on the Balearics (*Arenaria balearica, Cymbalaria aequitriloba, Stachys corsica*, etc.) or similarly *Hypericum balearicum* within the Balearic group.

Patroendemics

Patroendemics constitute, with palaeoendemics, the ancient element of the flora, but their significance is different. These are ancestral taxa which have survived on the islands where they are sometimes very restricted (e.g. *Dianthus gyspergerae*, Corsican endemic, recorded from only one locality on the island) and which have remained diploid while their corresponding taxa, more widely distributed, are polyploid (auto- or allopolyploids).

Cytotaxonomic studies are not yet sufficiently advanced to reveal the real importance of this element in the island floras of the western Mediterranean and its precise distribution. However, the application of cytotaxonomic methods to the study of species complexes and "à celle des races insignifiantes considérées souvent à tort par les taxonomistes, comme des néoendémiques" (Contandriopoulos and Favarger, 1974) has revealed in insular floras several cases of patroendemism of which the corresponding taxa inhabit other floristic domains (often boreal) or are

TABLE 2   Patroendemics. (These are taxa which have not varied in a given region while in neighbouring territories corresponding taxa have arisen by polyploidy and generally occupy wider areas of distribution)

Anthoxanthum odoratum L. var. *corsicum* (Briq.) Rouy (Corsica) diploid and *A. odoratum* L. (northern hemisphere), tetraploid

Phalaris arundinacea L. var. *rotgesii* (Husn) R. Lit. (Corsica) diploid and *P. arundinacea* L. vars. *picta* L. and *typica* (Junge) Graebn. (northern hemisphere) tetraploids

Arrhenatherum elatior L. J. & C. Presl ssp. *elatior* (Coutinho) R. Lit. var. *sardoa* (Schmidt) R. Lit. (Corsica and Sardinia) diploid and var. *vulgaris* Fries and *bulbosa* (Willd.) St. Amans (Northern Hemisphere) tetraploids

Dianthus gyspergerae Rouy (Corsica) diploid and species related to *D. furcatus* Balb. (Alps, Pyrenees) tetraploids

Crepis triasii (Camb.) Fries (Gymnesian islands) diploid and *C. vesicaria* L. ssp. *vesicaria* and *haenseleri* (Boiss, ex DC.) P. D. Sell (Europe) tetraploids

---

situated within the Mediterranean region. "Ils peuvent nous renseigner sur les territoires privilégiés à partir desquels se sont produits au Tertiaire ou au Quaternaire des courants d'immigration vers d'autres secteurs" (Contandriopoulos and Favarger, 1974).

Arrhenatherum elatior L. whose circumboreal area includes Europe excepting arctic regions, western Asia and North Africa etc. is represented in Corsica and Sardinia by ssp. *elatior* (Coutinho) R. Lit and var. *sardoa* (Schmidt) R. Lit. and *eriantha* (Boiss. & Reuter) R. Lit. which have remained diploid while most taxa related to *Arrhenatherum elatior* are polyploid. De Litardière (1949) considered these two taxa to have given rise to the tetraploid var. *vulgaris* Fries and *bulbosa* (Willd.) St. Amans.

Dactylis glomerata L. var. *hispanica* Koch, a tetraploid, is represented on Ibiza and Formentera by a diploid, forma *ibizensis* (Gand.) Knoche, which has, therefore, been conserved in the Pithyusan islands (Stebbins and Zohary, 1959). It should be noted, however, that these authors listed other diploid taxa related to *Dactylis glomerata*, though solely from the Mediterranean region.

Anthoxanthum odoratum L., widespread throughout the northern hemisphere, is tetraploid (diploid forms are associated with a high alpine habitat and are referable to *A. alpinum* A. & D. Löve). However in Corsica, specimens of *A. odoratum* var. *corsicum* (Briq.) Rouy, which were studied by de Litardière (1949) are diploids.

The same situation applies to the Corsican endemic *Phalaris arundinacea* L. var *rotgesii* (Husn.) R. Lit., where vars. *arundinacea* and *picta*, much more widespread in the Northern Hemisphere, are polyploids.

In the *Paeonia corallina* Retz group (central and southern Europe, W. Asia) many taxa are tetraploid, but *P. cambessedesii* (Willk.) Willk., endemic to the Gymnesian islands, is diploid (Stern, 1942–43; Cardona, 1977; Stebbins, 1938). Similarly, *Crepis triasii* (Camb.) Fries, another diploid Gymnesian endemic, is related to the Mediterranean tetraploid subspecies of *C. vesicaria* ssp. *vesicaria* and *haenseleri* (Boiss. ex DC.) P. D. Sell.

In the *Dianthus furcatus* Balbis group, which contains several taxa distributed in the Alps, Pyrenees and mountains of Spain, only two diploid taxa have been recognised: *D. gyspergerae* Rouy, Corsican endemic, and *D. brachyanthus* Boiss. var. *alpinus* from the mountains of Spain. All the other taxa which have been investigated from the caryological point-of-view are polyploids, namely *D. furcatus* Balb. and its different subspecies in the Alps, *D. subacaulis* from Mont Ventoux and *D. brachyanthus* from the Pyrenees and Sierra Nevada. The Corsican endemics and *D. brachyanthus* var. *alpinus* represent a primitive type which appears not to have evolved (Contandriopoulos, 1964). Likewise, there are those Corsican patroendemics *Pinguicula corsica* L. (*P. vulgaris* group) and *Leucanthemopsis tomentosa* (Loisel.) Heywood (= *Chrysanthemum tomentosum* Loisel.) belonging to the *Leucanthemopsis alpina* (L.) Heywood complex which has diversified in the Alps and Pyrenees (Contandriopoulos and Favarger, 1959).

From Sardinia (and perhaps the south of Italy) mention can be made of *Petrorhagia saxifraga* (L.) Link var. *glomerata* (Favarger, 1966).

These examples show the role played by insular Mediterranean environments in the conservation of primitive taxa. The patroendemics studied are referable only to "mediterranean", "boreal-montane" and "South and Central European montane" floristic elements, which leads us to consider that these elements arrived in the islands of the western Mediterranean before their isolation, that is at the beginning of the Tertiary. Their origin is therefore very ancient.

But if it is incontestable that the islands of the western Mediterranean have served as refuges, their role in the differentiation of taxa is even more important. In fact the study of endemism in Corsica (Contandriopoulos, 1962, 1964) and in the Balearics (Cardona, 1973, 1976, 1977, 1978) as well as numerous notes on Sardinian endemics (Martinoli, 1940, 1949a, 1949b, 1949c, 1954 etc; Arrigoni, 1970, 1972, 1975 etc; Garbari, 1968, 1973, etc; Valsecchi, 1976; Valsecchi and Corrias, 1973, etc.) have shown that ideas about vicariance and schizoendemism have been used to investigate territories which have a common stock of species. Their study permits us effectively to determine the connections which have existed between the islands themselves, between the islands and the adjacent Mediterranean territories, a knowledge of palaeogeography contributing to discovering, when this is possible, their age. Lastly, it tells us about evolutionary processes of speciation, gradual speciation resulting from genetic drift or from adaptive radiation as a function of isolation and sometimes also of new ecological conditions as shown by the work of Snogerup (1967) and Strid (1970) on *Erysimum* sect. *Cheiranthus* and the *Nigella arvensis* complex in the Aegean islands.

Schizoendemics

Schizoendemics form the group with the most taxa, but not all are of the same evolutionary significance. Some, like the palaeoendemics, are of very ancient origins and sometimes occur in relict stations. Others are more recent, and yet others are undergoing evolution (inchoative schizoendemism).

The distribution of schizoendemics permits us to understand the geographical aspect of the relationships of insular floras and to classify the endemics, depending upon the present-day distribution of vicariant taxa, among the various floristic elements.

(*a*) There is one kind of schizoendemism of very ancient origin as represented by Cyrno-Sardinian, Corsican or Sardinian endemics with Balearic endemics: *Helleborus trifolius* ssp. *corsicus* (C.S.) and *H. trifolius* ssp. *lividus* (B.), $2n = 32$; *Erodium corsicum* (C.S.) and *E. reichardii* (Gymnesian islands), $2n = 20$; *Pastinaca latifolia* (C.) and *P. lucida* (Majorca, Minorca), $2n = 22$; *Sesleria insularis* Somm. ssp. *insularis* (Majorca, Sardinia) and *S. insularis* ssp. *corsica* (Hackel) Ujh. (Corsica) $2n = 18$; *Micromeria filiformis* (Aiton) Benth. ssp. *filiformis* (Balearics, Corsica), $2n = 30$ and ssp. *cordata* (Moris ex Bertol.) Briq. (Sardinia) etc.

(*b*) The remarkable schizoendemism existing between orophile Cyrno-Sardinian, Corsican or Sardinian endemics and those of the mountains of central and southern Europe which is proof of the existence of an ancient mountain system at the beginning of the Tertiary linking the Cyrno-Sardinian massif with the mountains of Europe. These orophytes are related mainly to the orophile element of southern and central Europe.

The *Potentilla* belonging to the *Crassinerviae* Wolf group have been studied by Contandriopoulos (1962) and grouped by Pawlowski (1965) into two parallel related series: series *Crassinerviae* (Wolf) Pawł. with *Potentilla crassinervia* Viv., a silicolous Cyrno-Sardinian endemic of $2n = 14$, and series *Valderiae* Pawł. uniting those mostly very localised endemics in the mountains of central and southern Europe – *P. valderia* L. (Alpes Maritimes, silicolous), *P. grammopetala* Moris (west-facing north-Italian alps and southern Switzerland, silicolous), *P. haynaldiana* Janka, (eastern Balkan peninsula, silicolous, $2n = 14$), *P. doerfleri* Wettst. (W. Macedonia, silicolous) *P. nivalis* Lap. with a disjunct distribution in the Cantabrian mountains, the Pyrenees, the western and southern Alps,

TABLE 3   Schizoendemics. (These are taxa which result from the slow and progressive differentiation of a primitive taxon in different parts of its area. They have the same chromosome number)

I   *Schizoendemism between Tyrrhenian and Balearic endemics.* (They are of very ancient origin – beginning of the Tertiary)
Helleborus trifolius Mill. ssp. *corsicus* Briq. (Corsica-Sardinia) and ssp. *lividus* Schiff. (Majorca, Cabrera) 2n = 32
Erodium corsicum Lam. (Corsica, Sardinia) and *E. reichardii* DC. (Majorca, Minorca) 2n = 20
Pastinaca latifolia DC. (Corsica) and *P. lucida* L. (Majorca, Minorca) 2n = 22
Micromeria filiformis (Aiton) Benth. ssp. *filiformis* (Corsica, Balearics) and ssp. *cordata* Moris ex Bertol. 2n = 30
Sesleria insularis Somm. ssp. *insularis* (Sardinia, Majorca) and ssp. *cordata* (Hackel) Ujh. (Corsica) 2n = 18
II   *Schizoendemism between Corsican and Cyrno-Sardinian orophytes with orophytes from mountains of south and central Europe* (They are of very ancient origin–beginning of the Tertiary)
Potentilla crassinervia Viv. and *Potentilla* grex *crassinerviae* Wolf. distributed in the Alps, the Balkans and western Asia
Phyteuma serratum Viv. and *Phyteuma* section *Capitata* DC., series *Alpina* Schulz from the Alps, the Pyrenees and mountains of Spain
III   *Schizoendemism between insular endemics and widespread species*
Festuca pumilla Chaix from central and southern European mountains and *F. sardoa* Hackel (Corsica, Sardinia)
Calamagrostis varia Host. (Eurasian mountains) and var. *corsica* Hack. (Corsica)
Ligusticum lucidum Miller from mountains of southern Europe and ssp. *huteri* (Porta & Rigo) O. Bolòs (Majorca) and *L. corsicum* Gay (Corsica)
Primula vulgaris Huds. (Western, central and southern Europe, Corsica, Algeria, western Asia) and ssp. *balearica* (Willk.) W.W.Sm. & Forrest (mountains of Majorca)
IV   *Mediterranean schizoendemism*
A   Between Mediterranean orophytes
Ranunculus marschlinzii Steud. (Corsica) and *Ranunculus* group *demissus* DC.
Helichrysum frigidum Willd. (Corsica, Sardinia) and *H. montelisanum* Schmid (Sardinia) with *Helichrysum* section *virginea* DC. (Mediterranean)
B   Endemics which are differentiated throughout the Mediterranean
Astragalus balearicus Chater (Gymnesian islands) and *A. sirinicus* Ten. ssp *genargenteus* (Moris) Briq. (Corsica, Sardinia) and *Astragalus* species related to *A. sempervirens* Lam.
Brassica balearica Pers. (Majorca) and *B. insularis* Moris (Corsica, Sardinia) with *Brassica* group *oleracea* L.
C   Schizoendemics from the western Mediterranean basin
Nepeta foliosa Moris (Sardinia), *N. multibracteata* Desf. (Portugal) and species of section *pycnonepta* distributed in the southwest Mediterranean
Hippocrepis balearica Jacq. (Balearics) and *H. valentina* Boiss. (Cap de la Nau)
Launaea cervicornis (Boiss.) Font Quer & Rothm. (Gymnesian islands), *L. arborescens* (Batt.) Murb. (SE Iberian Peninsula) and *L. acanthoclada* Maire (NW Africa)
D   Schizoendemism within the islands of the western Mediterranean
Bellium bellidioides Cyr. (Tyrrhenian and Balearic endemic), *B. nivale* Req. (mountains of Corsica) and *B. crassifolium* Moris (mountains of Sardinia)
Thymus richardii Pers. ssp. *richardii* (Majorca) and ssp. *ebusitanus* (Font Quer) Jalas (Ibiza)
V   *Schizoendemics of the boreo-meridional element*
These are very numerous, particularly in Corsica, but are taxa of lower rank, subspecies or varieties

151

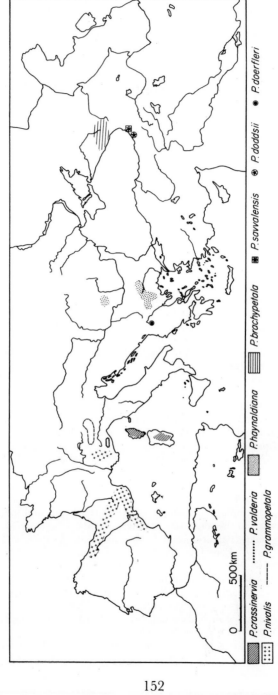

Fig. 8 Geographical distribution of *Potentilla* (from Pawłowski, 1965)

P.crassinervia ······· P.valderia ▓▓ P.haynaldiana ▦ P.brachypetala ▓ P.savvalensis ⊕ P.doddsii ◉ P.doerfleri
P.nivalis ───── P.grammopetala

0 ___ 500km

calcicolous, 2n = 14, *P. brachypetala* Fisch. from the Caucasus and *P. savalensis* Pawł. and *P. doddsii* Davis from Asia-Minor (Fig. 8).

The Cyrno-Sardinian endemic, isolated since the beginning of the Tertiary, shows a greater degree of speciation than the members of *Potentilla* series *Valderiae*. The latter, according to Pawłowski, form 3 principal groups, those of *P. valderia*, *P. nivalis* and *P. grammopetala*.

The Corsican endemic *Phyteuma serratum* Viv. is a member of a Tertiary alpine genus (Schulz, 1904) distributed in the Alps, the Pyrenees and the mountains of Spain. The section *Capitata* DC., series *Alpina* Schulz of *Phyteuma*, to which *P. serratum* belongs, includes the alpine species which grow in meadows, rocky places and moraines of high siliceous mountains (*P. hemisphaericum* L., Pyrenees and Sierra de Guadarrame to the Styrian Alps, the Appennines and the Carpathians, *P. gaussenii* Chouard, Pyrennean endemic, *P. serratoides* Chouard, Pyrennean endemic, *P. humile* Schleich., endemic to the Pennine Alps of Switzerland and Italy, *P. hedraianthifolium* Schulz endemic to the Dolomites and the Grisons). These are very often polymorphic taxa which are centred upon *P. hemisphaericum*, the most widespread species, and which have the same chromosome number of 2n = 14 (Contandriopolous, 1962). *Phyteuma serratum* appears to have retained a certain amount of morphological variability depending upon local factors, Fig. 9.

Among other alpine orophytes are: *Silene requienii* Otth., Cyrno-Sardinian endemic whose schizoendemics are *S. elizabethae* Jan.

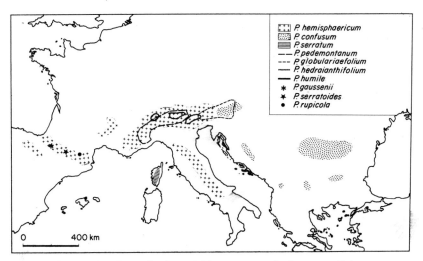

FIG. 9 Geographical distribution of *Phyteuma* sect. *Capitata* ser. *Alpina*.

(southeastern Alps), *S. zawadskii* Herbich (eastern Carpathians), *S. auriculata* Sibth. and Sm. (Apuani Alps and Greece). Unlike the *Potentilla*, all these *Silene* are calcicoles except for the Cyrno-Sardinian endemic which is silicolous.

   (c) Schizoendemism also often involves widespread taxa which are represented on the islands by endemics. For example: *Festuca pumila* Chaix of the mountains of southern and central Europe and *F. sardoa* Hackel in Corsica and Sardinia; *Calamagrostis varia* Host from Eurasian mountains and *C. varia* var. *corsica* Hackel in the mountains of Corsica; *Primula vulgaris* Hudson, western, central and southern Europe, Corsica, Algeria and western Asia and ssp. *balearica* (Willk.). W. W. Sm. & Forrest in the mountains of Majorca; *Ligusticum lucidum* Miller from mountains of Southern Europe, and the montane ssp. *huteri* (Porta & Rigo) O. de Bolòs from Majorca and *L. corsicum* J. Gay from Corsica.

   (d) Schizoendemics which belong to the Mediterranean element can be found either throughout the Mediterranean basin or only in certain sectors.

   (1) Among Mediterranean orophytes can be mentioned the species of *Ranunculus* of the *R. demissus* DC. group with *R. marschlinsii* Steudel (Corsica, 2n = 16) Contandriopoulos, 1962, *R. hayekii* Dörfler (northern Albania), *R. demissus* var. *graecus* Boiss. (northern Peloponnese), var. *major* Boiss. (Taurus and Anti-Taurus), var. *demissus* (Syria and Lebanon) and ssp. *hispanicus* Boiss. (Sierra Nevada, 2n = 16) Küpfer and Favarger, 1967.

   Likewise, concerning the species of *Helichrysum* section *Virginea* DC. of the Mediterranean basin, we have tentatively classified *Helichrysum frigidum* Willd. (Contandriopoulos, 1962), a Cyrno-Sardinian endemic which Beguinot (1935) considered as "le type le plus archaïque de la Corse et du Mont Limbara en Sardaigne", among the palaeoendemics by virtue of its distant affinities with the Helichrysums of section *Elegantissima* of central and southern Africa. However, the presence in the Eastern Mediterranean basin of *Helichrysum* section *Virginea*, narrowly localised, rupicolous endemics such as *H. amorgineum* Boiss. & Orph. (Amorgos in the Cyclades), *H. doerfleri* Rech. fil. (Crete), *H. sibthorpii* Rouy (Mount Athos, Greece) and *H. montelinasum* Schmid (Sardinia), leads us to consider that here we have relictual schizoendemics whose speciation is certainly much more advanced than, say, the *Ranunculus demissus* group. Only *H. montelinasum*, the Sardinian endemic, approaches *H. frigidum* and is, perhaps, of less ancient origin.

   (2) Mediterranean schizoendemics can also belong to large groups which have differentiated throughout the Mediterranean basin, as for

example *Astragalus sempervirens* Lam. and related species, with *A. balearicus* Chater (Gymnesian islands 2n = 16), *A. sirinicus* Ten. ssp. *sirinicus* (Appenines, Dalmatia, Montenegro), *A. sirinicus* ssp. *genargenteus* (Moris) Briq. (Corsica, Sardinia), 2n = 16, *A. ibrahimianus* Maire (Morocco), *A. sempervirens* Lam. ssp. *sempervirens* (Alps, Appenines and north east Spain). *A. sempervirens* ssp. *cephalonicus* (C. Presl) Ascher. & Graebn. (Greece, 2n = 16), *A. sempervirens* ssp. *muticus* (Pau) Rivas Goday & Borja (central and eastern Spain) and *A. sempervirens* ssp. *nevadensis* Boiss. (Sierra Nevada and Pyrenees, 2n = 16). All these species, with the exception of *A. massiliensis* which is a coastal species, are orophytes. *A. balearicus* is found from sea level up to mountain summits, but its habitat is always associated with the presence of winds, particularly of the Tramontane (Cardona, 1978; Contandriopoulos, 1962; Damboldt and Phitos, 1971, Baudière and Cauwet, 1968; etc.), Fig. 10.

Mention can also be made of the *Brassica oleracea* L. complex, with *B. balearica* Pers. (Majorca, 2n = 18), *B. insularis* Moris (Corsica and Sardinia, 2n = 18), *B. rupestris* Rafin. (Sicily, 2n = 18), *B. cretica* Lam. (SE. Greece, Crete and Aegean Islands), *B. incana* Ten. (S. and W. Italy, Sicily, Yugoslavia), *B. oleracea* ssp. *oleracea* (western coasts of France, N. Spain, England, 2n = 18), *B. oleracea* ssp. *robertiana* (Gay) Rouy & Fouc., 2n = 18 (from N. Spain to S. Italy).

In the *Genista acanthoclada* DC. group, Valsecchi (1975) showed that the following subspecies are vicariants: *G. acanthoclada* ssp. *acanthoclada* (Greece and Aegean Islands), ssp. *echinus* (Spach) Vals. (S. Anatolia), ssp. *sardoa* (Beg. & Lardi ex Lardi) Vals. (Sardinia), ssp. *balearica* (P.R.) Willk. (Majorca). The chromosome numbers of these taxa are not yet known.

We can also cite *Anthyllis fulgurans* Porta from the Gymnesian islands (Majorca, Minorca, Cabrera) and *A. hermanniae* (Couderc, 1975; Larsen, 1956), whose area extends from Corsica and Sardinia to Greece and Turkey (Cardona, 1973).

Finally we can note *Thymelaea velutina* (Pourr. ex. Camb.) Meissner from the Gymnesian islands with the *T. tartonraira* (L.) Alp. group from the Mediterranean basin, or again, *Senecio rodriguezii* Willk. from the eastern Balearics with the *S. leucanthemifolius* Poiret complex from the western and central Mediterranean region (Cardona, 1977, 1978; Dahlgren *et al.*, 1971; Fernandes and Queiros, 1970–71, Aymonin, 1974).

(3) Schizoendemics of the western Mediterranean basin. These are very numerous and we will mention only a few. However, they are of particular interest as they illustrate an affinity not only with species of the Iberian Peninsula but also with taxa distributed in N. Africa. *Nepeta foliosa* Moris (2n = 36), a Sardinian endemic, shows affinities with *N. multi-*

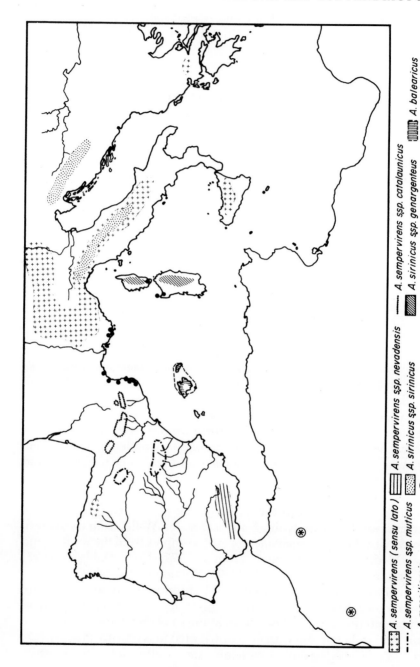

Fig. 10 Geographical distribution of *Astragalus*

bracteata Desf. from Portugal, and belongs to a group of species in section *Pycononepeta* distributed in the southwestern Mediterranean. Most of them are endemics "qui en raison de l'isolement geographique ont été soumises à une différenciation lente et progressive" (Valsecchi *et al.*, 1973).

Saxifraga corsica (Duby) Gren & Gordon (= *S. granulata* L. var. *russü* Engl.), a Cyrno-Sardinian endemic, is a vicariant of *S. corsica* ssp. *cossoniana* (Boiss.) D. A. Webb from Ibiza and the Valencien coast. The case of *Hippocrepis balearica* Jacq., 2n = 14, from the Cap de la Nau (Valencia region) is similar (Guern and Gorenflot, 1966), Fig. 11. *Launaea cervicornis* (Boiss.) Font Quer & Rothm. is more complicated; this endemic of the Gymnesian islands has a chromosome number 2n = 18

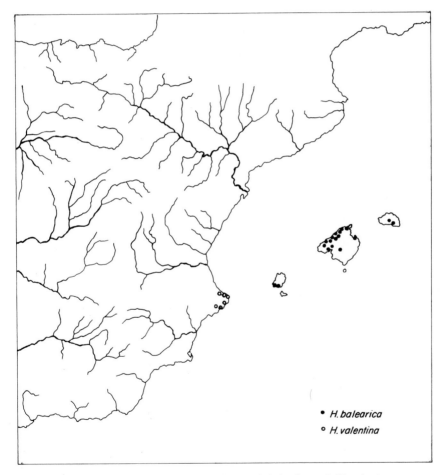

FIG. 11   Geographical distribution of *Hippocrepis balearica* and *H. valentina*

(Dahlgren *et al.*, 1971; Cardona, 1978). It is closely related to two other species of the same section: *L. lanifera* Pau (= *L. acanthoclada* Maire), 2n = 16 (Fernández Casas, 1973), whose area covers SE Spain, N Africa, Fuerteventura (?) and Arabia, and *L. arborescens* (Batt.) Murbeck, 2n = 14 (Larsen, 1960; Borgen, 1969; Gagnier *et al.*, 1973), which is recorded from SE Spain, NW Africa and the Canaries (Fig. 12a, b). It is possible that the differentiation of these three taxa was accompanied by dysploidy comparable with that noted by Cauwet (1976) in connection with the Balearic endemic (Majorca, Ibiza) *Bupleurum barceloi* Cosson whose basic number is x = 6 and which is a vicariant of *B. frutescens* L., inhabiting the coastal strip of the Iberian peninsula opposite the Balearics, with a basic number of x = 8.

Schizoendemism is not always a very old phenomenon, as for example, that which exists between two neighbouring islands or on a single island. Within the Balearics there has been a microdifferentiation of *Thymus richardii* Pers. with ssp. *richardii* and ssp. *ebusitanus* (Font Quer) Jalas, endemics of Majorca and Ibiza respectively, or again, in *Teucrium subspinosum* Pourr. ex Willd. in the Gymnesian islands (Majorca, Minorca, Cabrera) and var. *spinescens* Porta restricted to Minorca.

Bellium bellidioides L., a Tyrrhenian and Balearic endemic, has differentiated into the Corsican mountains as the schizoendemics *B. nivale* Req., and in Sardinia as *B. crassifolium* Moris (Contandriopoulos, 1962; Pogliani, 1968).

In Sardinia the endemic *Centaurea filiformis* Viv. is represented by two schizoendemics, ssp. *filiformis* and *ferulacea* (Martelli) Arrigoni (Arrigoni and Mori, 1975), or again, *Vinca difformis* Pourret is represented by the schizoendemic spp. *sardoa* Stearn (Garbari *et al.*, 1973).

If the different aspects of schizoendemism in the western Mediterranean are considered along with their biogeographical significance, the following three statements can be made:

1 Schizoendemism exists between Corsican or Sardinian endemics with taxa from the Iberian Peninsula and/or N. Africa but without representatives in the Balearics.

2 There is similarly schizoendemism between endemics from the Gymnesian islands and taxa in the Iberian Peninsula and/or N. Africa but not including the Pithyusan Islands.

3 The schizoendemics of the Pithyusan Islands are most often with Iberian taxa which generally occur round the Valencia region. Most cases are subspecies or varieties.

Finally, in the boreomeridional element, if schizoendemics are numerous particularly in Corsica, it is because they are most often taxa of lower rank-subspecies or varieties.

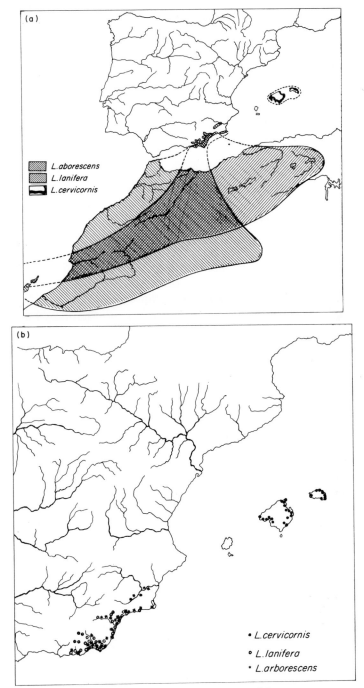

Fig. 12(a) and (b)   Geographical distribution of *Launaea*

F*

To sum up, the degree of speciation of endemics, their relative isolation and severity of their requirements are the factors which indicate the age of schizoendemics. For example, in Corsica, schizoendemics of the orophil element of the mountains of central and southern Europe are more ancient than those of the boreomeridional element which are only represented by varieties and subspecies.

Apoendemics

Apoendemism seems to be relatively poorly represented in the islands of the western Mediterranean, and this is not surprising if one considers the long isolation of the islands. It is through the cytotaxonomic study of "microendemics" that we are able to judge the relative importance of the different classes.

Among apoendemics whose corresponding taxa have been identified by cytotaxonomic analysis we can mention: *Genista cinera* (Will.) DC. ssp. *leptoclada* (Willk.) O. Bolòs, R. Mol. & P. Monts., tetraploid of Majorca while *G. cinerea* ssp. *cinerascens* (Lange) Rivas-Martínez is diploid (Cardona, 1976; Sanudo, 1972), *Santolina insularis* Genn. ex Fiori and *S. corsica* Jordan & Fourr. Cyrno-Sardinian endemics related to *S.chamaecyparissus* L. (Marchi and d'Amanto, 1973), *Byronia dioica* L. var. *angulosa* Let., tetraploid while ssp. *dioica* is diploid (Contandriopoulos, 1964), and *Paeonia coralina* Retz var. *leiocarpa*, tetraploid on Corsica while *P. cambessedesii*, a Balearic endemic is diploid.

Also among apoendemics are *Cymbalaria mulleri* (Moris) Cheval. in Sardinia, *Nepeta foliosa* Moris, also Sardinian, whose affinities are N. African (Valsecchi *et al.*, 1973), or again, *Medicago arborea* L. ssp. *citrina* (Font Quer) O. Bolòs & Vigo from the Espartar islands near Ibiza, Bledes near Majorca and Ferrera (Columbrets) near Alicante is tetraploid $(2n = 32)$ while *M. arborea* ssp. *arborea* of the southern Mediterranean region is hexaploid $(2n = 32)$ (Escarré, unpub.)

What are the origins of the endemic flora of the western Mediterranean? We have seen that they were diverse. First and foremost it is a Palaeogene Mediterranean flora which has developed *in situ*. It is the flora which might have populated the "Protoligurian massif" of Alvarez (1976) and which corresponds to a large extent with the Tyrrhenian flora which might have inhabited the Tyrrhenian islands (Corsica, Sardinia, the Tuscan archipelago, the Hyères islands) and the north of Minorca and which is composed mostly of palaeo- and patroendemics. With the Alpine orogenesis, this flora was enriched with species from the "central and southern European orophile" and "montane boreal" elements. The former has remained in the mountains of Corsica and Sardinia and is characterised by a very important degree of endemism (50% of the orophile flora of Corsica is endemic). The latter has survived in Corsica and Sardinia but also in the mountains of Majorca whose flora presents in fact much greater affinities with the mountains of southern Europe than with those of the Baetic chains.

In addition, the endemic floras of the islands of Corsica, Sardinia and the Balearics present Mediterranean affinities:

1 Either they may be large species-groups which are differentiated in the Mediterranean basin into schizoendemics.

2 Or they may be related to taxa from the eastern Mediterranean domain (*Anthyllis hermanniae* L., common in the eastern Mediterranean, also occurs in Corsica and Sardinia and has differentiated in Majorca and Minorca into an endemic subspecies, ssp. *hystrix* Willk.).

3 Or they may show affinities with taxa of the western Mediterranean domain as we have seen on p. 155. The degree of speciation of schizoendemics is related to the age of the connections between the islands and neighbouring territories.

Lastly, the boreomeridional element seems to be a later arrival in these islands particularly in Corsica (at the beginning of the Quaternary) where it is represented by numerous subspecies and varieties.

If the geographical distribution of endemics and of corresponding taxa allows us to trace, in a sense, the history of the colonisation of the islands of the western Mediterranean, it is equally useful to look at the species with disjunct distributions, present in these islands, and those that are at the limit of their ranges, whose distribution might complete the information provided by the study of endemism. The distributions of *Satureia thymbra* Willd., a species very common in the eastern Mediterranean basin and which occurs elsewhere only in southern Sardinia (Martinoli, 1949b) (Fig. 13), and of *Buxus balearica* Willd., a widely distributed species in N Africa which exists elsewhere only in the south of Spain, in Majorca and in the extreme south of Sardinia (Martinoli, 1949c) (Fig. 14) or again of *Micromeria inodora* (Desf.) Bentham whose area covers N. Africa, southern Spain and the Valencia region, as well as the Pithyusan islands and northeast Majorca, show the connections which have existed between different Mediterranean domains (Fig. 15).

Conclusion

In conclusion, the importance of palaeoendemics (monospecific genera, species very isolated taxonomically), the presence of patroendemics, the

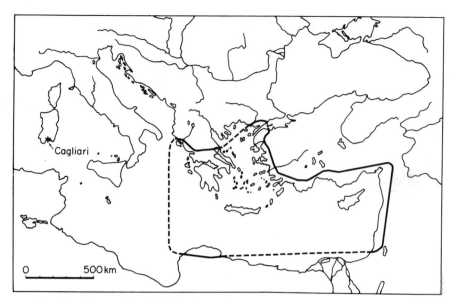

Fig. 13   Geographical distribution of *Satureia thymbra* (from Martinoli, 1949)

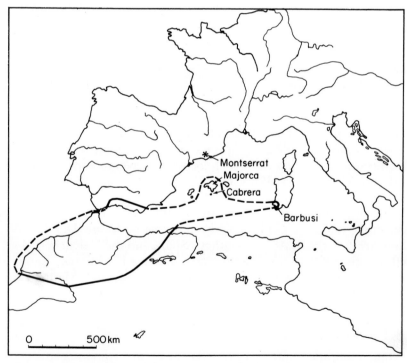

Fig. 14   Geographical distribution of *Buxus balearica* (from Martinoli, 1949)

162

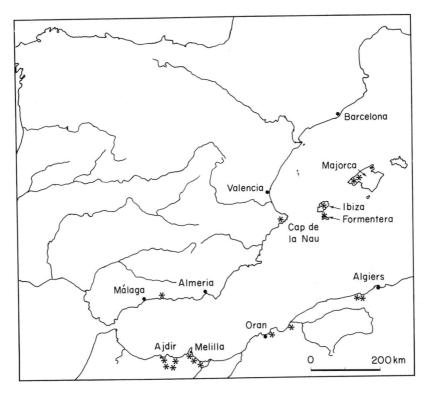

FIG. 15 Geographical distribution of *Micromeria inodora* (from Font Quer, 1927)

abundance of relictual schizoendemics, emphasise the ancient character of the endemic island floras of the western Mediterranean. But while "endemism par conservation" (Briquet, 1901) predominates and results principally from insular isolation, endemism "par novation" exists but is more difficult to detect as speciation is an extremely slow phenomenon which sometimes requires some tens of thousands of years and can be detected only when genetic changes are reflected in morphology. Speciation can have been a very ancient phenomenon, as we have seen, and resulted in endemics which are easy to recognise and whose characters are well fixed. The phenomenon can also be less ancient, subrecent or recent, the differentiation of the taxa being less pronounced. However it has often been noticed that each isolated territory has a tendency "à façonner les plantes qui le colonisent" (Gaussen and Leredde, 1949). Are these micromorphic local forms, ecotypes, or taxa undergoing speciation? Such are problems that only detailed analysis in the field and laboratory, comparative growth experiments, crossing experiments and cytotaxonomic studies can help to resolve.

However, if the flora of the Tyrrhenian islands and those of the Balearics appears, as a whole, relictual, it does not follow that it is static; one only needs to list the very important number of microendemics, subspecies and varieties, which have been described as much for Corsica (Briquet, 1910–13; de Litardière, 1935–55, etc.) and for Sardinia (Moris, 1837–59; Barbey, 1884; Fiori, 1969; Zangheri, 1976 etc.), as for the Balearic islands (Font Quer, 1927; Knoche, 1923, etc.). In addition, the presence of schizoendemics and sympatric apoendemics as well as that of highly polymorphic species, endemic or not, indicates well that insular floras of the western Mediterranean have not lost their potential for variability. An example is *Ruta corsica* DC., which is considered as a relictual palaeoendemic species completely isolated taxonomically. It is diploid in Corsica (Contandriopoulos, 1957) (Vallée du Prunelli, Col de Vergio) while Honsell (1957) studied a tetraploid race on Mount Genargentu, Sardinia. Under the influence of certain factors (particularly soil microenvironments in ecological niches), the mechanisms of speciation (adaptive radiation, genetic drift, mutation, hybridisation, polyploidy etc.) effect the formation of new biotypes. However, ecological conditions not remaining stable, these periods of active endemism dependent on variations in the environment, are followed by periods of passive endemism in this alternating cycle which governs biological phenomena.

Acknowledgements

We express our gratitude to Professors F. Garbari, University of Pisa, P. Arrigoni, University of Florence and B. Corrias, University of Sassari, for all the information with which they have been kind enough to furnish us regarding Sardinian endemics, as well as Professoro de Bolòs, University of Barcelona who has shared with us his knowledge of the Balearics. Finally, we thank Mme Verlaque and M. Sierra for drawing the maps.

REFERENCES

Alvarez, W. (1973). The application of plate Tectonics to the mediterranean region. In *Implication of Continental Drift to the Mediterranean Sciences* (D. H. Tarling and S. K. Runcorn, eds.), Vol 2, 893–908. Academic Press, London and New York

Arrigoni, P. V. (1970). Contributo alla conoscenze delle Armerie sardo-corse. *Webbia* 25, 137–182

Alvarez, W. (1976). A former continuation of the Alps. *Geol. Soc. Amer. Bull.* 87, 891–896, 2 figs., Doc. 6069

— (1972). Sulla distribuzione e il rango sistematico di *Centaurea filiformis* Viv. e *Centaurea ferulacea* Mart. *Webbia* **27**, (i), 279–287

— (1974). Raporti floristici tran l'Arcipelago Toscano e le terre vicine. *Lav. Soc. ital. biogeogr.* N.S. **5**, 1–11

— and Mori, B. (1971). Numeri cromosomici per la Flora italiana. *Inf. Bot. Ital.* **3**, 226–227

Aymonin, G. G. (1974). Polymorphisme chez les *Thymelea tartonraira* L. All. et position du *Passerina thomasii* Duby de la Corse. *Bull. Soc. Bot. Fr.* **121**, 95ème sess. extr. 41–43

Babcock, E. B. (1942). Systematics, cytogenetics and evolution in *Crepis*. *Bot. Rev.* **8**, (3), 139–190

— (1947). The genus *Crepis*, part. 2: Systematic treatment. *Univ. Calif. Publ. Bot.* **22**, 198–1030

Barbey, W. (1884). *Florae Sardoae Compendium*. Georges Bridel, Lausanne

Baudière, A. and Cauwet, A. (1968). Sur quelques plantes inédites, rares ou critiques de la flore des Pyrénées orientales et des Corbières audoises. *Nat. Monsp. Série Bot.* **19**, 179–200

Beguinot, A. (1935). Lo stato attuale delle conescenze sulla flora della Sardegna ed i problimi fitogeografici che vi si collegano. *Arch. Bot.* **ii** (i), 21–34, N.S.I.

Bellot, F. (1947). Revisión crítica de las especies del genero *Hippocrepis* de la Península e Islas Baleares. *Ann. Jard. Bot. Madrid* **7**, 197–334

Blanc, J. (1972). *Initiation à la Géologie Marine*. Doin, Paris

Boissier, E. (1839–45). *Voyage Botanique dans le Midi de l'Espagne*. 2ème vol. 757p. Gide et Cie, Paris

Bolòs, O. de (1958). Grupos corológicos de la flora balear. *P. Inst. Biol. Apl.* **27**, 49–71

— (1965). Etude comparative entre la végétation méditerranée-montagnard de Majorque et celle due midi valencien. *Rapports et Procès-verbaux des réunions de la C.I.E.S.M.M.* **18** (2), 483–488

— (1969). La vegetación de las Islas Baleares. V. Simposio de Flora Europaea, 81–89. Universidad Hispalense Sevilla

— and Molinier, R. (1960). Vue d'ensemble de la végétation des îles Baléares *Vegetatio* **17** (1–6), 251–270

Borgen, L. (1960). Chromosome numbers of vascular plants from Canary Islands with special reference to the occurrence of polyploidy. *Nytt. Mag. Bot.* **16**, 81–121

Bramwell, D. and Z. (1974). *Wild Flowers of the Canary Islands*. Stanley Thorne (Publishers) Ltd, Cheltenham

Briquet, J. (1901). Recherches sur la flore des montagnes de la Corse et ses origines. *Ann. Conserv. Jard. Bot. Genève* **5**, 12–119

— (1910–13). *Prodrôme de la flore corse*. **1**, Georg, Ed., Genève et Bâle 1910; **2**, part I, *ibid.* 1913

Cardona, M. A. (1973). Contribution à l'étude cytotaxinomique de la flore des Baléares, I. *Act. Phytotax. Bardionensi* **14**, 1–20

— (1976). Contribución al estudio citotaxonómico de la flora de las Baleares, IV. *Lagascalia* **6** (2), 265–274

— (1977). Contribució a l'estudi citotaxonómic de flora de les Balears, III. *Bull. Inst. Cat. Hist. Nat.* **41** (*Ser. Bot. 2*), 83–94

— (1978). Contribució a l'estudi citotaxonómic de la flora de les Balears, II. *Col. Soc. Cat. Biol.* **10**, 51–67

— and Contandripopoulos, J. (1977). L'endémisme dans les flores insulaires méditerranéennes. *Mediterranea*, Depart. Biol. Fac., Ciencias, Alicante, Univ. Valencia, **2**, 49–77

Cauwet, A.-M. (1976). Biosystématique des espèces vivaces de *Bupleurum* L. (Umbelliferae) du bassin méditerraneen occidental. 3 Fasc. Doctorat d'état, Université des Sciences et Techniques du Languedoc, Centre Universitaire de Perpignan.

Contandriopoulos, J. (1957). Contribution à l'étude caryologique des endémiques de la flore corse. *Ann. Fac. Sc. Marseille* **26**, 51–65

— (1962). Recherches sur la flore endémique de la Corse et sur ses origines. *Ann. Fac. Sc. Marseille* **32**, 354pp

— (1964). Recherches sur la flore endémique de la Corse et sur origines II. *Rev. Gen. Bot.* **71**, 361–384

— and Favarger, C. (1959). Existence de races chromosomiques chez *Chrysanthemum alpinum* L., leur répartition dans les Alpes. *Rev. Gen. Bot.* **66**, 341–357

— and Favarger C. (1974). Problèmes posés par l'endemisme en Méditerranée. In "La Flore du bassin méditerranéen, essai de systématique synthétique." *Coll. intern. C.N.R.S.* No. 235, 174–194

Couderc, H. (1975). Etude biosystématique des espèces françaises du genre *Anthyllis* et notamment de l'*A. vulneraria* L. Thèse, Paris

Cuerda, J. (1965). Données paléontologiques por l'etude de la malocofaune terrestre des Baléares orientales. *Rapports et Proces Verbaux du C.I.E.S.M.* **18** (2), 507–510

— (1975). *Los tiempos cuaternarios en Baleares.* 304p. Dip. Prov. Baleares, P. Palma de Mallorca

Dahlgren, R., Karlsson, T. and Lassen, P. (1971). Studies on the flora of the Balearic Islands I. Chromosome numbers in Balearic Angiosperms. *Bot. Not.* **124** (2), 249–269

Damboldt, J. and Phitos, D. (1971). In I.O.P.B. chromosome reports 34, *Taxon* **20**, 785–797

Duvigneaud, J. (1974). *Excursion du 21–28.6.74 à Majorque. Catalogue Provisoire de la Flore des Baléares.* Sart. Tilman, Liège

Favarger, C. (1962). Contribution de la biosystématique à l'étude des flores alpine et jurassienne. Colloque sue la Caryosystématique et la Taxinomie experimentale. In *Rev. Cytol et Biol. veg.* **25** (3–4), 397–410

— (1966). Contribution à la cytotaxinomie du genre *Petrorhagia* (= *Tunica*). *Bull. Soc. Bot. Suisse* **76**, 270–278

— and Contandriopoulos, J. (1961). Essai sur l'endémisme. *Bull. Soc. Bot. Suisse* **71**, 384–408

Fernandes, A. and Queiros, M. (1970–71). Sur la caryologie de quelques plantes récoltées pendant la 3ème réunion de Botanique péninsulaire. *Mem. Soc. Broteriana* **21**, 343–385

Fernandez Casas, J. (1973). Numeros cromosomicos de plantas españolas, 1 *Cuad. C. Biol.* **2** (1), 39–41

Fiori, A. (1969). *Nuova Flora Analitica Italiana.* Edizioni Agricole. Bologna

Font Quer, P. (1927). La flora de las Pitiusas y sus afinidades con la de la Península ibérica. *Mem. Real. Acad. Ciencias y Artes Barcelona* **20** (4), 3–48

Gagnieu, A., Linder, R. and Voggenreiter, V. (1973). Caryotypes de la flore insulaire de Tenerife. *Monogr. Biol. Canar.* **4**, 126–133

Garbari, F. (1968). Il genere Muscari (Liliacaea) contributo alla revisione citotassisinomia. *Giorn. Bot. Ital.* **102** (2), 87–105

—, Tornadore, N. and Pecori, E. (1973). Numeri cromosomici per la Flora italiana. *Inf. Bot. Ital.* **5** (2), 161–169

Gaussen, H. and Leredde, C. (1949). Les endémiques pyrénéo-cantabriques dans la région centrale des Pyrénées. *Bull. Soc. Bot. Fr.* **96**, 57–83

Guern, M. and Gorenflot, R. (1966). Caryologie du genre *Hippocrepis* L. *C. R. Ac. Sc. Paris*, Sér. D, **263**, 5, 509–512

Honsell, E. (1957). Ricerche cario-embryologische in *Ruta corsica* DC. *Delpinoa*, **10**, 141–153

Knoche, H. (1921–23). *Flora Balearica.* 4 vols. Montpellier

Küpfer, P. and Favarger, C. (1967). Premières prospections caryologiques dans la flore orophile des Pyrénées et de la Sierra Nevada. *C. R. Ac. Sc. Paris*, Sér. D, **264**, 2463–2465

Larsen, K. (1956). Chromosome studies in some Mediterranean and south European flowering plants. *Bot. Not.* **109** (3), 283–307

Larsen, K. (1960). Cytological and experimental studies on the flowering plants of the Canary Islands. *Biol. Skr. Dan. Vid. Selks.* **11** (3), 1–60

Litardière R. de (1935–55). *Prodrôme de la Flore de la Corse de Briquet, continué par R. de Litardière.* **2** (2). Paul Lechevalier, Paris, 1935; **3** (1). Paul Lechevalier, Paris, 1938; **3** (2). Paul Lechevalier, Paris, 1955

— (1949). Observations caryologiques et caryosystématiques sur différentes Graminées principalement de la flore méditerranéenne. *Mem. Soc. Hist. Nat. Afr. N.* **2**, 199–208

Marchi, P. (1972). Numeri cromosomici per la flora italiana. *Inf. Bot. Ital.* **4** (I), 60–66

— and d'Amato, G. (1973). Numeri cromosomici per la flora italiana. *Inf. Bot. Ital.* **5** (I), 92–100

Martinoli, G. (1940). Contributo all' embriologia delle Asteraceae. *Nuov. Giorn. Bot. Ital.* 2ème sér., **47** (4–5), 287–322

— (1949a). Ecologia della *Morisia monantha* Asc. Sull'altimiana della Campeda e nuova stazione della specie sulla gara di Gesturi. *Rend. Sem. Fac. Sc. Univ. Cagliari* **19** (2)

— (1949b). *Satureia thymbra* L. Elemento mediterraneo-orientale della Sardegna. *Nuov. Giorn. Bot. Ital.* N.S. **56**, 576–592

— (1949c). *Buxus balearica* Willd. Elemento mediterraneo-occidentale della

Sardegna. *Nuov. Gior. Bot. Ital.* N.S. **56** (4), 557–575

— (1954). La cytotaxinomie expérimentale appliquée aux espèces végétales de la Sardaigne et en particulier aux endémiques. *5éme Congr. Intern. Bot. Rapports et Communications, section 9, Paris,* 78–89.

— (1961). L'écologia della *Morisia monantha* Asch. e la nuova stazione di Nurri (Sardegna). *Arch. Bot. et Biogeog. Ital.* **37**, 4éme sér. VI (4), 1–7

Moris, J. H. (1837–59). *Flora Sardoa son Historia Plantarum in Sardegna et Adjacentibus Insulis.* 4 vols. Taurini

Obrador, A. (1972–73). *Estudio Estratigráfico y Sedimentológico de los Materiales Miocénicos de la Isla de Menorca.* 183p. Talleres Gráficos Coll. Maó

Pawłowski, B. (1965). De generis *Potentilla* L. serie *Crassinerviae* (T. Wolf) B. Pawl. nec non de taxis affinibus. *Fragm. Flor. et geobot.* **2** (I), 53–91

Pecorini, G., Rage, J. C. and Thaler L. (1974). La formation continentale du Cap Mannu, sa faune de vertébrés pliocènes et la question du Messinien en Sardaigne. In *Palaeogeografia del terziario sardo nell'ambito del Mediterraneo occidentale.* suppl. *Rend. Sem. Fac. Sc. Univ. Cagliari, 305–319*

Pogliani, M. (1968). Ricerche cariologische in *Bellium crassifolium* Moris (Asteraceae). *Boll. Soc. Sardo. Sci. Nat.* **2**, 55–57

Quezel, P. and Santa, S. (1963). *Nouvelle Flore de l'Algérie et des Régions Désertiques Méridionales.* Vol. II, 1170p. Ed. C.N.R.S, Paris

Rigual, A. (1972). *Flora y vegetación de la provincia de Alicante.* Inst. Est. Alicantinos. Exma. Dip. Prov. de Alicante. 403p. Alicante

Ríos, J. M. (1975). El mar Mediterráneo occidental y sus cosáts ibéricas. *Bol. R. Soc. Esp. Hist. Nat.* **70**, 1–473

Sañudo, A. (1972). Variabilidad cromósomica de les Genísteas de la flora española en relación con su ecología. *Cuad. C. Biol.* **2**, 43–52

Schmid, E. (1933). Beiträge zur Flora der Insel Sardinien. *Vierteljahrsschr. Naturf. Ges. Zürich* **78**, 232–255

Schulz, R. (1904). Monographische Bearbeitung der Gattung *Phyteuma.* Thèse, Zürich

Snogerup, S. (1967). Studies in the aegean Flora, VII: *Erysimum* sect. *Cheiranthus* A: *Taxonomy*; B: Variation and evolution in the small population system. *Opera Bot.* **13** and **14**

Stebbins, G. L. (1938). Cytogenic studies in *Paeonia* II. The cytology of the diploid species and hybrids. *Genetics* **23**, 83–110

— and Zohary, M. (1959). Cytogenetic and evolutionary studies in the genus *Dactylis*, morphology, distribution and interrelationships of the diploid species. *Univ. Calif. Publ. Bot.* **31**, 1–40

Stern, F. C. (1942–43). Geographical distribution of the genus *Paeonia. Proc. Linn. Soc. Lond.* Part. 2, 72–79

Strid, A. (1970). Studies in the aegean flora, XVI: Biosystematics of *Nigella arvensis* complex with special reference to the problem of non-adaptative radiation. *Opera Bot.* **28**, 1–169

Thaler, L. (1973). Nanisme et gigantisme insulaire. *La recherche* **37** (4), 741–73

— (1975). Contributo alla conoscenza sistematica del genere *Genista in Sardegna Genista acanthoclada* DC. *Giorn. Bot. Ital.* **109**, 239–249

Valsecchi, F. (1976). Il genere *Anchusa* in Sardegna. *Webbia* **30** (I), 43–68

— and Corrias, S. D. (1973). Notizie ecologische e sistematische su *Nepeta foliosa* Moris. *Giorn. Bot. Ital.* **107** (4), 73–180

Westphal, M., Orsini, J. and Vellutini, P. (1976). Le Microcontinent corse-sarde, sa position initiale, données paleomagnétiques et raccords géologiques. *Tectonophysics* **30**, 141–157

Willkomm, M. (.1893). *Supplementum Prodromi Florae Hispanicae*, 370p. Schweizerbart, Stuttgart.

— and Lange, J. (1870–80). *Prodromus florae hispanicae*. Vol. II, 680p.; Vol. III, 1144p. Schweizerbart, Stuttgart

Zaffran, J. (1967). Note sur le genre *Launaea* Coss. en Afrique du Nord et au Sahara. *Ann. Fac. Sc. Marseille* **39**, 195–210

Zangheri, F. (1976). *Flora Italica*. Vols. I and II. Cedam, Padua

9 Endemism and Evolution in Macaronesia

C. J. HUMPHRIES   *Department of Botany, British Museum (Natural History), London, England*

Como ya ha sido definido por varios biogeógrafos, Macaronesia lo constituyen las 30 islas e innumerables islotes de las Azores, Madeiras, Canarias, Salvajes y el Archipiélago de Cabo Verde. Ecológicamente, son extremadamente diversas clasificándose desde las islas tropicales oceánicas de Cabo Verde en el Sur, hacia las húmedas, templadas islas de las Azores, en el Norte. La distribución de habitats en las islas, particularmente en las islas más grandes de las Canarias, es bastante increible. Esto es a causa de grandes diferencias climáticas entre las costas Norte y Sur, debido a los vientos dominantes y zonación horizontal causada por las diferencias topológicas. Discretos habitats incluyen los acantilados costeros de las zonas bajas xerofíticas, la franja de bosques montañosos e incluso el cinturón subalpino en Tenerife.

El elemento endémico de la flora Macaronésica constituye alrededor de un 20% o alrededor de 680 especies de un total de algo así como 3200 fanerógamas. Comparando con áreas de medidas semejantes de otras partes, la región macaronésica alberga una inordenada y rica flora por unidad de área.

Las especies endémicas son morfológicamente y fisiológicamente muy diversas. En este trabajo se intentará ilustrar los orígenes de estas especies y sus pautas de derivación en las islas macaronésicas mirando los procesos de evolución de unos pocos ejemplos seleccionados. Se dán estadísticas concernientes a la distribución de endemismos en general como un corolario preliminar para aspectos casuales de evolución. Claramente, las islas más ricas son aquellas más grandes y las más diversas ecologicamente. Una clasificación artificial de endemismos usando criterios citológicos propone que tres cuartas partes de ellos se han desarrollado por especiación gradual y aislamiento intrínseco. Consecuentemente, la flora es rica en schizoendemismos, (aquellas especies desarrolladas al mismo nivel de ploide que los grupos hermanos continentales o macraronésicos) con sólo un puñado de apoendemismos (especies neopoliploide con grupos diploide hermanos continentales o macaronésicos), y patroendémicos (diploides con grupos poliploides hermanos continentales). El elemento palaeoendemico no será considerado en ningún detalle en este trabajo, y que consiste en su mayoría en aquellos taxones de antaño de mucha mas amplia distribución, con un remoto e indefinido parentesco del grupo hermano. Generalmente se cree que estos taxones han llegado simplemente a aislarse por cambios en condiciones climáticas continentales y que ahora solo sobrevivien en un puñado de habitats relictuales apropiados. Citológicamente parece que consisten en un grupo de taxones diploides y poliploides que han variado muy poco desde su temprana llegada a las islas macaronésicas.

Las pruebas acumulades de morfología, distribución, citología y la citogenética de híbridos artificiales y naturales proponen que la mayoría de los endemismos en Macaronesia son epibióticos activos. Estos están caracterizados como grupos monofiléticos, unigenómicos de especies evolucionadas por radiación adaptativa en las islas desde el Terciario y a menudo ascendientes palaeoendémicos. Esencialmente están mucho mejor adaptadas en poblaciones relativamente homocigóticas, discretas, con especies fértiles en cruzamiento que han llegado a quedar aisladas y separadas espacialmente por una selección poderosa en el ancho gradiente ecológico. Parece probable, que el proceso de radiación adaptativa cuente igualmente para divergencias en taxones en gran medida diferentes asi como en vicariantes cercanos similares.

Estudios detallados sobre la naturaleza de evolución por poliploide e hibridación en fanerogamas macaronésicas son muy escasos. Las observaciones iniciales sobre *Lotus, Geranium* y *Asparagus* sugieren que los poliploides apoendémicos aparecen en condiciones severas fuera de la normal distribución de poliploides. Sin embargo, esta hipótesis no parece que tenga sentido en poliploides del género *Aeonium* y *Aichryson*; tampoco para los neopoliploides de *Silene* y *Asphodelus*.

Introduction

The Macaronesian region consists of the five Atlantic island archipelagos of the Azores, the Madeiras, the Salvage Islands, the Canary Islands and the Cape Verde Islands. Within this region there are approximately 3200 species of flowering plants of which some 680, representing 20% of the total, constitute the endemic element. The total area as given by Sunding (1973b; chapter 2) is about 14 400 km². In this paper an attempt is made to consider why such a high degree of endemism occurs in a small area.

Statistical data on endemism

Because of the difficulties of understanding different authors' criteria I have restricted my account to taxa that I recognised at the species or higher level (Table 1). Following the examples of Turrill (1929) and Favarger (1972) for Balkan and European mountain floras I have added up the endemic taxa for each archipelago and expressed these as a percentage of the total flora. Because Macaronesian endemics are not confined to one archipelago I have considered them separately. Totals for the whole region are given in the last column. To give some indication of the diverse origins for the endemics I have also included figures for the total number of genera with endemic species, the number of genera endemic to one archipelago, the number of Macaronesian endemic genera and the number of non-Macaronesian genera with endemic species

TABLE 1   Endemic flowering plant species in Macaronesia

	Az	M	S	C	CV	Total
Total number of species in the native flora	760	1135	91	±1800	65	3200
No. of endemics confined to one archipelago	40	92	2	460	92	680
Percentage of endemics	5.2	8.16	2.2	25.5	15	20.4
No. of Macaronesian endemic species	7	50	9	62	16	66
No. of endemic species per genus	1.3	1.4	1.0	3.4	1.8	2.5
Total number of genera with endemic species	31	63	3	134	49	232
No. of endemic genera	0	1	0	17	0	18
No. of Macaronesian genera	4	13	2	13	1	13
No. of non-Macaronesian genera	27	48	1	104	47	220
Area of the islands (km^2)	2304	728	15	7273	4033	14 400

Az, Azores; M, Maderia; S, Salvage I.; C, Canary I.; CV, Cape Verde I.

Sources of data include: the checklist for Macaronesia of Eriksson *et al.* (1974), the checklist and paper of Sunding (1973a, b) and Chevalier's Flora (1935) for the Cape Verde Islands, the checklist of Hansen (1969) for Madeira, the list of Pickering and Hansen (1969) for the Salvage Islands, Bramwell's papers (1972b and 1976) and Bramwell and Bramwell (1974) for the Canary Islands. Corrections from recent monographs, e.g. Humphries (1976a) were used when necessary.

Interpretation of the data

The data are extremely interesting. The Canary Islands are by far the richest islands with 460 endemics representing 25% of the whole flora and about 45% of the native flora. By contrast, and at the other extreme, the Salvage Islands, which are indeed only slightly emergent rocks, harbour a flora of 91 species, only two of which are endemics. Madeira, without a doubt has the richest flora per unit area, but a low percentage of endemics with less than 100 species. The Azores have a small flora of 760 species and an equally small endemic flora of about 40 species representing only about 5·2% of the total. For Macaronesian endemic species the Canaries and Maderia share most of these taxa (see Sunding, chapter 2). The Azorean Macaronesian endemics are those mostly shared by Madeira and the Canaries, but the Cape Verdes group are shared largely by the Canaries (Sunding, 1973b). A consideration of the total number of genera with endemic species in Macaronesia as a whole suggests that no one genus is particularly well represented in the islands. Even in the Canary Islands there are on average only 3·4 species per genus, as compared with 1 or 2 species per genus for the remaining archipelagos and a total of 2·5 species per genus for the whole of Macaronesia. It is quite obvious that nearly all of the endemic species in Macaronesia

TABLE 2   Genera endemic to Macaronesia

	Number of species								
	Az	M	S	C	CV	N	A	Total	
Picconia	1	1		1				2	(*excelsa* M/C)
Bencomia		1		3				4	
Marcetella				1				1	
Dendripoterium		1		1				1	
Argyranthemum	(1)	3	1	18				22	
Aichryson	1	3		11				14	(*villosum* Az/M/C)
Greenovia				4				4	
Monanthes		1	1	16				16	(*brachycaulon* M/S/C)
Sinapidendron		2		2	5			9	
Cedronella	1	1		1				1	
Pleiomeris		1		1				1	
Phyllis		1		2				2	(*nobla* M/C)
Isoplexis		1		3				4	
Visnea		1		1				1	
Chamaemeles		1						1	
Tinguarra				1				1	
Drusa		1		1		1		1	
Gonospermum				4				4	
Schizogyne				2				2	
Allagopappus				2				2	
Heywoodiella				1				1	
Vieraea				1				1	
Sventenia				1				1	
Todaroa				2				2	
Dicheranthus				1				1	
Gesnouinia				1				1	
Neochamaelea				1				1	
Parolinia				3				3	
Ixanthus				1				1	
Spartocytisus				2				2	
Plocama				1				1	
Kunkeliella				2				2	

Key: see Table 4

belong to more widespread genera with continental sister groups in the mainland floras. However, there are 12 genera which are endemic to more than one archipelago in Macaronesia, all of them occurring in the Canaries and Madeira, four in the Azores and only one in the Cape Verde Islands. Of the 18 genera which are restricted to one archipelago all of them are found in the Canary Islands apart from the monotypic *Chamaemeles coriacea* Lindl. from Madeira. A complete list of these are given in Table 2. Some of the more diverse examples include *Argyranthemum* (22 species), *Aichryson* (14 species), *Monanthes* (16 species), *Sinapidendron* (9 species), *Isoplexis* (4 species), *Bencomia* (4 species), *Greenovia* (4 species) and *Gonospermum* (4 species). The remainder are mono- or ditypic. Altogether they account for a total of 110 species, about 14% of the endemic flora and 3.4% of the total flora.

If we consider the diversity of all phanerogamic genera occurring in Macaronesia (Table 3) we see that most of them are represented there by only one or two species and most of them with more than four species per genus occur in the Canary Islands. Amongst the most diverse examples we can cite *Aeonium* with 36 species in the Canaries, Madeira and the Cape Verde Islands, *Sonchus* (incl. *Taeckholmia* and *Babcockia*) with a total 29 species occurring in all of the islands except the Azores, *Echium* with 28 species in the Canaries, Madeira and the Cape Verde Islands and *Lotus* with 27 species widely distributed in all of the island groups.

It seems therefore, that each archipelago represents a distinct centre of diversity. Clearly the Canary Islands are the richest and most diverse group of islands followed by the Cape Verdes, Madeira and the Azores. The Salvage Islands are obviously the least rich. As an interpretation it might be possible to suggest that the largest islands might be the richest in endemics. This is certainly true for Tenerife but it does not explain the fact that some of the small islands, e.g. Gomera, harbour a much richer flora than the much larger islands of Fuerteventura and Lanzarote etc. (Table 4). Secondly, it can be supposed that those islands closest to the

TABLE 3   Generic diversity. Figures in the table refer to the number of genera

	Number of species																	
	1	2	3	4	5	6	7	8	9	10	11	12	14	15	16	18	22	31
Azores	41	4	2		1													
Madeira	51	11	4	4	1	1												
Salvage I.	2																	
Canary I.	67	25	14	10	2	3	2		1	2	1	1	2	2	1	1	2	1
Cape Verde I.	30	10	5		2		1			1								

TABLE 4   Area and diversity

Island		No. of endemic species	Area (km²)
Az	S Santa Maria	22	95
	M São Miguel	47	713
	T Terceira	40	400
	G Graciosa	8	59
	J São Jorge	43	236
	P Pico	43	428
	F Faial	41	166
	L Flores	43	141
	C Corvo	27	192
M	M Maderia	136	730
	D Desertas	26	10
	P Porta Santo	41	56
	S Salvage Islands	20	15
C	L Lanzarote	92	717
	F Fuerteventura	109	1717
	C Gran Canaria	242	1625
	T Tenerife	320	2355
	G Gomera	190	425
	H Hierro	141	307
	P Palma	191	789
Cv	A Sant Antao	75	637
	V São Vincente	45	207
	L Santa Luzia	6	10
	N São Nicolau	49	375
	S Sal	19	206
	B Boa Vista	17	393
	M Maio	8	216
	T São Tiago	46	1026
	F Fogo	45	443
	B Brava	18	55

mainland would be richer in endemics. Here, again the islands of Lanzarote and Fuerteventura, lying closest to the mainland, harbour far fewer endemic species than any of the Canary Islands to the west of them. Thirdly, it is possible to assume that all of the Macaronesian islands are about the same age, or at least have had the same opportunities for colonisation from adjacent continental floras. Thus, the best interpretation for the high levels of endemism which are found in the western Canary Islands as compared with the larger eastern islands and those of comparable size in the Azores and Cape Verdes must be directly related to a greater diversity of microhabitats into which the endemics have migrated or in which they have speciated and can survive, and the stability that these habitats have had over long periods of time.

Ecological diversity

As a measure of the range of niches which might occur in a particular island or archipelago we can briefly summarise the climatic and floristic components which have been discussed by various authors (Ceballos and Ortuño, 1951; Lems, 1960; Bramwell, 1971, 1972b) for the Canary Islands and compare them with data for the other archipelagos (Fig. 1).

The Canary Islands can be divided up into two major phytogeographical units – the eastern islands of Lanzarote and Fuerteventura (including the islets of Lobos and Graciosa) forming one

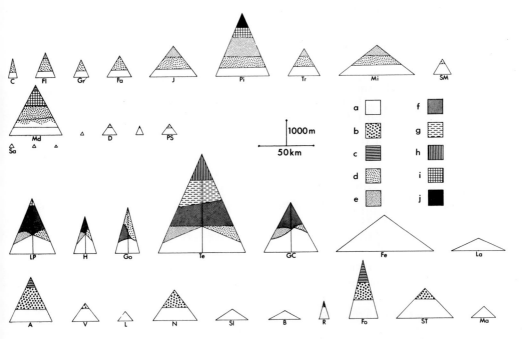

FIG. 1   Schematic representation of ecological diversity in the Macaronesian Islands

Azores: C, Corvo; Fl, Flores; GR, Graciosa; Fa, Faial; J, São Jorge; Pi, Pico; Tr, Terceira; Mi, São Miguel; SM, Santa Maria. *Madeiras*: Md, Maderia; D, Desertas; P, Porto Santo. *Salvage Islands*, Sa. *Canary Islands*: LP, La Palma; H. Hierro; Go, Gomera; Te, Tenerife; GC, Gran Canaria; Fe, Fuerteventura; La, Lanzarote. *Cape Verde Islands*: A, Sant Antao; V, São Vincente; L, Santa Luzia; N, São Nicolau; Sl, Sal; B, Boa Vista; R, Brava; F, Fogo; ST, São Tiago; Ma, Maio.

Key to vegetation zones: a, xerophytic zone; b, *Compositae/Labiatae* scrub zone; grass zone; d, broadleaved forest zone; e, *Juniper* zone; f, pine savannah zone; g, subalpine zone; h, *Viola cheiranthifolia* zone; i, *Erica* zone; j, *Gymnomitrium* zone. *Scale*: horizontal scale, longest distance across the islands; vertical scale, tallest island peak region and the western islands of Gran Canaria, Tenerife, Gomera, Hierro and La Palma forming the other. The two eastern islands have a low elevation (approx. 650 m maximum) and are arid most of the time. Being close to Africa they tend to be influenced by Saharan climatic conditions. The western islands, however, situated between 200 and 360 km from continental North Africa, are far less influenced by the Saharan conditions and enjoy an equable oceanic climate. Their comparatively much higher elevations (3717 m on Tenerife) together with prevailing northerly winds have produced a very wide range of microclimates as indicated by the development of obvious vegetation zones and strong north-south differences. The complete range of conditions occurs on Tenerife which is approximately 80 km in length and 50 km wide. Localities above 1900 m are snow-covered for about 5 months of the year, between November and April. Microphyllous shrubs are the predominant constituent of the vegetation which ultimately gives way to a monospecific Macaro-alpine *Viola cheiranthifolia* zone at about 2700 m. The mountain zone consists mainly of endemic pine savannah, but there are many other communities too. On the northern slopes of the western islands, for example, are found tree heath and evergreen broadleaved forests. The lowland xerophytic zone is very variable in relation to aspect, local topography and position. Extremes include the wet coastal halophyte communities on exposed northern cliffs, the steep sheltered inland cliffs, the dry succulent scrub areas and the very dry exposed coastal flats on east and south facing areas.

The main island of Madeira like the western Canary Islands, is also very much influenced by northern prevailing winds and thus shows a distinct north-south difference. However, because the temperature and humidity differentials are much lower, the vegetation zones, although easily identifiable, show only gradual transitions between one another. On the south of the island between 0 and 300 m is found the coastal halophyte community, and between 300 and 700 m is the lowland xerophytic zone mixed with cloud layer species. At 700 to 1200 m is the evergreen tree heath above which is found the true evergreen forest. Grassland communities occur at about 1850 m. On northerly aspects, by contrast, the cloud belt comes down to 100 m and the heath broadleaf forest down to 300 m. The Desertas and Porto Santo have little more than a lowland xerophytic zone and patches of the mixed zone (Sjögren, 1974).

The Azores are much colder and wetter than any of the southerly archipelagos. Furthermore, they have more or less constant temperatures throughout the year and are covered in cloud most of the time. There is some gradual zonation of the vegetation, like Madeira, but no north-south differential. The pattern is more or less the same for all of the islands, the only real variation due to differences in altitude, varied geological conditions (e.g. acidic ash on São Miguel and limestone on S. Maria) and the forest zones being lower in the wetter western islands. The coastal halophyte communities and lowland xerophytic scrub merge at 100 m into the *Myrica faya* Ait. broadleaved woodland which occurs on most of the islands up to about 500 m. This is replaced at 500 up to 1350 m by the cloud belt *Juniperus brevifolia* (Seub.) Antoine zone and above this the *Calluna/Daboecia* belt (Tutin, 1953; Sjögren, 1973). On Pico, a unique zone dominated by *Gymnomitrium* occurs at the summit.

The vegetated Salvage Islands of Salvagem Grand, Great Piton and Little Piton are little more then emergent rocks up to 150 m with a similar climate to the north-facing xerophytic zone of the western Canary Islands.

By comparison to the four other archipelagos, there appears to be little in the way of vegetation zonation in the Cape Verde Islands. There are no real differences between the montane and coastal habitats in terms of species composition although the dominance of various species changes at different levels. Schmidt (1852), as modified by Chevalier (1935), suggested that four microclimatic layers can be distinguished. All of the islands are subtropical, characterised between sea level and 800 m by various Saharo-Sindian elements such as *Ziziphus mauritianus* (L).) St-Hil. and *Acacia albida* Del., various tropical elements and a few Mediterranean species. Between 800 and 1200 m the islands are characterised by a number of shrubby Compositae, notably species of *Nidorella, Conyza, Odontospermum, Phagnalon* and *Artemisia* together with several woody Labiatae such as *Lavandula* and *Micromeria*: These tend to fade away around 1200 m when the peaks assume a grass-steppe appearance dominated by the tufted grasses *Hyparrhenia hirta* (L.) Stapf. and *Cenchrus ciliaris* L. European elements, e.g. *Epilobium parviflorum* Schreb. and *Brachypodium sylvaticum* (Huds.) P. Beaver, often occur around the wet places in this zone.

Summarising the ecology of the Macaronesian islands, the Azores represent the most uniformly wet and coldest archipelago. Madeira by comparison, is much warmer with gradual transitions between the forest zone and the lower xerophytic zone but differences in precipitation much more marked between the zones. Although there is a north-south differential, the composition of the zones are still relatively uniform all around the island. The Canaries by contrast show extremes both in a north/south and an east/west direction. Cloud belts are restricted to northerly or north-easterly slopes and the southern slopes are more arid. The two eastern islands are like deserts but lush vegetation occurs on the western islands. Furthermore, here we find the widest range of altitudinal zones, with very discrete margins and little overlap between them.

The Cape Verde Islands represent the opposite end of the spectrum to the Azores. They are subtropical, uniformly arid, suffering long periods of drought throughout the year, and show only a slight zonation.

Distribution of endemics and ecological diversity

Ecological diversity to the extent found in the Canary Islands obviously means that there are many particular niches which are very small, frequently found on one island and restricted to one vegetation zone. It

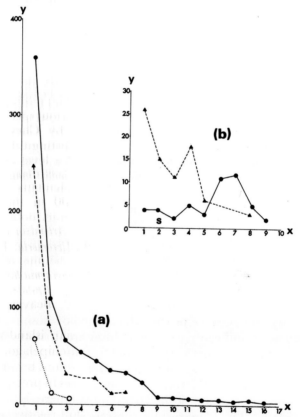

Fig. 2   Distribution patterns of endemics in the Macaronesian archipelagos
(a) ●———●, Combined data for Macaronesia; ▲ – – – ▲, Canary Islands; ○·····○, Madeiran Archipelago. (b) ●———●, Azores; ▲ – – – ▲, Cape Verde Islands; S, Salvage Islands. x-axis, number of islands; y-axis, number of species

would be expected therefore that many of the endemics in the Canaries would be microspecies occurring in small populations in restricted localities. Since there are great ecological extremes in the Canary Islands, even apparently similar habitats on different islands will harbour different resident endemics. It can be seen in Fig. 2 that 47·6% of the endemics for the whole of Macaronesia only occur on one island. Another 15% occur on two islands. The picture is very much the same for the Canary Islands, as would be expected, since they account for two thirds of the endemic element. However, where there is great uniformity from one island to the next, the number of different available niches is low, the same niche is repeated on different islands, and the number of endemics is low. This is exemplified by the Azores and the Cape Verde Islands (Fig. 2b). In the Azores there is a much lower number of endemics than in the Canaries, 60% of them occur on six or more of the islands, and they are invariably associated with the more widespread habitats such as broadleaved woodland and lowland scrub. It is possible to predict then that the genera which have radiated into many different habitats should reflect the first pattern. Table 5 illustrates the picture for four of the better known Macaronesian genera – *Argyranthemum, Sonchus, Echium* and *Aeonium.* More widespread genera of the Canary Islands which have an obligate ecology and have not radiated into widely differing habitats show slighter differences between related species and those which occur in uniform habitats occur on several of the islands. An example here, might include the vicariant endemics of *Centaurea* section *Cheirolophus* which are generally restricted to the basalt cliffs of the lower xerophytic zone in the western Canaries. By contrast, most Azorean endemics occur on six or more islands and Cape Verdes have a peak around four islands as a result of habitat uniformity depending on which vegetation zone they are likely to occur. Typical examples here might include *Daboecia azorica* Tutin & Warb. and *Spergularia azorica* (Kindb.) Lebel of the forest zone and lower xerophytic zone respectively.

TABLE 5   Species distribution in four adaptively radiated genera

Genus	Islands	Az	M	S	P	H	G	T	C	F	L	CV
					Number of species							
Argyranthemum		(1)	3	1	3	3	3	8	5	1	1	
Sonchus			3		5	4	5	11	8	2	2	2
Echium			2		5	3	4	9	6	2		3
Aeonium			3		7	4	9	12	6	1	2	2

Key: see Table 4

All of these results are best interpreted to mean that ecological isolation is the dominant selective force in Macaronesia and eco-geographical speciation the prevailing evolutionary situation in the flowering plants.

Evolution of the endemic flora

Stebbins and Major (1965) were able to conclude that the principal speciation processes in flowering plants are:

(*i*) Gradual divergence of previously similar populations, associated either with diversifications and breaking up of previously continuous, homogeneous habitats, or with migration from one area to a neighbouring one with somewhat the same or radically different ecological conditions.

(*ii*) Sudden differentiation of a population with respect to morphology and particularly in respect to chromosomal repatterning, with consequent reproductive isolation.

(*iii*) Hybridisation between related, previously isolated populations followed by introgression, polyploidy or both.

Detailed explicit phylogenies and data on the actual processes of evolution in Macaronesian endemics are extremely scarce. However, because of the number of chromosome-number papers available, it is possible to make some comments on the evolutionary origins of Macaronesian endemics by applying the somewhat artificial system of Favarger and Contandriopoulos (1961) which classifies an endemic in terms of its sister-group relationship. This was previously undertaken by Bramwell *et al.* (1972) and Bramwell (1976) and the main conclusions to be reached then were that the Macaronesian Islands contain mostly schizo- and palaeoendemics with only a handful of patro- or apoendemics. In fact, out of 350 species which I have looked at myself, 90% of the endemic flora appears to have evolved by gradual speciation (schizoendemism) and the rest by abrupt speciation involving polyploidy and chromosomal repatterning. There are no convincing examples of patroendemics but several good examples of apoendemism.

There are two points about diploids and polyploids which need further consideration here. Firstly, it is wrong to assume that because the Macaronesian flora is apparently rich in diploid taxa that it is relictual. Undeniably, judging from Liv Borgen's 1977 estimate (chapter 16) of 24·4% polyploidy for the endemic flora there are a considerable number of diploids as compared to surrounding areas. All this seems really to mean is that gradual evolution has mainly proceeded at the diploid level. Secondly, as Borgen (1969) pointed out, polyploids are equitably dispersed amongst the apparently relictual groups (palaeopolyploids) as much as they are in the derivative taxa (meso-neopolyploids). Thus, we find in the oft quoted palaeopolyploid genera *Isoplexis, Bencomia, Bystropogon, Cytisus* and *Scrophularia*, that the polyploid event is an old one and those genera with more than one Macaronesian endemic have gradually speciated in the islands. For example, *Isoplexis* with $2n = 56$ (12x) chromosomes must be considered to be a palaeopolyploid since the base number for the Scrophulariaceae is 7 (Borgen, 1969). However, since its sister group, the European genus *Digitalis*, mostly has the chromosome number of $2n = 56$, but incidentally also 112, the polyploid event is an old one and the four Macaronesian species have all arisen by gradual speciation.

As seen in Table 3 many single endemics have arisen "passively" through isolation. Quite clearly those species with remote or undefinable sister-group relationships can represent either relicts or derivative taxa. Others with well-defined but disjunct sister groups of the east and west Mediterranean countries, South and East Africa, Asia and America, must be considered relict derivatives of formerly wider distribution. These have been discussed at length by Bramwell (1972b, 1976). Bramwell and Richardson (1973) and Sunding (1973; chapter 2) when concerning themselves with the origin of Macaronesian flora so will not be discussed here. It is obvious at the same time though, that a number of the single endemics have evolved as a result of more recent migrations from predominantly Mediterranean stock. Most of the ditypic and widely elaborated genera are monophyletic groups which have diversified within the islands. This has largely come about as a process of gradual speciation conforming to Stebbins and Major's (1965) first type of "gradual divergence . . . by migration from one area to a neighbouring one with somewhat the same or radically different ecological conditions". The most spectacular examples are those which have adaptively radiated into a wide range of habitats. There are also a few exceptional examples of apoendemism by abrupt speciation involving polyploidy and chromosomal repatterning which will be considered separately.

Gradual speciation: adaptive radiation   The most fruitful lines of evidence to demonstrate the process of adaptive radiation by gradual speciation come from consideration of: (*a*) changes in morphology on a gross scale and at the population level; (*b*) cytology of natural populations; (*c*) cytogenetics of artificial hybrids and analysis of natural hybrids.

Morphological changes associated with evolution in the islands and details of relationships based on gross structural changes have only been described in any detail in *Aeonium* (Lems, 1960), *Echium* (Bramwell, 1972a, 1975; Lems and Holzapfel, 1968), *Sonchus* (Bramwell, 1972b) and

G

Argyranthemum (Humphries, 1973; 1976a, b). Chromosome numbers are available for a good half of the endemics but detailed karyotypes are known in only a few genera. There have been quite a number of reports of natural hybrids in Macaronesian genera but detailed studies on natural and artificial hybrids are only available for *Echium* (Bramwell, 1973), *Argyranthemum* (Humphries, 1976b; Borgen, 1976) and *Lavandula* (Murphy, pers. comm.)

(*a*) *Morphology and adaptive radiation* As we have already seen, greatest areas of species diversity are associated with areas of greatest ecological diversity. So too, in the genera mentioned above, the most spectacular changes in morphology occur in such features as habit and leaf morphology in areas of greatest ecological diversity. Data to support natural selection of adaptive phenotypes is provided by examples of convergent morphology in species of different genera occurring in similar habitats and parallel morphology in species of the same genus occupying habitats of similar ecological amplitude. To explain regional responses to natural selection in Macaronesia the results obtained for *Argyranthemum* (Humphries, 1976b) are given in Fig. 3. The "shrubbiest" member of the genus is *A. broussonetii* (Pers.) Humphries (A), a species from the broadleaved forests of Tenerife and Gomera, which can in some instances attain a diameter of 6 m and a height of 2 m. The bipinnatifid, shortly petiolate or subsessile leaves are of a very unreduced type. These are similar to other shade or forest species, e.g. *A. adauctum* ssp. *jacobaeifolium* (Schulz Bip.) Humphries (A2) and *A. pinnatifidum* (L. fil.) Lowe (A3) from Madeira. A number of adaptive trends can be distinguished from these. In south-facing lowland arid environments reduction in lignification, habit, capitulum size and leaf area produces forms of the B and C type, such as *A. frutescens* ssp. *gracilescens* (Christ) Humphries (C2) and *A. gracile* Schultz Bip. (C3) on Tenerife and *A. filifolium* (Schultz Bip.) Humphries (C1) on Gran Canaria. Plants of very xeric conditions discontinue growth after shedding seed at the end of the spring and remain fairly inactive in the hot summer months. The most extreme condition of this type is found in *A. filifolium*, a species often consisting of a single slender unbranched stem up to about 1 m in height with trifid pinnatisect, filiform leaves and extremely narrow capitula.

A reduction trend also occurs in taxa of subalpine and high montane environments (type D). Here, *A. tenerifae* Humphries and *A. adauctum* ssp. *dugourii* (Bolle) Humphries are unable to grow for up to 5 months of the year owing to persistent snow cover in the Cañadas region of Tenerife. Old shoots die down after flowering at the end of the year and new ones are produced each year from low lying stems which are only woody at their bases. The leaves of these species are again highly dissected and they

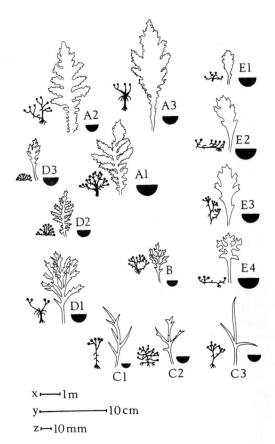

x ⊢—⊣ 1 m

y ⊢————————⊣ 10 cm

z ⊢—⊣ 10 mm

FIG. 3   Adaptive trends in leaf shape, habit and capitulum diameter in *Argyranthemum*

Species	Ecology
A1 *A. broussonetii*	Sheltered, warm wet forest
A2 *A. adauctum* ssp. *jacobaeifolium*	
A3 *A. pinnatifidum* ssp. *pinnatifidum*	
B *A. frutescens* ssp. *frutescens*	Xerophytic zone
C1 *A. filifolium*	
C2 *A. frutescens* ssp. *gracilescens*	Arid, south facing slopes of xerophytic zone
C3 *A. gracile*	
D1 *A. foeniculaceum*	Low montane (xerophytic zone) in sheltered ladera.
D2 *A. adauctum* ssp. *adauctum*	Arid, high montane regions
D3 *A. tenerifae*	Submacaro-alpine zone
E1 *A. pinnatifidum* ssp. *succulentum*	Halophytic coastal cliffs of the north facing
E2 *A. coronopifolium*	slopes of the xerophytic zone
E3 *A. maderense*	
E4 *A. frutescens* ssp. *succulentum*	

Scales: x, plant height/width; y, leaf length/width; z, capitulum diameter tend to have increased hairiness at the higher altitudes. The flowers are moderately small and the plants set seed in a matter of four or five months.

In exposed north coastal areas of the Canary Islands plants of type E with a reduced habit, pinnatilobed or pinnatifid leaves and increased succulence, large capitula, and reduced inflorescences can be found. Characteristic species of this type include *A. coronopifolium* (Willd.) Humphries, *A. frutescens* ssp. *canariae* (Christ) Humphries and ssp. *succulentum* Humphries, and *A. maderense* (D. Don) Humphries. In very exposed places the stems can be very short or procumbent and adpressed to the substrate. Taxa from similar environments in different localities on one or more islands develop similar morphological adaptations. For example, the spectacular *A. broussonetii* of the laurel forests of Tenerife and Gomera is replaced in the laurel forest of La Palma by its most closely related but nevertheless quite, distinct species *A. webbii* Schultz Bip. Similarly, *A. adauctum* (Link) Humphries is the dominant species of montane habitats of Gran Canaria, Tenerife and Hierro. Despite its great variability in form it is replaced in similar habitats on La Palma by *A. haouarytheum* Bramwell & Humphries and on Gomera by the montane endemic, *A. callichrysum* (Svent.) Humphries.

Species of *Argyranthemum* sect. *Monoptera* are very distinct from all other sections of the genus but it is quite clear that *A. filifolium* from the lowland xeric *Euphorbia* scrub of Gran Canaria has a convergent morphology with *A. frutescens* ssp. *gracilescens* and *A. gracile* from comparable arid environments on Tenerife. Similarly, south-slope upland ecotype specimens of *A. adauctum* ssp. *dugourii* from Tenerife have frequently been named as the subalpine *A. tenerifae* on the basis of convergent vegetative morphology when in fact both species are quite distinct when flowers and fruits are observed.

Other convergent pairs include the Grand Salvage coastal species *A. thalassophilum* (Svent.) Humphries and *A. frutescens* (L.) Schultz Bip. ssp. *frutescens* on Tenerife and Gran Canaria, which are superficially very similar; *A. winteri* from the Handia mountains of Fuerteventura, and *A. lidii* Humphries from the west facing cliffs of the Tamadaba Massif on Gran Canaria.

Since parallel and convergent trends occur in different taxa occupying similar habitats it follows that allopatric species occurring in habitats of narrow ecological amplitude will resemble one another. It is considered, therefore, that the minor differences which occur in the "super species" groups of *Centaurea* section *Cheirolophus* and the *Sonchus radicatus* Ait. complex probably reflect slight edaphic and microclimatological differences rather than being divergence as a result of genetic drift (Bramwell, 1972b).

Although each adaptively radiated group looks superficially very diverse the constituent species do not differ as fundamentally from one another as they do from continental sister groups. *Argyranthemum*, for example, is one of the most distinctive Old World genera of the Compositae tribe Anthemideae, being closely allied to the Mediterranean sister-group annuals of *Chrysanthemum* and *Heteranthemis*. These three taxa can be distinguished from all other members of the *Chrysanthemum* complex by the joint possession of heteromorphic cypselas with thick unmodified pericarp walls, particularly in those of the ray florets. All species of *Argyranthemum* from a monophyletic assemblage distinct from the sister group by their perennial habit, their unique bisporic embryo-sac development (Harling, 1951; Borgen, 1972) as well as their flavonoid and enzyme biochemistry (Greger, 1969; Krisper and Puff, 1976). Other adaptively radiated groups studied so far have been found to be monophyletic whether they be endemic genera or endemic sections of much wider genera as demonstrated in *Aeonium* (Lems, 1960) and *Echium* (Bramwell, 1972a).

(*b*)   *Cytology*   Over the last few years there has been a considerable number of papers on the chromosome numbers of Macaronesian and particularly Canary Islands flowering plants (Borgen, 1969, 1970, 1974, 1975; Bramwell *et al.*, 1971, 1972, 1976; Bramwell and Murray, 1972; Gagnieu *et al.*, 1973; Larsen, 1958, 1960, 1962; Michaelis, 1964; Van Loon, 1974). The most salient point to emerge from these papers is that adaptively radiated groups all show the same chromosome number. Critical karyotype studies however are much scarcer although the karyotypes appear to be remarkably uniform in the different species of such groups as *Argyranthemum* (Humphries, 1975), *Echium* (Bramwell, 1973), *Sonchus* (Roux and Boulos, 1972) and *Gonospermum* (Humphries, unpub.).

Observations on meiosis of natural populations and hybrids provide some more definitive generalisations about speciation in adaptively radiated groups. A survey of chiasma-frequency variation in natural populations of *Argyranthemum* (Humphries, 1975) indicated that there was a wider range of significantly different chiasma frequencies for populations for widespread endemics than narrowly restricted ones. Such variation is due to genetical control of individual variability. Pioneer populations of widespread species and isolated populations of narrow endemics such as *A. filifolium* (Schultz Bip.) Humphries and *A. lidii* Humphries tend to have a high chiasma frequency and hence increased chances of recombination. Large populations of variable species, e.g. *A. adauctum* and *A. frutescens* were observed to have a much lower chiasma frequency and in some cases even reciprocal translocations between non-homologous chromosomes, indicating a restriction in recombination.

　　　　　　　　　　　　　　　　　　　　　C. J. HUMPHRIES

The high chiasma frequencies of the pioneer or specialised endemic is interpreted as being due to depleted variability in relatively homozygous populations. Inversely, the low chiasma frequencies and structural changes of the more widespread species are probably conservation mechanisms for adaptive and relatively heterozygous genotypes. Such differences provide a very effective genetic control of variability in highly adaptable natural populations in closely related species of a similar genomic constitution.

(c) *Cytogenetics and hybrids*　　Hard evidence on the nature of speciation can only come from detailed crossing studies. The only hybrids of Macaronesian phanerogamic endemics to have been studied so far are all within genera of the Compositae; *Argyranthemum*, *Sventenia*, *Sonchus*, *Gonospermum* and *Lugoa*. Pairing behaviour at meiosis in F_1 hybrids in all of these genera including two apparently intergeneric hybrids *Sventenia bupleuroides* Font Quer × *Sonchus leptocephalus* Cass. (× *Sonchustenia decipiens* Svent.) (Perez de Paz, 1976) and *Gonospermum canariense* Less. × *Lugoa revoluta* DC. (Humphries, unpublished) was invariably normal.

The results for *Argyranthemum* can be considered in more detail and are shown in Fig. 4. These can be considered in the four categories of: (*i*) crossability in terms of fruit set; (*ii*) hybrid morphology; (*iii*) pollen fertility; (*iv*) meiosis.

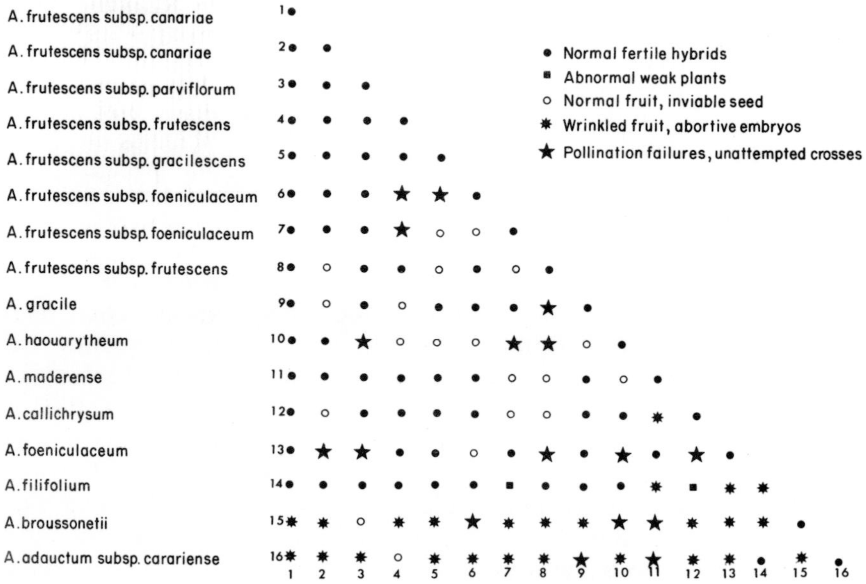

A. frutescens subsp. canariae　　1

A. frutescens subsp. canariae　　2

A. frutescens subsp. parviflorum　　3

A. frutescens subsp. frutescens　　4

A. frutescens subsp. gracilescens　　5

A. frutescens subsp. foeniculaceum　　6

A. frutescens subsp. foeniculaceum　　7

A. frutescens subsp. frutescens　　8

A. gracile　　9

A. haouarytheum　　10

A. maderense　　11

A. callichrysum　　12

A. foeniculaceum　　13

A. filifolium　　14

A. broussonetii　　15

A. adauctum subsp. carariense　　16

● Normal fertile hybrids
■ Abnormal weak plants
○ Normal fruit, inviable seed
✴ Wrinkled fruit, abortive embryos
★ Pollination failures, unattempted crosses

FIG. 4　Crossing relationships between Canary Island species of *Argyranthemum* (*i*) Wrinkled, abortive cypselas containing non-viable embryos were invariably produced in the crosses between *Argyranthemum* and other genera of the Anthemideae (e.g. *Chrysanthemum*) and also between *A. broussonetii* and species of sect. *Argyranthemum*, sect. *Preauxia* and sect. *Monoptera*. Other crosses involving intra- and interspecific hybridisations in sect. *Argyranthemum* together with intersectional crosses involving *A. coronopifolium* of sect. *Sphenismelia*, *A. filifolium* of sect. *Monoptera* and *A. adauctum* of sect. *Preauxia* showed little evidence of barriers to gene exchange. The apparently random failures that did occur and the overall reduction of cypsela production were considered to be the result of unsuccessful pollinations rather than due to disharmonious interactions.

(*ii*) Hybrid morphology and vitality. In nearly all cases of successful crosses the hybrids developed as normal plants of intermediate morphology between the parents. However, in some F_1 crosses e.g. *A. frutescens* ssp. *foeniculaceum* (Pitard & Proust) Humphries × *filifolium* and *A. filifolium* × *callichrysum* chlorotic and dwarf individuals were produced. Similar individuals were obtained in F_2 generations of the hybrids *A. maderense* × *foeniculaceum*. In reciprocal F_1 hybrids between *A. filifolium* × *adauctum* ssp. *canariense*, Borgen (1976) observed that the cypselas usually looked like the maternal parent. One F_1 plant raised from the cross *A. frutescens* ssp. *frutescens* × *callichrysum* produced abnormal capitula without florets, although the reciprocal was normal.

(*iii*) Pollen fertility. Parental plants had a pollen stainability (in 0·3% cotton blue in lactophenol) between 98 and 100%. Vigorous hybrids produced similar results. The lowest figures of about 60% recorded were in F_2 and later generation hybrids of *A. frutescens* × *coronopifolium* and *A. filifolium* × *adauctum* ssp. *canariense*. Such results indicate considerable genetic affinity.

(*iv*) Meiosis in F_1 and F_2 hybrids. As with parental populations nine bivalents were invariably found in all fertile hybrids. The only measurable variation seen to occur was a slight depression in overall chiasma frequency when compared to parental populations (see Humphries, 1975). This suggests either that minor cryptic cytological differences exist between different populations, or more likely that there is increased heterozygosity and varying degrees of genic imbalance between parental genomes, causing some overall effect on meiotic pairing.

In the genus *Argyranthemum* there seem to be only two examples of natural hybridisation. Hybrids between the two species *A. coronopifolium* and *A. frutescens* hybrids have developed on Tenerife at the Teno peninsula since the formation of scree-slopes from material produced by tunnelling activities through the cliffs connecting the Teno promontory with the Buenavista region (Humphries, 1976b). The hybrid population has developed since the construction of the tunnel in 1965 (and it is significant that no pre-1965 specimens of it exist). Although restricted entirely to the disturbed scree-slope for about 6 years and found directly between the two parental populations, the cliff population of *A. coronopifolium* and the coastal population of *A. frutescens*, the hybrid now seems to be spreading along the roadside. Introgression of *frutescens* genes has occurred to such an extent that the former species has almost disappeared in the pure form. Examination of meiosis in bud samples collected from the field shows that all of the naturally occurring hybrids are diploid (2n = 18) with apparently normal pairing. However, in root tips from cultivated plants raised from wild hybrid cypselas, the range of somatic mitotic chromosome numbers varied between 2n = 18 and 2n = 36 (Humphries, 1975. 1976b). Pairing at meiosis in these individuals showed a large number of trivalents and an equal number of bivalents and univalents, suggesting considerable genome homology between the parents. Absence of aneuploids in natural populations suggests that even in disturbed habitats selection pressures are still very strong and sufficient to eliminate such plants.

A somewhat similar situation between two Gran Canarian species has been observed by Liv Borgen (1976). The two parents. *A. adauctum* ssp. *canariense* and *A. filifolium* belong to the two sections *Preauxia* and *Monoptera* respectively.

The two species are remarkably distinct from one another in morphology, distribution and ecology. Among the most conspicuous features, *A. adauctum* ssp. *canariense* is an upland montane shrub with large woody stems, densely pubescent to tomentose tripinnatifid leaves with about 20 primary lobes. *A. filifolium* by contrast is a slender, virtually herbaceous lowland xerophytic scrub species with glabrous filiform leaves with always less than 10 primary lobes.

A. adauctum ssp. *canariense* occurs in the moister habitats of Gran Canaria ranging from Tafira Alta in the east to Cruz de Tejeda in the montane region. *A. filiform* is restricted to southwestern coast of Gran Canaria from Maspalomas to Puerto de Mogán. A large hybrid swarm occurs at Mogán at the edges of the range of both species and the area of hybridisation looks as though it is restricted to a region affected by grazing activity. As with the other natural hybrids the parental species seem to be perfectly interfertile with completely viable fertile hybrids exhibiting normal pairing at meiosis. Pollen fertility was extremely high and similar to the parents. There seems to be some introgression of *adauctum* genes into *filifolium* and Borgen (1976) indicates that there is considerable evidence here to suggest that other plants collected in western Gran Canaria known as *A. escarrei* (Svent.) Humphries may in fact represent the only worked out example of a stabilised natural hybrid within an adaptively radiated group.

The significance of hybridisation: Natural hybridisation in other genera. From the limited experimental work available it is possible to suggest that species swarms which have evolved in Macaronesia are essentially interfertile. Casual observations on their breeding systems e.g. gynomonoecy in *Argyranthemum* (Humphries, 1973), gynodioecy in *Echium* (Bramwell, 1973) suggest too that they are mostly outbreeders. This view is backed up considerably by a number of anecdotal accounts from the literature, so one might ask what significance does hybridisation have as regards evolution in the Macaronesian region?

Thirty-three hybrid combinations in twenty-five species of *Aeonium* and *Greenovia*, its close ally, have been recorded by various authors (Voggenreiter, 1974; Praeger, 1929, 1932; Kunkel, 1972). Hybrids occur in 3 of the 4 sections in the genus, namely sects. *Canariensia*, *Goochia* and *Urbica*, (but not *Holochrysa*) and between these sections and two species in the closely allied genus, *Greenovia*. The hybrids *A. simisii* (Sw.) Stearn × *canariense* (L.) Webb & Berth. and *A. simsii* (Sw.) Stearn × *spathulatum* (Hornem.) Praeger are of garden origin but the remainder are from genuine field records. There are no experimental studies on these hybrids. Nevertheless, all of them seem to be one-off events, as they are extremely rare and only ever occur in intermediate habitats between adjacent parents (Lems, 1960). They all seem to be unstable hybrids, suggesting recent origin, and there seem to be few really suitable habitats for their expansion. The morphological distinctiveness of all the described species would suggest that there is no convincing evidence to suggest that hybridisation has played a major role in the evolution of this group.

Unstable hybrids of recent origin occur in various different groups. The hybrid between *Micromeria benthamii* Webb & Berth. and *M. pineolens* Svent. for example is very common in the *Pinus canariensis* Chr. Sm. ex D.C. forest in the region of Tamadaba on Gran Canaria. Similarly, Bramwell (1973) reported hybridisation in *Echium* between *E. brevirame* Sprague & Hutch. and *E. webbii* Coincy along the canal margin and mule tracks of Bco. de los Angustias on La Palma. Because of a high degree of male sterility in this hybrid, introgression to both parental species has taken place.

In *Lavandula* and *Adenocarpus* a number of relatively stable hybrids have been detected. On Tenerife, *Lavandula canariensis* Miller frequently hybridises with *L. pinnata* L. fil. particularly in the region south of the Anaga peninsula. The hybrids in this area mostly resemble F_1 or F_2 crosses without any real introgression between the parents. However,

G*

Paul Murphy (pers. comm.) has demonstrated that "pure" *pinnata* only seems to occur on the Teno peninsula in the west of the island and the natural populations seem to accumulate "*canariensis*" characteristics in an easterly direction towards the Anaga peninsula suggesting an old hybridisation event and the stabilisation of the hybrid variants. Lems (1958) has studied the two sister species *Adenocarpus foliolosus* (Ait.) DC. and *A. viscosus* (Willd.) Webb & Berth. in considerable detail. *A. foliolosus* is a lower montane species of Tenerife, Gomera and La Palma, whereas *A. viscosus* is a subalpine species from the Cañadas region of Tenerife. *A. foliolosus* appears to extend into the pine forest between the two species on Tenerife but the variability of these populations is due to introgression from *A. viscosus* and they seem to be clearly associated with ancient deforestation activities of the endemic pine.

It seems then that in most genera hybridisation can readily occur as evidenced by the few examples of natural populations which have been demonstrated to be of hybrid origin, but these seem always to be associated with disturbed habitats. It is obvious too from the presence of hybrids that pollen transfer must be operative in many quite widely separated allopatric outbreeding populations. However, stabilised hybrids are still very rare in the Macaronesian flora and it seems that ecological differentiation sufficiently maintains species integrity in most groups and hybridisation has played only a minor role in the formation of species.

Abrupt speciation: apoendemism   Genuine examples of abrupt speciation are rather scarce. The most obvious examples of apoendemism are found in the genera *Asparagus*, *Lotus* and *Forsskoalea* and in the infraspecific polyploids of *Adenocarpus foliolosus* and *Reseda crystallina* Webb & Berth.

Chromosome counts on *Lotus* section *Pedrosia* show that seven out of the eighteen species studied (Ortega, 1976) from a total of twenty-five are tetraploids ($2n = 4x = 28$). Despite the fact that all other perennial *Lotus* groups contain diploid and tetraploid species (Bolkovskikh *et al.*, 1969) with a base number of $x = 7$, the Macaronesian species do seem to constitute a monophyletic group, meaning that the tetraploids have arisen autochthonously within the islands. The genus ranges throughout most of the vegetation zones particularly within the Canary Islands. However, all of the polyploids occur in the xerophytic zone and apart from *L. mascaensis* Burch., the endemic of the Masca valley on Tenerife, all tetraploid populations have been found in coastal habitats.

The small shrubs and perennial herbs of the predominantly N. African genus *Forsskaolea* (Urticaceae) provide a straighforward example of apoendemism in the Cape Verde Islands. *F. angustifolia* Retz. common to the lowland dry areas on all the Canary Islands and *F. tenacissima* L. from the Sahara region (Reese, 1957) have shown to have 2n = 22 chromosomes. Populations from the dryer parts of São Vicente and Sant Antao of *F. procridifolia* Webb however have been shown to have 44 chromosomes (Borgen, 1975). The distinctive morphology of this species seems to indicate that it probably represents an old antopolyploid.

The most common chromosome number in *Asparagus* is 2n = 20 for North African and Mediterranean species. However, the tetraploid number (2n = 40) (Borgen, 1969) has been recorded for *A. pastorianus* Webb & Berth., a scrambling shrub from the coastal and xerophytic regions of Tenerife, Gran Canaria and Gomera, and a hexaploid count (2n = 60) (Bramwell *et al.*, 1976) has been recorded for *A. nesiotes* Svent., a narrow, obviously coastal endemic from the Salvage Islands.

Intraspecific polyploidy has been demonstrated by Bramwell *et al.* (1976) to occur in *Adenocarpus foliolosus*, an erect, leafy aggressive coloniser of sub-climax communities in woodlands throughout Gran Canaria, Tenerife and Gomera. Populations with chromosome numbers of 2n = 26 and 52 have been reported. A similar phenomenon seems to occur in the polymorphic annual or perennial therophyte, *Reseda crystallina* Webb & Berth. which occurs on the coasts of the eastern Canary Islands. In *Reseda* section *Resedastrum* the diploid number is normally 2n = 12, but in this species Bramwell *et al.* (1972) found the octoploid, 2n = 48, and Borgen (1974) the tetraploid, 2n = 24, both from Fuerteventura.

In all of these examples, the higher polyploid species occupy distinctly allopatric habitats away from related and putatively parental lower-ploid taxa. There seems to be no obvious correlation, therefore, between polyploidy and species isolation. What is more likely is that the higher polyploids extend the range of diploid species in the seemingly more severe conditions or confer advantage to colonizing species in unstable and changing habits, typical of the "breakdown" communities. However, several actively epibiotic groups such as *Aeonium, Aichryson, Monanthes* and *Descurainia* contain a low frequency of polyploid species which have no appreciably different distribution patterns to their diploid relatives.

Discussion

On the basis of the evidence presented above, the endemic element of the Macaronesian phanerogamic flora constitutes about one quarter of the native flora. It is obvious from the large number of genera within the islands that many groups have only one or two Macaronesian endemics, which originated from a well diversified continental flora. Several of these belong to genera with unusual disjunct distributions, which indicates that the Macaronesian region contains a number of palaeoendemics which must have migrated in the Tertiary or late Cretaceous period (Sunding, chapter 2). However, several also belong to uniquely distinctive, monotypic genera with only remote affinities to continental sister groups which may or may not be primitive. The retention of plesiomorphous features, i.e. ancestral morphological attributes and the same chromosome numbers as sister groups, together with the fact that many are taxonomically isolated are rather dubious lines of evidence on which to estimate the age of species. Most groups in fact have diverged since their original Tertiary migration into the Macaronesian islands, and the fact that many possess synapomorphic features (uniquely derived attributes) shared by sister groups is indicative of a monophyletic origin from a single island ancestor. Logically, monophyletic Macaronesian groups with more than one species in the islands can only be of equivalent age to their sister groups. The generic pair *Digitalis* and *Isoplexis* serve to illustrate the point.

The distribution and morphological variation of endemics is so intimately associated with areas of habitat diversity that eco-geographical isolation has been the most important selective force in divergence. The fact that many genera have a low number of species is indicative that many groups have a narrow ecological preference and cannot adapt to widely different habitats. Those notably few groups with a large number of species have generally adaptively radiated into a wide range of different conditions.

The cytological and limited cytogenetic data available together with information on the fundamental morphological coherence of more widespread Macaronesian endemic groups indicates that evolution in the large and small groups has proceeded mostly by gradual speciation. In *Argyranthemum* (and this also seems to be true for those groups which form natural hybrids) differences within and between species result from genic changes rather than from major chromosomal reorganisation. Should there have been even minor structural chromosome differences, such as inversions or translocations, there would be considerable decrease in pollen fertility. The high fertility of species hybrids in *Argyranthemum*, *Lavandula*, *Gonospermum*, *Sonchus* and *Aeonium* and generic hybrids between *Aeonium* and *Greenovia*, and *Lugoa* and *Gonospermum* endorses the considerable chromosomal homology which occurs in closely related groups of species. Since radiation can be defined as the dispersal and isolation of a group into a variety of different or similar habitats, and in our case often over short distances, it is important to consider how speciation comes about. It is McArthur and Wilson's thesis (1967) that towards the periphery of the dispersal range in an organism speciation and change into new autochthonous endemics readily occurs. Bramwell (1975) suggests that this definition parallels Grant's (1971) definition of quantum speciation, which is described as "the budding-off" of a new, different daughter species from a semi-isolated peripheral population of a parental species. This has been amply demonstrated in the California Flora in *Clarkia, Gilia* and several other genera. These groups are predominantly annual, having diploid endemic species that are morphologically very similar to neighbouring, more widespread diploid species which occupy similar habitats. Hybridisation is rarely involved in speciation and in most cases the endemics have evolved by chromosomal re-organisation. In fact hybrids are rare and when formed are very infertile. Quantum speciation is primarily associated with rapidly changing habitats as in areas of periodic or exceptional drought in ecologically marginal sites (Lewis, 1972). Most Macaronesian groups by contrast have clearly evolved without major chromosomal change. Furthermore, the populations of many widely dispersed groups are small of similar size, and more widespread species exhibit stepped clinal patterns (Humphries, 1976a).

The key for gradual speciation to have occurred in Macaronesia lies in two ecological features of importance: diversity and stability (Lems, 1960). It is ecological diversity, the steep ecological gradients between habitats and the isolation of habitats which provides the fabric for radiation or vicariance phenomena. It is the stability of the island habitats ensured by the oceanic climate which then preserves the endemic. Stebbins and Major (1965) concluded for the California Flora that regions with ample moisture or regions with marked aridity are likely to be relatively stable and harbour the (older?) endemics. On the borderlines between these two extremes even small climatic shifts move the local conditions beyond the tolerance of resident species. In times of rapid fluctuation, rapid speciation must follow. In the Macaronesian region the only abrupt or major shifts in habitat conditions have been caused by volcanic eruptions. However, these are and have been extremely localised and have not taken place wholesale at any one time. Obviously there must have been and still must be periods of readjustment and colonisation but not frequent fluctuations as encountered in California. There have been major climatic changes in Macaronesia but only as a gradual drying out since the Tertiary. Thus, the Macaronesian habitats are on the whole discrete, stable and generally small with sharp distinctions between them, particularly when on different islands and in vegetation zones.

The widespread, adaptively radiated groups such as *Aeonium*, *Argyranthemum* and *Sonchus* exhibit considerable plasticity so as to be able to occupy this wide range of habitats. Although this implies the need for variability, the general absence of heterozygous hybrids in undisturbed habitats, despite obvious gene transfer, is further support for the importance of ecological stability for the evolution of adaptive radiants and the relative homozygosity of well adapted species. That many taxa are potentially infertile outbreeders suggests too that stabilising selection in steep ecological gradients has played a major part and internal pre-zygotic isolating factors only a minor role in keeping species apart.

Those genera which have diverged in a limited range of habitats usually have a lower number of vicariant species. Gradual speciation has essentially been the same for such genera as *Crambe* and *Centaurea* which occur in relatively uniform habitats as for adaptively radiated genera but without the spectacular changes associated with those groups. Those species which occur in unstable or disturbed habitats have undergone some degree of disruptive selection by polyploidy and chromosomal repatterning.

Acknowledgements

I would like to thank the Cabildo Insular de Las Palmas for contributing towards the expenses of my participation in the symposium. My thanks are also due to Bob Press for drawing the figures, to Peter York for photographing them and to Marilyn Humphries for typing the manuscript.

REFERENCES

Bolkovskikh, Z., Grif, V., Matvejera, T. and Zakharyeva, O. (1969). *Chromosome Numbers of Flowering Plants*. 926p. Komorov Botanical Institute, Leningrad

Borgen, L. (1969). Chromosome numbers of vascular plants from the Canary Islands with special reference to the occurrence of polyploidy. *Nytt. Mag. Bot.* **16**, 81–121

— (1970). Chromosome numbers of Macaronesian flowering plants. *Nytt. Mag. Bot.* **17**, 145–161

— (1972). Embryology and achene morphology in endemic Canarian species of *Chrysanthemum* L. Hoffm., subgenus *Argyranthemum* (Webb) Harling (Asteraceae). *Norw. J. Bot.* **19**, 149–170

— (1974). Chromosome numbers of Macaronesian flowering plants 11. *Norw. J. Bot.* **21**, 195–210

— (1975). Chromosome numbers of vascular plants from Macaronesia. *Norw. J. Bot.* **22**, 71–76

— (1976) Analysis of a hybrid swarm between *Argyranthemum adauctum* and *A. filifolium* in the Canary Islands. *Norw. J. Bot.* **23**, 121–137

— (1977). Karyology of the Canarian Flora. (this volume)

Bramwell, D. (1971) *Studies in the Flora of the Canary Islands*. Unpubl. PhD. Thesis, University of Reading. 335p.

— (1972a). A revision of the genus *Echium* in Macaronesia. *Lagascalia* **2**, 37–115

— (1972b). Endemism in the flora of the Canary Islands. In *Taxonomy, Phytogeography and Evolution* (D. H. Valentine, ed.), 141–159. Academic Press, London and New York

— (1973). Studies in the genus *Echium* from Macaronesia. *Monogr. Biol. Canar.* **4**, 71–82

— (1975). Some morphological aspects of the adaptive radiation of Canary Islands *Echium* species. *Anal. Inst. Bot. Cavanilles* **32** (2), 241–254

— (1976). The endemic flora of the Canary Islands. In *Biogeography and Ecology in the Canary Islands* (G. Kunkel, ed.), 207–240. *Monogr. Biol.* **30**. Junk, The Hague

— and Bramwell, Z. (1974). *Wild Flowers of the Canary Islands*. 261p. Stanley Thornes, (Publishers) Ltd. London and Burford

—, Humphries, C. J., Murray, B. G. and Owens, S. J. (1971). Chromosome numbers in plants from the Canary Islands. *Bot. Notiser* **124**, 376–382

— (1972). Chromosome studies in the flora of Macaronesia. *Bot. Notiser* **125**, 139–152

— and Richardson, I. B. K. (1973). Floristic connections between Macaronesia and the East Mediterranean region. *Monogr. Biol. Canar.* **4**, 118–125

— and Murray, B. G. (1972). A preliminary report on the cytology of some Cape Verde Islands plants. *Cuad. Bot. Canar.* **14/15**, 27–29

—, Perez de Paz, J. and Ortega, J. (1976). Studies in the flora of Macaronesia: Some chromosome numbers of flowering plants. *Botanica Macaronesica* **1**, 9–16

Ceballos, F. and Ortuño, F. (1951). *Estudio sobre la Vegetación y la Flora Forestal de las Canarias Occidentales*. 465p. Instituto Forestal, Madrid

Chevalier, A. (1935). Les îles du Cap vert. Flore de l'archipel. *Rev. Bot. Appl.* **15**, 753–1090

Eriksson, O., Hansen, A. and Sunding, P. (1974). *Flora of Macaronesia. Checklist of Vascular Plants*. 66p. The University, Umeå

Favarger, C. (1972). Endemism in the montane floras of Europe. In *Taxonomy, Phytogeography and Evolution* (D. H. Valentine, ed.), 191–204. Academic Press, London and New York

— and Contandriopoulos, J. (1961). Essai sur l'endemisme. *Bull. Soc. Bot. Suisse* **71**, 383–408

Gagnieu, A., Linder, R. and Voggenreiter, V. (1973). Caryotypes de la Flore Insulaire de Tenerife. *Monogr. Biol. Canar.* **4**, 126–133

Grant, V. (1971). *Plant Speciation*. Columbia University Press, New York and London

Greger, H. (1969). Flavonoid und Systematik der Anthemideae (Asteraceae). *Naturwissenschaften* **56**, 467–468

Hansen, A. (1969). Checklist of the vascular plants of the Archipelago of Madeira. *Bol. Mus. Mun. Funchal* **24**, 62p.

Harling, G. (1951). Embryological studies in the Compositae. Part 11. Anthemideae – Chrysantheminae. *Acta Horti Berg.* **16**, 1–56

Humphries, C. J. (1973). *A Taxonomic study of the genus Argyranthemum.* Unpubl. Ph.D. Thesis, Univeristy of Reading. 376p.

— (1975). Cytological studies in the Macaronesian genus *Argyranthemum* (Compositae – Anthemideae). *Bot. Notiser* **128**, 239–255

— (1976a). A revision of the Macaronesian genus *Argyranthemum* Webb ex Schultz Bip. (Compositae – Anthemideae). *Bull. Br. Mus. (Nat. Hist.), Bot.* **5** (4), 147–240

— (1976b). Evolution and Endemism in *Argyranthemum* Webb ex Schultz Bip. (Compositae: Anthemideae.) *Botanica Macaronesica* **1**, 25–50

Krisper, J. and Puff, C. (1976). Peroxidasemuster und Systematick von *Argyranthemum* und *Chrysanthemum* S. str. (Asteraceae – Anthemideae). *Plant Syst. Evol.* **124**, 291–301

Kunkel, G. (1972). Plantas Vasculares de Gran Canaria. *Monogr. Biol. Canar.* **3**, 86p.

Larsen, K. (1958). Preliminary note on the cytology of the endemic Canarian element. *Bot. Tidsskr.* **54**, 167–169

— (1960). Cytological and experimental studies, on the flowering plants of the Canary Islands. *Biol. Skr. Dan. Vid. Selsk.* **11**, (3), 1–60

— (1962. Contribution to the cytology of the endemic Canarian element. *Bot. Notiser* **115**, 196–202

Lems, K. (1958). Botanical notes on the Canary Islands. I. Introgression among the species of *Adenocarpus* and their rôle in the vegetation of the islands. *Bot. Inst. Nac. Invest. Agron.* **18** (39), 351–370

— (1960). Botanical notes on the Canary Islands. II. The evolution of plant forms, in the islands: *Aeonium. Ecology* **41**, 1–17

— and Holzapfel, C. M. (1968). Evolution in the Canary Islands. 1. Phylogenetic relations in the genus *Echium* (Boraginaceae) as shown by trichome development. *Bot. Gazette* **129**, 95–107

Lewis, H. (1972). The origin of endemics in the California flora. In *Taxonomy, Phytogeography and evolution* (D. H. Valentine, ed.), 179–189. Academic Press, London and New York

McArthur, R. H. and Wilson, E. O. (1967). *The Theory of Island Biogeography* (Monographs in Population Biology No. 1) Princetown University Press, New Jersey

Michaelis, G. (1964). Chromosomzahlen einiger Kanarischen Endemismen. *Planta* **62**, 194

Ortega, J. (1976). Citogenética del Genero *Lotus* en Macaronesia 1. Números de cromosomas. *Botanica Macaronesica.* **1**, 17–24

Perez de Paz, J. (1976). Observaciones sobre la biologia y relaciones de *Sventenia bupleuroides* F.Q. *Botanica Macaronesica* , 51–66

Pickering, C. H. C. and Hansen, A. (1969). Scientific Expedition to the Salvage Islands, July 1963. ix. List of Higher plants and Cryptogams known from the Salvage Islands. *Bol. Mus. Mun. Funchal* **25**, 63–71

Praeger, R. L. (1929). Semperviva of the Canary Islands area *Proc. Roy. Irish Acad.* **38**, Sect. B, 454–499

— (1932). *An Account of the Sempervivum Group.* 265p. The Royal Horticultural Society, London

Reese, G. (1957). Über die Polyploidiespektren in der Nordsaharischen Wüstenflora. *Flora* **144**, 598–634

Roux, J. and Boulos, L. (1972). Révision systématique du genre *Sonchus* L. s.l. II. Etude Caryologique. *Bot. Notiser* **125**, 306–309

Schmidt, J. A. (1852). *Beiträge zur Flora der Cap-Verdischen Inseln, mit Berücksichtigung aller bis jetzt daselbst bekannten wildwachsenden und kultivierten Pflanzen.* 8 + 358p. Ernst Mohr, Heidelburg

Sjögren, E. (1973). Plant communities of the natural vegetation of Madeira and the Azores. *Monogr. Biol. Canar.* **4**, 107–111

— (1974). Local climatic conditions and zonation of vegetation on Madeira. *Agron. Lusit.* **36**, 95–139

Stebbins, G. C. and Major, J. (1965). Endemism and Speciation in the California Flora. *Ecol. Monogr.* **35**, 1–35

Sunding, P. (1973a). *Checklist of the Vascular Plants of the Cape Verde Islands.* 36p. Mimeogr. Bot. Garden. Univ. of Oslo

— (1973b). Endemism in the flora of the Cape Verde Islands with special emphasis on the Macronesian flora element. *Monogr. Biol. Canar.* **4**, 112–117

— (1977). Origins of the Macaronesian flora. (this volume)

Turrill, W. B. (1929). *The Plant Life of the Balkan Peninsula.* 490p. The Clarendon Press, Oxford

Tutin, T. G. (1953) The vegetation of the Azores. *J. Ecol.* **41**, 53–61

Van Loon, J. C. (1974). A cytological investigation of flowering plants from the Canary Islands. *Acta Bot. Neer.* **23**, 113–124

Voggenreiter, V. (1974). Geobotanische Untersuchungen an der Natürlichen Vegetation der Kanareninsel Tenerife. (Anhang; Vergleiche mit La Palma und Gran Canaria) Als Grundlage für den Naturschutz. *Diss. Bot.* **26**, 718p. Cramer, Leutershausen

10 Biogeographical Elements in the New Zealand Lichen Flora

D. J. GALLOWAY   *Botany Division, DSIR, Christchurch,*
New Zealand

Las islas de Nueva Zelanda se alzan como anchas cordilleras desde el suelo del oceano Pacífico Sur, unos 1600 km. hacia el Este de Australia. Ocupando un area de 26·9 millones de hectáreas, son así de una medida similar al Reino Unido y Japón. Las tres islas principales, Norte, Sur y Stewart están entre 34°6'S y 47°20'S con las islas subantártica de Auckland y la isla Campbell, que están generalmente incluidas dentro de la región botánica de Nueva Zelanda, situada más al Sur alrededor de 50°S. La masa de tierra de Nueva Zelanda se extiende a lo largo del eje SW y NE paralela a la dirección de su cadena de montañas, estando las tres islas mayores separadas solamente por Estrechos relativamente reducidos.

Aunque se ven llanos muy estensos, el país es, en su totalidad, montañoso, con sus más altas elevaciones alcanzadas en la isla Sur, donde existe un extenso sistema glacial asociado a los Alpes Sureños. Las montañas de la isla Norte son más bajas y están dominadas por 4 picos volcánicos, dos de los cuales están todavía en activo – la evidencia de glaciación es mucho menos obvia.

El clima de Nueva Zelanda es fuertemente oceánico, aunque en partes de la isla Sur hacia el Este de los Alpes sureños sea marcadamente continental. Los vientos son predominante en todas las áreas del Oeste, con una tendencia a aumentar en fuerza de Norte a Sur. La cadena de montañas actuaa como una barrera a estos vientos y producen agudos contrastes climáticos entre el Este y el Oeste mayores que los que se obtienen entre Norte y Sur.

Nueva Zelanda contiene una gran diversidad de paisajes, desde los pantanales subantárticos hasta los bosques de lluvias subtropicales y desde las playas del oceano a los picos glaciados de montañas. Esta gran diversidad de topografía ofrece una escala muy amplia de habitats para la colonización de líquenes, siendo éstos encontrados desde el nivel de mar, a las más altas rocas expuestas sobre Mt Cook a una altitud de 3750 m.

Según los estudios actuales que están todavía muy fragmentados e incompletos, la flora de liquen de Nuveva Zelanda, comprende alrededor de 1500–2000 especies distribuidas entre 150 géneros. El presente trabajo se refiere solamente a los macrolíquenes, ya que estos son grandes, de fácil recolección y ya identificados y, frecuentemente, son componentes importantes de la vegetación áreas especiales. Entre los macrolíquenes es posible definir varios elementos o agrupamientos fitogeográficos, siendo propuestos y discutidos los siguientes elementos: 1). templado Sur o Austral; 2. Antártic-subantártico; 3. Pantropical; 4. Este Asiático; 5. cosmopolita; 6. bipolar y 7. endémico.

El elemento endémico en la flora liquen de Nueva Zelanda es muy pequeño, alrededor de 1–2% contiene solamente un género endémico, y con un marcado contraste con el altisimo grado de endemismo mostrado por grupos dentro de la flora vascular

Son examinados los factores de influencia en la distribución de liquenses en Nueva Zelanda.

Introduction

New Zealand is an isolated archipelago in the southwest Pacific Ocean 1600 km to the east of Australia and 12 000 km to the west of South America. It is a narrow, predominantly mountainous country of three major and numerous smaller islands, the main islands (North, South and Stewart) extending 1900 km from latitude 34°8′S to latitude 47°17′S. With a land area of 26·9 million hectares, New Zealand is similar in size to the United Kingdom, or to Japan. Recent accounts of the geological history of New Zealand (Fleming, 1975), of the climate (Coulter, 1975), and of the flora and vegetation (Godley, 1975) are relevant to any discussion of New Zealand's lichen vegetation.

Lichens were first collected from New Zealand over 200 years ago by Joseph Banks and Daniel Solander during Captain Cook's *Endeavour* voyage (1768–1771) and the first descriptions of New Zealand species *viz. Lichen filix (Sticta filix* (Sw.) Nyl.) and *Lichen linearis (Ramalina linearis* (Sw.) Ach.) were published by Olof Swartz (1783) from material collected in 1774 by Georg and Rheinold Forster during Cook's *Resolution* voyage (1772–1775). Archibald Menzies, naturalist to Vancouver's *Discovery* (1791–1795) expedition collected 17 lichen species from Dusky Sound in 1791 (unpublished observations) but details of these and other lichen collections made during that voyage were never published.

The nineteenth century saw a steady increase in the knowledge of New Zealand's lichens beginning with the rather restricted collection of D'Urville (Bory de St. Vincent, 1828; Richard, 1832) Cunningham (1836) and Raoul (1846), and receiving considerable impetus from the visit of Joseph Hooker to the Bay of Islands in 1841 (Hooker and Taylor, 1844; Babington, 1855). Hooker encouraged local botanists (including Colenso, Haast, Hector, Knight, Monro, Lyall and Sinclair) to collect lichens and send them to Kew for identification and on the basis of these collections, supplemented by those made by Lauder Lindsay in Otago (Lindsay, 1866, 1868; Nylander, 1866) he prepared the substantial account of New Zealand lichens in the second part of his *Handbook of the New Zealand Flora* (Hooker, 1867). Large New Zealand lichen collections were reviewed by Nylander (1888) and Müller-Argoviensis (1894), and

Berggren's lichen collections of 1874–5 were published by Hellbom (1896).

In the present century, the Swedish botanist G. Einar Du Rietz who visited New Zealand with his wife Greta Sernander-Du Rietz in 1926–1927, was the first to collect lichens intensively from all parts of the New Zealand botanical region. Although he never published a general account of his work in New Zealand, his example and enthusiasm encouraged local botanists (see Galloway, 1976) to examine New Zealand's lichen flora much more thoroughly and his inspiration and influence can fairly be said to have determined the course of much recent lichenological research in this country.

The New Zealand lichen flora is estimated to comprise 120–150 genera (comparable figures for Australia are 170 genera (Weber and Wetmore, 1972) and Tasmania 90 genera (Wetmore, 1963)) and 1000–1500 species. Of these only the 90-odd genera of macrolichens are at all well known since they are conspicuous, easily collected and readily identified, and frequently may be important components of the vegetation. New Zealand's lichen vegetation is composed of many varied communities of foliose, fruticose and crustose species ranging from taxa that have arisen in New Zealand after its separation from Australia, South American and Antarctica, to species introduced within the short span of European settlement. Lichens are found from the sea shore to the summit rocks of Mt. Cook at 3500 m (Wilson, 1976).

Although there is now an extensive literature relating to New Zealand lichenology (Galloway, 1974), which grows at an increasing rate, there is not an authoritative lichen flora upon which ecological work can be based. Consequently, knowledge of New Zealand distributions of many genera is still severely limited and ecological studies on even such obvious and floristically important genera as *Pseudocyphellaria, Parmelia* sens. lat., *Stereocaulon* and *Sticta* are still in their infancy. Lichenometric studies have been made in the central Southern Alps of South Island (Burrows and Lucas, 1967; Burrows and Orwin, 1971; Burrows, 1973; Orwin, 1970, 1972; Wardle, 1963) while Daly (1970) discussed lichens as indicators of atmospheric pollution in the city of Christchurch.

In recent years, studies on the large modern collections of New Zealand lichens in herbaria in London (BM) Uppsala (UPS and UPSV) and New Zealand (CHR and OTA) have allowed some preliminary observations to be made on the phytogeographical relationships of New Zealand's lichen flora. It must be stressed however that the discussion which follows is provisional, since many areas of New Zealand are still unexplored lichenologically and in addition there are no modern lichen floras of Australia, or the Pacific Islands available for comparison. A consideration of the Australian lichen literature (see Wetmore, 1963; Weber and Wetmore, 1972) which is based in large part upon nineteenth century collections from restricted areas of Tasmania, Victoria, New South Wales and southern Queensland, suggests that the lichen floras of New Zealand, Tasmania and southeastern Australia are closely similar. However until lichens of all of these regions are better documented it will not be possible to assess the degree of endemism of each.

This paper attempts to delineate the several phytogeographical elements discernible in New Zealand's macrolichen flora, since at present the complex array of microlichens forming a large part of our lichen flora is almost unknown. Names of the biogeographical elements are based on the proposals of Fleming (1963).

Phytogeographical elements

The cosmopolitan element New Zealand has a number of lichen species which are represented in the floras of most continents. Such species of cosmopolitan distribution include:

Collema coccophorum Tuck., *C. fasciculare* (L.) Web., (Degelius, 1974); *Heterodermia leucomela* (L.) Poelt (Kurokawa, 1973; Swinscow and Krog, 1976a); *Hypotrachyna laevigata* (Sm.) Hale (Hale, 1975a); *Lobaria scrobiculata* (Scop.) DC., *Normandina pulchella* (Borr.) Nyl. *Omphalodiscus decussatus* (Vill.) Schol. (Llano, 1950); *Parmelia saxatilis* (L.) Ach.; *Parmotrema crinitum* (Ach.) Choisy; *Peltigera polydactyla* (Neck.) Hoffm. (Murray, 1960b); *Physcia adscendens* (Th. Fr.) Oliv. em. Bitt., *P. stellaris* (L.) Nyl.; *Placopsis gelida* (L.) Linds. (Lamb, 1947); *Pseudocyphellaria aurata* (Ach.) Vain., *P. crocata* (L.) Vain., *P. intricata* (Del.) Vain.; *Pseudoparmelia caperata* (L.) Hale, *P. soredians* (Nyl.) Hale (Hale, 1976a); *Sphaerophorus melanocarpus* (Sw.) DC. (Murray, 1960a); *Stereocaulon vesuvianum* Pers. (Lamb, 1951); *Thamnolia vermicularis* (Sw.) Ach. ex Schaer. (Sato, 1965, 1966); *Umbilicaria cylindrica* (L.) Del., *U. hyperborea* (Ach.) Hoffm., *U. polyphylla* (L.) Hoffm. (Llano, 1950); *Xanthoparmelia conspersa* (Ach.) Hale and *Xanthoria parietina* (L.) Th.Fr.

The wide distribution of *Thamnolia vermicularis* in arctic and alpine habitats, although frequently commented upon (see Culberson, 1972) is not readily explained since the species produces neither asexual propagules nor spores. Species of the genus *Siphula*, especially *S. decumbens* Nyl., and *S. roccellaeformis* Nyl., share similar habitat niches in New Zealand with *Thamnolia vermicularis*, and although they too produce neither spores nor asexual propagules and rely on fragmentation of the thallus for dispersal, their ranges of distribution are much narrower.

Species of the federation *Xanthorion* in New Zealand, especially

Xanthoria parietina, Physcia adscendens, P. stellaris and *Ramalina linearis* are found most commonly on the bark of deciduous introduced trees and shrubs particularly species of *Acer, Fraxinus, Malus, Populus* and *Salix,* although the federation is also encountered on some native species such as *Avicennia resinifera* Forst. f. (mangrove), *Discaria toumatou* Raoul (matagouri), and cultivated *Sophora microphylla* Ait. (kowhai).

The bipolar element This element, first noted by Du Rietz (1928, 1940) contains the following species: *Alectoria nigricans* (Ach.) Nyl.; (Hawksworth, 1972); *Cetraria ericetorum* Opiz; *Cornicularia aculeata* (Schreb.) Th.Fr.; *Pannaria hookeri* (Borr.) Nyl.; *Pertusaria dactylina* (Ach.) Nyl.; *Pseudephebe miniscula* (Nyl. ex Arn.) Brodo & D. Hawksw.; *P. pubescens* (L.) Choisy (Brodo and Hawksworth, 1977) and *Solorina crocea* (L.) Ach. (Murray, 1960b). In New Zealand bipolar lichens are found at high elevations and are more richly represented in South Island than in North Island. A similar finding was reported by Schofield (1974) for bipolar mosses. Most of these lichen species are restricted to high-alpine zones of Central Otago (Mark and Bliss, 1970; Bliss and Mark, 1974) and eastern Canterbury (Burrows, 1969), although *Alectoria nigricans* ranges more widely, from Mt. Hikurangi and the summits of the Kaimanawa and Ruahine Ranges in North Island to the summits of Mt. Anglem (Galloway, 1968a) and Frazer Peaks (Galloway, 1968b) in Stewart Island. *Cornicularia aculeata* and *Pseudephebe pubescens* have also been recorded from exposed subalpine areas in Stewart Island (Galloway, 1968a, b). It is noteworthy that *Pannaria hookeri* is found only on schistose rocks throughout its known world range of Central Otago, New Zealand, Scotland, the European Alps and Arctic Scandinavia (P. M. Jørgensen, pers. comm.). Its presence in New Zealand, as with the other species mentioned above, is not readily explained as none produce vegetative diaspores capable of efficient and widespread dispersal. Long-distance dispersal of thallus fragments from Northern Hemisphere populations seems an unsatisfactory explanation since the distribution of the species in alpine regions of New Zealand is limited, but it appears this is the only mechanism that will explain the observed disjunct distributions.

The eastern Asian element This element, which may yet be shown to be equivalent to the Malayo-Pacific element of Fleming (1962, 1963), contains a small number of species which are characteristic of the lichen flora of Japan. Some of the species are also found in eastern Australia and it is likely that they will be found also in New Guinea, the Philippines, Java and the Malesian archipelago. The species from this element known from New Zealand are: *Cetrelia braunsiana* (Müll.

Arg.) Culb. & Culb. (Culberson and Culberson, 1968); *Coccotrema cucurbitula* (Mont. in Gay) Müll. Arg., *C. porinopsis* (Nyl.) Imsh. (Oshio, 1968); *Collema japonicum* (Müll. Arg.) Hue (Degelius, 1974); *Heterodermia japonica* (Sato) Swinsc. & Krog (Swinscow and Krog, 1976a); *Leprocaulon arbuscula* Nyl. (Lamb and Ward, 1974) and *Placopsis cribellans* (Nyl.) Räs. (Lamb, 1947).

The pantropical element   This element is most noticeable in the forests of North Island north of latitude 40°S where many lichen species reach the southerly limit of their ranges there. A good example is *Teloschistes flavicans* (Sw.) Norm., a striking epiphyte of coastal trees and shrubs on the Three Kings and Poor Knights, offshore island groups of northern New Zealand (unpublished observations). The genera *Coccocarpia* (Swinscow and Krog, 1976b), *Erioderma* (Galloway and Jørgensen, 1975), *Everniastrum* (Hale, 1976d), *Heterodermia* (Kurokawa, 1973; Swinscow and Krog, 1976a), *Hypotrachyma* (Hale, 1975a), *Leptogium* (Sierk, 1964), *Parmotrema* (Hale, 1965, 1974), *Physma*, *Phyllopsora*, *Ramalina* and *Teloschistes* are characteristic components of this element and associations of species from these genera are often common on such northern trees as kauri (*Agathis australis* Salisb.) and pohutukawa (*Metrosideros excelsa* Sol. ex Gaertn.). Other common substrates for pantropical species are the successional shrubs kanuka (*Leptospermum ericoides* A. Rich.) and manuka (*Leptospermum scoparium* J. & G. Forst.). A few lichens of tropical origin such as *Baeomyces absolutus* Tuck., *Cladia aggregata* (Sw.) Nyl. and *Coccocarpia cronia* Tuck. range more widely throughout New Zealand.

A feature of species in this element is the development of asexual propagules such as isidia, phyllidia and soredia in many taxa, allowing them to act as efficient colonisers of disturbed habitats. Many of the recent introductions to the New Zealand lichen flora are from this element as the epiphytic vegetation of introduced trees and shrubs fenceposts, gates and wooden farm buildings amply testifies.

The austral element   According to Fleming (1963) the austral element in New Zealand ". . .includes plants and animals distributed by the west wind drift of air and water masses and its contribution to the biota has apparently been greatest when climatic zones moved northwards (in the Pliocene and Pleistocene) and also perhaps . . . when a temperate and vegetated Antarctica provided a route broken by narrow sea barriers than in post-Pliocene time. . ." The austral element in New Zealand accordingly has affinities with the lichen floras of the subantarctic islands (Auckland, Campbell, Macquarie), with the Antarctic Continent, with southern South America (including Juan Fernandez and the Falkland Islands), with Tristan da Cunha and with Kerguelen.

The southern Hemisphere is the centre of distribution of several lichen genera which are thought to have evolved there and which are represented in the Northern Hemisphere, by only one or two species. The best known of these *southern* lichen genera are *Menegazzia* (Santesson, 1942a), *Neuropogon* (Lamb, 1939, 1948a, 1964) and *Placopis* (Lamb, 1947). *Menegazzia* contains about 50 species, many still undescribed. All except *M. terebrata* (Hoffm.) Koerb., which ranges widely in the Northern Hemisphere (being found in Asia, Europe and North America) are restricted to the Southern Hemisphere. *Neuropogon*, related to *Usnea*, has its richest speciation in antarctic regions but *N. sulphureus* (König) Hellb., ranges via the Andes and Rockies into the Arctic. The remaining 12–15 species of the genus are restricted to southern latitudes. *Placopsis* is an oceanic genus of some 25 species and all are restricted to the Southern Hemisphere. The exception is *P. gelida* which, like *Menegazzia terebrata,* is widely distributed in the Northern Hemisphere (Formosa, Korea, Japan, Aleutian Islands, Alaska) and in the Southern Hemisphere is known from the Galapagos Islands, Chile, Fuegia, Tristan da Cunha and New Zealand.

In addition to genera discussed above, others, notably *Psoroma, Pseudocyphellaria, Sphaerophorus* and *Sticta* also have most species in the Southern Hemisphere although several species of each are also found in Northern Hemisphere floras.

By contrast, lichen genera which are thought to have evolved in the Northern Hemisphere are often poorly represented or absent altogether in the Southern Hemisphere. Such *northern* genera[1] include; *Alectoria, Bryoria, Cetrelia, Cladina, Dactylina, Evernia, Fulgensia, Oropogon*+ *Parmeliopsis*+, *Platismatia*+, *Pseudevernia*+, *Roccella*+, *Solorina* and *Toninia.*

The similarities in the phanerogamic floras of New Zealand and southern South America are well known (see Dawson, 1958; Godley, 1960; Raven, 1972; Raven and Axelrod, 1972) and not surprisingly there are many affinities between the lichen floras of Chile and Fuegia (Montagne, 1852; Darbishire, 1912; Santesson, 1944; Lamb, 1949, 1958; Redon, 1973) and New Zealand, with the following genera being widely distributed in both regions; *Agyrophora, Cladia, Cladonia, Coccocarpia, Coccotrema, Collema, Erioderma, Heppia, Heterodermia, Leptogium, Lopadium, Menegazzia, Nephroma, Pannaria, Pannoparmelia, Parmelia, Parmeliella, Peltigera, Physma, Placopsis, Pseudocyphellaria, Psoroma, Siphula, Sphaerophorus, Stereocaulon, Sticta, Teloschistes, Thamnolia, Umbilicaria, Usnea.*

[1] Genera absent from New Zealand are marked +

Despite considerable congeneric links between the two floras, the numbers of lichen species which are shared between New Zealand and South America are surprisingly small and include the following: *Agyrophora zahlbruckneri* (Frey) Llano (Llano, 1950); *Cladia aggregata, C. schizopora* (Nyl.) Nyl., *C. sullivanii* (Müll, Arg.) Martin (Galloway, 1977a); *Collema laeve* Hook.f. & Tayl. (Degelius, 1974); *Erioderma chilense* Mont. (Galloway and Jørgensen, 1975); *Hypogymnia logubris* (Pers.) Krog.; *Leptogium malmei, L. menziesii* (Jørgensen, 1975); *Menegazzia globulifera* R. Sant., *M. sanguinascens* (Räs.) Lamb (P. W. James, pers. comm.); *Nephroma cellulosum* (Sm. ex Ach.) Ach.; *Neuropogon ciliata* (Nyl.) Kremp., *N. acromelana* (Stirt.) Lamb (Lamb, 1939, 1948a); *Parmeliella pycnophora* (Nyl.) R. Sant (Santesson, 1944); *Physma chilense* Hue; *Placopsis cribellans, P. gelida, P. brevilobata* (Zahlbr.) Lamb, *P. parellina* (Nyl.) Lamb, *P. perrugosa* (Nyl.) Müll. Arg., *P. rhodophthalma* (Müll. Arg.) Räs. (Lamb, 1947); *Pseudephebe miniscula, P. pubescens* (Lamb, 1958); *Pseudocyphellaria aurata, P. crocata, P. delisea* (Fée in. Del.) D. Gall & P. James, *P. faveolata* (Del.) Malme, *P. intricata* (Huneck *et al.*, 1973); *Psoroma leprolomum* (Nyl.) Räs., *P. sphinctrinum* (Mont.) Nyl. (Lamb, 1958); *Sphaerophorus melanocarpus, S. ramulifer* Lamb, *S. tener* Laur. (Lamb, 1958) and *Stereocaulon corticatulum* Nyl., *S. ramulosum* (Sw.) Räusch. and *S. vesuvianum* (Lamb, 1958).

Although the number of lichen species common to New Zealand and to South America is relatively small it is noteworthy that similar ecological niches in both countries are filled by related taxa. This development of vicariant taxa in the floras of New Zealand and South America has already been documented for several phanerogamic communities and in particular cushion bog vegetation (Godley, 1960). In the lichens, vicariant taxa are well developed in the genera *Pseudocyphellaria, Psoroma, Stereocaulon* and *Usnea*. As examples of vicariants, the South American species *Usnea pallida* Mot., and *U. noblis* Mot., do not occur in New Zealand, the ecological niches they would otherwise occupy there being filled by the New Zealand species *U. contexta* Mot., and *U. xanthopoga* Mot. Other examples will be discussed in the section dealing with the endemic element in the New Zealand lichen flora.

While there are many similarities between the two lichen floras several genera found in South America are not represented in New Zealand. These include: *Darbishirella; Desmazieria* (Follman, 1976); *Dolichocarpus* (Santesson, 1949); *Endocena; Everniopsis; Lepolichen; Oropogon; Plastismatia* (Culberson and Culberson, 1968); *Protousnea* (Krog, 1976); *Roccella; Roccellaria; Roccellinastrum; Tornabenia, Xanthopeltis* (Santesson, 1949) and *Zahlbrucknerella* (Henssen, 1977).

Juan Fernandez (Zahlbruckner, 1924) shares 14 lichen species with

New Zealand although in the genera *Pseudocyphellaria* and *Stereocaulon* South American taxa predominate. Of the 84 foliose and fruitcose species recorded from Tristan de Cunha (Jørgensen, 1977), 26 occur in New Zealand, however of these only *Parmeliella pycnophora* and *Stereocaulon corticatulum* belong to the austral element.

The austral element in the New Zealand lichen flora also has a recognisable antarctic component reflecting affinities with Antarctica and with the subantarctic islands to the south of New Zealand (Dodge, 1948, 1970, 1973). The only antarctic lichens known to occur in New Zealand are *Neuropogon antarctica* (DR.) Lamb, which is sparingly present on the summits of the Central Otago mountains (Mark and Bliss, 1970), and *Mastodia testellata* Hook.f. & Harv., a distinctive maritime species known from the Snares Islands, Milford Sound and the Open Bay Islands. In addition, several lichens are restricted to the subantarctic islands of New Zealand and although often common components of the lichen vegetation of exposed subalpine moorlands there, they have apparently been unable to extend their ranges to any major land mass. It is conceivable that they are relicts of once more widely dispersed genera lost from New Zealand and/or South America during the Pleistocene glaciations. The intensely oceanic climates of the Auckland and Campbell Islands and on the coasts and islets around Stewart Island and Foveaux Strait have permitted the survival of the phanerogamic genus *Stilbocarpus* through the last glaciation (Wardle, 1963) and possibly the following lichens are also such relict species: *Argopsis megalospora* Th.Fr., – Auckland and Campbell Islands (Lamb, 1974); *Stereocaulon argus* Hook.f. & Tayl. – Auckland, Campbell and southern Stewart Islands (Galloway, 1968b); *Steinera* species – Auckland, Campbell, Macquarie Islands, Kerguelen and southern New Zealand (P. W. James, pers. comm.). The curious monotypic genus *Knightiella* – *K. splachnirima* (Hook.f. & Tayl.) Gyeln., is found in southern New Zealand in subalpine cushion bogs as far north as latitude 46°S, but is more common in moorlands on the subantarctic islands and Stewart Island. It also occurs in Tasmania where it was first discovered.

In the New Zealand lichen flora the austral element is characteristic of undisturbed habitats and is well developed in the epiphytic vegetation of beech and podocarp forests flanking the southern Alps, and in subalpine scrub associations and subalpine grasslands from 47°S to 39°S. However in the northern part of this range many species appear to be replaced by those with tropical affinities.

The Australian element   The similarity of the phanerogamic floras of New Zealand and Australia (including Tasmania) has been noted many times

(Hooker, 1853, 1860; Cockayne, 1928; Fleming, 1975). This similarity extends also to their lichen floras (Martin, 1965a. 1966; Wetmore, 1963; Weber and Wetmore, 1972). The lichen floras of Tasmania and of southeastern Australia (Victoria and New South Wales) share many species with New Zealand, particularly in the commonly occurring macrolichen genera. This is in contrast to the predominantly vicariant relationship which exists between species in the shared macrolichen genera of New Zealand and southern South America. This congruence of large parts of the eastern Australian and New Zealand lichen floras can be accounted for by the relative proximity of the two countries (derived from a common ancestral landmass) and the effective means of wind dispersal of taxa which exists between them (Raven, 1972, 1973; Raven and Axelrod, 1972; Raven and Raven, 1976). In several macrolichen genera the number of species present in the Australian flora is greater than in the New Zealand flora and often also the species ecological and geographical ranges are wider in Australia. This lends support to the notion that many lichen species evolved in Australia and were subsequently transported to New Zealand and established when corresponding habitats became available.

The monotypic genus *Chondropsis semiviridis* (Nyl.) Nyl. in Cromb., is characteristically developed in the cooler, drier parts of southern Australia (Filson, 1967; Rogers, 1971; Rogers and Lange, 1972) and it occurs also in the driest areas of New Zealand, the semi-arid intermontane basins of Central Otago and the Mackenzie Country. The genus *Cladia*, which is the Southern Hemisphere equivalent of the reindeer lichens (*Cladina* species) of the Arctic tundras, is most richly represented in the Australian flora with eight species (Filson, 1970); the New Zealand flora has five (Martin, 1965b; Galloway, 1977a). Of the 77 known species of the genus *Collema*, 16 species are found in both New Zealand, and Australia (Degelius, 1974) although three species in the Australian flora are not in New Zealand. *Gymnoderma melacarpa* (F.Wils.) Yoshim., which was recently reported from Tasmania (Yoshimura, 1973) also occurs widely throughout New Zealand, and the species *Heterodea muelleri* (Hampe) Nyl. (Blackman *et al.*, 1973; Jahns and Knapp, 1973) formerly thought to be restricted to Australia is now known from sand-dune vegetation at Ninety-Mile Beach, North Auckland.

In the lichen family Parmeliaceae there are many similarities between the Australian and New Zealand floras with the closest affinities being found in the genera *Hypogymnia* (Weber and Wetmore, 1972; Elix, 1975); *Parmelia*; *Parmelina* (Hale, 1976c) and *Pseudoparmelia* (Hale, 1976a) although of the 16 species of this last genus known from Australia only six occur in New Zealand. In contrast, the genera *Bulbothrix* (Hale, 1976b) and *Relicina* (Hale, 1975b) have species in the Australian flora but are not known from New Zealand. Few of the New Zealand species of *Menegazzia* occur in Australia. *Xanthoparmelia* has many species in Australia, particularly in the drier inland areas where there is a high proportion of endemic taxa (Filson, 1967; Kurokawa, 1969; Kurokawa *et al.*, 1971; Kurokawa and Elix, 1971; Kurokawa and Filson, 1975; Baker *et al.*, 1973; Elix, 1976) although several species, *Xanthoparmelia amphixantha* (Müll. Arg.) Hale, *X. furcata* (Müll. Arg.) Hale, *X. scabrosa* (Tayl.) Hale, and *X. tasmanica* (Hook.f. & Tayl.) Hale, are known from New Zealand and are presumably derived from Australian populations.

In the Stictaceae too there are strong Australian affinities at the species level in the genera *Lobaria, Pseudocyphellaria* and *Sticta*. In both *Lobaria* and *Sticta* there are more species in the Australian flora than in the New Zealand flora. Of the four species of *Lobaria* known from New Zealand three are found in Australia and of the nine species of *Sticta* from New Zealand 7 occur in Australia. Seventeen of New Zealand's 40 species of *Pseudocyphellaria* are endemic, and the following are confined to New Zealand and Australia: *P. australiensis* H.Magn., *P. billardierii* (Del.) Räs., *P. colensoi* (Bab. in Hook.f.) Vain., *P. coronata* (Müll. Arg.) Malme, *P. flavicans* (Hook.f. & Tayl.) Vain and *P. multifida* (Laur. in Nyl.) D. Gall & P. James.

Other lichen genera having species common to both countries are: *Siphula* – *S. coriacea* Nyl. (Rogers and Lange, 1972), *S. decumbens* and *S. fragilis* (Hook.f. and Tayl.) R. Sant.; *Stereocaulon* – *S. caespitosum* Redgr., *S. corticatulum, S. ramulosum, S. trachyphloeum* Lamb (Galloway *et al.*, 1976); *Thysanothecium* – *T. hyalinum* (Tayl.) Nyl. (Des Abbayes, 1968; Galloway, 1977b); and *Umbilicaria* – *U. cylindrica, U. hyperborea, U. polyphylla* (Llano, 1950; Blackman *et al.*, 1974).

A relationship between the lichen floras of New Zealand and Lord Howe Island can be demonstrated in the occurrence of distinctive species common to both regions. *Pseudocyphellaria poculifera* (Müll. Arg.) D. Gall & P. James, a marginally isidiate-sorediate, yellow-medulla species related to *P. aurata* was originally described from material collected at Mt. Gower, Lord Howe Island and has recently been found on the Three Kings Islands and several other localities in northern New Zealand. In addition, an undescribed, isidiate, non-perforate species of *Menegazzia*, first collected from New Zealand in 1926 by G. Einar Du Rietz from the bark of *Nothofagus truncata* (Col.) Ckn. at York Bay, Wellington, and which has subsequently been found in many North Island localities is also known to occur on Lord Howe Island.

Several species characteristic of the South African lichen flora also occur in New Zealand. *Siphula decumbens* (Mathey, 1971) has a wide range in subalpine localities in New Zealand from the Coromandel Peninsula in the north to Port Pegasus, Stewart Island, in the south. Two species of *Xanthoparmelia, viz. X. congensis* (Stein.) Hale, and *X. molliuscula* (Ach.) Hale which are characteristic of the South African lichen flora and sometimes regarded as endemic to that region, have a limited occurrence in New Zealand where they are found on the schist rocks and arid soils of lowland Central Otago.

The endemic element In the vascular flora of the New Zealand biological region about 78% of the species are endemic (Cockayne, 1928). Mark and Adams (1973) have stated that the level of endemism in the alpine species of the New Zealand biological region is as high as 93%. In contrast to this the level of endemism in New Zealand's macrolichen flora is very low, being of the order of 1–2%, with most of the endemics occurring in austral genera. It is probable that a higher level of endemism exists in the microlichen flora, particularly in alpine regions where they are frequently physiognomically dominant, but at present no taxonomic studies have been made in this large and varied group to support this supposition. It must be stressed however that as the lichen flora of Australia (particularly of the eastern states) is at present so poorly understood, the following account of lichens endemic to the New Zealand flora must be regarded as an interim statement liable to modification once the Australian lichens are better documented.

There is one endemic lichen genus in New Zealand, the monotypic *Thysanophoron* (*T. stereocauloides* (Nyl.) Sato) (Stirton, 1883; Sato, 1967), which is closely related to the genus *Sphaerophorus* but differs from it in having cephalodia and an organised system of secondary branches arising from a well-developed central stalk which is firmly attached to the substrate by a strong holdfast. This species grows on canopy branches of species of *Nothofagus* (especially *N. menziesii* Oerst. and *N. solandri* (Hook.fil.) Oerst. var. *cliffortioides*) and is found in both North and South Islands, being most common in forests on the eastern slopes of the Southern Alps. The monotypic genus *Cladoniopsis* (*C. caespitosa* Zahlbr.) proposed by Zahlbruckner (Zahlbruckner, 1941; Lamb, 1953) is merely a weakly branching form of the polymorphic species *Baeomyces heteromorphus* Nyl. ex Bab. & Mitt. in Hook.f.

In addition to *Thysanophoron* several other genera (predominantly southern temperate ones) have species which appear to be restricted to New Zealand. An isidiate species of *Anzia* (*A. jamesii* D. Gall., belonging to section *Nervosae*) is endemic to New Zealand and is widespread though rare and local being found from Auckland in the north to Paterson Inlet,

Stewart Island in the south. It is the first species from section *Nervosae* known from the South Pacific region. Of the seven species of *Coccocarpia* known from the New Zealand flora, three are endemic (Arvidsson and Galloway, unpublished observations) including the taxon invalidly published as *Parmeliella coronata* (Henssen, 1969; Henssen and Jahns, 1973).

Collema novozelandicum Degel. is known from the South Island where it is found from sea level to alpine localities (Degelius, 1974). *Cladonia murrayi* Martin, and *C. southlandica* Martin are interesting endemics (Martin, 1962; Ahti, 1973) and it is likely that more will be found once the New Zealand species of *Cladonia* are reassessed. Other endemic species include: *Heppia spectabilis* Zahlbr. (Zahlbruckner, 1941); *Lobaria asperula* (Stirt.) Yoshim. (Stirton, 1877); *Nephroma lyallii* Bab. in Hook.f. (Murray, 1960b); *Neuropogon subcapillaris* (D. Gall) D. Gall. (Galloway, 1968c); *Omphalo-discus subaprinus* (Frey) Llano (Frey, 1936; Llano, 1950); *Parmelia bratti* Essl. (Culberson and Esslinger, 1976); *P. epheboides* Zahlbr. (Zahlbruckner, 1941); *Polychidium contortum* Henss. (Henssen, 1963); *Sagenidium citrinum* Follm. (Follmann, 1975); and *Spilonema dendroides* (Henssen, 1963).

In the genus *Menegazzia*, six of the 10 species known from the New Zealand flora are endemic and although two of these are named (*M. aucklandica* Zahlbr., *M. nothofagi* Zahlbr. (Zahlbruckner, 1941)) the rest are undescribed. These species appear to be more closely related, chemically at least, to Asiatic and Australian taxa than to the South American species (P. W. James, pers. comm.).

Six species of *Placopsis* are endemic to New Zealand (*P. gelidoides* DR. ex Lamb, *P. illita* (Kn.) Lamb, *P. lateritiodies* Lamb, *P. salazina* Lamb, *P. subgelida* (Nyl.) Nyl., and *P. subparellina* Nyl.). A useful phytogeographical account of this genus is available (Lamb, 1947).

Of the 40 species of *Pseudocyphellaria* known at present from New Zealand 17 are endemic (Galloway and James, unpublished observations). Of these endemic species several are highly polymorphic and frequently have a complex and variable chemistry with development of well-defined chemotypes of only slight taxonomic significance (A. L. Wilkins, unpublished observations). It seems likely that the present populations of *Pseudcyphellaria* characteristic of New Zealand, South America and southeastern Australia (including Tasmania) were derived from common ancestors arising at a time when these land masses were joined or in close proximity. Upon separation of the continents, parallel speciation gave rise to a number of related vicariant species which occupy similar ecological niches. An example is the distribution of those species of *Pseudocyphellaria* having a conspicuous yellow medulla; New Zealand has the following species: *P. aurata, P. colensoi, P. coronata, P. berberina* (G. Forster)

D. Gall and P. James, *P. flavicans, P. poculifera and P. rubella* (Hook.f. & Tayl.) D. Gall. and P. James., Australian species in this group include: *P. aurata, P. colensoi, P. flavicans, P. flavissima* (Müll. Arg.) D. Gall. *in litt., P. poculifera, P. podocarpa* (Müll. Arg.) D. Gall. *in litt., and P. rubella,* and the South American species are: *P. aurata, P. berberina, P. clathrata, P. coerulescens* (Mont.) H. Magn., *P. compar* (Nyl.) H. Magn., *P. endochrysa* (Del.) Vain., *P. pilosella* Malme, and *P. scabrosa* R. Sant. (Galloway and James, 1977). While there are similarities in the species found in Australia and New Zealand there are only two species common to New Zeland and South America. Most of the South America species mentioned above have blue-green algae as their phycobiont, while the Australian species have only green phycobionts.

Although several isidiate species of *Pseudocyphellaria* are found in New Zealand only one, *P. delisea,* is at all widely distributed in the southern temperate zone. Its fertile species-pair (see Poelt, 1970) *P. homoeophylla* (Nyl.) Dodge is however known only from New Zealand. While both morphological and chemical variation is apparent in several New Zealand *Pseudocyphellaria,* none show the peculiar and striking dimorphism of some species of the related genus *Sticta* where different morphotypes are formed by the same mycobiont in association with different phycobiont genera (James and Henssen, 1976).

The genus *Psoroma* has a proliferation of species in New Zealand, many of them endemic, e.g. *P. dureitzii* P. James & A. Henss. (James and Henssen, 1975. *Stereocaulon* has four species endemic to New Zealand, the most widespread being subalpine *S. colensoi* Bab. in Hook.f., having distinctive North and South Island races, the North Island plants very possibly being influenced by growth on volcanic soils. *S. colensoi* is related to *S. implexum* Th.Fr., of South America and to *S. staufferi* Lamb, of New Guinea (Frey, 1967). The remaining endemic species, *S. fronduliferum* Lamb, and the dwarf alpine *S. gregarium* Redgr., and *S. loricatum* Lamb (Galloway *et al.,* 1976) have more restricted distributions.

Factors influencing lichen distribution in New Zealand

The distribution of lichens in New Zealand is influenced by two main interrelated processes: the diversity of habitats available for lichen establishment, and the presence of lichen sources for exploitation of newly available habitats. The low level of endemism is a reflection of both processes. Disturbance of habitats over a long period has probably led to a loss of endemic species. Recolonisation of altered habitats has been, in historical times at least, primarily by long-distance dispersal of non-endemic species. The austral and Australian components of the lichen flora comprise taxa which, on the whole, produce few asexual propagules and seem less fitted to compete with adventive species (frequently with vegetative propagules) which are often the successful colonisers of mostly Man-induced or Man-modified habitats.

Significant modification of habitats relevant to their present ecology has occurred in New Zealand since Pleistocene times and has been considerable in certain areas as a result of Polynesian and European settlement. For instance, natural and Polynesian fires that deforested large areas of the eastern South Island (Molloy *et al.*, 1963), and widespread volcanic activity in the central North Island no doubt led to the extinction of many lichen species. Re-establishment of lichens in these severely modified landscapes involved a redistribution of lichen species, many of which would be new to the New Zealand lichen flora and which were probably wind-carried as isidia or soredia, or thallus fragments, from remote sources. The ecological factors determining production and dispersal of lichen propagules have been reviewed by Hawksworth (1973), Pyatt (1974), Bowler and Rundel (1975) and Bailey 1976).

Many lichens produce large numbers of isidia and/or soredia which are easily transported by wind, and the wide distribution of sorediate and isidiate species in the floras of New Zealand, Australia and South America has undoubtedly been assisted by strong westerly winds characteristic of latitudes between 35°S and 45°S (Mason, 1971). An account of the viability of spores of New Zealand mosses during various simulated conditions of long-distance, trans-oceanic dispersal was reported by van Zanten (1976) and has relevance for any investigation of long-range dispersal of lichen diaspores. Also, dispersal of diaspores and even thallus fragments by birds must be considered as a mechanism for long-range dispersal of lichens between New Zealand, the subantarctic islands and South America (Godley, 1967; Bailey, 1976).

There is good evidence for carriage by wind from Australia to New Zealand of pollen grains, ash, insects and birds (Raven, 1973; Raven and Raven, 1976) and it is probable that lichen progagules and also thallus fragments may have been transported in this way. An example is seen in the Australian distribution of the unattached or vagant species *Chondropsis semiviridis*, characteristic of the arid sclerophyll shrublands of Australia (Filson, 1967; Rogers, 1971; Rogers and Lange, 1972). It is possible that *Chondropsis* is derived from *Xanthoparmelia* since the species *X. amphixantha* and *X. australiensis* (Cromb.) Hale show a clear tendency towards the vagant condition and their distribution is also affected by wind. In New

H

Zealand, *C. semiviridis* and *X. amphixantha* are found in the inter-montane basins of Central Otago, the Mackenzie Country, and in the upper Awatere valley, Marlborough (L. B. Moore, pers. comm.), areas with low rainfall and induced steppe as a consequence of burning and over-grazing. Since these areas were once wooded, at least in part, it seems that the two lichen species were introduced by wind from Australia within probably the last 500 years. Unfortunately their continued existence in New Zealand is threatened by the flooding of large areas of the upper Clutha and Waitaki valleys in the continuing programme of hydro-electric power development. Long-distance dispersal by wind probably also accounts for the distribution of *Xanthoparmelia molliuscula* in South Africa, Western Australia and New Zealand (Central Otago), and *Parmeliella pycnophora* (isidiate) and *Stereocaulon corticatulum* (sorediate) in New Zealand, South American and Tristan da Cunha.

The effects of trampling on lichen distribution and habitat availability can be seen in certain subalpine species of the asexual genus *Siphula*. *S. decumbens* and *S. roccellaeformis* Nyl., and to a less extent *S. complanata* R. Sant., and *S. fragilis* (Hook.f. & Tayl.) R. Sant., appear to be effectively distributed along tracks in subalpine grasslands and in the upper reaches of the forest by the trampling activity of both deer and mountaineers.

Alteration of the landscape (by burning, deforestation and drainage) as a result of European settlement has eliminated lichen species from many areas and has allowed a rapid expansion of the range of certain non-endemic species. Examples are: *Xanthoparmelia scabrosa* on roofing tiles, bitumen paths and roads; *Stereocaulon ramulosum* and *Baeomyces heteromorphus* on disturbed earth, particularly along roadsides, and the associations of predominantly sorediate species of *Parmelia, Parmotrema, Ramalina* and *Usnea*, characteristic of fenceposts in all parts of the country. The uniformity of much of the country's farmland has led to a loss of species diversity in the lichen cover here and to the emergence of certain lichens as weed species of wide distribution.

The effects of atmospheric and terrestrial pollution on lichens in urban and industrial environments has been little studied in New Zealand except for the work of Daly (1970), and nothing at all is known of the effects of widespread aerial application of fertilisers and herbicides on lichen communities. The replacement of native forests with exotic trees over large areas, and the planting of exotic trees in parks and gardens and as windbreaks on farms has allowed an extension of range of some lichen species formerly of restricted distribution such as the species association *Xanthoria parietina, Teloschistes chrysophthalmus* (L.) Th.Fr., *Physcia stellaris, P. adscendens* and *Physciopsis adglutinata* (Flk.) Choisy.

Rich in species and luxuriant in growth as the lichen flora of New

Zealand is, it is also particularly susceptible to changes in the environment caused by continuing land utilisation and human settlement. New Zealand's mountain lands have for centuries provided habitats for a wide diversity of lichen genera and species, but these are now a diminishing resource in the face of current developments in tourism, mining, forest utilisation and hydro-electric power generation. Adequate conservation measures must therefore be insisted upon if we are to preserve the element of the lichen flora which is uniquely developed there.

Acknowledgements

During the preparation of this paper I enjoyed fruitful discussions with Mr. P. W. James, Botany Department, British Museum (Natural History) London, and Dr. A. L. Wilkins, Chemistry Department, University of Waikato, Hamilton, New Zealand and to them I tender my thanks. Fil.Lic. P. M. Jørgensen, Botanical Museum, University of Bergen generously made available to me unpublished work on Tristan da Cunha and also contributed useful phytogeographical data which I gratefully acknowledge. I have also benefitted from discussions on the distributions of Australian lichens with Mr. N. Sammy, Botany Department, University of Western Australia, and most particularly with the late Dr. G. C. Bratt of Hobart, Tasmania. The following New Zealand colleagues, Dr. E. J. Godley, Professor A. F. Mark, Dr. M. J. Parsons, Mr. K. R. West and Mr. H. D. Wilson critically read the manuscript and made many constructive comments on it and for their help I am particularly grateful.

REFERENCES

Ahti, T. (1961). Taxonomic studies on reindeer lichens (*Cladonia* subgenus *Cladina*). *Ann. Bot. Soc. Zool.-Bot. Fenn. Vanamo* **32**, 1–160

— (1973). Taxonomic notes on some species of *Cladonia* subsect. *Unciales*. *Ann. Bot. Fennici* **10**, 163–184

Babington, C. (1855). Lichenes. In Hooker, J. D., *Botany of the Antarctic Voyage of H.M. Discovery Ships* Erebus *and* Terror, *in the Years 1839–1843*. II, Flora Novae Zelandiae. Part II Flowerless Plants, 266–311. L. Reeve & Co, London

Baker, C., Elix, J. A., Murphy, D. P. H., Kurokawa, S. and Sargent, M. V. (1973). *Parmelia reptans*, a new lichen species producing the depsidone, succinprotocetraric acid. *Aust. J. Bot.* **21**, 137–140

Bailey, R. H. (1976). Ecological aspects of dispersal and establishment in lichens. In *Lichenology: Progress and Problems* (D. H. Brown, D. L. Hawskworth and R. H. Bailey, eds.), 215–247. Academic Press, London and New York

Blackman, A. J., Bratt, G. C. and Cashin, J. A. (1973). Distribution and chemistry of *Heterodea muelleri* (Hampe) Nyl. *Bryologist* **76**, 410–413

—, Bratt, G. C. and Cashin, J. A. (1974). Umbilicariaceae in Tasmania. *Lichenol.* **6**, 112–114

Bliss, L. C. and Mark, A. F. (1974). High-alpine environments and primary production on the Rock and Pillar Range, Central Otago, New Zealand. *N.Z. J. Bot.* **12**, 445–483

Bory de Saint Vincent, M. (1828) *Voyage autour du monde sur la corvette Coquille pendant les années 1822, 1823, 1824 and 1825.* 232p. Paris

Bowler, P. A. and Rundel, P. W. (1975). Reproductive strategies in lichens. *Bot. J. Linn. Soc.* **70**, 325–340

Bratt, G. C., Blackman, A. J. and Cashin, J. A. (1976). The genus *Anzia* in Tasmania. *Lichenol.* **8**, 69–77

Brodo, I. M. and Hawksworth, D. L. (1977). *Alectoria* and allied genera in North America. *Opera Bot.* **42**, 1–164

Burrows, C. J. (1969). Alpine grasslands. In *The Natural History of Canterbury* (G. A. Knox, ed.), 117–132. A. H. and A. W. Reed, Wellington

— (1973). Studies on some glacial moraines in New Zealand. 2. Ages of moraines of the Mueller, Hooker and Tasman glaciers. *N.Z. J. Geol. Geophys.* **16** (4), 831–855

— and Lucas, J. (1967). Variations in two New Zealand glaciers during the past 800 years. *Nature, Lond.* **216**, 467–468

— and Orwin, J. (1971). Studies on some glacial moraines in New Zealand. 1. The establishment of lichen growth curves in the Mount Cook area. *N.Z. J. Sci.* **14** (2), 327–335

Cockayne, L. (1928). *The Vegetation of New Zealand.* 2nd edn., 456p. Wilhelm Engelmann, Leipzig

Coulter, J. D. (1975). The climate. In *Biogeography and Ecology in New Zealand* (G. Kuschel, ed.), 87–138. Junk, The Hague

Culberson, C. F. and Esslinger, T. L. (1976). 4-0-Methylolivetoric and loxodellic acids: New depsides from new species of brown *Parmeliae. Bryologist* **79** (1), 42–46

Culberson, W. L. (1972). Disjunctive distributions in the lichen-forming fungi. *Ann. Miss. Bot. Gard.* **59**, 165–173

— and Culberson, C. F. (1968). The lichen genera *Cetrelia* and *Platismatia* (Parmeliaceae). *Contr. U.S. Nat. Herb.* **34** (7), 449–558

Cunningham, A. (1836). Flora insularum Novae Zelandiae precursor, or a specimen of the botany of the islands of New Zealand. *Hook. Comp. Bot. Mag.* **11**, 327–335

Daly, G. T. (1970). Bryophyte and lichen indicators of air pollution in Christchurch, New Zealand. *Proc. N.Z. Ecol. Soc.* **17**, 70–79

Darbishire, O. V. (1912). The lichens of the Swedish Antarctic Expedition. *Wiss. Ergebn. schwed. Südp.-Expedn. 1901–1903* **4** (2), 1–74

Dawson, J. W. (1958). Interrelationships of the Australasian and South American floras. *Tuatara* **7**(1), 1–6

Degelius, G. (1974). The lichen genus *Collema* with special reference to the extra-European species. *Symb. Bot. Upsal.* **20** (2), 1–215

Des Abbayes, H. (1968). Les lichens du genre *Thysanothecium* Mont. et Berk., (Cladoniacées) et leur constitution chimique. *J. Jap. Bot.* **43**, 302–304

Dodge, C. W. (1948). Lichens and lichen parasites. *B.A.N.Z.A.R.E. Repts* **7**, 1–276

— (1970). Lichenological notes on the flora of the Antarctic continent and subantarctic islands. *Nova Hedwigia* **19**, 439–502

— (1973). *Lichen Flora of the Antarctic Continent and Adjacent Islands.* 399p. Phoenix Publ., Canaan, New Hampshire

Du Rietz, G. E. (1928). The discovery of an arctic element in the lichen flora of New Zealand and its plant geographical consequences. *Rept. A.N.Z.A.A.S.* **19**, 628–635

— (1940). Problems of bipolar plant distribution. *Acta Phytogeogr. Sueic.* **13**, 215–282

Elix, J. A. (1975). 2′-0-Methylphysodic acid and hydroxyphysodic acid: Two new depsidones from the lichen *Hypogymnia billardierii*. *Aust. J. Chem.* **28**, 849–858

— (1976). Three new species of *Parmelia* subgen. *Xanthoparmelia* (Lichens) from south-eastern Australia. *Aust. J. Bot.* **24**, 663–668

Filson, R. B. (1967). Supplementary descriptions for two Victorian desert lichens. *Mulleria* **1**, 197–202

— (1970). Studies in Australian lichens I. *Cladonia* and *Hypogymnia*. *Vict. Nat.* **87**, 324–327

Fleming, C. A. (1962). New Zealand biogeography. A palaeontologist's approach. *Tuatara* **10** (2), 53–108

— (1963). The nomenclature of biogeographic elements in the New Zealand biota. *Trans. Roy. Soc. N.Z. (General)* **1** (2), 13–22

— (1975). The geological history of New Zealand and its biota. In *Biogeography and Ecology in New Zealand* (G. Kuschel, ed.), 1–86. Junk, The Hague

Follman, G. (1975). Vorarbeiten zu einer Monographie der Flechtenfamilie Roccellaceae Chev. I. Die Gattung *Sagenidium* Stirt. *Bot. Jahrb. Syst.* **96**, 45–52

— (1976). Zur Nomenklatur der Lichenen III. Über *Desmazieria* Mont. (Ramalinaceae) und andere kritische Verwandtschaftskreise. *Philippia* **3** (2), 85–89

Frey, E. (1936). Vorarbeiten zu einer Monographie der Umbilicariaceen. *Ber. Schweiz. Bot. Ges.* **45**, 198–230

— (1967). Die Lichenologischen Ergebnisse der Forschungsreisen des Dr Hans Ulrich Stauffer in Zentralafrika (Virunga-Vulkane 1954–55) und Südafrika-Australien-Ozeanien-USA 1963–64. *Bot. Jahrb.* **86**, 209–255

Galloway, D. J. (1968a). The lichens of Stewart Island 1. The Mount Anglem highlands. *Trans. Roy. Soc. N.Z. (Bot.)* **3**, 231–236

— (1968b). The lichens of Stewart Island 2. Port Pegasus. *N.Z. J. Bot.* **6**, 309–314

— (1968c). A new variety of *Usnea (Neuropogon) ciliata* (Nyl.) DR., in southern New Zealand. *N.Z. J. Bot.* **6**, 470–472

— (1974). A bibliography of New Zealand lichenology. *N.Z. J. Bot.* **12**, 397–422

— (1976). H. H. Allan's early collections of New Zealand lichens. *N.Z. J. Bot.* **14**, 225–230

— (1977a). Additional notes on the lichen genus *Cladia* Nyl., in New Zealand. *Nova Hedwigia* **28**, 475–486

— (1977b). The lichen genus *Thysanothecium* Mont. and Berk., an historical note. *Nova Hedwigia* **28**, 499–513

— and Jørgensen, P. M. (1975). *Erioderma sorediatum*, a new lichen from New Zealand. *Lichenol.* **7**, 139–142

— Lamb, I. M. and Bratt, G. C. (1976). Two new species of *Stereocaulon* from New Zealand and Tasmania. *Lichenol.* **8**, 61–67

— and James, P. W. (1977). *Pseudocyphellaria berberina* (G. Forster) D. Gall. and P. James: Notes on its discovery and synonymy. *Lichenol.* **9**, 95–105

Godley, E. J. (1960). The Botany of Southern Chile in relation to New Zealand and the subantarctic. *Proc. Roy. Soc. B.* **152**, 457–475

— (1967). Widely distributed species, land bridges and continental drift. *Nature, Lond.* **214**, 74–75.

— (1975). Flora and vegetation. In *Biogeography and Ecology in New Zealand* (G. Kuschel, ed.), 177–229. Junk, The Hague

Hale, M. E. (1965). A monograph of Parmelia subgenus *Amphigymnia*. *Contr. U.S. Nat. Herb.* **36** (5), 193–358

— (1974). New combinations in the lichen genus *Parmotrema* Massalongo *Phytologia* **28** (4), 334–339

— (1975a). A revision of the lichen genus *Hypotrachyna* (Parmeliaceae) in tropical America. *Smiths. Contr. Bot.* **25**, 1–73

— (1975b). A monograph of the lichen genus *Relicina* (Parmeliaceae). *Smiths. Contr. Bot.* **26**, 1–32

— (1976a). A monograph of the lichen genus *Pseudoparmelia* Lynge (Parmeliaceae). *Smiths. Contr. Bot.* **31**, 1–62

— (1976b). A monograph of the lichen genus *Bulbothrix* Hale (Parmeliaceae). *Smiths. Cont. Bot.* **32**, 1–29

— (1967c). A monograph of the lichen genus *Parmelina* Hale (Parmeliaceae). *Smiths. Cont. Bot.* **33**, 1–60

— (1976d). Synopsis of a new lichen genus *Everniastrum* Hale (Parmeliaceae). *Mycotaxon* **3** (3), 345–353

Hawksworth, D. L. (1972). Regional studies in *Alectoria* (Lichenes) II. The British species. *Lichenol.* **5**, 181–261

— (1973). Ecological factors and species delimitation in the lichens. In *Taxonomy and Ecology* (V. H. Heywood, ed.), 31–69. Academic Press, London and New York

Hellbom, P. J. (1896). Lichenaea noe-zelandica seu lichens Novae Zelandiae a Sven Berggren annis 1874–1875 collecti. *Bihang Kongl. Sv. Vet.-Akad. Handl.* **21**, 1–150

Henssen, A. (1963). Eine Revision der Flechtenfamilien Lichinaceae und Ephebaceae. *Symb. Bot. Upsal.* **18** (1), 1–120

— (1969). Die Entstehung des Thallusrandes bei den Pannariaceen (Lichens). *Ber. Dtsch. Bot. Ges.* **82**, 235–248

— (1977). The genus Zahlbrucknerella. *Lichenol.* **9**, 17–46

— and Jahns, H. M. (1973) ["1974"]. *Lichens. Eine Einführung in die Flechtenkunde.* 467p. Georg Thieme, Stuttgart

Hooker, J. D. (1853). Introductory essay to the flora of New Zealand. In *Flora Novae Zelandiae*. Part I. L. Reeve & Co, London

— (1860) *Introductory essay to Flora Tasmaniae*. L. Reeve & Co, London

— (1867) *Handbook of the New Zealand Flora*, 550–594. L. Reeve & Co, London

— and Taylor, T. (1844). "Lichens Antarctici"; being characters and brief descriptions of the new *Lichens* discovered in the southern circumpolar regions Van Diemen's Land and New Zealand during the voyage of H.M. Discovery ships *Erebus* and *Terror*. *Hook. Lond. J. Bot.* **3**, 634–658

Huneck, S., Redon, J. and Quilhot, W. (1973). Mitteilungen über Flechteninhaltsstoffe XCVII. Zur Phytochemie südamerikanischer *Pseudocyphellariaceen. J. Hattori Bot. Lab.* **37**, 539–562

Jahns, H. M. and Knapp, P. van der (1973). Die Flechtengattung *Heterodea* Nyl., Systematik und Ontogenie der Fruchtkörper. *Herzogia* **2**, 437–451

James, P. W. and Henssen, A. (1975). A new species of *Psoroma* with sorediate cephalodia. *Lichenol.* **7**, 143–147

— and Henssen, A. (1976). The morphological and taxonomic significance of cephalodia. In *Lichenology: Progress and Problems* (D. H. Brown, D. L. Hawksworth and R. H. Bailey, eds.), 27–77. Academic Press, London and New York

Jørgensen, P. M. (1975). Contributions to a monograph of the *Mallotium*-hairy *Leptogium* species. *Herzogia* **3**, 433–460

— (1977). Foliose and fruticose lichens from Tristan da Cunha. *Det Norske Videnskaps-Akad. Skrift. I. Mat.-Nat.Kl.Ny Ser.* **36**, 1–40

Krog, H. (1976). *Lethariella* and *Protousnea* two new lichen genera in Parmeliaceae. *Norw. J. Bot.* **23**, 83–106

Kurokawa, S. (1969). On the occurrence of norlobaridone in *Parmeliae. J. Hattori Bot. Lab.* **32**, 205–215

— (1973). Supplementary notes on the genus *Anaptychia. J. Hattori Bot. Lab.* **37**, 563–607

— and Elix, J. A. (1971). Two new Australian Parmeliae. *J. Jap. Bot.* **46** (4), 113–116

— Elix, J. A., Watson, P. L. and Sargent, M. V. (1971). *Parmelia notata*, a new lichen species producing two new depsidones. *J. Jap. Bot.* **46** (2), 33–36

— and Filson, R. B. (1975). New species of *Parmelia* from South Australia. *Bull. Nat. Sci. Mus. Tokyo Ser. B (Bot.)* **1** (1), 35–47

Lamb, I. M. (1939). A review of the genus *Neuropogon* (Nees and Flot.) Nyl., with special reference to the Antarctic species. *J. Linn. Soc. Lond.* **52**, 199–237

— (1947). A monograph of the lichen genus *Placopsis* Nyl. *Lilloa* **13**, 151–288

— (1948a). Further data on the genus *Neuropogon. Lilloa* **14**, 139–168

— (1948b). New, rare or interesting lichens from the Southern Hemisphere I. *Lilloa* **14**, 203–251

— (1949). La importanica de los liquenes como indicadores fitogeograficos en el hemisferio austral. *Lilloa* **20**, 65–68

— (1951). On the morphology, phylogeny and taxonomy of the lichen genus *Stereocaulon*. *Can. J. Bot.* **29**, 522–584

— (1953). New, rare or interesting lichens from the Southern Hemisphere II. *Lilloa* **26**, 401–438

— (1958). La vegetación liquénica de los Parques Nacionales Patagónicos. *Ann. Parques Nacion. Buenos Aires* **7**, 1–188

— (1964). Antarctic lichens I. The genera *Usnea, Ramalina, Himantormia, Alectoria* and *Cornicularia*. *Br. Ant. Surv. Sci. Rept.* **38**, 1–34

— (1974). The lichen genus *Argopsis* Th.Fr. *J. Hattori Bot. Lab.* **38**, 447–462

— and Ward, A. (1974). A preliminary conspectus of the species attributed to the imperfect lichen genus *Leprocaulon* Nyl. *J. Hattori Bot. Lab.* **38**, 499–553

Lindsay, W. L. (1866). List of lichens collected in Otago, New Zealand. *Trans. Bot. Soc. Edin.* **8**, 349–358

— (1868). *Contributions to New Zealand Botany.* 102p. Williams and Norgate, Edinburgh

Llano, G. A. (1950). A monograph of the lichen family Umbilicariaceae in the Western Hemisphere. 281p. Off. Nav. Res. Dept. of the Navy, Washington, D.C.

Malme, G. O. A. N. (1899). Beiträge zur Stictaceen Flora Feuerlands und Patagoniens. *Bihang Kongl. Sv. Vet.-Akad. Handl.* **25.III (5)**, 1–40

Mark, A. F. and Adams, N. M. (1973). *New Zealand Alpine Plants.* 262p. A. H. and A. W. Reed, Wellington

— and Bliss, L. C. (1970). The high-alpine vegetation of Central Otago, New Zealand. *N.Z. J. Bot.* **8**, 382–451

Martin, W. (1958a). The *Cladoniae* of New Zealand. *Trans. Roy. Soc. N.Z.* **85**, 603–632

— (1958b). Notes on *Cladonia*, subgenus *Clathrina*. *Bryologist* **61**, 78–81

— (1962). Notes on some New Zeland species of *Cladonia* with descriptions of two new species and one new form. *Trans. Roy. Soc. N.Z. (Bot.)* **2**, 39–44

— (1965a). Comparison of lichen floras of New Zealand and Tasmania. *Trans. Roy. Soc. N.Z. (Bot.)* **3**, 1–6

— (1965b). The lichen genus *Cladia*. *Trans. Roy. Soc. N.Z. (Bot.)* **3**, 7–12

— (1966). Census catalogue of the lichen flora of New Zealand *Trans. Roy. Soc. N.Z. (Bot.)* **3**, 139–159

— (1968). Supplement to census catalogue of New Zealand lichens. *Trans. Roy. Soc. N.Z. (Bot.)* **3**, 203–208

Mason, B. J. (1971). Global atmosphere research programme. *Nature, Lond.* **233**, 382–388

Mathey, A. (1971). Contribution à l'étude du genre *Siphula* (Lichens) en Afrique. *Nova Hedwigia* **22**, 795–878

Molloy, B. P. J., Burrows, C. J., Cox, J. E., Johnston, S. A. and Wardle, P.

(1963). Distribution of subfossil forest remains, eastern South Island, New Zealand. *N.Z. J. Bot.* **1**, 68–77

Montagne, J. C. F. (1852). *Liquenes.* In Gay, C., *Hist. fis. y pol. Chile* **8**, 53–228

Motyka, J. (1936–38). *Lichenum Generis Usena Studium Monographicum.* Pars Systematica I (1–304) and II (305–651). Leopoli

Müller-Argoviensis, J. (1894). Conspectus systematicus lichenum Novae Zelandiae. *Bull. Herb. Boiss.* **2**, 2–16, 17–114

Murray, J. (1960a). Studies of New Zealand lichens. I. The Coniocarpineae. *Trans. Roy. Soc. N.Z.* **88**, 177–195

— (1960b). Studies of New Zealand lichens. III. The family Peltigeraceae. *Trans. Roy. Soc. N.Z.* **88**, 381–391

Nylander, W. (1866). Lichenes Novae Zelandiae, quos ibi legit anno 1861 Dr Lauder Lindsay. *J. Linn. Soc. Lond. (Bot.)* **9**, 244–259

— (1888). *Lichenes Novae Zealandiae.* 156p. P. Schmidt, Paris

Orwin, J. (1970). Lichen succession on recently deposited rock surfaces. *N.Z. J. Bot.* **8**, 452–477

— (1972). The effect of environment on assemblages of lichens growing on rock surfaces. *N.Z. J. Bot.* **10**, 37–47

Oshio, M. (1968). Taxonomical studies on the family Pertusariaceae of Japan. *J. Sci. Hirosh. Univ. ser. B.Dov. 2 (Bot.)* **12** (1), 81–163

Poelt, J. (1970). Das Konzept der Arten-Paare bei den Flechten. *Dtsch. Bot. Ges. N.F.* **4**, 187–198

Pyatt, F. B. (1974) ["1973"]. Lichen propagules. In *The Lichens* (V. Ahmadjian and M. E. Hale, eds.), 117–145. Academic Press, London and New York

Raoul, E. (1846). *Choix de plantes de la Nouvelle Zélande.* 56p. Fortin, Masson & Cie, Paris

Raven, P. H. (1972). Plant species disjunctions: a summary. *Ann. Miss. Bot. Gard.* **59** (2), 234–246

— (1973). The evolution of subalpine and alpine plant groups in New Zealand. *N.Z. J. Bot.* **11**, 177–200

— and Axelrod, D. I. (1972). Plate tectonics and Australasian palaeobiogeography. *Science* **176**, 1379–1386

— and Raven, T. E. (1976). The genus *Epilobium* (Onagraceae) in Australasia: a systematic and evolutionary study. *N.Z. D.S.I.R. Bull.* **216**, 1–321

Redon, J. (1973). Beobachtungen zur Geographie und Ökologie der chilenischen Flechtenflora. *J. Hattori Bot. Lab.* **37**, 153–167

Richard, A. (1832). Essai d'une flore de la Nouvelle Zélande. Lichens. In A. Lesson and A. Richard, *Voyage de découvertes de l'Astrolabe éxecuté par ordre du Roi pendant les années 1826–1829, sous le commandement de M. J. Dummont-D'Urville,* 22–38. Part. Bot. Tastu, Paris

Rogers, R. W. (1971). Distribution of the lichen *Chondropsis semiviridis* in relation to its heat and drought resistance. *New Phytol.* **70**, 1069–1077

— and Lange, R. T. (1972). Soil surface lichens in arid and sub-arid south-eastern Australia. I. Introduction and floristics. *Aust. J. Bot.* **20**, 197–213

Santesson, R. (1942a). South American *Menegazziae.* *Ark.f. Bot.* **30A** (3), 1–35

— (1942b). The South American *Cladinae.* *Ark.f. Bot.* **30A** (3), 1–27

— (1944). Contributions to the lichen flora of South America *Ark.f. Bot.* **31A** (3), 1–28

— (1949). *Dolichocarpus* and *Xanthopeltis* two new lichen genera from Chile. *Sv. Bot. Tidskr.* **43**, 547–567

Sato, M. (1965). The mixture ratio of the lichen genus *Thamnolia* in New Zealand. *Bryologist* **68**, 320–324

— (1966). Mixture ratio of the lichen genus *Thamnolia* in New Zealand. *Misc. Bryol. Lichenol.* **4**, 1

— (1967). A new genus of the lichen family Sphaerophoraceae. *Misc. Bryol. Lichenol.* **4**, 107–109

Schofield, W. B. (1974). Bipolar disjunctive mosses in the Southern Hemisphere with particular reference to New Zealand. *J. Hattori Bot. Lab.* **38**, 13–32

Sierk, H. A. (1964). The genus *Leptogium* in North America north of Mexico. *Bryologist* **67** (3), 295–317

Stirton, J. (1877). On new genera and species of lichens from New Zealand. *Proc. Glasg. Phil. Soc.* **10**, 285–306

— (1883). On lichens (1) from Newfoundland collected by Mr A. Gray with a list of species; (2) from New Zealand; (3) from the south of Scotland. *Trans. Bot. Soc. Edin.* **14**, 355–362

Swartz, O. (1783). "Methodus Muscorum Illustrata". Praes Carolus a Linne. *Act. Med. Suec.* **1**, 155–204

Swinscow, T. D. V. and Krog, H. (1976a). The genera *Anaptychia* and *Heterodermia* in East Africa. *Lichenol.* **8**, 103–138

— and Krog, H. (1976b). The genus *Coccocarpia* in East Africa. *Norw. J. Bot.* **23**, 251–259

Wardle, P. (1963). Evolution and distribution of the New Zealand flora as affected by quaternary climates. *N.Z. J. Bot.* **1**, 3–17

Weber, W. A. and Wetmore, C. M. (1972). Catalogue of the lichens of Australia exclusive of Tasmania. *Beith. Nova Hedwigia* **41**, 1–137

Wetmore, C. M. (1963). Catalogue of the lichens of Tasmania. *Rev. Bryol. Lichenol.* **32**, 223–264

Wilson, H. D. (1976). Vegetation of the Mount Cook National Park, New Zealand. *Nat. Parks Authority Sci.* **Ser. I**, 1–138

Yoshimura, I. (1973). Notes on *Gymnoderma melacarpum* comb. nov. *J. Jap. Bot* **48** (9), 283–288

Zahlbruckner, A. (1924) Die Flechten der Juan Fernandez Inseln. *Nat. Hist. Juan Fernandez, Easter Island* **2**, 315–408

— (1941). Lichens Novae Zelandiae. *Denkschr, Akad. Wiss. Wien* **104**, 249–380

Zanten, B. O. van (1976). Preliminary report on germination experiments designed to estimate the survival chances of moss spores during aerial transoceanic long-range dispersal in the Southern Hemisphere, with particular reference to New Zealand. *J. Hattori Bot. Lab.* **41**, 133–140

11 Endemism and Evolution in Galapagos Islands Vascular Plants

DUNCAN M. PORTER   *Dept. of Biology, Virginia Polytechnic Institute and State University, Blacksburg, U.S.A.*

La actividad volcánica ha dado origen a las islas Galápagos, las cuales son auténticas islas volcánicas. A pesar de algunas controversias en el pasado, no existe evidencia física que indique que estuvieran alguna vez conectadas a Sur o Centro América por medio de una lengua de tierra. La actividad volcánica continúa en la actualidad, existiendo muchos rios de lava que han aparecido tan recientemente que aún en ellos no ha crecido la vegetación. La geología del Archipiélago es bien conocida y los estudios más recientes indican que tiene una probable antiguedad máxima de 3 millones de años. Aunque están en el Ecuador, las Galápagos están mas cercanas a las islas desiertas que lo están de las islas de fresca y abundante vegetación que suelen asociarse con el trópico. Las plantas dependen principalmente de la lluvia esporádica que cae de Diciembre a Junio, aunque las que alcanzan mayor altura (por encima de 200 m) las grandes islas, pueden ser envueltas en neblinas casi diariamente. El promedio de lluvia caida es menor de 75 cm/año, y existe una marcada variación de año en año. La cantidad de lluvia caida también varía según la dirección de las laderas (las del Sur son más húmedas, ya que la lluvia viene principalmente del Sur-Este), altitud (más a una altitud mediana, 200 a 500 m) y corrientes oceánicas. De Julio a Noviembre, el Archipiélago es fresco y brumoso con pocas precipitaciones. El promedio más alto de temperatura durante la estación cálida lluviosa es de aproximadamente 29°C. Durante la estación fresca y seca, 19°C. Este régimen climático resulta de la interacción de dos factores principales. Durante la estación seca, hay grandes afloramientos de aguas frias subterráneas en el Oeste del Archipiélago, mientras que la estación de lluvias coincide con la llegada de aguas calientes de superficie arrastradas desde el Norte.

Siete zonas de vegetación deben ser reconocidas en el Archipiélago: zona litoral (aparece al nivel del mar); zona árida (inmediatamente hacia el interior desde la zona del litoral a altitudes de 80 a 300 m o más altas); zona de transición (por encima de la zona árida, desde, raramente, las cercanias del nivel del mar a una altitud de aproximadamente 320 m); zona *Scalesia* (en las islas más largas y altas desde 180 a 550 m); zona *Morena*; zona *Miconia* (por encima de la zona de *Scalesia* desde 400 a 700 m); y zona de helechos (desde 500 m hasta las cimas de los volcanes).

Cada zona tiene sus propias características dominantes, aunque muchas especies pueden distribuirse a través de más de una zona. La zona de helechos es la más húmeda. Los aguaceros van decreciendo abajo de las laderas.

La flora consiste en 543 taxones indigenas aparte de 192 malas hierbas y especies escapadas de jardines introducidas por el hombre, dando un total de 735

225

plantas vasculares. El cuarenta y tres por ciento (231) de la taxa indígena (especies, subspecies o variedades) son endémicas. Esto incluye 8/107 pteridofitas, 18/85 monocotiledones, y 205/351 dicotiledones. Existen también siete géneros endémicos que aparecen en las Asteraceae (*Darwiniothamnus*, *Lecocarpus*, *Macraea* y *Scalesia*), Cactaceae (*Brachycereus* y *Jasminocerus*), y Cucurbitaceae (*Sicyocaulis*). El parentesco geográfico de la flora está en su vecina Sur América. Los pájaros han jugado el papel más importante en la dispersión de plantas a las islas.

Las islas Galápagos son bién conocidas a través de los trabajos de Charles Darwin, que visitó del Archipiélago en 1835. Su fauna jugó una parte muy significante en las ideas de Darwin referente al papel de la selección natural en evolución. Los pinzones de las Galápagos han servido como un ejemplo clásico de radiación adaptativa. Menos conocidas son las radiaciones adaptativas que han tenido lugar en los géneros de plantas como *Acalypha* (6 taxones), *Alternanthera* (8), *Aristida* (4), *Borreria* (6), *Chamaesyce* (9), *Cordia* (3), *Croton* (4), *Darwiniothamnus* (4), *Froelichia* (5), *Jasminocereus* (3), *Lecocarpus* (3), *Mollugo* (9), *Opuntia* (14), *Paspalum* (3), *Polygala* (5), *Scalesia* (20), y *Tiquilia* (3). Estas radiaciones, excepto para las *Darwiniothamnus* y *Paspalum*, han tenido lugar básicamente en la zona arida. La mayor diversidad de especies también se encuentra en esta zona.

El endemismo por zonas de vegetación es como sigue: Litoral (10 taxones), Arida (137), Transición (17), Scalesia (56), Morena (1), Miconia (1), y Helechos (9), Esto llega a ser incluso más sorprendente cuando las zonas están divididas dentro del Litoral (10), básicamente árida (Arida y Transición – 154), y básicamente mésica (Scalesia, Miconia y Helechos – 67).

Estudios recientes sobre la historia vegetativa de las islas basados en polen y esporas fósiles indican que en los pasados 25 000 años hubo un periodo seco de 15 000 años seguido de 10 000 años donde habitats más mésicos se presentaron. Esta historia está reflejada en las distribuciones y radiaciones de las plantas vasculares endémicas.

Introduction

The Galapagos Islands lie astride the equator in the eastern Pacific Ocean between about 800 and 1100 km west of the South American continent. They extend from approximately 89° 14′ to 92° 01′ west longitude, and from 1° 40′ north to 1° 25′ south latitude. This archipelago consists of some 45 islands, islets, and rocks, including nine islands of over 50 km² in area (Fig. 1). The largest, Isabela, covers approximately 4700 km², over half of the total land surface of the archipelago, which is about 7900 km². Isabela is four times the size of Santa Cruz, the second largest island. It and Fernandina have volcanoes that reach up to 1500 m in elevation or higher, but most of the land is relatively low. For a discussion of Galapagos soils, see van der Werff's paper, chapter 20.

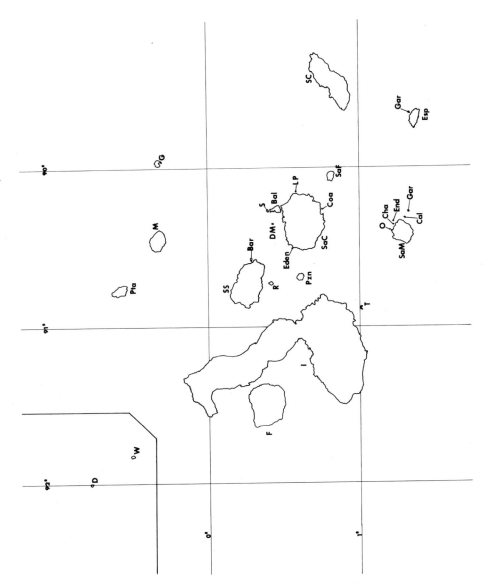

Fig. 1 Map of the Galapagos Islands. Key to island abbreviations (English names where they differ follow the official Ecuadorean names in parentheses): Bal, Baltra (South Seymour); Bar, Bartolomé (Bartholomew); Cal, Caldwell; Cha, Champion; Coa, Coamaño; D, Darwin (Culpepper); DM, Daphne Major; Eden, Eden; End, Enderby; Esp, Española (Hood); F, Fernandina (Narborough); G, Genovesa (Tower); Gar (Esp), Gardner (cerca de Española) (Gardner (near Hood)); Gar (SaM), Gardner (cerca de Santa Maria) (Gardner (near Charles)); I, Isabela (Albemarle); LP, Las Plazas; M, Marchena (Bindloe); O, Onslow; Pta, Pinta (Abingdon); Pzn, Pinzón (Duncan); R, Rábida (Jervis); S, Seymour (North Seymour); SaC, Santa Cruz (Indefatigable); SaF, Santa Fé (Barrington); SaM, Santa María (Charles); SC, San Cristóbal (Chatham); SS, San Salvador (James); T, Tortuga (Brattle); W, Wolf (Wenman)

227

The islands are a province of Ecuador, which claimed them in 1832. They are known officially as El Archipiélago de Colón, although they are rarely referred to as such. In addition, each island has at least one English and one Spanish name, the latter being official. The administrative capital is Puerto Baquerizo Moreno (Wreck Bay) on San Cristóbal. The Charles Darwin Research Station, founded under the auspices of UNESCO in 1964, is at Bahía Academía (Academy Bay) on Santa Cruz. It is the centre for biological investigations in the archipelago.

Volcanic activity has given rise to the Galapagos, which are true oceanic islands. In spite of some past controversy, there is no physical evidence to indicate that they were ever connected to the mainland of South or Central America via a landbridge. Volcanic activity continues today, and there are many lava flows which have occurred so recently that they have not yet been vegetated. The archipelago's geology is well covered in McBirney and Williams (1969). The most recent evidence indicates that it has a probable maximum age of three million years (Bailey, 1976).

Although they are on the equator, the Galapagos are closer to desert islands than they are to the lushly vegetated islands that one usually associates with the tropics. The lowland plants depend mainly upon the sporadic rain that falls from January to June, although those at higher elevations (above approximately 200 m) on the larger islands may be bathed in fog almost daily. Average rainfall in the lowlands is less than 75 cm/year, and there is marked variation from year to year as well. From July to December, the archipelago is cool and foggy with little precipitation in the lowlands, but with much at higher elevations (see van der Werff's Fig. 1).

The rainfall pattern also varies with slope direction (south slopes being wetter, rains coming mainly from the south east), with elevation (rainfall being higher the higher up one goes, with the exceptions of the highest volcanoes, which penetrate above the clouds), and with ocean currents. The highest average temperatures during the warm season are about 29°C, during the cool season about 19°C. This climatic regime appears to result from the interaction of two main factors (Houvenaghel, 1974). During the cool season there are large upwellings of cold subsurface waters to the west of the archipelago, while the warm season coincides with the arrival of warm surface waters drifting down from the north. A more detailed discussion of the Galapagos climate will be found in van der Werff's paper (chapter 20).

Vegetation

Seven principal vegetation zones may be recognised in the archipelago (zonation is discussed in detail in Wiggins and Porter, 1971, but more thorough studies are badly needed): *Littoral Zone* (occurring at sea level); *Arid Zone* (immediately inland from the Littoral Zone to elevations of 80 to 300 m or higher); *Transition Zone* (above the Arid Zone, from rarely near sea level to an elevation of about 320 m); *Scalesia Zone* (on the larger, higher islands from 180 to 550 m); *Brown Zone* (intermediate between the Scalesia Zone and the next);, *Miconia Zone* (above the Brown Zone from 400 to 700 m); and *Fern-Sedge Zone* (from 500 m to the summits of most of the volcanoes).

The Fern-Sedge Zone is the wettest, rainfall decreasing downslope from it. The highest volcanoes (Wolf and Cerro Azul on Isabela) project above the cloud cover and are arid. In addition, as pointed out to me by van der Werff, the vegetation on the cinder soils of Fernandina, Isabela, and Santa María does not fall into the above scheme. Other, less widespread vegetation types occur as well, but they have not yet been studied. Each zone has its own characteristic dominants, although many species may range through more than one zone. The vegetation zones on southern Santa Cruz, representative for those islands with human settlements, are discussed in van der Werff's chapter.

All vegetation zones will be found only on the larger, higher islands, which have higher rainfall. The lower, smaller, drier islands generally contain only the lower two or three zones. Distribution of the zones also is dependent upon exposure. South-facing slopes being wetter, the zones will be found at lower elevations on them than on northern slopes. The plant ecology of the archipelago needs much work. The most comprehensive field study of Galapagos vegetation remains that of Stewart (1915). The first priority for ecological studies is the construction of a vegetation map, which is in progress under UNESCO auspices.

Flora

The Galapagos Flora consists of 543 indigenous taxa (species, subspecies, or varieties), plus 192 weeds and garden escapes introduced by Man, for a total of 735 vascular plants. These figures are slightly higher than those of Porter (1976), reflecting the recent reports of Adsersen (1976a, b) and van der Werff (1977). The geographical relationships of the flora are with adjacent South America. Birds have played the most important role in the dispersal of plants to the islands (Porter, 1976). In addition to the endemic species discussed in the next section, there are seven endemic genera, occurring in the Asteraceae (*Darwiniothamnus, Lecocarpus, Macraea* and *Scalesia*), Cactaceae (*Brachycereus* and *Jasminocereus*), and Cucurbitaceae (*Sicyocaulis*).

The Galapagos Islands are well known through the works of Charles Darwin, who visited the archipelago in September and October 1835. Their fauna played a significant role in Darwin's ideas regarding the role of natural selection in evolution. Less well appreciated has been the effect that the flora had on his scientific work. Darwin's life-long interest in plant geography and dispersal mechanisms can be directly attributed to his visit to the Galapagos. There was much correspondence in the 1840s between Darwin and J. D. Hooker, later Director of the Royal Botanic Gardens, Kew on the derivation and relationships of the island's plants. The first flora of the archipelago, in fact, was based primarily on Darwin's collections (Hooker, 1847a).

The Galapagos finches have served as a classical example of adaptive radiation, the evolution of several divergent forms, each adapted to a different niche, from a single ancestral form. Less well known are the adaptive radiations that have led to the evolution of three or more taxa in 19 genera of Galapagos vascular plants. These are in the families Amaranthaceae (*Alternanthera*, 8 taxa; *Froelichia*, 5); Asteraceae (*Darwiniothamnus*, 4; *Lecocarpus*, 3; *Scalesia*, 20); Boraginaceae (*Cordia*, 3; *Tiquilia*, 3); Cactaceae (*Jasminocereus*, 3; *Opuntia*, 5 and 9); Euphorbiaceae (*Acalypha*, 6; *Chamaesyce*, 9; *Croton*, 4); Lamiaceae (*Salvia*, 3); Molluginaceae (*Mollugo*, 9); Piperaceae (*Peperomia*, 4); Poaceae (*Aristida*, 4; *Paspalum*, 3); Polygalaceae (*Polygala*, 5); and Rubiaceae (*Borreria*, 6). In addition, two taxa have evolved autochthonously in ten other genera. Field and laboratory studies of any of these genera should increase our knowledge of this basic evolutionary phenomenon and of plant evolution on islands in general.

The endemics

A list of endemic vascular plant taxa follows. Arrangement is alphabetical by family, genus, and species. Pteridophytes come first, followed by monocots, then dicots. Included, in order, are the names of the taxa, their distributions by island (see the legend to Fig. 1 for island abbreviations), habitats, chromosome numbers when known, and discussions of their relationships.

Lycopodophyta

LYCOPODIACEAE

Lycopodium setaceum ssp. *galapagense* O. Hamann – I, Pta, SaC, SS; Scalesia and Brown Zones. *Lycopodium setaceum* Lam. is pantropical in distribution; Proctor (1977) refers it to synonomy under *L. verticillatum* L. f.

Pteridophyta

ASPIDIACEAE

Ctenitis pleiosoros (Hook. f.) Morton – I, Pta, SaC, SC, SS; upper Scalesia Zone into Fern-Sedge Zone. Svenson (1935, p. 304): "close to the polymorphic West Indian and Andean *D. [Dryopteris] subincisa*". (= the tropical American *C. subincisa* (Willd.) Ching).

ASPLENIACEAE

Asplenium formosum var. *carolinum* (Maxon) Morton – F, I, Pta, SaC, SaM, SC, SS; characteristic of the Scalesia Zone. *Asplenium formosum* Willd. is pantropical in distribution.

CYATHEACEAE

Cyathea weatherbyana (Morton) Morton – I, SaC, SC, SS; common in the Miconia Zone, characteristic of the Fern-Sedge Zone. Most closely related to the tropical American *C. andina* (Karst.) Domin (Tryon, 1976).

POLYPODIACEAE

Polypodium insularum (Morton) de la Sota – I, Pta, SaC, SS; Scalesia Zone; n = 74, tetraploid (Jarrett *et al.*, 1968; as *P. bombycinum* var. *insularum* Morton). Probably related to the Andean *P. bombycinum* Maxon or *P. balaonense* Hieron.

 P. tridens Kunze – Esp, F, I, M, Pta, Pzn, R, SaC, SaF, SaM, SC, SS; common in the Transition Zone; n = 37, diploid (Jarrett *et al.*, 1968). de la Sota (1966) includes 22 species in the *P. squamulatum* L. group, stating that the affinities of *P. tridens* are not with South America, but that it shares primitive characters with more northern species. The group contains one West Indian species and nine from Mexico and Central America. Svenson (1938) reported *P. tridens* from mainland Ecuador, but de la Sota found no collections to back up this statement.

SINOPTERIDACEAE

Notholaena galapagensis Weatherby & Svenson – F, I, SaC, SS – rocky habitats, sea level to c. 900 m. Most closely related to *N. candida* (Mart. & Gal.) Hook. (Svenson, 1935; Tryon, 1956), which occurs from southern Texas and northern Mexico to Honduras.

THELYPTERIDACEAE

Thelypteris tetragona ssp. *aberrans* Morton – I, SaC; Scalesia Zone. *Thelypteris tetragona* (Sw.) Small is tropical American in distribution.

Magnoliophyta: Monocotyledonae

BROMELIACEAE

Tillandsia insularis Mez – F, I, Pan, SaC, SaM, SC, SS; frequent in the Scalesia Zone. Closely related to the Andean (Ecuador and Peru) *T. multiflora* Benth. (L. B. Smith, pers. comm.), next to which it falls in Smith's (1970) key to *Tillandsia*.

(*T. insularis* var. *latilamina* Gilmartin = *T. insularis* (van der Werff, 1977).

CYPERACEAE

Cyperus anderssonii Boeck. – Bal, Bar, D, F, G, Gar (Esp), I, LP, M, Pta, Pzn, R, SaC, SaF, SaM, SC, SS, W; common in the Arid and Transition Zones. Perhaps related to the tropical American *C. hermaphroditis* (Jacq.) Standl.

C. elegans ssp. *rubiginosus* (Hook.f.) Eliass. – Bal, Esp, Pzn, SaC, SaF, SC; common in the Arid Zone. *Cyperus elegans* L. is tropical American in distribution.

C. grandifolius Anderss. – SaC, SaM, SC; characteristic of the Fern-Sedge Zone. Perhaps related to the tropical American *C. meyenianus* Kunth.

ORCHIDACEAE

Cranichis lichenophila D. Weber – I; known from only three localities in the wet zones. Related to the West Indian *C. tenuis* complex (L. A. Garay, pers. comm.).

Epidendrum spicatum Hook.f. – F, I, Pta, SaC, SaM, SC, SS; characteristic of the Scalesia Zone. Related to the Andean (Ecuador) *E. neglectum* Schltr. (L. A. Garay, pers. comm.).

(*Erythrodes weberiana* Garay also occurs in mainland Ecuador (L. A. Garay, pers. comm.).)

POACEAE

Aristida. Henrard (1929) placed the Galapagos species in section *Pseudarthratherum*, with about 21 species, five in the archipelago, two (*A. doelliana* Henr. and *A. setifolia* HBK.) in Brazil, and the rest in Africa to India. The Galapagos species are closely related (Reeder and Reeder in Wiggins and Porter, 1971), probably have resulted from a single original introduction, and probably are most closely related to the Brazilian species.

A. divulsa Anderss. – I, M, Pta, SaC, SC, SS; Arid Zone?

A. repens Trin. – F, G, I, Pta, SaC, SaF, SaM, SC, SS; characteristic of the Arid Zone.

A. supbspicata Trin. & Rupr. – Bal, Bar, F, G, Gar (Esp), I, M, S, SaC, SaF, SC, SS; characteristic of the Arid Zone.

A. villosa Robins. & Greenm. – Bal, Pzn, R, S, SaF, SaM, SS; Arid Zone.

Cenchrus platyacanthus Anderss. – Bal, D, Esp, F, G, Gar (Esp), I, LP, M, R, S, SaC, SaM, SC, SS, T; common in the Arid Zone. Most closely related to the pantropical *C. incertus* M. A. Curtis (DeLisle, 1963).

Paspalum. A genus of warmer areas with about 250 species. The Galapagos endemics probably have evolved from a single original introduction and are related to South American (Andean) species.

P. galapageium Chase var. *galapageium* – F, I, M, SaC, SaM, SS; higher elevations, Fern-Sedge Zone?

P. galapageium var. *minoratum* Chase – F, I, Pzn, SaC, SaM, SC; sea level to c. 830 m.

P. redundans Chase – SaC; Arid Zone. Apparently last collected in 1932.

Pennisetum pauperum Steud. – F, I, SS; common in arid areas on cinder soils at higher elevations. Perhaps related to the Andean (Ecuador and Peru) *P. intectum* Chase.

Trichoneura. The Galapagos taxa apparently are most closely related to the Andean (Peru) *T. weberbaueri* Pilger. Otherwise, there are one species in North America and six in tropical Africa.

T. lindleyana (Kunth) Ekman var. *lindleyana* – Bal, F, G, Gar (Esp), I, LP, M, Pta, Pzn, R, S, SaC, SaF, SaM, SS; Arid and Transition Zones.

T. lindleyana var. *albemarlensis* (Robina. & Greenm.) Reeder & Reeder – G, I, Pta, SaC, SaM, SS; mainly in the Arid and Transition Zones.

Trisetum howellii Hitchc. – I, SaC, SC; characteristic of the Fern-Sedge Zone. According to Reeder and Reeder (in Wiggins and Porter, 1971, p. 887), "apparently most closely related to *T. deyeuxioides* (HBK.) Kunth", a tropical American species.

Magnoliophyta: Dicotyledonae

ACANTHACEAE

Justicia galapagana Lindau – F, I, Pta, SaC, SS; chiefly in the Scalesia Zone. Apparently most closely related to the Andean (Bolivia) *J. kuntzii* Lindau (Svenson, 1935).

AIZOACEAE

Sesuvium edmonstonei Hook.f. – Bar, Cal, Cha, DM, End, Esp, G, Gar (Esp), LP, Pzn, R, S, SaF, SaM, SC, T; chiefly in the Littoral Zone. Probably most closely related to the pantropical *S. portulacastrum* L., which also occurs in the Galapagos.

AMARANTHACEAE

The Galapagos members of this family are currently under study by J. A. Mears. It is expected that his revision will reduce the number of taxa recognised below.

Alternanthera. A tropical and subtropical genus of about 200 species. The Galapagos endemics have been derived from probably five introductions from Andean South America.

A. filifolia (Hook.f.) Howell ssp. *filifolia* – Esp, F, I, Pzn, SaC, SaF, SaM, SC, SS; in more arid areas from sea level to 1180 m.

A. filifolia ssp. *glauca* Howell – T; Arid Zone.

A. filifolia ssp. *glaucescens* (Hook.f.) Eliass. – SC; Littoral and Arid Zones.

A. filifolia ssp. *microcephala* Eliass, – Bar, SS; Arid Zone.

A. filifolia ssp. *nudicaulis* (Hook.f.) Eliass. – SaM; Arid Zone. Perhaps not endemic, as "plants collected in Chile have been referred to *A. filifolia* ssp. *nudicaulis* in the literature". (Eliasson in Wiggins and Porter, 1971, p. 187.)

A. filifolia ssp. *pintensis* Eliass. – Pta; Transition Zone?

A. filifolia ssp. *rabidensis* Eliass. – R; Arid Zone.

A. flavicoma (Anderss.) Howell – SaM, SC; Arid Zone. Closely related to *A. filifolia* (Howell, 1933b).

A. galapagensis (Stewart) Howell – Cal, End, Gar (SaM), SaC; Arid Zone.

A. helleri (Robins.) Howell – D, W; Arid Zone.

A. nesiotes I. M. Johnst. – SaM; Arid Zone. According to Johnston (1923,

p. 83), "a very distinct member of *Alternanthera* and apparently without any close described relative".

A. snodgrassii (Robins.) Howell – Bal, S, SaC; Arid Zone. Closely related to the Andean (Chile) *A. vestita* (Anderss.) Howell (Howell, 1933b; Eliasson, 1966), which also occurs in the Galapagos Islands.

Amaranthus. A tropical and temperate genus of about 60 species. The Galapagos endemics appear to have been evolved from two original introductions, presumably from Andean South America.

A. anderssonii Howell – Bal, Esp, Pzn, SaF, SS; Arid Zone. Apparently related to *A. squamulatus* (Eliasson, 1966).

A. furcatus Howell – I, SaC, SS; Transition and Scalesia Zones? Closely related to *A. sclerantoides* (Howell, 1933b; Eliasson in Wiggins and Porter, 1971).

A. sclerantoides (Anderss.) Anderss. – Bal, Coa, D, DM, Esp, G, Gar (Esp), I, LP, Pta, SaC, SaF, SaM, SC, SS, W; Littoral Zone.

A. squamulatus (Anderss.) Robins. – Bal, G, I, Pzn, R, S, SaC, SaM, SS, T; Arid Zone.

Froelichia. The two Galapagos species are closely related and certainly have evolved from a single original introduction. They perhaps are related to the tropical American *F. interrupta* (L.) Moq.

F. juncea Robins. & Greenm. ssp. *juncea* – I; arid zones from near sea level to 900 m.

F. juncea ssp. *alata* Howell – SaC; Arid Zone; n = 16 (Kyhos in Wiggins and Porter, 1971).

F. nudicaulis Hook.f. ssp. *nudicaulis* – SS (reported also from SaM and SC by Howell, 1933b); Arid Zone.

F. nudicaulis ssp. *curta* Howell – Pzn; Transition and Scalesia Zones?

F. nudicaulis ssp. *lanigera* (Anderss.) Eliass. – F, I; on fresh fields, from sea level to 1600 m.

Lithophila. The Galapagos species probably have resulted from a single original introduction. The other 13 or so species of *Lithophila* are Caribbean in distribution.

L. radicata (Hook.f.) Standl. – Esp, SaM, SC; Littoral Zone. This species "bears a generic resemblance to the species of *Lithophila* in northern South America and the West Indies, *L. muscoides* Sw". (Howell, 1933b, p. 97).

L. subscaposa (Hook.f.) Standl. – Pzn, SaM, SS; Scalesia Zone?

Philoxerus rigidus (Robins. & Greenm.) Howell – SS; Littoral Zone?; known from only two collections, apparently not recollected since 1906. The 10 species of the genus occur along tropical coasts.

Pleuropetalum darwinii Hook.f. – I, SaC, SS; Scalesia Zone; 2n = 34 (Eliasson, 1970). Suessenguth (1938) points out the resemblances between this species and the Costa Rican *P. standleyi* Suess., but both appear to be related to the tropical American *P. sprucei* (Hook.f.) Standl.

APIACEAE

Hydrocotyle galapagensis Robins. – I, SaC, SC; in and near ponds in Scalesia Zone. Probably only a form of the widespread *H. umbellata* L., which has recently been reported from the same area (van der Werff, 1977).

APOCYNACEAE

Vallesia glabra var. *pubescens* (Anderss.) Wiggins – Esp, I, SaC, SC, SS; Arid and Transition Zones. *Vallesia glabra* is tropical American in distribution, including the Galapagos Islands, where it is sympatric with var. *pubescens*. The latter may prove to be merely a pubescent form, not worthy of taxonomic recognition.

ASCLEPIADACEAE

Sarcostemma angustissimum (Anderss.) R. W. Holm – Bal, Bar, F, I, Pta, Pzn, R, SaC, SaM, SC, SS; Arid Zone, less common in Transition Zone. "Little can be said about the relationships of *S. angustissimum* since it has been so rarely collected and is so reduced morphologically." (Holm, 1950, p. 535). Holm places this species in a monotypic section of the genus. There are a number of Andean or South American taxa to which it might be related.

ASTERACEAE

Baccharis steetzii Anderss. – I, SaC, SaM, SC; Scalesia Zone. Probably related most closely to the Andean (Ecuador) *B. gnidiifolia* HBK., which also occurs in the Galapagos.

Chrysanthellum pusillum Hook.f. – F, I, SaC, SaF, SaM, SC, SS; Arid and Transition Zones. Most closely related to *C. mexicanum* Greenm. from south-central Mexico (B. L. Turner, pers. comm.). Although Eliasson (1972) has argued for the recognition of *C. fagerlindii* Eliass. as a separate taxon, it is best included under *C. pusillum* (B. L. Turner, pers. comm.), as was done by Cronquist (in Wiggins and Porter, 1971).

Darwiniothamnus. An endemic genus, for which Cronquist (in Wiggins and Porter, 1971) recognised one species with three varieties. However, Harling's (1962) treatment, which more accurately represents the populations in the field, is followed below. The genus is most closely related to *Erigeron*. "The nearest relatives of *Darwiniothamnus* within *Erigeron*, as this genus is at present circumscribed, should probably be sought among the somewhat shrubby species from the coast of Central Chile, e.g. *E. berterianus* DC. and *E. litoralis* (Phil.) Skottsb. (cf. Skottsberg, 1950, pp. 158–164), and the Juan Fernandez Islands."

D. lancifolius (Hook.f.) Harling ssp. *lancifolius* – F, I; common in the Transition Zone and above. Included in Wiggins and Porter (1971) under *D. tenuifolius* var. *glabriusculus* (Stewart) Cronq.

D. lancifolius ssp. *glandulosus* Harling – F, I; common in shrubby vegetation on cinders. Included in Wiggins and Porter (1971) under *D. tenuifolius* var. *glandulosus* (Harling) Cronq.

D. tenuifolius (Hook.f.) Harling ssp. *tenuifolius* – I, Pta, Pzn, SaM, SS; common in the Transition and Scalesia Zones. Included in Wiggins and Porter (1971) as var. *tenuifolius*.

D. tenuifolius ssp. *santacruzianus* Harling – SaC; Scalesia Zone. Included in Wiggins and Porter (1971) under var. *tenuifolius*.

Delilia. A genus of three species, the third being the tropical American *D. biflora* (L.) Kuntze, recently reported from the Galapagos as an introduced weed (van der Werff, 1977). Included in Wiggins and Porter (1971) as *Elvira*, but Stuessy (1975) has pointed out that the former is the older name.

D. inelegans (Hook.f.) Kuntze – SaM; known only from the type collection, made by Darwin in 1835. Included in Wiggins and Porter (1971) as *Elvira inelegans* (Hook.f.) Robins.

D. repens (Hook.f.) Kuntze – F, I, SaC, SS; occurring in woody vegetation from sea level to 1400 m. Included in Wiggins and Porter (1971) as *Elvira repens* (Hook.f.) Robins.

Encelia hispida Anderss. – SaF, SaM, SC, SS; Arid Zone. According to Cronquist (in Wiggins and Porter, 1971, p. 331), "closely related to *E. canescens* Lam., of the Peruvian coast, and the 2 may eventually prove to be conspecific".

Jaegeria gracilis Hook.f. – F, I, SaC, SaM, SC, SS; common in the Miconia and Fern-Sedge Zones; 2n = 36, tetraploid (Torres, 1968). Most closely related to the tropical American *J. hirta* (Lag.) Less. (Torres, 1968; Cronquist in Wiggins and Porter, 1971). Includes *J. crassa* Torres (van der Werff, 1977), recognised as separate in Wiggins and Porter (1971).

Lecocarpus. An endemic genus most closely related to *Acanthospermum* and *Melampodium* (Stuessy, 1970; Eliasson, 1971), both of which contain a number of tropical American species.

L. lecocarpoides (Robins. & Greenm.) Cronq. and Stuessy – Esp, Gar (Esp), SC; Arid Zone.

L. leptolobus (Blake) Cronq. & Stuessy – Sc; Arid Zone; known only from the type collection, made by Stewart in 1906. Perhaps not distinct from *L. lecocarpoides*.

L. pinnatifidus Decne. – SaM; on cinders in the Arid Zone; 2n = 22 (Eliasson, 1970; as *L. foliosus* Decne.).

Macraea. A monotypic endemic genus. "The greatest affinities to *Macraea* are found in *Wedelia*, particularly among the American species of this genus." (Harling, 1962, p. 98). *Wedelia* is a tropical and warm temperate genus of about 70 species.

M. laricifolia Hook.f. – F, I, Pta, R, SaC, SaF, SaM, SC, SS; in open shrubby vegetation on cinders from near sea level to 1200 m or higher.

Pectis. "Both Galapagos Islands species are members of an unnamed South American section of *Pectis*." (Keil, 1977, p. 92).

P. subsquarrosa (Hook.f.) Schultz Bip. – Bal, Bar, Eden, Esp, F, Gar (Esp), I, Pta, Pzn, R, S, SaC, SaF, SaM, SC, SS; Arid Zone; n = 36, hexaploid (Kyhos in Wiggins and Porter, 1971; Keil, 1977).

P. tenuifolia (DC.) Schultz Bip. – F, I, G, SaC, SC; Arid Zone.

Scalesia. The fourth and largest endemic composite genus. It is a member of tribe Heliantheae, subtribe Verbesininae, being closely related to *Tithonia* and *Viguiera* (Ono, 1967a, b) or to *Helianthus* and *Viguiera* (Eliasson, 1974), with which it shares the basic chromosome number of x = 17 (all taxa of *Scalesia* so-far counted are tetraploids, 2n = 68). *Helianthus* has about 100 species in North and South America, *Tithonia* about 10 species in Mexico, Central America, and the West Indies, and *Viguiera* about 150 species in the warmer parts of the Americas. *Scalesia* appears to be most closely related to the South American representatives of *Helianthus* (subgenus *Viguieropsis*) and *Viguiera* (Eliasson, 1974), many of which have Andean distributions. A single original introduction has given rise to this genus, the prime example of adaptive radiation in Galapagos plants. The treatment of *Scalesia* follows that of Eliasson's (1974) monograph.

S. affinis Hook.f. ssp. *affinis* – SaM (W. side); Arid Zone.

S. affinis ssp. *brachyloba* Harling – SaC (S. side); Arid and Transition Zones; 2n = 68 (Ono, 1967a; Eliasson, 1970; both as *S. affinis*).

S. affinis ssp. *gummifera* (Hook.f.) Harling – F, I; Arid Zone; 2n = 68 (Eliasson, 1974).

S. aspera Anderss. – Eden, SaC (N. side); Arid and Transition Zones; 2n = 68 (Eliasson, 1974).

S. atractyloides Arn. var. *atractyloides* – SS; Transition Zone.

S. atractyloides var. *darwinii* (Hook.f.) Eliass. – SS; Transition Zone; 2n = 68 (Eliasson, 1974).

S. baurii Robins. & Greenm. ssp. *baurii* – Pzn; Scalesia Zone?; 2n = 68 (Ono, 1971).

S. baurii ssp. *hopkinsii* (Robins.) Eliass. – Pta, W; Arid and Transition Zones; 2n = 68 (Eliasson, 1970; as *S. hopkinsii*).

S. cordata Stewart – I (S. half); cinder soils at both low (100–350 m) and high (1280–1600 m) elevations.

S. crockeri Howell – Bal, S, SaC (N. side); Arid Zone; 2n = 68 (Eliasson, 1970).

S. divisa Anderss. – SC; Arid Zone; 2n = 68 (Eliasson, 1974).

S. helleri Robins. ssp. *helleri* – SaC (S. side), SaF; Arid Zone; 2n = 68 (Eliasson, 1974).

S. helleri ssp. *santacruzana* Harling – SaC (S. side); Arid Zone.

S. incisa Hook.f. – SC (N. side); Arid Zone; 2n = 68 (Ono, 1971; Eliasson, 1974).

S. microcephala Robins. var. *microcephala* – F, I; more common at higher elevations; 2n = 68 (Eliasson, 1970; Ono, 1971).

S. microcephala var. *cordifolia* Eliass. – I (N. side); 400–1600 m, apparently in mesic woodlands.

S. pedunculata Hook.f. – SaC, SaM, SC, SS; Scalesia Zone; 2n = 68 (Ono, 1967a, 1971; Eliasson, 1974).

S. retroflexa Hemsl. – SaC (SE part); Arid Zone.

S. stewartii Riley – Bar, SS (E. side); Arid Zone; 2n = 68 (Ono, 1971).

S. villosa Stewart – Cal, Cha, Gar (SaM), O, SaM; on cinder soils in the Arid Zone; 2n = 68 (Eliasson, 1974).

Spilanthes darwinii D. M. Porter – SaM, SC, SS; Scalesia Zone. *Spilanthes* is a tropical genus of about 60 species; *S. darwinii* is presumably related to one of the many tropical American species. It was listed by Cronquist (in Wiggins and Porter, 1971) as *S. diffusa* Hook.f., a later homonym of *S. diffusa* Poepp. & Endl.

BORAGINACEAE

Cordia. The four Galapagos endemics belong to section *Varronia*, with *C. revoluta* "probably not immediately related" to the other three (Johnston, 1935, p. 175), which are closely related. "While it may be generally stated that they are most closely related to the species of western Peru and Ecuador, their immediate relationships on the continent are quite obscure." (Johnston, 1935, p. 174). Svenson (1946) points out the morphological resemblance between the Andean (Colombia, Ecuador, and Peru) *C. polyantha* Benth. and *C. anderssonii*, *C. leucophlyctis*, and *C. scouleri*. Thus, the endemic cordias appear to have resulted from two separate introductions from Andean South America.

C. anderssonii (Kuntze) Gürke – Esp, I, Pta, Pzn, SaC, SC, SS; Transition and Scalesia Zones.

C. leucophlyctis Hook.f. – Esp, F, I, SaC, SaF; characteristic of the Arid Zone, but also occurring higher up in drier areas.

C. revoluta Hook.f. – F, I, SaM, SS; common in the Arid and Transition Zones, but also occurring higher up in drier areas.

C. scouleri Hook.f. – I, SaC, SaM, SS; Arid Zone?

Heliotropium anderssonii Robins. – SaC; Arid Zone and lower parts of the Transition Zone. Johnston (1928) places this species in section *Orthostachys*, subsection *Ebracteata* of *Heliotropium* with eight other species, all but one of Andean distribution.

Tiquilia. The three Galapagos species are most closely related to the Andean (Ecuador, Peru, Bolivia, Chile) *T. paronychioides* (Phil.) A. Richardson (Johnston, 1924; Svenson, 1946; Richardson, 1977), and have been derived from a single original introduction. Typification and the application of names to the Galapagos species are discussed in Porter (1977) and Richardson (1977).

T. darwinii (Hook.f.) A. Richardson – Bal, Esp, I, LP, SaC, SaF, SC, SS, T; characteristic of the Littoral Zone. Included in Wiggins and Porter (1971) as *Coldenia darwinii* (Hook.f.) A. Gray.

T. galapagoa (Howell) A. Richardson – Bal, Bar, DM, F, G, I, M, Pta, R, SaC, SaM, SC, SS; characteristic of the Arid Zone. Included in Wiggins and Porter (1971) as *Coldenia fusca* (Hook.f.) A. Gray (Richardson, 1977).

T. nesiotica (Howell) A. Richardson – Bar, SS; characteristic of the Arid Zone. Included in Wiggins and Porter (1971) as *Coldenia nesiotica* Howell.

Tournefortia. The two endemic Galapagos species are closely related, and represent a single original introduction. This pantropical genus contains perhaps 100, mostly American species. Hooker (1847a, p. 197) refers *T. rufo-sericea* "to the neighbourhood of *T. velutina* HBK". (the tropical American *T. volubilis* L.).

T. pubescens Hook.f. – F, I, Pzn, SaC, SaM, SC, SS, W; common in the Transition and Brown Zones.

T. rufo-sericea Hook.f. – F, I, Pta, SaC, SaM, SC, SS; characteristic of the Scalesia Zone.

BURSERACEAE

Bursera malacophylla Robins. – Bal, DM, S; Arid Zone. Closely related to and probably derived from the Andean (Venezuela, Colombia, Ecuador, Peru) *B. graveolens* (HBK.) Trian. & Planch., also a common Galapagos species.

CACTACEAE

Brachycereus. A monotypic, endemic genus.

B. nesioticus (K. Schum.) Backbg. – Bar, F, G, I, Pta, SS; characteristic of the

Arid Zone. Most closely related to the Andean (Ecuador) *Armatocereus cartwrightianus* (Britt. and Rose) Backb. (Dawson, 1962, 1966).

Jasminocereus. An endemic genus of three taxa. Most closely related to the Andean (Ecuador) *Monvillea maritima* Britt. and Rose (Dawson, 1962, 1966).

J. thouarsii (Weber) Backbg. var. *thouarsii* – Cha, SaM, SC; Arid and lower Transition Zones.

J. thouarsii var. *delicatus* (Dawson) Anderson & Walkington – Bar, SaC, SS; characteristic of the Arid Zone.

J. thouarsii var. *sclerocarpus* (K. Schum.) Anderson & Walkington – F, I; on open lava flows, from near sea level to c. 700 m.

Opuntia. The Galapagos opuntias can be separated into two evolutionary groups, the "*O. helleri* line" (*O. galapageia, O. helleri, O. insularis, O. megasperma, O. saxicola*) and the "*O. zacana* line" (*O. echios*) (Dawson, 1964, 1965; Walkington and Anderson, 1967), which represent two separate original introductions. Within each group, the arborescent habit, thought to be advanced by Dawson (1964, 1965, 1966), probably is primitive and the shrubby, spreading habit advanced (Arp, 1973). They do not appear to be closely related to the opuntias of coastal Ecuador. "Either sufficient time has passed since their migration to permit extensive morphological and chemical changes, or the nearest relatives and/or ancestral stock may be within the Andes Mountains or farther to the south along coastal Peru". (Anderson and Walkington, 1968, p. 22).

O.. echios Howell var. *echios* – Bal, DM, LP, SaC; Arid to Scalesia Zones.

O. echios var. *barringtonensis* Dawson – SaF; characteristic of the Arid Zone.

O. echios var. *gigantea* (Howell) D. M. Porter – SaC; Arid and lower Transition Zones.

O. echios var. *inermis* Dawson – I; Arid Zone.

O. echios var. *zacana* (Howell) Anderson & Walkington – S; Arid Zone.

O. galapageia Hensl. var. *galapageia* – Bar, Pta, SS; Arid Zone.

O. galapageia var. *macrocarpa* Dawson – Pzn; shrubby and forested areas, c. 175–300 m.

O. galapageia var. *profusa* Anderson & Walkington – R; Arid Zone.

O. helleri K. Schum. – D, G, M, W; Arid Zone.

O. insularis Stewart – F, I; Arid Zone and higher in drier areas.

O. megasperma Howell var. *megasperma* – Cha, SaM; Arid and lower Transition Zones.

O. megasperma var. *mesophytica* J. Lundh – SC; upper Transition and Scalesia Zones.

O. megasperma var. *orientalis* (Howell) D. M. Porter – Esp, Gar (Esp), SC; Arid and lower Transition Zones.

O. saxicola Howell – drier areas from sea level to c. 1500 m.

CARYOPHYLLACEAE

Drymaria monticola Howell – SaC; Fern-Sedge Zone. Closely related to several Andean species: *D. firmula* Steyrm. (Venezuela), *D. glaberrima* Bartl. (Peru), *D. ovata* (Venezuela to Argentina); "these four poorly known species seem to form a closely knit group". (Duke, 1961, p. 233).

CONVOLVULACEAE

Ipomoea habeliana Oliv. – Cha, Gar (Esp), G, M, Pta, Pzn, SaC, SaM; Arid Zone. This is a huge genus of some 500 tropical and warm-temperate species; *I. habeliana* presumably has its relationships with tropical America.

I. linearifolia Hook.f. – DM, F, G, I, Pta, Pzn, R, SaC, T, W; Arid Zone and common in the Transition Zone. Closely related to, or perhaps conspecific with (Svenson, 1946), the basically Andean *I. incarnata* (Vahl) Choisy.

I. tubiflora Hook.f. – SS; Arid Zone? Known only from the type, collected by Darwin in 1835. Presumably related to tropical American species.

CUCURBITACEAE

Elaterium carthagenense var. *cordatum* (Hook.f.) Svens. – Pta, SS; Arid and Transition Zones. The typical variety is Andean (Ecuador and Peru) in distribution and is also sympatric with var. *cordatum* in the archipelago. They differ only in minor characters of leaf shape, and var. *cordatum* is a questionably distinct taxon.

Sicyocaulis. A monotypic, endemic genus. Presumably, it is allied to *Sicyos*, a pantropical, mostly American genus of about 15 species.

S. pentagonus Wiggins – I, SaC; Scalesia Zone.

Sicyos villosa Hook.f. – SaM; known only from the type collection, made by Darwin in 1835. Perhaps related to the Andean *S. chaetocephalus* Harms (Peru) or *S. malvifolius* Griseb. (Peru, Bolivia, and Argentina).

CUSCUTACEAE

Cuscuta acuta Engelm. – Bal, D, Esp, F, G, I, M, SS; lower and middle elevations. "Possibly present on the coast of Peru" (Wiggins and Porter, 1971, p. 371). Closely related to *C. globosa* Ridley of northeastern Brazil and the Island of Fernando Noronha according to Yuncker (1932), who also included the Andean *C. andina* Phil. (Chile) and *C. haughtii* Yuncker (Peru) in the same small (five species) subsection of the genus.

C. gymnocarpa Engelm. – G, I, SaC, SaM, SS; lower and middle elevations. Closely related to the Andean (Argentina) *C. stuckertii* Yuncker (Yuncker, 1932).

ERICACEAE

Pernettya howellii Sleumer – I, SaC; characteristic of the Fern-Sedge Zone. Apparently most closely related to the Andean (Chile) *P. mucronata* (L. f.) Gaud. (Sleumer, 1935).

EUPHORBIACEAE

Acalypha. A genus of about 400 species, chiefly tropical, with its greatest concentration in the Caribbean region. Pax and Hoffman (1924) place the Galapagos taxa in a section of 50 species, mostly South American. They probably have evolved from a single original introduction (Robinson and Greenman, 1895).

A. flaccida Hook.f. – SS; known only from the type collection, made by Darwin in 1835.

A. parvula Hook.f. – DM, Esp, F, I, Pzn, R, SaC, SaF, SaM, SC, SS; from sea level to over 1000 m, in various vegetation types. Includes var. *chathamensis* (Robins.) Webster, var. *reniformis* (Hook. f.) Muell.-Arg., and var. *strobilifera* (Hook. f.) Muell.-Arg. (van der Werff, 1977), recognised as separate by Webster (in Wiggins and Porter, 1971).

A. sericea Anderss. var. *sericea* – I, M, Pta; Arid Zone?

A. sericea var. *baurii* (Robins. & Greenm.) Webster – F, I, SaC, SC; Transition and lower Scalesia Zones. Includes var. *indefessus* Webster (van der Werff, 1977), recognised as separate by Webster (in Wiggins and Porter, 1971).

A. velutina Hook.f. – SaM; Arid Zone? Apparently not collected since 1891.

A. wigginsii Webster – SaC; Scalesia Zone and above.

Chamaesyce. A cosmopolitan genus of about 250 species, about 3/4 of them American. "Eight of the ten species of *Chamaesyce* found are endemic. They share a number of characteristics, and for the most part are rather distinct from other New World species." (Burch, 1969, p. 173). Thus, there is a possibility that they have radiated from a single original introduction, presumably from tropical America.

C. abdita Burch – Bal, Cha, Esp, SaC, SaF; Arid Zone. "It has some resemblance to *Chamaesyce micromera* (Boiss. ex Engler) Wooton & Standley, a North American [southwestern United States and Mexico] species also reported from Peru" (Burch, 1969, p. 178).

C. amplexicaulis (Hook.f.) Burch – Bal, Bar, DM, End, G, Gar (Sam), M, O, Pzn, R, SaC, SC, T, W; characteristic of the Arid Zone.

C. bindloensis (Stewart) Burch – Bar, M, R, SaC; Arid Zone.

C. galapageia (Robins. & Greenm.) Burch – I, Pta, SaC, SaM, SS; arid habitats, 50–1230 m. This species, *C. bindloensis*, and *C. recurva* "are much more similar in overall appearance to other New World species than are most of the endemic species". (Burch, 1969, p. 177). *Chamaesyce galapageia* has similarities with the tropical American *C. hyssopifolia* (L.) Small and *C. lasiocarpa (Kl.)* Arthur and the more temperate *C. nutans* (Lag.) Small (Burch, 1969; Burch in Wiggins and Porter, 1971).

C. nummularia (Hook.f.) Burch var. *nummularia* – Bar, Gar (Esp), SaF, SC, W; common in the Arid Zone.

C. nummularia var. *glabra* (Robbins. & Greenm.) Burch – SaM; common in the Arid Zone.

C. punctulata (Anderss.) Burch – Bal, Bar, DM, Eden, F, I, M, Pta, Pzn, R, SaC, SaF, SaM, SC, SS; common in the Arid Zone.

C. recurva (Hook.f.) Burch – Bal, Eden, Esp, G, Gar (Esp), I, Pta, Pzn, R, S, SaC, SaF, SC, SS; Arid Zone.

C. viminea (Hook.f.) Burch – Bar, G, I, LP, M, Pta, R, SaC, SaF, SaM, SC, SS; characteristic of the Arid Zone and also common in the Transition Zone. Similar in appearance to *C. vaginulata* (Griseb.) Millsp. of the Bahamas Islands (Burch, 1969; Burch in Wiggins and Porter, 1971).

Croton. The Galapagos species appears to be closely related to the Andean (Ecuador) *C. rivinifolius* HBK. (Svenson, 1946; Webster, 1970).

C. scouleri Hook.f. var. *scouleri* – Cha, DM, Esp, F, G, Gar (Esp), I, M, Pta, R,

S, SaC, SaF, SaM, SC, SS, T; characteristic of the Arid Zone, common in the Transition Zone.

C. scouleri var. *brevifolius* (Anderss.) Muell.-Arg. – SaM; common in the Transition Zone, also in the Scalesia Zone.

C. scouleri var. *darwinii* Webster – D, G, W; characteristic of the Arid Zone.

C. scouleri var. *grandifolius* Muell.-Arg. – I, Pta, R, SaC, SC, SS; common in the Transition Zone, also in the Scalesia Zone.

Euphorbia equisetiformis Stewart – I; known from only two or three localities at 600–880 m on the S. side of the island. Apparently a member of section *Alectoroctonum* (Schlecht.) Boiss., "but it does not appear to be close to other species of this group". (Burch, 1969, p. 178). This section contains 17 tropical American species, six of which occur in northern South America (Boissier, 1862).

FABACEAE

Dalea tenuicaulis Hook.f. – I, SaC, SaM, SC, SS; Arid and Transition Zones. Perhaps related to the Andean (Colombia, Ecuádor, Peru) *D. coerulea* (L. f.) Schinz and Thellung.

Phaseolus mollis Hook.f. – F, I, SaC, SS; Transition Zone and above. "Endemic, or possibly a variant of the widespread species *P. lunatus* L." (Rudd in Wiggins and Porter, 1971, p. 631). The latter is a tropical American (now a pantropical weed) species, sometimes cultivated.

LAMIACEAE

Hyptis gymnocaulos Epling – F, I; Arid Zone, cinder soils. Epling (1949) placed this species in his subsection *Eriocephalae* with 14 other South American, mostly Andean, species.

Salvia. Epling (1938) placed the three Galapagos endemics in his section *Micranthae* with eight other species from Florida, the West Indies, and southern Mexico, including *S. tenella* Sw. They probably have been derived from a single original introduction.

S. insularum Epling – SC; known only from the type collection, made by Wood in 1846.

S. prostrata Hook.f. – SaM, SC, SS; Scalesia Zone? ". . . allied to *S. tenella* Sw., a West Indian species." (Hooker, 1847a, p. 201).

S. pseudoserotina Epling – SaM; occurring at the highest elevations.

LINACEAE

Linum. There may be as many as 17 or 18 taxa of the genus in South America, which has centres of diversity in Peru and Chile (Rogers and Mildner, 1976). The two Galapagos species were not discussed by Rogers and Mildner; they appear to be related to the Andean (Peru) *L. oligophyllum* Willd., and probably represent a single original introduction.

L. cratericola Eliass. – SaM; Scalesia Zone?

L. harlingii Eliass. – I; open shrubby vegetation on bare cinders at higher elevations.

MALVACEAE

Abutilon depauperatum (Hook.f.) Robins. – DM, Esp, G, Gar (Esp), I, M, Pta, Pzn, R, SaC, SaF, SaM, SC, SS; Arid and Transition Zones. According to Bates (in Wiggins and Porter, 1971, p. 670), "a polymorphic species closely related to if not conspecific with the more widely distributed, tropical American *A. umbellatum* (L.) Sweet".

Gossypium barbadense var. *darwinii* (Watt) J. B. Hutch. – Esp, Gar (Esp), I, Pta, Pzn, R, S, SaC, SaF, SaM, SC; common in the Arid and Transition Zones. The other two varieties of *G. barbadense* are Andean (Ecuador and Peru) in distribution.

G. klotzschianum Anderss. – F, I, M, SaC; Arid and Transition Zones. Most closely related to the Mexican *G. davidsonii* Kellogg (Kearney, 1952), often considered a variety of *G. klotzschianum* (cf. Stephens, 1958).

Urocarpidium insulare (Kearney) Krapov. – F, I; dry rocky slopes and crater rims, 1350–1600 m. Related to the Andean (Argentina) *U. pentandrum* Krapov. (Krapovicas, 1954).

MELASTOMATACEAE

Miconia robinsoniana Cogn. – SaC, SC; dominant in the Miconia Zone. Also reported from Panama (Wurdack in Gleason, 1958). Related to a group of eight Andean (Colombia and Venezuela) species (Gleason, 1958).

MENISPERMACEAE

(*Cissampelos galapagensis* Stewart = *C. glaberrima* St. Hil. (Rhodes, 1975)).

MIMOSACEAE

Acacia rorudiana Christoph. – Esp, I, SaC, SaM, SS; characteristic of the Arid Zone. "Possibly also on the mainland, in Chile" (Rudd in Wiggins and Porter, 1971, p. 646).

MOLLUGINACEAE

Mollugo. The Galapagos endemics are closely related to the widespread *M. verticillata* L. and have probably radiated from a single original introduction (Howell, 1933a; Eliasson, 1966).

M. crockeri Howell – SS (E. side); Arid Zone.

M. flavescens Anderss. ssp. *flavescens* – SaC, SC; Arid Zone.

M. flavescens ssp. *gracillima* (Anderss.) Eliass. – Bal, Bar, F, I, M, Pta, Pzn, R, SaC, SaF, SaM, SC, SS, T; mainly in the Arid Zone.

M. flavescens ssp. *insularis* (Howell) Eliass. – SaM, SC; Arid Zone.

M. flavescens ssp. *striata* (Howell) Eliass. – W; Arid Zone. Known only from the type collection, made in 1906.

M. floriana (Robins.) Howell subsp. *floriana* – O, SaM; Arid Zone.

M. floriana ssp. *gypsophiloides* Howell – Pzn; Arid Zone? Apparently not collected since 1932.

M. floriana ssp. *santacruziana* (Christoph.) Eliass. – SaC; Arid Zone? Known only from the type collection, made in 1927.

M. snodgrassii Robins. – F, I; recent lava fields, sea level to 1600 m.

MYRTACEAE

Psidium. The endemic Galapagos species is most closely related to the basically Mexican and Central American (Mexico to northern Colombia and Venezuela) *P. sartorianum* (Berg) Ndzu. (Porter, 1968).

P. galapageium Hook.f. var. *galapageium* – F, I, Pta, SaC, SS; common in the Transition and Scalesia Zones.

P. galapageium var. *howellii* D. M. Porter – I, SaC, SC; Transition and Scalesia Zones.

NOLANACEAE

Nolana galapagensis (Christoph.) I. M. Johnst. – Coa, I, S, SaC, SaM, SC, T; Littoral Zone. Most closely related to the Chilean species of the genus, rather than those of Peru (Johnston, 1936).

NYCTAGINACEAE

Pisonia floribunda Hook.f. – I, Pta, Pzn, SaC, SaM, SC, SS; Transition and Scalesia Zones. Apparently related to the pantropical *P. aculeata* L.

PASSIFLORACEAE

Passiflora colinvauxii Wiggins – SaC; Scalesia Zone. This species could be related to any of a number of the several hundred South American members of the genus.

P. foetida var. *galapagensis* Killip – Cha, I, SaC, SaM, SC; from near sea level to the Scalesia and Miconia Zones. *Passiflora foetida* L. is a polymorphic tropical American species, in which Killip (1938) recognised 37 varieties! "This is very close to var. *hirsuta* [Amazonian Peru and Brazil], and I am separating the two mainly because of their different geographical distribution." (Killip, 1938, p. 505).

PIPERACEAE

Peperomia. The Galapagos endemics belong to the Central and (mainly) South American subgenus *Sphaerocarpidium* (Yunker, 1933). They perhaps represent a single original introduction.

P. galapagensis Miq. var. *galapagensis* – I, Pta, Pzn, SaC, SaM, SC, SS; common in the Scalesia Zone.

P. galapagensis var. *ramulosa* (Anderss.) Yunker – I, Pta, SaC, SaM; common in the Scalesia Zone.

P. obtusilimba C. DC. – I, SaC, SS; Transition and Scalesia Zones and above.

P. petiolata Hook.f. – F, I, Pta, Pzn, SaC, SaM, SS; common in the Transition Zone.

PLANTAGINACEAE

Plantago galapagensis Rahn – I, SaC, SaM, SC; Transition Zone? and above. Closely related to the North American (southwestern United States and northern Mexico) *P. rhodosperma* Decne., "and separated only by the much smaller floral parts". (Rahn, 1974, p. 135). Included in Wiggins and Porter (1971) as *P. paralias* var. *pumila* (Hook.f.) Wiggins.

POLYGALACEAE

Polygala. The Galapagos species are closely related to one another and appear to be most closely related to the tropical American *P. paludosa* St.-Hil. or *P. paniculata* L. (Howell and Porter, 1968). They probably represent a radiation from a single past introduction from South America.

P. *anderssonii* Robins. – I, SaC, SS; Arid Zone; apparently not collected since 1939. Perhaps not distinct from *P. galapageia* (van der Werff, 1977).

P. *galapageia* Hook.f. var. *galapageia* – I, M, SaM, SC; Arid Zone.

P. *galapageia* var. *insularis* (A. W. Bennett) Robins. – M, Pta, SaC, SaM, SC; Arid Zone.

P. *sancti-georgii* Riley var. *sancti-georgii* – SaM (N. side); Littoral Zone.

P. *sancti-georgii* var. *oblanceolata* Howell – R, SaC, SS; Arid Zone.

POLYGONACEAE

Polygonum galapagense Caruel – I, SaC, SC; Fern-Sedge Zone. Perhaps related to the widespread American *P. hydropiperoides* Michx.

PORTULACACEAE

Calandrinia galapagosa St. John – SC (N. part); Arid Zone. Most similar to the Andean (Chile) *C. splendens* Barn. (St. John, 1937).

Portulaca howellii (Legr.) Eliass. – Bar, Cal, Cha, D, DM, Eden, End, G, Gar (Esp), Gar (SaM), LP, M, Pta, R, S, SaF, SaM, T, W; Littoral Zone. Most closely related to the Andean (Argentina) *P. fulgens* Griseb. (Legrand, 1953, 1962).

RHAMNACEAE

Scutia spicata var. *pauciflora* (Hook.f.) M. C. Johnst. – Bar, Esp, I, LP, M, Pzn, R, SaC, SaF, SaM, SC, SS; common in the Littoral Zone, also in the Arid Zone. The typical variety occurs in Ecuador and Peru (Johnston, 1974). Included in Wiggins and Porter (1971) as *S. pauciflora* (Hook.f.) Weberb.

RUBIACEAE

According to Standley (1931, p. 180), "the few Rubiaceae existing in the Galapagos, chiefly species of *Borreria*, perhaps are as closely related to those of Ecuador as to those of any other region".

Borreria. The Galapagos endemics are closely related and certainly represent an evolutionary radiation from a single original introduction.

B. *dispersa* Hook.f. – I, Pta, SaC, SaM, SC, SS; characteristic of the Arid Zone.

B. *ericaefolia* Hook.f. – F, I, Pta, R, SaM, SC, SS; characteristic of the Arid Zone.

B. *linearifolia* Hook.f. – I, SaM, SS; Arid Zone. Apparently not collected since 1932.

B. perpusilla Hook.f. – SaC, SS; Arid and Transition Zones.

B. rotundifolia Anderss. – SaC; Known only from the type collection, made by Andersson in 1852.

B. suberecta Hook.f. – I, Pzn, SaF, SC; Arid and Transition Zones. Apparently not collected since 1932.

Galium galapagoense Wiggins – I, SaC, SaM; Scalesia to Miconia Zones. This cosmopolitan genus contains about 400 species, but *G. galapagoense* is "unlike any of the known species of *Galium* on the mainland of South America". (Wiggins, 1970, p. 250). However, this is where its relatives are to be sought.

Psychotria. This pantropical genus has some 1000 species, and has its centre of distribution in Andean South America. The two Galapagos species are closely related and represent a single original introduction.

P. angustata Anderss. – SaM; Scalesia Zone? Not collected since 1852.

P. rufipes Hook.f. – F, I, Pta, SaC, SC, SS; characteristic of the Scalesia Zone, common in the Transition Zone, and also in the Brown and Miconia Zones.

SAPINDACEAE

Cardiospermum galapageium Robins. & Greenm. – I, SaC, SS; common in the Transition Zone. Perhaps only a narrow-leaved form of the pantropical *C. halicacabum* L. (Svenson, 1946), which also occurs in the archipelago.

Dodonaea viscosa var. *galapagensis* (Sherff) D. M. Porter – I; cinder soils, mostly above 900 m. *Dodonaea viscosa* (L.) Jacq. is a widespread, polymorphic species; the genus is badly in need of revision from a modern systematic viewpoint (Porter, 1970). The relationships of the endemic taxon are with tropical America.

SCROPHULARIACEAE

Galvezia. The Galapagos species has as its "nearest relative on the mainland *G. fruiticosa* Gmelin". (Wiggins, 1968, p. 4). The latter is Andean (Peru) in distribution.

G. leucantha Wiggins ssp. *leucantha* – I, SC; Arid Zone.

G. leucantha ssp. *pubescens* Wiggins – R, SS; Arid Zone.

SIMAROUBACEAE

Castela galapageia Hook.f. – Bal, Esp, F, I, LP, M, Pta, Pzn, R, S, SaC, SaF, SaM, SC, SS; common in the Arid and Transition Zones. Most closely related to the Caribbean (Lesser Antilles to northern Venezuela and Colombia) *C. erecta* Turp. and North American (Texas to southern Mexico) *C. tortuosa* Liebm. (Cronquist, 1944). The three sometimes are recognised as subspecies of a single species (Cronquist, 1945).

SOLANACEAE

Acnistus ellipticus Hook.f. – F, I, Pzn, SaC, SaM, SC, SS; Scalesia Zone and above. The genus contains about 20 species, mostly Andean in distribution.

Capsicum galapagense Heiser & Smith – I, SaC, SS; Transition and Scalesia Zones; $n = 12$, diploid (Heiser and Smith, 1958). Hunziker (1958) places *C.*

galapagense with 23 other species in section *Capsicum*, 13 of them Andean in distribution. According to Heiser and Smith (1958, p. 200), "the untoothed calyx is similar to that of *C. shottianum* Send." from Brazil. Included in Wiggins and Porter (1971) as *C. galapagoense* A. T. Hunziker, a name that was not validly published until 1961.

Exedeconus miesii (Hook.f) D'Arcy – Bar, Cha, Esp, F, Gar (Esp), Gen, I, Pta, Pzn, R, SaC, SaM, SC, SS; Littoral Zone. According to D'Arcy (pers. comm.) the Galapagos populations probably are morphologically distinct from those of mainland Ecuador and Peru. Included in Wiggins and Porter (1971) as *Cacabus miersii* (Hook.f.) Wettst.

Lycium minimum C. L. Hitchc. – Bal, Esp, Gar (Esp), I, Pta, Pzn, SaC, SaF, SaM; Arid Zone. Apparently most closely related to the North American (Sonoran Desert) *L. californicum* Nutt.

Lycopersicon. "The closest approach to the Galapagos tomatoes in terms of morphology and genetic compatibility is found in forms of *L. pimpinellifolium* from coastal Ecuador and Peru." (Rick, 1963, p. 74).

L. cheesmanii Riley var. *cheesmanii* – Bal, Esp, F, I, SaC, SaM, SC; Arid Zone.

L. cheesmannii var. *minor* (Hook.f.) D. M. Porter – Bar, F, Gar (Esp), Gar (SaM), I, Pta, Pzn, R, SS; Arid Zone, occasionally in the Littoral Zone. Included by Rick in Wiggins and Porter (1971) as *L. cheesmanii* f. *minor* (Hook.f.) Muller.

Physalis galapagoensis Waterfall – Esp, Gar (Esp), I, R, S, SaC, SaM, SC; Arid and Transition Zones; n = 12 (Waterfall, 1968). Apparently most closely related to *P. cordata* Miller, distributed from southern Mexico to Panama and in the West Indies, which also occurs in the Galapagos.

Solanum edmonstonei Hook.f. – SaM; known only from the type collection, made by Edmonston in 1846. "The supposedly endemic *S. edmonstonei* shows stronger affinities to some South American species of Sect. *Regmandra* and, indeed, may only represent an accidental introduction or waif." (Roe in Wiggins and Porter, 1971, p. 479). Indeed, it may not have been collected in the archipelago. Edmonston was killed in mainland Ecuador soon after leaving the Galapagos, and other specimens are known to have been mislabled following his death (see Svenson, 1938, p. 304).

URTICACEAE

Pilea baurii Robins. – Esp, F, I, Pta, SaC, SaM, SC, SS; Transition to Fern-Sedge Zones. This species keys in Killip (1936) to his group *Capillatae*, which includes nine Andean species (Killip, 1936, 1939).

VERBENACEAE

Clerodendrum molle var. *glabrescens* Svens. – SaC; common in the Arid and Transition Zones. Questionably distinct from the tropical American var. *molle*, which is sympatric with it in the archipelago.

Lantana. The Galapagos species is closely related to the Andean (Ecuador and Peru) *L. sprucei* Hayek (Svenson, 1946).

L. peduncularis Anderss. var. *peduncularis* – Bal, Cha, Esp, Gar (Esp), I, M, Pta,

I

Pzn, R, SaC, SaF, SaM, SC, SS; common in the Arid and Transition Zones.

L. peduncularis var. *macrophylla* Moldenke – G, Gar (Esp); dominant in the Arid and Transition Zones. Questionably distinct from var. *peduncularis*.

Lippia. A genus of nearly 200 species, mostly tropical American. The relationships of the Galapagos endemics undoubtedly are with Andean South America. A single original introduction is likely.

L. rosmarinifolia Anderss. var. *rosmarinifolia* – F, I, Pta, SS; cinder soils. Includes var. *stewartii* Moldenke (van der Werff, 1977), recognised as a separate taxon by Moldenke in Wiggins and Porter (1971).

L. rosmarinifolia var. *latifolia* Moldenke – SS; Transition and Scalesia Zones. Questionably distinct from var. *rosmarinifolia*.

L. salicifolia Anderss. – SaM; Scalesia Zone.

Verbena. A genus of about 250 species, all but two or three in tropical or temperate America. The Galapagos endemics appear to have resulted from two original introductions.

V. grisea Robins. & Greenm. – Pzn; higher elevations.

V. sedula Moldenke var. *sedula* – SaC; Fern-Sedge Zone.

V. sedula var. *darwinii* Moldenke – SS; known only from the type collection, made by Darwin in 1835. Questionably distinct from var. *sedula*.

V. sedula var. *fournieri* Moldenke – SC; Scalesia Zone. Questionably distinct from var. *sedula*.

V. townsendii Svens. – F, I, Pta, SaC; drier open habitats, 15–845 m. Includes *V. galapagosensis* Moldenke, *V. glabrata* var. *tenuispicata* Moldenke, and *V. stewartii* Moldenke (van der Werff, 1977), all listed as separate taxa by Moldenke in Wiggins and Porter (1971).

VISCACEAE

Phoradendron henslovii (Hook.f.) Robins. – F, I, Pta, Pzn, R, SaC, SaM, SC, SS; may be found wherever woody plants occur; $n = 28$, tetraploid (Wiens and Barlow, 1971). Apparently most closely related to the West Indian (Cuba) *P. dichotomum* Krug and Urb. (Weins and Barlow, 1971).

ZYGOPHYLLACEAE

Kallstroemia adscendens (Anderss.) Robins. – Cha, Esp, Gar (Esp), I, Pzn, SaF, SaM, SC; Arid Zone. Most closely related to the North American (southwestern United States and northern Mexico) *K. californica* (S. Wats.) Vail (Porter, 1969).

Discussion

From the above, it may be seen that 43% (231/543) of the indigenous taxa (species, subspecies, or varieties) are endemic. This includes 8/107 pteridophytes, 18/85 monocots, and 205/351 dicots. Table 1 gives figures for Galapagos vascular plant endemism from previous publications.

As Table I indicates, as the floras of the archipelago and adjacent South America have become better known, the percentage of endemism

TABLE 1   Percentages of vascular plant endemism reported for the Galapagos Islands in previous floristic studies

Investigators		Per cent endemism
Hooker (1847b)		49 (123/253 taxa)
Andersson (1885)		54 (179/333 taxa)*
Robinson (1902)		41 (239/590 taxa)
Stewart (1911)		41 (252/615 taxa)
Wiggins and Porter (1971)		32 (228/702 taxa)
Johnson and Raven (1973)		26 (163/635 taxa) †
Porter (1976)	total flora—	34 (236/703 taxa)
	indigenes—	45 (236/522 taxa)

* Andersson included only angiosperms in his flora.

† Johnson and Raven did not include infraspecific taxa in their calculations.

in the islands has dropped. It has also dropped with the fewer number of forms being recognised by modern systematists. In addition, previous calculations of endemism have been somewhat misleading, in that they have been based on the total flora, both aliens and indigenes. The present study gives an endemism of 31% when calculated for the total flora of 735 taxa, but when the Man-introduced taxa are excluded, endemism for the islands rises to 43% of the vascular plants.

The above figures are most liberal. Six of the taxa in the above list are questionably endemic, while 14 are questionably distinct from other taxa. Assuming this to be correct, recalculation yields the somewhat more conservative figure of 40% (211/523) endemism. In addition, nine taxa are known only from type collections (one is also questionably distinct), and four have not been collected for 45 years, one for 71 years, one for 85 years, and one for 125 years. For those taxa known only from their types, one was collected in 1927, two in 1906, one in 1852, one in 1846, and four in 1835. If we assume that all are now extinct, the most conservative figure for endemism today becomes 37% (186/498), or 27% (186/690) for the total flora. Thus, endemism in the indigenous vascular flora of the archipelago lies somewhere between 37% and 43%. This contrasts markedly with that other botanically well-known Pacific archipelago, the Hawaiian Islands, where 94·4% of angiosperm species are endemic (Carlquist, 1965). One must agree with Carlquist (1965, p. 307) that this difference is due to the Galapagos Islands being "more recent, nearer to the mainland, and drier than the Hawaiian Islands". Indeed, endemism in the Galapagos is strikingly high considering the low diversity of habitats. This is undoubtedly due to the openness of the habitats that are present and to the basic weediness of the flora, both of which provide opportunities for rapid evolutionary change.

TABLE 2 Geographical relationships of the endemic vascular plants of the Galapagos Islands

	Neotropical	Pantropical	Andean	Mexico and C. America	S. America	Caribbean	N. America	Total
Pteridophytes	3	2	1	2				8
Monocotyledons	4	1	8		4	1		18
Dicotyledons	55	15	120	4		8	3	205
Total	62 (27%)	18 (8%)	129 (56%)	6 (3%)	4 (2%)	9 (4%)	3 (1%)	231
No. of single original introductions from each area	32 ((27%)	10 (8%)	61 (52%)	5 (4%)	1 (1%)	6 (5%)	3 (3%)	118

Geographical areas are defined as follows: Neotropical (distributed generally in the American tropics); Pantropical (distributed in both the Old and New World tropics); Andean (occurring only in western South America from Venezuela to Chile, generally or in part); Mexico and Central America (occurring only in Mexico and/or Central America, and in one case also in northern Colombia and Venezuela); South America (occurring only in extra-Andean South America); Caribbean (occurring in the West Indies and often also on the edges of the surrounding continents); North America (occurring in the southwestern United States and adjacent northern Mexico).

Like 92% of the rest of the indigenous vascular plants, the closest relatives of most of the Galapagos endemics occur in adjacent South America (Table 2). The most obvious difference here is the presence of Caribbean and North American relationships shown by a few of the endemics, relationships not found in the other indigens (cf. Porter, 1976).

Endemism by vegetation zones is roughly as follows: Littoral (10 taxa), Arid (137), Transition (17), Scalesia (56), Brown (1), Miconia (1), and Fern-Sedge (9). This becomes even more striking when the vegetation is divided into the three major ecological zones that occur in the archipelago (Johnson and Raven, 1973): littoral (10 taxa, 4% of the endemism), basically arid (Arid Zone, Transition Zone, and arid habitats occurring elsewhere – 154 taxa, 67% of the endemism), and basically mesic (Scalesia, Brown, Miconia, and Fern-Sedge Zones – 67 taxa, 29% of the endemism). Johnston and Raven (1973) have pointed out that endemism here is low in the littoral zone because of high immigration and extinction rates, high in the arid zone because of its extent and presumed age, and low in the mesic zone because it is so recent in the archipelago.

In addition, almost all of the evolutionary radiation that has taken place in the endemic flora has done so in the arid regions, also the areas of greatest species diversity in the islands. The only adaptive radiations that appear to have taken place in mesic habitats are in the genera *Darwiniothamnus* and *Peperomia*. It is true that several taxa of *Scalesia* have penetrated the mesic regions, but the largest number remain in the Arid Zone, where the initial radiation of the genus took place. I agree with Johnson and Raven (1973) that the mesic regions have been populated mainly by dispersal from adjacent South America, not by plants evolved from related species in more arid habitats below as in most other island groups.

Recent studies on the vegetational history of the islands based on fossil pollen and spores (Colinvaux and Schofield, 1976a, b) indicate for the past 25 000 years a dry period of 15 000 years followed by 10 000 years when more mesic habitats were present. Such history is mirrored in the distributions and radiations of the endemic vascular plants.

Acknowledgements

Field studies in the Galapagos Islands in 1967 and 1977 were made possible through the National Science Foundation and the Friends of the Museum of Comparative Zoology, Harvard University. The American Philosophical Society and the VPI and SU Education Fund provided funds so that Galapagos collections at the Royal Botanic Gardens, Kew and at Cambridge University could be consulted. The Excmo. Cabildo Insular de Gran Canaria and the VPI and SU Education Foundation provided funds so that this paper could be presented at the symposium "Plants and Islands". H. van der Werff, H. Adsersen, O. Hamann, and U. Eliasson generously provided valuable information on distribution and ecology, as did W. G. D'Arcy (Solanaceae), L. A. Garay (Orchidaceae), L. B. Smith (Bromeliaceae), and B. L. Turner (*Chrysanthellum*) on their various specialties. All are most gratefully acknowledged, as is I. L. Wiggins, who first piqued my interest in the islands.

REFERENCES

Adsersen, H. (1976a). *Ombrophytum peruvianum* (Balanophoraceae) found in the Galapagos Islands. *Bot. Not.* **129**, 113–117
— (1976b). New records of pteridophytes from the Galapagos Islands. *Bot. Not.* **129**, 429–436
Anderson, E. F. and Walkington, D. L. (1968). A study of some neotropical opuntias of coastal Ecuador and the Galapagos Islands. *Noticias de Galápagos* **12**, 18–22
Andersson, N. J. (1855). Om Galapagos öarnes vegetation. *Kgl. Svenska Vetenskapsakad. Handl.* **1**, 61–256
Arp, G. K. (1973). The Galapagos opuntias: Another interpretation. *Noticias de Galápagos* **21**, 33–37
Bailey, K. (1976). Potassium-Argon ages from the Galapagos Islands *Science* **192**, 465–467
Boissier, E. (1862). Subordo Euphorbieae. In D.C. *Prodr.* **15** (2), 3–188
Bowman, R. I. (ed.) (1966). *The Galapagos.* University of California Press, Berkeley and Los Angeles
Burch, D. (1969). Notes on the Galapagos Euphorbieae (Euphorbiaceae). *Ann. Mo. Bot. Gard.* **56**, 173–178
Carlquist, S. (1965). *Island Life.* Natural History Press, New York
Colinvaux, P. A. and Schofield, E. K. (1976a). Historical ecology in the Galapagos Islands. I. A Holocene pollen record from El Junco Lake, Isla San Cristóbal. *J. Ecol.* **64**, 989–1012
— and Schofield, E. K. (1976b). Historical ecology in the Galapagos Islands. II. A Holocene spore record from El Junco Lake, Isla San Cristóbal. *J. Ecol.* **64**, 1013–1028
Cronquist, A. (1944). Studies in the Simaroubaceae. I. The genus *Castela. J. Arn. Arbor.* **25**, 122–128
— (1945). Additional notes on the Simaroubaceae. *Brittonia* **5**, 469–470
Dawson, E. Y. (1962). Cacti of the Galapagos Islands and of coastal Ecuador. *Cact. Succ. J. (Los Angeles)* **34**, 67–74, 99–105

— (1964). Cacti in the Galapagos Islands. *Noticias de Galápagos* **4**, 12 13

— (1965). Further studies of *Opuntia* in the Galapagos Archipelago. *Cact. Succ. J. (Los Angeles)* **37**, 135–148

— (1966). Cacti in the Galapagos Islands, with special reference to their relations with tortoises. In *The Galapagos* (R. I. Bowman, ed.), 209–214. University of California Press, Berkeley and Los Angeles

DeLisle, D. G. (1963). Taxonomy and distribution of the genus *Cenchrus*. *Iowa State Coll. J. Sci.* **37**, 259–351

Duke, J. A. (1961). Preliminary revision of the genus *Drymaria*. *Ann. Mo. Bot. Gard.* **48**, 173–268

Eliasson, U. (1966). Studies in Galapagos plants. III. Centrospermae. *Sv. Bot. Tidskr.* **60**, 393–439

— (1970). Studies in Galapagos plants. VIII. Chromosome numbers of some endemic species. *Bot. Not.* **123**, 149–154

— (1971). Studies in Galapagos plants. X. The genus *Lecocarpus* Decaisne. *Sv. Bot. Tidskr.* **65**, 245–277

— (1972). Studies in Galapagos plants. XIII. Three new floristic records and two supplementary remarks. *Bot. Not.* **125**, 320–322

— (1974). Studies in Galapagos plants. XIV. The genus *Scalesia. Opera Bot.* **36**, 1–117

Epling, C. (1938/39). A revision of *Salvia*: Subgenus *Calosphace. Feddes Repert. Spec. Nov. Regni Veg. Beih.* **110**, 1–380

— (1949). Revisión de género *Hyptis* (Labiatae). *Revista Mus. La Plata, Secc. Bot.* **7**, 153–497

Gleason, H. A. (1958). Melastomataceae. Flora of Panama, Part VIII, Family 141. *Ann. Mo. Bot. Gard.* **45**, 203–304

Harling, G. (1962). On some Compositae endemic to the Galapagos Islands. *Acta Horti Berg.* **20**, 63–120

Heiser, C. B., Jr. and Smith, P. G. (1958). New species of *Capsicum* from South America. *Brittonia* **10**, 194–201

Henrard, J. T. (1929). Monograph of the genus *Aristida*. Vol. 1. *Meded. Rijks-Herb.* **59**, 1–153

Holm, R. W. (1950). The American species of *Sarcostemma* R. Br. (Asclepiadaceae). *Ann. Mo. Bot. Gard.* **37**, 477–560

Hooker, J. D. (1847a). An enumeration of the plants of the Galapagos Archipelago, with descriptions of those which are new. *Trans. Linn. Soc. Lond.* **20**, 163–233

— (1847b). On the vegetation of the Galapagos Archipelago as compared with that of some other tropical islands and of the continent of America. *Trans. Linn. Soc. Lond.* **20**, 235–262

Houvenaghel, G. T. (1974). Equatorial undercurrent and climate in the Galapagos Islands. *Nature, Lond.* **250**, 565–566

Howell, J. T. (1933a). The Templeton Crocker Expedition of the California Academy of Sciences, 1932. No. 3. The genus *Mollugo* in the Galapagos Islands. *Proc. Calif. Acad. Sci., ser. 4* **21**, 13–23

— (1933b). The Templeton Crocker Expedition of the California Academy of

Sciences, 1932. No. 9. The Amaranthaceae of the Galapagos Islands. *Proc. Calif. Acad. Sci., ser. 4* **21**, 87–116

— and Porter, D. M. (1968). The plant genus *Polygala* in the Galapagos Islands. *Proc. Calif. Acad. Sci., ser. 4* **32**, 581–586

Hunziker, A. T. (1958). Synopsis of the genus *Capsicum. VIIIe Congr. Internat. Bot. Rapp. Comm. Sect. 3, 4, 5 et 6.* Pp. 73–74

Jarrett, F. M., Manton, I. and Ray, S. K. (1968). Cytological and taxonomic notes on a small collection of living ferns from Galapagos. *Kew Bull.* **22**, 475–480

Johnson, M. P. and Raven, P. H. (1973). Species number and endemism: The Galapagos Archipelago revisited. *Science* **179**, 893–895

Johnston, I. M. (1923). Diagnoses and notes relating to the spermatophytes chiefly of North America. *Contr. Gray Herb.* **68**, 80–104

— (1924). Studies in the Borginaceae. II. 2. A tentative classification of the South America coldenias. *Contr. Gray Herb.* **70**, 55–61

— (1928). Studies on the Boraginaceae—VII. 1. The South American species of *Heliotropium. Contr. Gray Herb.* **81**, 3–73

— (1935). Studies in the Boraginaceae. XI. *J. Arn. Arbor.* **16**, 145–205

— (1936). A study of the Nolanaceae. *Proc. Amer. Acad. Arts* **71**, 1–87

Johnston, M. C. (1974). Revision of *Scutia* (Rhamnaceae). *Bull. Torrey Bot. Club* **101**, 64–72

Kearney, T. H. (1952). Notes on Malvaceae II. *Leafl. West. Bot.* **6**, 165–172

Keil, D. J. (1977). Chromosome studies in North and Central American species of *Pectis* L. (Compositae: Tageteae). *Rhodora* **79**, 79–94

Killip, E. P. (1936). New species of *Pilea* from the Andes. *Contr. U.S. Natl. Herb.* **26**, 367–394

— (1938). The American species of Passifloraceae. *Publ. Field Mus. Nat. Hist., Bot. Ser.* **19**, 1–613

— (1939). The Andean species of *Pilea. Contr. U.S. Natl. Herb.* **26**, 475–530

Krapovicas, A. (1954). Estudio de especies de *Anurum*, nueva sección del género *Urocarpidium* Ulbr. (Malvaceae). *Darwiniana* **10**, 606–636

Legrand, C. D. (1953). Notas sobre *Portulaca. Comun. Bot. Mus. Hist. Nat. Montevideo* **2** (27), 1–21

— (1962). Las especies americanas de *Portulaca. Anal. Mus. Nac. Montevideo, ser. 2* **7** (3), 1–149

McBirney, A. R. and Williams, H. (1969). Geology and petrology of the Galapagos Islands. *Geol. Soc. Amer. Mem.* **118**, 1–197

Ono, M. (1967a). Chromosome number of *Scalesia* (Compositae), an endemic genus of the Galapagos Islands. *J. Jap. Bot.* **42**, 353–360

— (1967b). The systematic position of *Scalesia* from the viewpoint of chromosome number. *Noticias de Galápagos* **9/10**, 16–17

— (1971). Chromosome number of *Scalesia* (Compositae), an endemic genus of the Galapagos Islands (2). *J. Jap. Bot.* **46**, 327–334

Pax, F. and Hoffmann, K. (1924). Euphorbiaceae – Crotonoideae – Acalypheae – Acalyphinae. *Pflanzenreich IV.* **147–XVI** (Heft 85), 1–231

Porter, D. M. (1968). *Psidium* (Myrtaceae) in the Galapagos Islands. *Ann. Mo. Bot. Gard.* **55**, 368–371

— (1969). The genus *Kallstroemia* (Zygophyllaceae). *Contr. Gray Herb.* **198**, 41–153

— (1970). The genus *Dodonaea* (Sapindaceae) in the Galapagos Islands. *Occas. Pap. Calif. Acad. Sci.* **81**, 1–4

— (1976). Geography and dispersal of Galapagos Islands vascular plants. *Nature, Lond.* **264**, 745–746

— (1977). Typification of *Tiquilia darwinii* and *Tiquilia fusca* (Boraginaceae). *Rhodora* **79**, 288–291

Proctor, G. R. (1977). *Flora of the Lesser Antilles. Leeward and Windward Islands. Vol. 2. Pteridophyta.* Arnold Arboretum, Jamaica Plain, Mass.

Rahn, K. (1974). *Plantago* section *Virginica*. A taxonomic revision of a group of American plantains, using experimental, taximetric and classical methods. *Dansk Bot. Ark.* **30** (2), 1–180

Rhodes, D. G. (1975). A revision of the genus *Cissampelos*. *Phytologia* **30**, 415–484

Richardson, A. (1977). Monograph of the genus *Tiquilia (Coldenia, sensu lato)*, Boraginaceae: Ehretioideae. *Rhodora* **79**, 467–572

Rick, C. M. (1963). Biosystematic studies on Galapagos tomatoes. *Occas. Pap. Calif. Acad. Sci.* **44**, 59–77

Robinson, B. L. (1902). Flora of the Galapagos Islands. *Proc. Amer. Acad. Arts* **38**, 78–270

— and Greenman, J. M. (1895). On the flora of the Galapagos Islands as shown by the collections of Dr. Baur. *Amer. J. Sci., ser. 3* **50**, 135–149

Rogers, C. M. and Mildner, R. A. (1976). South American *Linum*, a summary. *Rhodora* **78**, 761–766

St. John, H. (1937). A new *Calandrinia* from the Galapagos Islands *Amer. J. Bot.* **24**, 95

Sleumer, H. (1935). Revision der Gattung *Pernettya* Caud. *Notizbl. Bot. Gart. Berlin-Dahlem* **12**, 626–655

Smith, L. B. (1970). Notes on Bromeliaceae, XXXI. Keys to *Tillandsia* and simulators. *Phytologia* **20** (3); 121–183

de la Sota, E. R. (1966). Revisión de las especies americanas del grupo *Polypodium squamatum* L. *Revista Mus. La Plata, Secc. Bot.* **10**, 69–186

Standley, P. C. (1931). The Rubiaceae of Ecuador. *Publ. Field. Mus. Nat. Hist., Bot. Ser.* **7**, 179–251

Stephens, S. G. (1958). Salt water tolerance of seeds of *Gossypium* species as a possible factor in seed dispersal. *Amer. Naturalist* **92**, 83–92

Stewart, A. (1911). A botanical survey of the Galapagos Islands. *Proc. Calif. Acad. Sci., ser. 4* **1**, 7–288

— (1915). Some observations concerning the botanical conditions in the Galapagos Islands. *Trans. Wisconsin Acad. Sci.* **18**, 272–340

Stuessy, T. F. (1970). The genus *Acanthospermum* (Compositae-Heliantheae-Melampodinae): Taxonomic changes and generic affinities. *Rhodora* **72**, 106–109

— (1975). *Delilia* (Compositae). Flora of Panama, Part IX, Family 184. *Ann. Mo. Bot. Gard.* **62**, 1057–1058

Suessenguth, K. (1938). Amarantaceen-Studien. *Feddes Repert. Spec. Nov. Regni Veg.* **44**, 36–48

I*

Svenson, H. K. (1935). Plants of the Astor Expedition, 1930 (Galapagos and Cocos Islands). *Amer. J. Bot.* **22**, 208–277

— (1938). Pteridophyta of the Galapagos and Cocos Islands. *Bull. Torrey Bot. Club* **65**, 303–333

— (1946). Vegetation of the coast of Ecuador and Peru and its relation to that of the Galapagos Islands. II. Catalogue of the plants. *Amer. J. Bot.* **33**, 427–498

Torres, A. M. (1968). Revision of *Jaegeria* (Compositae-Heliantheae). *Brittonia* **20**, 52–73

Tryon, R. (1956). A revision of the American species of *Notholaena*. *Contr. Gray Herb.* **197**, 1–106

— (1976). A revision of the genus *Cyathea*. *Contr. Gray Herb.* **206**, 19–98

Walkington, D. L. and Anderson, E. F. (1967). A study of some neotropical opuntias. II. Morphology and chemistry. *Amer. J. Bot.* **54**, 645–646

Waterfall, U. T. (1968). A new species of *Physalis* from the Galapagos Islands. *Rhodora* **70**, 408–409

Webster, G. L. (1970). Notes on Galapagos Euphorbiaceae. *Madroño* **20**, 257–263

Werff, H. van der (1977). Vascular plants from the Galapagos Islands: New records and taxonomic notes. *Bot. Not.* **130**, 89–100

Wiens, D. and Barlow, B. A. (1971). The cytogeography and relationships of the viscaceous and eremolepidaceous misletoes. *Taxon* **20**, 313–332

Wiggins, I. L. (1968). A new species and subspecies of *Galvezia* (Scrophulariaceae) from the Galapagos Islands. *Occas. Pap. Calif. Acad. Sci.* **65**, 1–8

— (1970). Studies on the plants of the Galapagos Islands. I. New species and combinations. *Madroño* **20**, 250–253

— and Porter, D. M. (1971). *Flora of the Galapagos Islands*. Stanford University Press, Stanford, Calif.

Yunker, T. G. (1932). The genus *Cuscuta*. *Mem. Torrey Bot. Club.* **18**, 109–330

— (1933). Revision of the Hawaiian species of *Peperomia*. *Bernice P. Bishop Mus. Bull.* **112**, 1–131

Special Topics

12 Pachycaul Plants and Islands

D. J. MABBERLEY   *Departments of Botany and Forestry, University of Oxford, England*

Las razones históricas para la supuesta correlación entre los habitats isleños y la distribución de paquicaules y otras especies leñosas en familias de plantas preponderantemente herbaceas, son examinadas e ilustradas con referencia al descubrimiento del *Senecio* spp. leñoso en Africa tropical. La verdera distribución de tales plantas y la extensa presencia de las formas de paquicaules en familias predominantemente leñosas así como herbáceas, se han expuesto.

La ecología de la forma de vida paquicaule es examinada con particular referencia a las condiciones del sotobosque del bosque lluvioso tanto para formas jóvenes de las especies arbóreas, como de los arbustos del sotobosque. Las adaptaciones de la forma de vida a las condiciones presentadas en habitats secos, ambientes tropicales montañosos y de otros, se comparan con aquellos de Paquicaules de islas. Geográfica y ecologicamente se muestra un paralelismo entre la ocupación de habitats insulares y la regeneración de bosque de lluvia.

Las teorías evolutivas enfocadas con plantas Paquicaules son brevemente examinadas. Se ha hecho una especial referencia a teorías derivadas de estudios de xilema secundario pero hacen falta más estudios urgentemente.

Las formas Paquicaules de islas están situadas en un contexto mundial, en primer lugar por el examen de su distribución geográfica y taxonómica y la ecología de un "modelo arquitectónico" particular; en segundo lugar, por un estudio de la distribución de plantas Paquicaules comparadas con las de parientes Leptocaules en el mismo género. Los ejemplos han sido tomados de Meliaceae malayos y los resultados comparados con estudios amteriores hechos en plantas predominantemente herbáceas así como en familias leñosas.

La importancia de los estudios en plantas Paquicaules está perfilada. Algunos discernimientos nuevos en biogeografía y probablemente evolutivos han sido ya señalados. El riesgo de estudiar plantas isleñas en aislamiento y la extrapolación de tales estudios es considerado, reclamándose una monografía que dé una aproximación auténtica, basada en sondeos taxonómicos.

Introduction

The attraction of islands to biologists is said to be that they embrace simple ecosystems, allegedly more simple to analyse than continental areas, and that they constitute natural "experiments", instructive to ecologists and evolutionists alike. The recent resurgence of interest in island biology has, according to Simberloff (1974), given biogeography "general laws of both didactic and predictive powers". To turn back from such heady heights to look at the history of a few ideas in island biology in

259

connection with the controversial theories surrounding evolutionary studies on higher plants seems appropriate to this book.

Early explorers were astonished to find that many of the trees and other large plants to be found on isolated islands belonged to groups which in the temperate countries are predominantly herbaceous, an observation which excited considerable interest in the botanical world. For example, Captain Cook discovered the massive crucifer, *Pringlea antiscorbutica* [R. Br. ex] Hook. f. on the remote South Atlantic island, Kerguelen, and later Joseph Hooker wrote (*Fl. Antarctica* 2: 239 (1845)) after the voyage of the *Erebus* and *Terror*, "This is perhaps the most interesting plant procured during the whole voyage. . . . The contemplation of a vegetable very unlike any other in botanical affinity and in general appearance, so eminently fitted for the food of man, and yet inhabiting one of the most desolate and inhospitable spots on the surface of the globe, must equally fill the mind of the scientific explorer and common observer with wonder".

The *Pringlea*, with its massive primary construction, large leaves and short internodes, may be described as pachycaul, when compared with the slender much branched, or leptocaul, construction of, say, limes and beeches, which have long internodes, small leaves and slender twigs (Corner, 1949; 1975). Such pachycaul plants on islands include species of *Centaurodendron* (Compositae) on Juan Fernandez, *Heterochaenia* (Campanulaceae) on Mauritius, *Richea pandanifolia* Hook. f. (Epacridaceae) in Tasmania and *Echium* (Boraginaceae) in Macaronesia.

Pachycaul distribution

Charles Darwin has been blamed (Hemsley, 1885) for an error which has had remarkable repercussions, still to be felt today. In his *Origin of Species* (p. 392), he wrote that islands "often possess trees or bushes belonging to Orders which elsewhere include *only* (my italics) herbaceous species". Clearly Darwin was a victim of the vicissitudes of botanical discovery, in that island floras, and indeed coastal ones, were investigated before the continents were explored, a fact that at first led to very curious ideas on the flora of the tropics (Stearn, 1957). As an example, of the seven woody *Senecio* species native to tropical Africa and the Atlantic islands, the first to be brought back to Europe were *Senecio leucadendron* (Forst. f.) Hemsl. and *S. redivivus* Mabberley, collected on St. Helena by Joseph Banks on Cook's *Endeavour* voyage in 1771 (Mabberley, 1975b). No pachycaul species native to the mainland was collected until 1859, when John Kirk gathered scraps of a woody species on Livingstone's Zambezi Expedition, a species found a few months later on Clarence Peak, Fernando Po by

Gustav Mann. Mann (1862) wrote, "The vegetation here consists mostly of herbaceous plants as Gramineae, *Rubus* etc. The largest trees here (50 feet high) are Araliaceae and Compositae", the latter being the *Senecio*, now known as *S. mannii* Hook. f. It was not until well over a century after the discovery of the St. Helena species that the most celebrated pachycaul species of the continent, namely the Giant Groundsels, were discovered on the Kilimanjaro expedition of 1884.

It is clear, then, why earlier workers could have been misled into making the spurious correlation repeated by Darwin. As Hemsley (1885) and many others since, notably in recent years van Steenis (1973) and Mabberley (1974b), have pointed out, woody species in predominantly herbaceous groups are not restricted to islands in the classical definition of the geographical term. But, here we encounter a difficulty. The classical distinction between "continental" and "oceanic" islands has become blurred (van Balgooy, 1969) and, furthermore, Simberloff (1974) defines an island as "Any patch of habitat isolated from similar habitat by different, relatively inhospitable terrain traversed only with difficulty by organisms of the habitat patch", which, he considers, could include bromeliad "vases", sand dunes and cowpats, besides classical "geographical" islands. As with the woody members of the "herbaceous" families, so with pachycaul plants, which are not restricted to "geographical" islands as we have seen, and not to predominantly herbaceous families either (D'Arcy, 1973). It seems, therefore, essential that pachycaul plants on islands be looked at in relation to those of so-called continental areas, particularly when even these are taken by e.g. Simberloff (1974) to be islands. Indeed from cowpats to South America, it is difficult to see what is not or at some time has not been an island.

By pachycaul plants is not meant gouty or podagric (van Steenis, 1955) plants with secondary fattening like baobabs, nor "giant" plants in the sense of eventual greatness as in giant redwoods, but primary obesity. There are families of flowering plants which are predominantly pachycaul, such as Palmae, their massiveness providing nutrition and, indeed, a whole culture for certain tropical peoples, as do, on a smaller scale, the pachycaul Pandanaceae and the pachycaul grasses, bamboos. A dicotyledonous example is Araliaceae: species of *Schefflera*, *Cussonia* and *Osmoxylon*, the ungainly *Arthrophyllum javanicum* Bl. (*A. diversifolium* auctt.) of Malesia, of which Corner (1940: 155) wrote, "This singularly unattractive tree . . . is perhaps as common as any tree can be and forms pure thickets in secondary jungle", and the mighty hapaxanthic *Harmsiopanax* of New Guinea, which attains some 9 m, with petioles to 2 m long, laminas 1 m across and terminal panicles to 5 m high and 6 m across (Philipson, 1970). Here tropical massiveness intrudes into the temperate zones as *Fatsia* and other pachycauls of restaurant and sittingroom, but also as the predominantly herbaceous Umbelliferae – included in Araliaceae by Thorne (1973) – of which the annual herbaceous overground parts are apparently homologous with the inflorescences of the tropical araliad (Mabberley, 1974a). The link is shown by the tree-like forms of *Peucedanum kerstenii* Engl. with woody aerial stems on the Rwenzori of the Uganda/Zaire border. Familiar pachycauls in herbaceous alliances are the so-called "architectural" plants of the horticulturist: giant hogweeds, rhubarb and gunnera. Examples with overground pachycaul stems include the palmiet, *Prionium serratum* (Thunb.) Drège (Juncaceae), a shrubby aloe-like plant of southern Africa, a pachycaul *Macrocarpaea* (Gentianaceae) of southern Venezuela (Steyermark, 1974) and, in woody groups, *Decaisnea* (Lardizabalaceae) of the Himalaya, *Diploglottis* (Sapindaceae) of Australia and *Phylloclinium* (Flacourtiaceae) of tropical Africa, and many others.

Pachycaul ecology

After the unsuccessful attempt to found a Scottish colony in Panama in 1698–1700, James Wallace (1700) wrote, "This place affords legions of monstrous Plants, enough to confound all the methods of Botany ever hitherto thought upon . . . some of their Leaves exceed three Ells [c. 3 m] in length and are very broad". It is not clear what the monsters were, but pachycaul construction of certain species in many woody groups is suited to the ecological "strategy" of rainforest understorey living (Ashton, 1977). Good examples including species in Lecythidaceae, Myrsinaceae, Ochnaceae, Rutaceae and Theophrastaceae are tabulated by D'Arcy (1973). These treelets flower and fruit in the understorey, while many tall forest trees pass through a pachycaul stage when young, such as *Artocarpus* spp. (Moraceae) in Malesia, where the treelets, notably Rubiaceae (Ridsdale, 1975) may be overlooked when growing with such saplings. Some of the tall trees are gap-fillers in the cycle of regeneration of the forest (Horn, 1970; 1975), and may remain in a shade-tolerant pachycaul juvenile state, ticking over for several years, until a gap is formed when they are "released" and grow up to fill the gap. This is also the "strategy" of certain lianes, as some Bignoniaceae, which, of course, do not climb in the sense of *Convolvulus*, but grow up from the sterile pachycaul rosette-tree stage as the canopy rises in the regenerating forest.

Those trees with a shade requirement and a pachycaul rosette-tree form when young include many of our important tropical hardwoods, e.g. the meliaceous *Carapa* of South America and both *Khaya* and *Entandrophragma* (Fig. 1) of Africa, but some trees typical of secondary forest also have this form in youth, e.g. *Campnosperma* (Anacardiaceae) of Malesia and *Anthocleista* (Loganiaceae *s.l.*) of tropical Africa, which have leaves up to 2 m long. Such pioneer trees as these and the "midnight horror", *Oroxylum indicum* (L.) Vent., of Malesia have been termed "nomads" by van Steenis (1958): typical examples of the species mentioned above are *Arthrophyllum* and *Senecio mannii*. Such trees regenerate in the light, often have large leaves, grow rapidly when young, both in height and girth, flowering and fruiting early and annually, producing pale, light wood and long-lived seeds which are dispersed by birds, bats or wind. They are frequently armed with stings, barbs or spines, making the secondary jungle the unpleasant place it is, but are rarely toxic. The activities of Man have opened up many new sites and, indeed, habitats for these plants, thereby making them far commoner than they can ever have been before. As with so many plant attributes, there is a complete gradation between the "strategy" of this pioneering light demander and that of the obligate shade demander. Unlike the pachycaul treelets, many of the pioneers and other tall trees put off flowering until their crowns are free of the understorey. Frequently, the juvenile stages are morphologically very different from the adult stages, resulting in habit-heteroblastism deriving from what Schaffalitzky de Muckadell (1959) called meristem ageing. Currently, it is fashionable to account for this switch or phase change (Brink, 1962), unavailable to the treelets, in terms of changes in RNA content in the meristematic cells (Riding, 1976).

The unbranched rosette habit is not restricted to woody plants in the rain forest, but is to be found in herbs of the understorey too, e.g. the "miniature palm tree" form of herbs such as species of *Cyrtandra*, *Didissandra*, *Didymocarpus* (Gesneriaceae), *Sonerila* (Melastomataceae) and *Neckia* (Ochnaceae) according to Burtt (1977). The pachycaul treelet "strategy" is clearly adapted to these conditions, for superficially similar architectural tree models (in the sense of Hallé and Oldeman, 1970) have the same ecological effect, e.g. Corner's model, i.e. monopodial unbranched with axillary inflorescences, such as *Colea* spp. (Bignoniaceae) of Madagascar and *Semecarpus* spp. (Anacardiaceae) of Malesia, but also other models comprising monopodial trunks with plagiotropic lateral branches resembling inflorescences such as *Tapeinosperma reinianum* Jacobs (Myrsinaceae) of New Guinea (Jacobs, 1976), *Ardisia* spp. (Myrsinaceae), and many Rubiaceae including *Bertiera* spp. (Leroy, 1974) and *Lasianthus* spp. etc. Examples outside the rain forest include *Euphorbia wakefieldii* N. E. Br., restricted to the island-like limestone outcrops of the East African coastal strip.

Indeed, the pachycaul is not restricted to rainforest and islands

Fig. 2 *Aloe capitata* Bak. var *cipoliniola* H. Perr. near Ambatofinandrahana, Madagascar, March 1971

Fig. 1 *Entandrophragma angolense* (Welw.) C. DC. at Kepong Arboretum, Malaysia, April 1974

264

FIG. 4 *Conyza vernonioides* (A. Rich.) Wild at 3000 m on Mt. Elgon, Kenya, December 1970

FIG. 3 *Canarium hirsutum* Willd. in Sepilok F. R., Sabah, May 1974

geographical and geological, but is found in deserts, e.g. *Yucca* (Agavaceae), Cactaceae and succulent Euphorbiaceae, and in the tropical alpine belt e.g. species of *Puya* (Bromeliaceae), *Lupinus* (Leguminosae) and *Espeletia* (Compositae) in South America and *Lobelia* (Campanulaceae) and *Senecio* in Africa (Mabberley, 1977). Both these habitats suffer great diurnal but little seasonal temperature fluctuation, for which pachycaul construction is admirably adapted. Similarly, the deep-seated or non-existent cambium pre-adapts pachycaul plants to tolerance of anthropogenic fires as seen in aloes in Madagascar (Fig. 2) as well as cycads and tree-ferns in New Guinea. Of pachycauls of such disparate habitats, some are hapaxanthic, such as rain forest pioneers like *Harmsiopanax* (Araliaceae) of Malesia and *Spathelia* (Rutaceae) of South America, as well as some *Lobelia* spp. of the alpine belt of central Africa, and certain *Echium* spp. of Macaronesia. Such unbranched hapaxanthic plants (Holttum's Model) are more familiar as monocotyledonous examples, such as *Agave* (Agavaceae), *Puya*, *Ensete* (Musaceae) and *Corypha* (Palmae), which in flower is "crowned by the largest inflorescence of any higher plant, a wide-spreading cream-coloured structure rising some 8 m above the crown" (Evans, 1976). Echoes of this construction can be seen in the biennials and other hapaxanthic plants of temperate countries, the basal rosette at ground level topped with a death-bringing inflorescence, from the carrot (Umbelliferae) to the Chinese lily, *Cardiocrinum giganteum* (Wall.) Makino (Liliaceae), *Megacarpaea polyandra* Benth. (Cruciferae) of Kashmir (Napier, 1976) and the alpine saxifrages with rosettes to 55 cm across and up to 3000 flowers (Anon., 1937). Temperate examples with above-ground pachycaul parts are few, but *Lavatera arborea* L. (Malvaceae) and *Brassica oleracea* L. of the cliffs of the British Isles, and, indeed, the declined Jersey long jack walking-stick industry of the Channel Islands (Parker and Cox, 1970) are conspicuous examples.

Pachycaul evolution

The pachycaul growth form is very widespread as we have seen and cannot be regarded merely as a "curiosity" or "exception" or "special case". It is to be found in many families of Angiosperms, besides Gymnosperms and Pteridophytes. In his Durian Theory, Corner (1949; 1964; 1975) has argued that the pachycaul condition is a primitive one, and antecedent to the leptocaul and that the radiation of the flowering plants into their major subgroupings occurred in the pachycaul stage. It is further argued that one would expect few of the so-called primitive families (i.e. ones with allegedly primitive floral construction) to exhibit the primitive growth form, for if such did exist the ancestors of the modern flowering plants would still be with us (cf. Kubitzki, 1975). Nevertheless, certain magnolias are somewhat pachycaul and Humphries has pointed out that a South American member of the Bonnettiaceae, *Neblinaria celiae* Maguire, is rather pachycaul too. Again, the most remarkable pachycaul temperate plants have their frost-sensitive pachycaul parts protected by the physics of water, namely the waterlilies with their massive rhizomes at the bottom of ponds. Here we have pachycaul plants with no vessels, with curious morphology of tropical abandon (Cutter, 1957), huge primitive cantharophilous flowers, and critical seedling and chemical characters (Haines and Lye, 1975; Fairbrothers *et al.*, 1975) putting them uncomfortably in either monocotyledons and dicotyledons. Their modified arils and their allegiance to the gigantic armed *Victoria amazonica* (Poepp.) Sowerby put pachycauls and the Durian Theory alarmingly close at hand. Corner (1976) has further argued that in *Ficus* (Moraceae) not only have leptocaul trees been derived from pachycaul ancestors, but also that the climbing figs in different groups have been derived in parallel from pachycaul stocks. In a predominantly herbaceous family, Compositae, Mabberley (1974a) argued that in *Senecio* the pachycaul woody forms with pleiochasial branching (Leeuwenberg's Model), as seen in *Dracaena draco* L. (Agavaceae), represent the primitive growth form in groups which comprise lianes, pachycauls and herbs (two groups in New Zealand, another in Africa), pachycauls and herbaceous plants (tropical montane and temperate), pachycaul and leptocaul trees (New Zealand), being also found in the West Indies, Central America, Macaronesia and elsewhere as well as in other *Senecioneae* and other tribes: *Astereae, Cichorieae, Cynareae* (Mabberley, 1974a) and *Inuleae* (*Allagopappus dichotomus* (L.f.) Cass. of the Canary Islands). In the tropical alpine taxa of pachycaul *Senecio*, an argument for a tropical forest ancestry rather than an extra-tropical one best fitted the facts, a conclusion which is supported by findings from studies in other genera, such as *Wahlenbergia* (Thulin, 1975: 103).

There is no doubt however that certain groups of plants can become even more pachycaul. This is made possible by the mode of growth of these plants, which have intercalary meristems manifest in features such as sympetaly, inferior ovaries, pachychalazal seeds and parallel-veined leaves. In some groups this has arisen as a response to occupation of alpine habitats, e.g. *Lobelia* in the African mountains, where an overall control of the development of the plant's morphology results in an "hyper-pachycaul" syndrome (cf. Beketoff, 1858; Bramwell, 1972; Mabberley, 1977), associated with a "new" system of cortical vascular bundles. Such innovation in other groups has given the phyllomorph of *Streptocarpus*

(Gesneriaceae; Burtt, 1974), but many examples of morphological "novelty" may merely point up the range of morphological possibility in tropical plants – supra-axillary inflorescences, cauliflory, epiphylly – which are not ecologically viable in the temperate zones, where only a narrow range of morphological variety survives.

The range of form from pachycaul to leptocaul is readily seen in large woody and herbaceous genera in the tropics, pachycaul species in such genera being *Miconia magnifica* Triana (Melastomataceae) of Mexico, *Canarium hirsutum* Willd. (Burseraceae) of Borneo (Fig. 3), *Vernonia conferta* Benth. (Compositae) of Uganda and *V. neocoursiana* Humbert of Madagascar, *Begonia luxurians* Schiedw. (Begoniaceae) of Brazil, *Conyza vernonioides* (A. Rich.) Wild (Compositae) of eastern Africa (Fig. 4) and many others. There is a complete gradation from pachycaul to leptocaul in many such groups, either to leptocaul trees or to herbs, which seem, as a group, to have been derived in several ways (Corner, 1964; Gatsuk, 1976), showing the intermediate stages of growth form through which such constructions could have been derived from the pachycaul. Many herbaceous plants retain the branching typical of their presumed ancestors, e.g. temperate *Cirsium* spp. (Jäger, 1977) with underground pleiochasial rhizome branching comparable with the aerial branching of the pachycaul relict, *Centaurodendron*, of the same tribe.

The enormous literature of wood anatomy includes little on the sappy, useless wood of pachycaul plants, except where there has been the usual interest in the woody members of predominantly herbaceous groups. In contradistinction to the deductions on the primitive nature of pachycauly made from observations on the overall morphology, anatomy, development, ecology and geography of pachycaul members of both woody and herbaceous groups, arguments have been adduced to support the notion that pachycauls in herbaceous groups, and indeed their leptocaul allies, are secondarily derived woody plants with an herbaceous ancestry. The arguments are not very convincing (see Mabberley, 1974b; but compare Gibson, 1973 and Koeke-Noorman, 1976) but the glib dubbing of woody plants in small herbaceous groups as "derived" has gained a little currency, e.g. in *Guizotia* (Compositae; Baagøe, 1974).

That pachycaul stages occur in the ontogeny of forest trees and that pachycaul treelets occur on continents as well as on islands in a wide range of habitats, seem to me, at least, to make it unnecessary to try to explain pachycauly as an island (classical) phenomenon and to bolster this idea up with ecological arguments of "evolutionarily active" groups or "all year round" growth, when both these possibilities obtain in the continental tropics. Until the wood anatomical studies are extended to juvenile stages of forest trees and care is taken to compare sections from morphologically equivalent parts of the plant body of different species, arguments from wood anatomy alone will continue to be unconvincing. Island biology is not well served by insular argument.

Island pachycauls in context

Varying degrees of pachycauly from the stoutest to the most slender leptocaul can be used as a quantitative way of looking at plant structure and in an evolutionary context this may be more useful than using such categories as "herbs", an ecological rather than an evolutionary concept (Gatsuk, 1976). A qualitative approach is the framework for tropical tree form as architectural models set out by Hallé and Oldeman (1970). Many of the understorey treelet pachycauls mentioned above correspond to Corner's Model, which is found in nearly all the larger families of dicotyledons (Hallé and Mabberley, 1977). In Campanulaceae, Mabberley (1975c) argued that Corner's Model was derived from Holttum's. The view of a derived status of Corner's Model is shared by Leroy (1976), who believes that it may have been evolved in several ways, perhaps by condensation of the lateral plagiotropic branches to lateral inflorescences as in certain Rubiaceae (Leroy, 1974). Whatever the origin of the model in different groups, there are, according to a survey published by Hallé and Mabberley (1977), excluding palms, most of which correspond to Corner's Model, 99 species in 72 genera in 36 families of dicotyledons and two families of monocotyledons corresponding to the model. Of course this modest list reflects the authors' knowledge and experience, and it can be increased by five more species, three more genera and one more family from the recent literature, *viz.* three New Guinea species of *Chaetostachydium* (Rubiaceae; Ridsdale, 1975), *Leea papuana* Merr. & Perry (Leeaceae; Ridsdale, 1976) also of New Guinea and, from southern Africa, *Harpephyllum caffrum* [Bernh. ex] Kr. (Anacardiaceae). Of the dicotyledons in this sample, 42 are to be found in continental Africa and America, 24 in Asia and Malesia (including 10 in New Guinea and New Ireland), two in Australia, nine in Madagascar, five in Hawaii, three in the Solomons, one in Mauritius and one in Macaronesia but, strikingly, 15 in New Caledonia.

The great majority are understorey treelets in rainforest such as *Jollydora duparquetiana* (Baill.) Pierre (Connaraceae) of equatorial Africa and, unforgettably, *Captaincookia margaretae* (Rubiaceae) of New Caledonia, but *Espeletia spicata* [Sch. Bip. ex] Wedd. (Compositae) is an equatorial alpine plant, some *Euphorbia* spp. inhabit dry country, and *Geranium canariense* Reuter of Macaronesia and *Mahonia bealei* Carr. (Berberidaceae) of China are not tropical. There is no doubt, however, that the pachycauls of this and other models and other woody species of isolated insular floras are in microspermous families. The question is not, however, "Why are there pachycaul Compositae or Campanulaceae on isolated islands?", but "Why are there no pachycaul Meliaceae or Rutaceae there, when the pachycaul habit seems to be well adapted to insular environments?". The answer was provided over a century ago by Alfred Russel Wallace (1876), "The combination of a great facility of distribution [of Compositae] . . . with a great attractiveness to insects, and the capacity of being fertilised by a variety of species of all orders".

Nevertheless the dwelling on pachycauls of islands can be most misleading. Some years ago Professor Corner pointed out to me the interesting example of tropical Asiatic Simaroubaceae. *Soulamea* is a genus extending from the Seychelles and the islands of Malesia to New Caledonia and Polynesia. The trees are rather pachycaul with simple leaves, except for some of the pinnate-leaved species of New Caledonia where there are six endemics. The ovary is syncarpous. Without looking beyond the islands, one might expect to argue that there was an island/pachycaul correlation and that pachycauly was a derived condition. But the allied genus, *Eurycoma*, an understorey treelet from Burma to Borneo, has an apocarpous ovary and pinnate leaves, allegedly primitive features, while the Chinese *Ailanthus*, the fast-growing "tree-of-heaven", has massive saplings, which feature is maintained by pollarding in horticulture to provide spectacular foliage. *Soulamea* is at once put into context and the spurious island/pachycaul correlation vanishes. But, if *Eurycoma* and *Ailanthus* had become extinct, authors might have interpreted the evidence differently!

When a large genus of megaspermous trees, including pachycauls, is examined, interesting patterns emerge. *Chisocheton* (Meliaceae) is a genus of 51 species of understorey trees and treelets and timber trees, pachycaul and leptocaul, native to the forested regions of eastern India and southern China through Malesia to northern Australia and eastwards to the New Hebrides. Of the four sections into which the species of this genus fall, two are notable for the wide range of pachycauly they exhibit. In sect. *Chisocheton* (Fig. 5), the two most pachycaul species, one from each of the two series in the section, are rather restricted in their geographical distribution, compared with their leptocaul allies. In sect. *Dasycoleum* (Fig. 6), this is even more marked, for the most pachycaul species, *C. perakensis* (Hemsl.) Mabberley[1], is restricted to Maxwell's Hill in West Malaysia, while *C. pentandrus* (Blanco) Merr. and *C. ceramicus* (Miq.) C. DC. range far eastwards into the islands of Malesia.

---

[1]*Megaphyllaea perakensis* Hemsl. in Hook., *lc. pl.* [18]: t.1708 (1887).

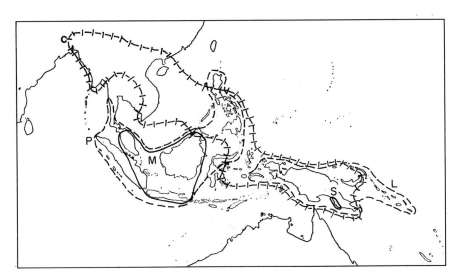

Fig. 5 Distribution of some species of *Chisocheton* sect. *Chisocheton*: ser. *Schumanniani*: S = *C. schoddei* Stevens (pachycaul), L = *C. lasiocarpus* (Miq.) Val., *s.l.* (leptocaul); ser. *Pariculati*: M = *C. macrophyllus* King (pachycaul), C = *C. cumingianus* (C. DC.) Harms and P = *C. patens* Bl. (both leptocauls)

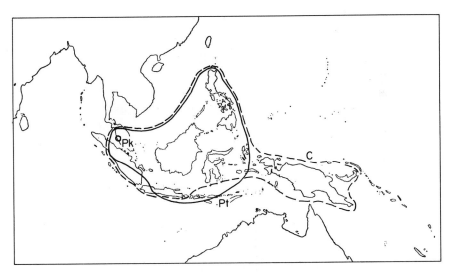

Fig. 6 Distribution of some species of *Chisocheton* sect. *Dasycoleum*: Pk, *C. perakensis* (pachycaul); C, *C. ceramicus* (Miq.) C. DC.; Pt, *C. pentandrus* (Blco.) Merr. (both leptocauls)

271

Such is not a new finding, for the pachycauls of the Solomon Island *Ficus* spp. are similarly restricted compared with their leptocaul allies (Corner, 1967). In *Senecio* sens. lat., Mabberley (1974a) showed that the pachycaul tropical species are much more restricted in their distribution than are their herbaceous allies. If the pachycaul is the primitive form then Willis's theory of "Age and Area" is turned on its head. Support for such an inversion comes from *Dolichandrone* (Bignoniaceae) where van Steenis (1927) pointed out that the most widespread species was advanced in several features. Again, Kubitzki (1975) has argued from completely different evidence that taxa with large numbers of primitive features in *Hernandia* (Hernandiaceae) and *Davilla* and *Dillenia* (Dilleniaceae) in Malesia are much more restricted in distribution than their allies with fewer such characteristics. These findings seem to support the general predictions of Corner's Durian Theory and the primitive nature of pachycaul construction.

Considering insular environments again, much has been made of the supposed similarity between conditions on isolated islands and on tropical mountains. There is no doubt that certain genera, as in Campanulaceae and Compositae, exist in pachycaul forms in both habitats, but the differences, notably that floras can pass up and down mountains without long-distance dispersal, are considerable (MacArthur and Wilson, 1967: 114; White, 1971). The colonisation and occupation of mountains perhaps has less in common with the same phenomena on islands than does the pioneering of forest gaps by early colonist trees. To return to Simberloff's definition of an island, rainforest could be thought of as a patchwork of isolated islands at different stages of regeneration and colonisation, admittedly not as isolated, particularly to animals, as true "geographical" islands (MacArthur and Wilson, 1967). As Ashton (1977) has pointed out, such colonisation begins with the light-demanding pioneers, often pachycauls, followed by increasingly shade-tolerant forms, such as the pagoda trees, like *Terminalia* spp. resembling gigantic cakestands, such "multilayers" (Horn, 1970, 1975) giving way to the shade-tolerant monolayers. This is exactly the evolutionary sequence proposed by Corner in his Durian Theory for the origin of the leptocaul, and is the ontogenetic sequence followed by habit-heteroblastic trees mentioned above. Now, when physical conditions become limiting, the "succession" on any site may become truncated, as in dry areas where multilayers dominate the "climax" vegetation (Horn, 1970, 1975). A stimulating study by Duncan and Gunn (1971) showed how an isolated loblolly pine plantation in Georgia, U.S.A. was colonised by 18 species of woody plants of which 84% were introduced by birds and the remainder by wind. The bat, bird and wind-dispersed, long-lived seeds and fruits of the tropical forest gap colonists would also be suited to island colonisation. If the late successional plants with their large seeds permitting shade tolerance in youth are not available, as on islands, then evolution will favour overtopping and leptocaul tree-making in those microspermous pachycaul groups, which are.

Variation patterns in groups of such microspermous pachycauls, e.g. Pacific *Bidens* (Compositae) and *Lobelioideae* have led some authors to postulate evolutionary mechanisms peculiar to islands. Whatever the origin of such patterns, there are many tropical continental examples of such taxonomically intractable "ochlospecies" as in *Diospyros* (White, 1962). Again, it has been asserted that early island colonists may have been self-pollinating, but that, later, gynodioecism[1] would be selected for, promoting outcrossing. The early colonists of rainforest clearings in the genus *Lobelia*, e.g. the pachycaul *L. giberroa* Hemsl. of eastern Africa is often self-pollinated, producing seeds in cultivation without the agency of birds which its floral structure indicates as pollinators. Such colonists with their self-compatibility or autogamy (Cruden, 1977) are suited to open habitats and have wind-, bird- and bat- dispersed seeds, which aerial transport and their selfing capacity would suit them to early colonisation of "oceanic" islands. Incidentally many such plants are armed but not toxic to generalised herbivores (Cates and Orians, 1975), again features of many island plants. As for gynodioecy, it is becoming increasingly apparent that many rainforest trees are functionally dioecious though many appear bisexual, perhaps to maintain their precise pollination symbioses (White, 1975). Bawa and Opler (1975) record that up to 50% of the species in some neotropical lowland rain forests are dioecious, and that outcrossing is apparently at a premium in such continental areas, too. Indeed, it would seem that many of the features of the island plant "syndrome" are to be found in rainforest trees. It would seem unnecessary, then, to postulate "new" mechanisms in island plant evolution. The regenerating mosaic that is continental rainforest and the distance between individuals of the same species create "island situations" *par excellence*. But, our lack of knowledge of rainforest biology puts us in Darwin's position when discussing island phenomena – we are in danger of falling into the trap that the Galapagos flora set for him.

The island pachycauls of "advanced" families, the microspermous pachycaul colonisers, exhibit, like deciduous leptocauls of temperate regions, just one of the many possible "strategies" seen in tropical trees. Other pachycaul groups seem to have given rise to climbers, others,

---

[1]N.B. The vernacular names of the pachycaul *Senecio* spp. of St. Helena, the He- and She-Cabbage Trees, have led some authors to assume that they are the male and female of one species.

through neoteny and condensation to herbs adapted to the temperate regions, others to tolerance of desert, mountain and fire. They seem to show us the way to interpret the evolution of the Angiosperm tree by reading the "Age and Area" theory inside out. As for the islands, studies of both the microspermous and macrospermous are instructive. The microspermous include species with remarkable wide-spread affinity, e.g. the woody *Senecio* spp. of St. Helena are said to have much in common with the pachycaul species of the islands of the New Zealand area (Drury, 1975). Such relationships are paralleled by continental examples, e.g. *Lobelia* spp. of Brazil and Rwanda (Mabberley, 1975a) and the amphi-atlantic affinities in other microspermous groups in Cactaceae, Bromeliaceae and Ericaceae (Stevens, 1970) which are well known. Less appreciated perhaps are the amphipacific affinities of macrospermous groups (van Steenis, 1963), which brings us to the richness of certain island floras in macrospermous groups including pachycaul species. Notable is New Caledonia (Thorne, 1965), which, like Madagascar, seems to be part of the ancient land surface of the Earth, but, unlike other parts, such as the Guyana Highlands and Brazilian Shield, also rich in endemics, has been cut off and preserves for us a veritable botanical *Thesaurus*, surely worth our attention and all possible conservational effort.

Conclusion

These are just some of the ideas stimulated by consideration of pachycaul plants. Piecemeal study will not reveal the patterns essential to an overall picture of a group. As has been repeatedly pointed out in this volume, it is essential to have a sound taxonomic basis for our hypotheses. Which "evolutionary biologists" find the time for monographs of large genera? It is impossible to grapple with a group of this size in a Ph.D. thesis or short-term research periods, or in the writing of regional floras, as important as this may be. Who has time to use his intellect to unravel the stories of *Cassia*, *Eugenia*, *Euphorbia*, *Piper*, *Solanum* or *Vernonia* and their pachycauls?

REFERENCES

Anon. (1937). Saxifraga longifolia. *Q. Bull. alp. Gdn Soc.* **5**, 264
Ashton, P. S. (1977). Ecology and the Durian Theory. *Gdns' Bull., Singapore* **29**, 19–23
Baagøe, J. (1974). The genus *Guizotia* (Compositae), a taxonomic revision. *Sv. Bot. Tidsskr.* **69**, 1–39
Balgooy, M. M. J. van (1969). A study on the diversity of island floras. *Blumea* **17**, 139–178

Bawa, K. S. and Opler, P. A. (1975). Dioecism in tropical trees. *Evolution* **29**, 167–179

Beketoff, A. (1858). Über die morphologischen Verhältnisse der Blatt-theile zu einander und zum Stengel. *Linnaea* **29**, 417–462

Bramwell, D. (1972). Endemism in the flora of the Canary Islands. *Taxonomy, Phytogeography and Evolution* (D. H. Valentine, ed.), 141–159. Academic Press, London and New York

Brink, R. A. (1962). Phase change in higher plants and somatic cell heredity. *Q. Rev. Biol.* **37**, 1–22

Burtt, B. L. (1974). Patterns of structural change in the flowering plants. *Trans. Bot. Soc. Edin.* **42**, 133–142

— (1977). Notes on rainforest herbs. *Gdns' Bull., Singapore* **29**, 73–80

Cates, R. G. and Orians, G. H. (1975). Successional status and the palatability of plants to generalized herbivores. *Ecology* **56**, 410–418

Corner, E. J. H. (1940). *Wayside Trees of Malaya*, Vol. I. Government Printer, Singapore

— (1949). The Durian Theory or the origin of the modern tree. *Ann. Bot.* N.S. **13**, 367–414

— (1964). *The Life of Plants*. Weidenfeld and Nicolson, London

— (1967). *Ficus* in the Solomon Islands and its bearing on the post-Jurassic history of Melanesia. *Phil. Trans. Roy. Soc.* B **253**, 23–159

— (1975). Prototypic organisms XIII. Tropical trees "Thick twig, big leaf". *Theoria to theory* **9**, 33–43

— (1976). The climbing species of *Ficus*: derivation and evolution. *Phil. Trans Roy. Soc.* B **273**, 359–386

Cruden, R. W. (1977). Pollen-ovule ratios: a conservative indicator of breeding systems in flowering plants. *Evolution* **31**, 32–46

Cutter, E. G. (1957). Studies of morphogenesis in the Nymphaeaceae. 1 – Introduction: some aspects of the morphology of *Nuphar lutea* (L.) Sm. and *Nymphaea alba* L. *Phytomorphology* **7**, 45–56

D'Arcy, W. G. (1973). *Correlliana* (Myrsinaceae), a new palmoid genus of the tropical rain forest. *Ann. Mo. Bot. Gdn* **60**, 442–448

Drury, D. G. (1975). A comparision of *Senecio kirkii* (New Zealand) and *Senecio insularis* (Lord Howe Island) with senecios endemic to the island of St. Helena. *N.Z. J. Bot.* **13**, 769–780

Duncan, W. and Gunn, W. (1971). Colonization of an isolated pine plantation by woody plants. *Bull. Ga Acad. Sci.* **29**, 191–199

Evans, G. C. (1976). A sack of uncut diamonds: the study of ecosystems and the future resources of mankind. *J. Ecol.* **64**, 1–39

Fairbrothers, D. E., Mabry, T. J., Scogin, R. L. and Turner, B. L. (1975). The bases of angiosperm phylogeny: Chemotaxonomy. *Ann. Mo. Bot. Gdn* **62**, 765–800

Gatsuk, L. E. (1976). The content of the concept "herbs" and the problem of their evolutional position [Russian; English summary]. *Trans. Moscow Soc. Nat.* **42** (Biol. ser., Bot. sect.), 55–132

Gibson, A. C. (1973). Comparative anatomy of secondary xylem in Cactoideae (Cactaceae). *Biotropica* **5**, 29–65

Haines, R. W. and Lye, K. A. (1975). Seedlings of Nymphaeaceae. *Bot. J. Linn. Soc.* **70**, 255–265

Hallé, F. and Mabberley, D. J. (1977). Corner's architectural model. *Gdns' Bull., Singapore* **29**, 175–181

— and Oldeman, R. A. A. (1970). *Essai sur l'Architecture et la Dynamique de Croissance des Arbres Tropicaux.* Masson, Paris

Hemsley, W. B. (1885). Report on the present state of knowledge of various insular floras. *Report of the Voyage of H.M.S. Challenger* (C. Wyville-Thomson and J. Murray, eds.). *Botany* **1** (1), 1–75. H.M.S.O., London

Horn, H. S. (1970). *The Adaptive Geometry of Trees.* Princeton University Press, Princeton

— (1975). Forest succession. *Sci. Amer.* **232** (5), 90–98

Jacobs, M. (1976). *Tapeinosperma reinianum* (Myrsinaceae), a new species from New Guinea. *Blumea* **23**, 3–5

Jäger, E. J. (1977). Wuchsform und Verbreitung der *Cirsium acaule* – Verwandtschaft in Eurasien. *Flora* **166**, 75–92

Koeke-Noorman, J. (1976). Juvenile characters in the wood of certain Rubiaceae with special reference to *Rubia fruticosa* Ait. *I.A.W.A. Bull.* **1976**/3, 38–41

Kubitzki, K. (1975). Relationships between distribution and evolution in some heterobathmic tropical groups. *Bot. Jahrb. Syst.* **96**, 212–230

Leroy, J.-F. (1974). Recherches sur la phylogenèse du développement. Mise en évidence d'une série de trois états dans le genre *Bertiera* (Rubiacées). *Adansonia* sér. 2, **14**, 53–59

— (1976). Essais de taxonomie syncrétique. 1. Étude sur les *Meliaceae* de Madagascar. *Ibid.* **16**, 167–203

Mabberley, D. J. (1974a). Branching in pachycaul Senecios: the Durian Theory and the evolution of angiospermous trees and herbs. *New Phytol.* **73**, 967–975

— (1974b). Pachycauly, vessel-elements, islands and the evolution of arborescence in "herbaceous" families. *Ibid.*, 977–984

— (1975a). The Giant Lobelias: pachycauly, biogeography, ornithophily and continental drift. *Ibid.* **74**, 365–374

— (1975b). The pachycaul *Senecio* species of St. Helena, "Cacalia paterna" and "Cacalia materna". *Kew Bull.* **30**, 413–420

— (1975c). The Giant Lobelias: toxicity, inflorescence and tree-building in the Campanulaceae. *New Phytol.* **75**, 289–295

— (1977). The origin of the afroalpine pachycaul flora and its implications. *Gdns' Bull., Singapore* **29**, 41–55

MacArthur, R. H. and Wilson, E. O. (1967). *The Theory of Island Biogeography.* Princeton University Press, Princeton

Mann, G. (1862). Letter describing his expedition to the Cameroon Mountains. *J. Linn. Soc. Bot.* **7**, 1–13

Napier, E. (1976). Propagating information. *The Garden* [*J. Roy. hort. Soc.*] **101**, 42–43

Parker, S. and Cox, G. S. (1970). The giant cabbage of the Channel Islands. *Guernsey hist. Monog.* No. 10

Philipson, W. R. (1970). Constant and variable features of the Araliaceae. *Bot. J. Linn. Soc.* **63**, supp. [*New research in plant anatomy*, N. K. B. Robson, D. F. Cutler and M. Gregory, eds.], 87–100

Riding, R. T. (1976). The shoot apex of trees of *Picea mariana* of differing rooting potential. *Can. J. Bot.* **54**, 2672–2678

Ridsdale, C. E. (1975). Notes on New Guinea Rubiaceae. *Chaetostachydium. Blumea* **22**, 267–269

— (1976). Leeaceae. *Flora malesiana* I, **7**, 755–782

Schaffalitzky de Muckadell, M. (1959). Investigations on aging of apical meristems in woody plants and its importance in silviculture. *Det. Forstlige Førsgsvaesen* **25**, 310–455

Simberloff, D. S. (1974). Equilibrium theory of island biogeography and ecology. *Ann. Rev. Ecol. & Syst.* **5**, 161–182

Stearn, W. T. (1957). Botanical exploration to the time of Linnaeus. *Proc. Linn. Soc. Lond.* **169**, 173–196

Steenis, C. G. G. J. van (1927). Malayan Bignoniaceae, their taxonomy, origin, and geographical distribution. *Recl Trav. Bot. Neerl.* **24**, 787–1049

— (1955). Podagric plants in Malaysia. *Webbia* **11**, 189–195

— (1958). Rejuvenation as a factor for judging the status of vegetation types: the biological nomad theory. In [U.N.E.S.C.O.,] *Study of Tropical Vegetation. Proceedings of the Kandy Symposium*, 212–218

— (1963). Transpacific floristic affinities, particularly in the tropical zone. In *Pacific Basin Biogeography* (J. L. Gressitt, ed.), 219–231. Bishop Museum Press, Honolulu

— (1973). Woodiness in island flora. *Taiwania* **18**, 45–48

Stevens, P.F. (1970). *Agauria* and *Agarista*: an example of tropical transatlantic affinity. *Notes Roy. Bot. Gdn Edin.* **30**, 341–359

Steyermark, J. A. (1974). The summit vegetation of Cerro Autana. *Biotropica* **6**, 7–13

Thorne, R. F. (1965). Floristic relationships of New Caledonia. *State Univ. Iowa Stud. Nat. Hist.* **20** (7), 1–14

— (1973). Inclusion of the Apiaceae (Umbelliferae) in the Araliaceae. *Notes Roy. Bot. Gdn Edin.* **32**, 161–165

Thulin, M. (1975). The genus Wahlenbergia *s. lat.* (Campanulaceae) in tropical Africa and Madagascar. *Symb. Bot. Upsal.* **21** (1)

Wallace, A. R. (1876). Opening address to the British Association, Section D, Biology. *Nature, Lond.* **14**, 403–412

Wallace, J. (1700). Part of a journal kept from Scotland to New Caledonia in Darien, with a short account of that country. *Phil. Trans. Roy. Soc.* **22**, 536–543

White, F. (1962). Geographic variation and speciation in Africa with particular reference to *Diospyros*. In *Taxonomy and Geography* [Syst. Assoc. Publ. No. 4] (D. Nichols, ed.), 71–103. Systematics Association, London

— (1971). The taxonomic and ecological basis of chorology. *Mitt. Bot. Stsamml., Münch.* **10**, 91–112

— (1975). Introduction. In T. D. Pennington and B. T. Styles, A generic monograph of the Meliaceae. *Blumea* **22**, 419–540

13 Evolution Within a Single Genus: *Sonchus* in Macaronesia

ANGELA E. ALDRIDGE   *Jardín Botánico, "Viera y Clavijo"*
Las Palmas de Gran Canaria, Spain

Las formas ancestrales de *Sonchus* parecen asemejarse al moderno subgénero macaronésico *Dendrosonchus* en caracteres tales como el hábito leñoso y la similitud de varios taxones N.W. Africanos al más derivado del grupo, *S. radicatus* de macaronesia, es una posible indicación de ello.

Una vez que estas formas ancestrales llegaron a estar establecidas en las islas Canarias, sufrieron una radiación adaptativa ocupando el taxon resultante todas las principales zonas climáticas y de vegetación. Los dos miembros modernos más primitivos del grupo se encuentran en antiguas áreas basálticas de Tenerife y Gran Canaria, siendo quizás el principal factor en la evolución del grupo la diversidad de habitats disponible y la escasez de competición. Las posibles rutas de migración para el *Sonchus* en las islas Canarias son señaladas en relación a esta oleada evolutiva.

La flora endémica de las islas Canarias está generalmente considerada como relicta del terciario y testimonio de ello ha sido extraido de la taxonomía, citología, morfología y paleobotánica.

En el género *Sonchus*, el autor muestra como los caracteres anatómicos pueden ser de utilidad para establecer la naturaleza relicta de algunas plantas isleñas y demostrar la naturaleza ancestral cuando se compara con parientes continentales.

Introduction

It is generally considered that endemic species in a flora are usually more ancient than the non-endemic element. This is because they must either have had their origin in the region (neoendemics), a process usually requiring a long period of time, or else they must be remnants of an older vegetation which has elsewhere become extinct (palaeoendemics) (Wulff, 1943). Insular floras are of particular value for evolutionary studies since they have not been exposed freely to a flood of immigration but have developed in comparative isolation and, therefore, possess a high percentage of endemics. Very many oceanic islands are known to have very ancient types in their floras and faunas which are regarded as remnants of life from a much earlier period.

The Canary Islands display a considerable degree of endemism with

K

about 35% of its species as endemics, 70% of these indigenous species are woody. It is generally accepted, mainly from anatomical evidence, that herbaceous plants have arisen from woody (Eames, 1911; Sinnott and Bailey, 1914, 1922; Whitaker, 1918; Jeffrey and Torrey, 1921). This has later been contested (Carlquist, 1962). The vegetation of these islands is regarded as more ancient than that of continental areas and it may, therefore, be considered as a vestige of an earlier and much more uniform flora which flourished over the Northern Hemisphere subtropical regions during the middle or later part of the Tertiary. Towards the end of the Tertiary this subtropical flora was displaced due to changes in the climatic zones and the probable southern migration of a cooler, drier climate which gave rise to the modern Mediterranean vegetation (Bramwell, 1972). This includes a number of tropical forms which have persisted as relicts to this day. As discussed by Sunding, chapter 2, many of the macrofossil floras from the Tertiary deposits of the western Mediterranean region have been shown to have a large number of species which still exist in the present-day Macaronesian flora.

The predominance of woody plants on oceanic islands was first noted by Darwin (1872) and he remarked that islands often have trees or shrubs belonging to groups which elsewhere include only herbaceous species. He explained that herbs probably became established on islands and then, by growing taller to gain advantage over other herbaceous plants, became first shrubs and eventually trees. This idea has been supported with a new anatomical theory called paedomorphosis (Carlquist, 1962). For the past six years I have examined sufficient material anatomically to dispute this theory and to provide other explanations for what has occurred in groups of woody plants on islands, and have attempted to show that the more generally accepted theory that herbs are derived from woody forms still applies to island floras as well as continental (Aldridge, 1975).

When the woody plants became established in oceanic island conditions they were isolated from their near neighbours and relatives. When the climate became too severe for their continental ancestors these became extinct but in the offshore islands where some had found refuge they were able to survive owing to the more favourable oceanic climates. From general observations of many oceanic island floras it is obvious that these plants diversified and many different types evolved which became adapted to the individual ecological and climatic areas of each island. All these types eventually became established, identifiable taxa. In many cases it is probable that originally more than one immigrant from the same source became established on the island before the continental members of that species group may have become extinct and each species may have diversified separately. The result would be that from each parent type the derived groups of species would probably be distinguishable. This vast adaptation to individual conditions is characteristic of oceanic islands probably because of the lack of competition from already established vegetation types. Competition for each ecological niche by the newly established plants would cause natural selection to favour the better adapted types and speciation would occur for those best adapted. This diversification and eventual speciation of groups of plants on oceanic islands is termed adaptive radiation. The phenomenon was first discussed in detail by Darwin in his *Origin of Species* (1872) when considering the Galapagos Islands. He stated that when an immigrant first settled on one of the islands or when it subsequently spread from one to another it would undoubtedly be exposed to different conditions in different islands for it would have to compete with a different set of organisms. A plant would find its most suitable niche occupied by different species in the different islands and it would also be exposed to attacks by different enemies. If it subsequently varied then natural selection would probably favour different variants in the different islands. Some species would, however, spread and still retain the same characteristics throughout the group. Once adaptation has proceeded the derived species are seldom found in the same habitat. When this occurs and the two are distinct morphologically, it is probably an indication of a much more distinct relationship. When they are very similar morphologically it is probably an indication of speciation in progress or that the habitats have been disturbed by Man. In these latter areas hybridisation between species is quite common (Aldridge, in press).

The problem with large groups of island species which have adaptively radiated is to distinguish which species is most like the ancestral type and which the most recently evolved. By solving this problem we will be determining the evolutionary pathways which the species have followed. Stebbins (1967) stated that most of the trends of phylogeny can be seen operating to a small extent within groups of genetically related species and are, therefore, open to study by experimental methods. The most established and reliable trends of phylogeny are probably those based on anatomical features of the secondary xylem as they are largely one-directional and irreversible (Bailey and Tupper, 1918; Record, 1919; Bailey, 1920, 1923; Wetmore, 1926; Frost, 1930a, 1930b, 1931; Kribs, 1935, 1937; Chattaway, 1936; Chalk, 1937; Gilbert, 1940). The present discussion is illustrated by a woody group of endemic Canary Islands plants. The subgenus *Dendrosonchus* of the genus *Sonchus* (family Compositae, tribe Lactuceae) comprises 17 species and 10 subspecies and is composed of two distinct

groups or sections, *Dendrosonchus* and *Atalanthus*. These sections can easily
be distinguished in the field by the shapes of their leaf-lobes and each
taxon may also be distinguished by its leaf-shape (Aldridge, 1976a).
Anatomical investigations within the subgenus have revealed several
potentially useful sources of information which could be considered as
relevant to the elucidation of the evolutionary and phylogenetic trends
within the group (Aldridge, 1977, 1978). Taking into consideration the
morphology, especially of the leaf, capitulum and habit, of the species,
possible lines of evolution based on anatomical information are proposed
for the subgenus.

Evolutionary studies in Sonchus

The Canarian *Sonchus* species of subgenus *Dendrosonchus* seem to be
basically Tertiary relicts of a once, more widespread Mediterranean forest
flora which has survived only in the Macaronesian region. Although
other members of the genus are found in the Mediterranean region I do
not consider any of these to be more primitive than the members of
Dendrosonchus. Their relictual nature is strongly supported by their woody
life-forms and their diploid chromosome numbers found throughout the
group. The nearest related continental members of the genus are annual
to perennial herbs of subgenus *Sonchus* which exhibit a range of polyploid-
levels and chromosome base numbers. Thirteen of the twenty-one species
of the subgenus *Sonchus* have either a slightly woody caudex, a woody
rhizome or a woody taproot (Boulos, 1973). It is, therefore, apparent that
the genus is basically woody and not herbaceous. The Compositae are
generally considered to be a predominantly herbaceous family but this
condition is certainly not reflected in the genus *Sonchus*. Babcock (1950)
considered the rhizomatous species of *Crepis* to have been derived from
tap-rooted ancestors. In some cases the rhizomatous condition could have
reverted back to the tap-rooted condition. All the members of
Dendrosonchus have tuberous tap-roots, whereas the majority of annual to
perennial species of the subgenera *Sonchus* and *Origosonchus* are
rhizomatous. In the more derived members of the subgenus *Sonchus* the
reversion to the tap-rooted condition has occurred. However, these tap-
roots are not tuberous as in *Dendrosonchus*.

 Babcock (1947) was of the opinion that *Sonchus*, *Launaea*, *Tolpis* and
Hieracium originated from *Dubyaea*-like ancestors. The genus *Dubyaea* has
its distribution in the Himalayas and western China. Its members are
perennial. According to Babcock, the genera given above developed as a
branch of the pre-Tertiary Arctic flora in the region of the northern Ural
mountains. Then in early Eocene times, before the Obic Sea separated

Europe from Asia, certain *Dubyaea*-like plants migrated into northern Europe where they continued to develop throughout the Tertiary period. They were then driven southward or exterminated by extreme cold.

This explanation could account for the absence of primitive members of *Sonchus* in the Mediterranean and North African regions at the present-day. The Canary Islands, being subcontinental with an oceanic climate, are protected from extremes of climate prevalent on the continent, and the migrating ancestors could possibly have found refuge in these islands during the Tertiary period. At this time the eastern and western parts of the archipelago are thought to have been separated following crustal movements along the fault lines separating Fuerteventura (and its related islands) from Gran Canaria (and the other more westerly islands) (Hausen, 1962, 1971).

Members of *Sonchus* subgenus *Dendrosonchus*, as recognised by Aldridge (1976b), present extremely varied anatomical characteristics which is unusual for such a closely related group of plants. They are woody pachycauls and thus could be considered as excellent material for evolutionary investigation (Mabberley, chapter 12; *see also* Mabberley, 1974). Many anatomical workers have supplied us with sound evidence for formulating the directions of evolution of features within the secondary xylem. It is on these principles that the present work has been based. These important works have been reviewed in detail by several authors (Chalk, 1937; Tippo, 1946; Bailey, 1951; Takhtajan, 1954; Dickison, 1975; Carlquist, 1975). Well-established trends in the tracheary elements have been of prime importance to the elucidation of evolutionary trends in *Dendrosonchus* and these trends have been clarified by consideration of the wood rays, the petioles and nodes, the cypsela and the general stem anatomy.

The details of this investigation are the subject of a separate publication (Aldridge, 1978) but the basic conclusions will be summarised here. Initially large numbers of vessel elements of each taxon were examined, measured and compared. The ratios between the lengths and widths of each vessel element and the means for each taxon were calculated. The evolutionary trend in vessel elements proposed in the early part of this century was based upon hundreds of species from hundreds of families of Angiosperms, Gymnosperms and fossil plants and it was, therefore, surprising that by examining the length to width ratios of the vessel elements a trend from primitive to derived was found in both sections of the subgenus *Dendrosonchus*. If we assume that the species having primitive vessel-elements are themselves primitive and the species with derived vessel elements are themselves derived then we find that in the section *Atalanthus* the most primitive species is *Sonchus arboreus* DC. and in the section *Dendrosonchus* the most primitive species is *Sonchus brachylobus* Webb ex Sch. Bip. The most derived species in section *Atalanthus*, from this particular body of evidence, is *Sonchus pinnatus* Ait. subspecies *palmensis* and the most derived species in the section *Dendrosonchus* is *Sonchus acaulis* Dum.-Cours.

Although evolutionary trends in vessel elements are considered to be reliable it is not acceptable to use this information alone in the estimation of relative primitiveness of any group of species. Neither is it acceptable to use any one single source of data for this purpose. From the data from vessel elements in *Dendrosonchus* it is only possible to show that there are two distinct lines of evolution, one within each of the two sections. It is not possible to say whether there has occurred several diverging lines of species as we would expect from a group which shows adaptive radiation. It is necessary, therefore, to examine other evidence to elucidate and support these probable trends in evolution. Another anatomical feature of the secondary xylem which was found to show an evolutionary trend was the wood rays. An evolutionary trend in wood rays was also discovered in the early part of this century. *Dendrosonchus* has a range of ray types which are primitive in those species with primitive vessel elements and more derived in those with more derived vessel elements. These trends were found in both of the sections of *Dendrosonchus* and they have been discussed previously in detail (Aldridge, 1978). This evidence, therefore, supported that from vessel elements.

Other anatomical features of the species were then examined and compared in order to clarify the relationships between the species and, if possible, to explain the directions of evolution within each section. The most rewarding of these was the comparative anatomy of the vascular tissue in the petioles and nodes. Four basic types of vascular supply were found for the subgenus (Aldridge, 1977). The vascular tissue in the petioles comprises small discrete bundles of xylem and phloem. There are two arrangements of these bundles in the petioles of *Dendrosonchus*, either O-shaped or U-shaped. There are also two types of development for each of these. In the simplest type the bundles move into the petiole from the stem and form a U-shape. From this type probably evolved a second in which some of the phloem elements moved to the adaxial side of the petiole and then almost immediately returned to the abaxial surface. When this type is examined in the petiole it appears as the basic U-type. From the U-type the more complex O-type has evolved in which phloem elements from the cortical phloem of the stem came to position themselves on the adaxial surface. The most complex type of petiolar vascular supply is that in which the O-shape is achieved by turning around in the petiole of bundles of xylem and phloem to the adaxial position. All these types are considered to have evolved from the basic U-type. The numbers of gaps left in the vascular cylinder of the stem after the bundles supplying the leaves had departed was also a useful comparative feature. In the more·primitive species the common number of leaf gaps was three. The more derived the species the more gaps were left in the stele. The highest number of gaps seen was ten in *Sonchus acaulis* (Aldridge, 1977).

With this extra anatomical information as well as some features of the cypsela anatomy (Aldridge, 1978) it was possible to show that the two basic trends of evolution that have occurred within the subgenus *Dendrosonchus*, which were based upon vessel elements and wood rays, are not straight lines of evolution but are a series of radiating branches from two ancestral types. I have already mentioned that anatomical evidence alone cannot be relied upon to show evolutionary trends within a group and, therefore, it must be correlated with evidence from morphological features (Aldridge, 1976a). The morphology of the leaves, the sizes of the capitula, the form of the pollen, the structure of the pappus and the general habit of each species were all correlated with this anatomical information and a pattern of radiating branches of evolution from two ancestral types emerged (Fig. 1).

As suggested before, the most primitive species in the section *Atalanthus* was found to be *Sonchus arboreus*. From this ancestral type two lines of evolution occurred. One culminating in *Sonchus leptocephalus* Cass. subspecies *capillaris* which has very reduced leaf-lobes. The other in *Sonchus pinnatus* subspecies *palmensis* with much broader leaf-lobes. In the section *Dendrosonchus* the most primitive species was found to be *Sonchus brachylobus*. This species is equally as primitive in all its anatomical features as *Sonchus arboreus*. If we consider *Sonchus brachylobus* to be something like the ancestral type for this section, then four major branches of evolution have occurred from it. Two of these are also branched. The most derived species of the whole of the subgenus was found to be *Sonchus acaulis*. From the research carried out it was not possible to determine the nature of the common ancestor to the two sections but it is probable that it was more woody and shrub-like than any of the present-day members of the rest of the genus *Sonchus*.

Conclusions

The largest centre of diversity for the section *Atalanthus* is the island of Tenerife in the Canary Islands. Four of the six taxa (species and subspecies) are found on this island. The largest centre of diversity for the section *Dendrosonchus* also occurs on Tenerife although the proposed ancestral type, *Sonchus brachylobus*, grows on Gran Canaria. *Sonchus*

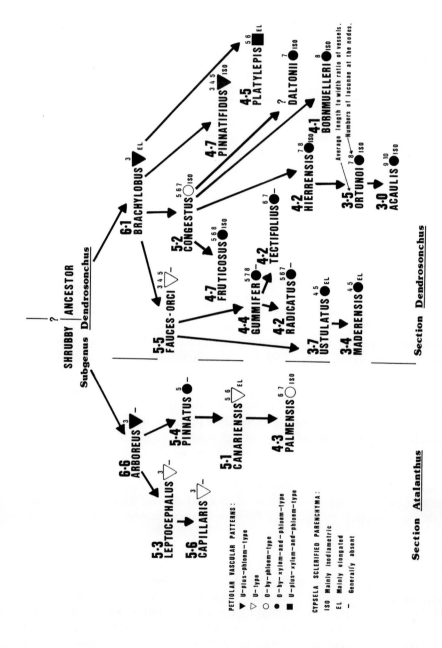

Fig. 1 Probable evolutionary relationships within *Dendrosonchus*

pinnatifidus Cav. is the only species of the subgenus which is found away from the island situation (Aldridge, in press). This species has become more shrubby and derived in its vessel elements but is morphologically and anatomically very similar to *Sonchus brachylobus*. The two species *S. platylepis* Webb ex Sch. Bip. and *S. pinnatifidus* are possibly the result of early adaptive radiations from the ancestral type. It is possible that *Sonchus pinnatifidus* migrated eastwards even before Fuerteventura and Lanzarote were separated from the African continent.

The subgenus is obviously composed of two distinct morphological groups which I have recognised previously as sections (Aldridge, 1976a). Two distinct ancestral types are considered to have given rise to this situation. Both types were probably woody shrubs having medium-sized capitula and leaves. These two types are not thought to have arisen from a common ancestor within the Canary Islands, but they may have evolved from a common ancestor during or before the Tertiary period and before they migrated to the Canaries.

Boulos (1960) considered the genus *Sonchus* to have originated in central Africa from the genus *Launaea*. He proposed that the species of the subgenus *Origosonchus* are the most primitive members of the genus and that they are a link between *Launaea* on the one hand and *Dendrosonchus* on the other. From the evidence put forward here it is possible to say that the subgenus *Dendrosonchus* is composed of members which are very primitive and it is more likely that the subgenera *Origosonchus* and *Sonchus* are derived from this group. The similarities in characters between the subgenus *Origosonchus* and *Launaea*, as discussed by Boulos, may indicate the derivation of *Launaea* from that subgenus, and that it is, therefore, more derived than the genus *Sonchus*. As pointed out by Boulos, the most primitive members of the subgenus *Sonchus* (*Sonchus pustulatus* Willk., *Sonchus fragilis* Ball and *Sonchus briquetianus* Gandonger) occur in northwest Africa. These species are in fact very similar to the *Sonchus radicatus* Ait. group of *Dendrosonchus*, which is considered here, on anatomical and morphological evidence, to be derived.

Once the ancestral types of the subgenus *Dendrosonchus* became established in the Canary Islands, they underwent rapid evolution, probably in the late or post-Tertiary period, which has resulted in a wide range of forms (17 species and 10 subspecies) occupying the major climatic and vegetation zones. It appears that such a wide range of forms can be maintained in the Macaronesian region, and in the Canaries in particular, as a result of two factors: the diversity of available habitats and the relative stability of major environmental factors including lack of competition over a long period of time. The diverging lines of evolution shown for *Dendrosonchus* are illustrative of adaptive trends to particular

K*

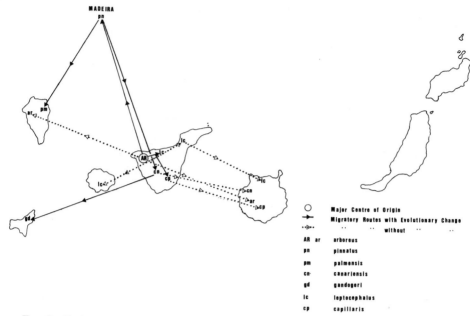

FIG. 2   Probable migration routes of members of *Atalanthus*

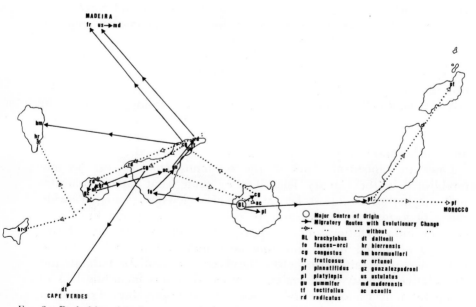

FIG. 3   Probable migration routes of members of *Dendrosonchus*

288

environmental conditions. Within each line are closely related taxa which may represent vicariads, being allopatric species which show similarities. The origin and evolution of the members of the subgenus *Dendrosonchus* can be summarised in Figs 2 and 3 which indicate the possible migration routes thought to have occurred in their evolution. The two most primitive members of the group are found in ancient basaltic areas of Tenerife and Gran Canaria respectively. It is, therefore, proposed that the present-day members of the subgenus originated from these centres, radiated to other areas of these islands and eventually migrated to other islands in the archipelago becoming distinct taxa at some time during this.

The endemic flora of the Canary Islands is generally considered to be relict and Tertiary. This view was based on several distinct sources of evidence such as taxonomy, cytology, morphology, palaeobotany and phytogeography. I have now demonstrated that the anatomy of certain island plants may also be useful in showing the relict nature of these island floras. In islands, such as the Canaries, we enjoy a situation which is a refugium for relict types of plants which in continental regions have become extinct. These groups of plants may be considered as living fossils and if we had as good a fossil history of plants as we have of animals it is highly probable that we would find many of the fossils to be like the plants now existing on oceanic islands. Because many of these woody, island groups have undergone a comparatively recent surge of evolution they are known as active epibiotics, and the anatomical information which I have attempted to explain briefly here is important for deciding which of these plants is nearer to the ancestral type. Similar work, now in progress, with other woody Macaronesian groups of plants is proving to be useful in substantiating this method of research.

REFERENCES

Aldridge, A. E. (1975). Taxonomic and anatomical studies in *Sonchus* L. subgenus *Dendrosonchus* Webb ex Schultz Bip. and related genera. Unpubl. Ph.D. thesis, University of Reading, England
— (1976a). A critical reappraisal of the Macaronesian *Sonchus* subgenus *Dendrosonchus* s.l. (Compositae-Lactuceae). *Bot. Macar.* **2**, 25–58
— (1976b). Macaronesian *Sonchus* subgenus *Dendrosonchus* s.l. (Compositae-Lactuceae), including a reappraisal of the species concept and new combinations. *Bot. Macar.* **2**, 81–93
— (1977). Anatomy and evolution in the Macaronesian *Sonchus* subgenus *Dendrosonchus* (Compositae-Lactuceae). Nodal and petiolar vascular patterns. *Bot. Macar.* **3**, 41–59

— (1978). Anatomy and evolution in the Macaronesian *Sonchus* subgenus *Dendrosonchus* (Compositae-Lactuceae). *Bot. J. Linn. Soc.* **76** (4), 249–285

— Cytology, reproductive biology and hybridization in Macaronesian *Sonchus* L. (Compositae-Lactuceae). *2° Congreso Pro Flora Macaronesia* (in press)

Babcock, E. B. (1947). The genus *Crepis*. Part two: Systematic treatment. *Univ. Calif. Publ. Bot.* **22**, 199–1030

— (1950). Supplementary notes on *Crepis* III. Taproot versus rhizome in phylogeny. *Evolution* **4** (4), 358–359

Bailey, I. W. (1920). The cambium and its derivative tissues II. Size variations of cambial initials in gymnosperms and angiosperms. *Amer. J. Bot.* **7**, 355–367

— (1923). The cambium and its derivative tissues IV. The increase in girth of the cambium. *Amer. J. Bot.* **10**, 499–509

— (1951). The use and abuse of anatomical data in the study of phylogeny and classification. *Phytomorphology* **1**, 67–69

— and Tupper, W. W. (1918). Size variations in tracheary cells I. A comparison between the secondary xylems of vascular cryptogams, gymnosperms and angiosperms. *Proc. Amer. Acad. Arts Sci.* **54**, 149–204

Boulos, L. (1960). Cytotaxonomic studies in the genus *Sonchus* 2. The genus *Sonchus* a general systematic treatment. *Bot. Not.* **113** (4), 400–420

— (1973). Révision systématique du genre *Sonchus* L. s.l. IV. Sous-genre 1. *Sonchus. Bot. Not.* **126**, 155–196

Bramwell, D. (1972). Endemism in the flora of the Canary Islands. In *Taxonomy, Phytogeography and Evolution* (D. H. Valentine, ed.), 141–159. Academic Press, London and New York

Carlquist, S. (1962). A theory of paedomorphosis in dicotyledonous woods. *Phytomorphology* **12**, 30–45

— (1975). *Ecological Strategies of Xylem Evolution.* University of California Press, Berkeley and Los Angeles

Chalk, S. (1937). The phylogenetic value of certain anatomical features of dicotyledonous woods. *Ann. Bot. (London)* N.S. **1** (3), 409–428

Chattaway, M. M. (1936). Relation between fibre and cambial initial length in dicotyledonous woods. *Trop. Woods* **46**, 16–20

Darwin, C. (1872). *On the Origin of Species by Means of Natural Selection or the Preservation of Favoured Races in the Struggle for Life*, 6th ed. Murray, London

Dickison, W. C. (1975). The bases of angiosperm phylogeny: Vegetative anatomy. *Ann. Mo. Bot. Gdn* **62**, 590–620

Eames, A. J. (1911). On the origin of the herbaceous type in the angiosperms. *Ann. Bot. (London)* **25** (97), 215–224

Frost, F. H. (1930a). Specialization in secondary xylem of dicotyledons I. Origin of vessels. *Bot. Gaz. (Chicago)* **89**, 67–94

— (1930b). Specialization in secondary xylem of dicotyledons II. The evolution of the end wall of the vessel segment. *Bot. Gaz. (Chicago)* **90**, 198–212

— (1931). Specialization in secondary xylem of dicotyledons III. Specialization of the lateral wall of the vessel segment. *Bot. Gaz. (Chicago)* **91**, 88–96

Gilbert, S. G. (1940). Evolutionary significance of ring porosity in woody angiosperms. *Bot. Gaz. (Chicago)* **102**, 105–120

Hausen, H. (1962). New contributions to the geology of Grand Canary (Gran Canaria, Canary Islands). *Soc. Sci. Fenn. Comm. Phys.-Math.* (*Helsinki*) **27** (1)

— (1971). Outlines of the geology of Gomera (Canary Islands) in relation to its surface forms. *Soc. Sci. Fenn. Comm. Phys.-Math.* (*Helsinki*) **41** (1)

Jeffrey, E. C. and Torrey, R. E. (1921). Physiological and Morphological correlations in herbaceous angiosperms. *Bot. Gaz.* (*Chicago*) **71** (1), 1–30

Kribs, D. A. (1935). Salient lines of specialization in the wood rays of dicotyledons. *Bot. Gaz.* (*Chicago*) **96**, 547–557

— (1937). Salient lines of structural specialization in the wood parenchyma of dicotyledons. *Bull. Torrey Bot. Club* **64**, 177–187

Mabberley, D. J. (1974). Pachycauly, vessel-elements, islands and the evolution of arborescence in "herbaceous" families. *New Phytol.* **73**, 977–984

Record, S. J. (1919). Storied or tier-like structure in certain dicotyledonous woods. *Bull. Torrey Bot. Club* **46**, 253–273

Sinnott, E. W. and Bailey, I. W. (1914). Investigations on the phylogeny of the angiosperms 4. The origin and dispersal of herbaceous angiosperms. *Ann. Bot.* (*Lond.*) **28** (112), 547–600

— (1922). The significance of the "folia ray" in the evolution of herbaceous angiosperms. *Ann. Bot.* (*Lond.*) **36** (144), 523–533

Stebbins, G. L. (1967). Adaptive radiation and trends of evolution in higher plants. In *Evolutionary Biology*, (Th. Dobzhansky, M. K. Hecht and W. C. Steere, eds.) Vol. 1, 101–142. Appleton-Century Crofts, New York

Takhtajan, A. L. (1954). *Essays on the Evolutionary Morphology of Plants* (Transl. by O. Hess Gankin. G. L. Stebbins, ed.). American Institute of Biological Sciences, Washington, D.C

Tippo, O. (1946). The role of wood anatomy in phylogeny. *Amer. Midl. Naturalist* **36**, 362–372

Wetmore, R. H. (1926). Organisation and significance of lenticels in dicotyledons I. Lenticels in relation to aggregate and compound storage rays in woody stems. Lenticels and roots. *Bot. Gaz.* (*Chicago*) **82**, 71–88

Whitaker, E. S. (1918). Anatomy of certain goldenrods. *Bot. Gaz.* (*Chicago*) **65**, 250–260

Wulff, E. V. (1943). *An Introduction to Historical Plant Geography*. Chronica Botanica Co., Waltham, Mass.

14 Reproductive Biology in Island Plants

F. EHRENDORFER   *Botanisches Institut und*
Botanischer Garten der Universität Wien, Austria

La biología reproductiva en plantas isleñas es un campo de investigación complejo y fascinante. En este trabajo se manejan los siguientes aspectos: llegada por medio de dispersión a larga distancia; establecimiento de poblaciones fundadoras y evolución insular que afecta el sistema de reproducción; polinización y biología floral y de la espora; biología del fruto y la semilla.

Se discute la llegada de plantas a islas volcánicas recientes, tales como Krakatoa y Surtsey, así como a islas más antiguas, por ejemplo la cadena hawaiana. Se discute también los mecanismos de transportes, como los de flotación, corrientes de aire y pájaros. Se citan ejemplos de cada uno de ellos.

Se describen las necesidades biológicas y reproductivas para el establecimiento de poblaciones fundadoras y la necesidad de vencer la propia incompatibilidad. Se muestra la radiación y diversificación de colonizadores triunfantes como resultado de hibridización y recombinación, pero también implica mecanismos especiales que refuerzan la reproducción para reconstruir los "pools" genéticos agotados. Estos mecanismos incluyen ginodioecismo y poligamo-dioecismo etc. Se comenta con detalle la pérdida de mecanismos de dispersión a larga distancia en el establecimiento de plantas isleñas.

Se señala el aumento del tamaño de la fruta en muchas plantas insulares y se dán algunas explicaciones probables.

El autor apremia para que se hagan más estudios sobre biología de polinización de plantas endémicas de islas y de su relación con insectos y pájaros endémicos polinizadores, ya que existe el peligro de que se pierda una información valiosa si uno u otro de los modelos simbiótico llega a extinguirse.

Introduction

Within the framework of this volume I would like to survey our present knowledge concerning the reproductive biology of vascular plants on islands, particularly on oceanic islands. This is an extensive, fascinating, and complex field of inquiry, still insufficiently covered by relevant work and factual evidence. For the most significant recent contributions and summaries in book form we have to be grateful to Carlquist (1965, 1974). This present survey will concentrate on the following problems of island plant reproductive biology:

1. Arrival by long-distance dispersal,
2. Establishment of founder populations,
3. Insular evolution, affecting (a) the breeding system, (b) pollination and floral biology, (c) spore, seed, and fruit biology.

293

Arrival by long-distance dispersal

The most dramatic natural experiments on long-distance dispersal of plants (and animals) to oceanic islands are afforded by volcanic catastrophes, destruction of old and origin of new biota, as on the North Atlantic island of Surtsey (since 1963), Krakatoa between Sumatra and Java (since 1883) or the Hawaiian Islands (during several millions of years). Within four years Surtsey had been reached by 5 Angiosperms (Einarsson, 1967), Krakatoa was settled by 271 species up to 1934 (Drs van Leeuwen, 1934), and the Hawaiian Islands, much more remote from source areas, have built up a native flowering plant flora of more than 1200 species from at least 256 separate introductions (Fosberg, 1963; Carlquist, 1967). Analyses demonstrate that such oceanic island floras are disharmonious with regard to their dispersal spectrum: adaptations to long-distance transport of diaspores are grossly over-represented; this applies particularly to transport by ocean drift (hydrochory), air currents (anemochory), and birds (zoochory: ornithochory); birds may carry seeds or fruits which they have eaten (endozoochory) or which adhere to their surface (epizoochory) (Ridley, 1930).

Classical examples of long-distance dispersal of floating fruits or seeds by ocean currents wide-spread island inhabitants are the coastal and pantropical *Cocos nucifera* L., the palaeotropical genera *Pandanus* and *Barringtonia* (Lecythidaceae), and the tropical amphiatlantic genus *Chrysobalanus*. Sea-water dispersal has effected the differentiation of the tropical mangrove flora (with *Rhizophora*, *Avicennia* etc.) into an Australian, E. African and a W. African-American province. Among Convolvulaceae the stoloniferous dune pioneers *Ipomoea pes-caprae* Roth and *Calystegia soldanella* R. Br. have reached most of the tropical, temperate continental, and island coasts of our globe. The typical Mediterranean littoral Umbellifer *Crithmum maritimum* L. has successfully extended its area to the Canary Islands, Madeira and the Azores.

Storms, particularly strong updrafts and high velocity "jet streams" in the upper atmosphere have been shown to be quite effective agents for long-distance dispersal of spores, seeds, and smaller fruits. Evidence for this comes from the extensive insular occurrence of several Pteridophytes with dust-like spores (e.g. *Psilotum* or *Pteridium*), of Angiosperms with very small seeds (e.g. *Metrosideros* among the Myrtaceae in the Pacific), or particularly of those with feathery appendages on seeds or fruits, as in certain Onagraceae (e.g. *Epilobium* in temperate habitats of both hemispheres), Asclepiadaceae, Compositae (e.g. *Senecio* and *Erigeron*, both world-wide, or *Vernonia* in the tropical zone) and Gramineae. The fact that Orchidaceae are less common on islands than one would expect from their minute, easily airborne seeds (e.g. only 3 species on the Hawaiian Islands), may be connected to their mycotrophy, specialised floral biology, and/or temperature sensitivity of the seeds.

Effective epizoochorous dispersal to oceanic islands has often been due to birds which carry small fruits or seeds (frequently mucilaginous when wet) in the mud on their feet. This applies for instance to many species of the world-wide genera *Drosera*, *Euphorbia*, *Plantago*, *Galium*, *Juncus* and *Scirpus*, to the N.Hemisphere-centred *Luzula*, to *Wahlenbergia* and *Cotula*, most abundant in the S.Hemisphere, and to the Antarctic Caryophyllacea *Colobanthus*. These genera include several taxa which have become island endemics. Similar considerations apply to several (sub)-tropical genera with viscid appendages on their fruits, as in the coastal Nyctaginaceae *Pisonia* and *Boerhaavia*, the Compositae *Adenostemma*, *Eclipta* and *Lagenophora*, and in *Plumbago*. Furthermore, successful attachment to birds may be due to hooks, spines, barbs or other adhesive structures. Such mechanisms are evidently responsible for the wide, often insular, and eventually endemic distribution of taxa within the genera *Geum*, *Sanicula* and *Cynoglossum* (all of Holarctic origin, but presently world-wide), the (sub)tropical *Desmodium*, *Triumfetta*, *Plectranthus* and *Aristida*, or the S.Hemisphere-centred *Acaena* and *Uncinia*. From the New World the Compositae genus *Bidens* has successfully expanded into the Old World and into the islands of the Pacific.

Endozoochory by birds appears to be of particular importance for the colonisation of oceanic islands. Among the very numerous examples it should suffice here to list representatives from the (sub)tropical Lauraceae, Piperaceae, *Ficus*, *Syzygium* and many other Myrtaceae, *Ilex*, *Scaevola* and *Smilax*, the S.Pacific-centred *Exocarpos*, *Styphelia* and *Coprosma*, the S.Hemisphere *Gunnera*, *Fuchsia* and *Nertera*, and the N.Hemisphere-centred *Rubus* and *Vaccinum*. *Cyrtandra* (Gesneriaceae) is a good example of how a berry-fruited and endozoochorous[1] genus has colonised the Pacific islands from Australasia and has extensively differentiated on the Hawaiian Islands (St. John, 1966).

A comparison of dispersal spectra of different insular seed-plant floras reveals remarkable differences (Carlquist, 1967, 1974; Porter, 1976). In the Pacific, the quite recent atolls of the equatorial Line Islands (L; original and natural introductions c. N = 33), the dry and volcanic Galapagos Islands (c. 3 million years; G; N = 281), and the certainly much older humid island of Samoa (S; N = 311) had the following approximate percentages of natural arrivals: by ocean drift L = 63·6%, G = 12%, S = 17·8%, by air flotation L = 0%. G = 11%, S = 8·1%, and by birds L = 30·3%, G = 77%, S = 64·6%; the latter includes

[1]But compare critical remarks by Balgooy (1971–75)!

introductions through epizoochory (barbs, bristles etc.) $L = 0\%$, $G = 27\cdot4\%$, $S = 4\%$ and endozoochory $L = 9\cdot1\%$, $G = 33\cdot2\%$, $S = 50\cdot8\%$. As a generalisation it appears that ocean drift is most effective on low islands (atolls etc.) with a prominence of coastal habitats, and that wind-dispersal becomes relatively important on islands closer to continental source areas; but most transport of seeds and fruits to more remote islands is due to birds. Epizoochory on muddy feet (with small, often mucilaginous diaspores) dominates in aquatic and marshy habitats, epizoochory on feathers (with barbs, bristles etc. on diaspores) in dry open habitats, and endozoochory (usually with fleshy diaspores) in woody habitats. It is obvious from this that the type of recipient insular ecosystem and the potential vectors involved have a strong selective "filtering" influence on the type of diaspores arriving and eventually establishing newcomers.

Much still remains to be done in the field of comparative, quantitative and experimental analyses of diaspores from island plants and their continental progenitors, and of diaspores in the actual course of transport by wind, water, and animals. Even if our relevant data are gradually improved, interpretations of long-distance dispersal will still have to be balanced and critical. A case in question is offered by the interesting occurrence of the herbaceous Umbellifer *Drusa glandulosa* (Poir.) Bornm. on the Canary Islands; all related taxa are confined to the New World (Bramwell, 1972). The suggestion of a relatively recent long-distance dispersal of the adhesive fruits with their hooked appendages is close at hand. But new localities of this species have been found in Morocco and Somalia (!), and they parallel several obviously ancient disjunctions (e.g. in *Aeonium* and *Dracaena*). *Drusa* therefore may be an ancient relict and not an actively migrating plant.

Establishment of founder populations

After arrival of propagules on an island, germination, maturation and reproduction are next obstacles to be overcome by all successful immigrant plant species. For zoophilous Angiosperms preadaptation to the available pollinating animals will be essential for survival. The establishment on the Hawaiian Islands of the ornithophilous Legumes *Erythrina sandwichensis* Deg. (endemic) and *Strongylodon lucidus* Seem. (widespread in the Pacific) must have been linked to the prior origin of flower-visiting bird species among the local Drepanididae. Migratory Angiosperms therefore often need less specialised pollination, e.g. by smaller insects, by wind, or most commonly by autogamy, i.e. by self-pollination. It is obvious that hermaphrodite and self-compatible plants which can produce offspring from single founder individuals after spontaneous selfing will be very much better preadapted for island colonisation than dioecious or self-sterile and obligatory outcrossing species, where at least two individuals need to mate before progeny can originate (Baker, 1955, 1967). Relevant proof for this thesis from systematic surveys of pollination systems in island floras is still very meagre. Exemplary studies by Rick (1966) on the Galapagos flora indicate a much lower degree of self-incompatibility and a much higher level of automatic self-fertilisation there than in the floras of continental source areas.

Apart from this, there is good evidence from a number of plant genera that island biota have been successfully colonised by autogamous representatives from among normally outbreeding continental populations. In the Gesneriaceae the Pacific genus *Cyrtandra* (cf. p. 295) has radiated on the basis of self-compatability coupled with a varying degree of insect visits to the conspicuous flowers, i.e. a balance between in- and outbreeding. Self-incompatibility is a primitive feature in *Galium* (Rubiaceae); the small species-group which has reached Australia, evidently by island-hopping across Indomalesia from the north, consists of inbreeders. In contrast to the outbreeding and more localised Pacific species of *Scaevola* (Goodeniaceae), the coastal pioneer *S. taccada* Roxb. (=*S. sericea*) has attained a very wide distribution with selfing, cleistogamous flowers and buoyant fruits (Carlquist, 1974). Similarly, long-distance dispersal of *Lycopersicon* to the Galapagos Islands was achieved by predominantly selfing biotypes (Rick, 1966).

In these and similar cases the break-down of a gametophytic system of self-incompatibility, common to many Angiosperm families, appears to be involved: One (or more) S-gene(s) with a series of alleles prevent the development of those pollen grains which have the same S-alleles as the recipient (stylar) plant; simple mutations of the S-gene(s) can inactivate the system (cf. Nettancourt, 1977 for further references).

In sporophytic systems of self-incompatibility the pollen reaction is determined by the genetic constitution of the pollen-producing plant, only two alleles are involved, and there is often close linkage with di-(or tri-) morphic flower structures (Vuilleumier, 1967). Classical cases of the breakdown of this outbreeding device in connection with long-distance dispersal and island colonisation have been presented for the Plumbaginaceae and Primulaceae (Baker, 1953a,b, 1959, 1966; Moore and Yates, 1974). In genetical terms, the flower dimorphism in these two families has originated by linkage of an incompatibility gene with genes for pollen, anther position and style dimorphism into a "super-gene". Breakdown was brought about several times, either be recombination within this "super-gene" and by loss of incompatibility, resulting in derived monomorphic and autogamous populations, or by apomixis. In *Limonium* the transition to autogamy has enabled members of sect. *Limonium* to expand from Europe and S.America to western and eastern N.America, and to reach from there to the Bermudas (*L. lefroyi*) and back to NW.Europe (*L. humile* Mill.). Apomictic types of sect. *Limonium* have settled on Malta and Pantellaria (*L. cosyrense* (Guss.) O. Kuntze), the Balearic Islands (*L. gougetianum* (Gir.) O. Kuntze), and Ireland (*L. paradoxum* Pugs., *L. transwallianum* Pugs.). Dimorphic and out-breeding members of sect. *Plathymenium*, centred in E. Asia, have given rise to the monomorphic and inbreeding species group of *L. japonicum-L. australe* which has reached Queensland, Tasmania and New Caledonia. From dimorphic and self-incompatible populations of *Armeria maritima* (Mill.) Willd. in Europe, one monomorphic and self-compatible line with the papillose pollen-type B has established itself as a pioneer on the Shetland Islands, while others with the reticulate pollen type A have extended their area over the Northern Hemisphere and with an enormous disjunction from N.America even down into southernmost S.America. A similar pattern is encountered in *Primula* subsect. *Farinosae* where the change from heterostyly and outbreeding to homostyly and inbreeding (together with polyploidy) has been connected with circumpolar and transequatorial migrations into N. and S.America, including the occupation of Iceland, Greenland and the Falkland Islands.

Even dioecy, still another mechanism to secure outbreeding, has been eliminated in some island colonisers in favour of hermaphroditism and inbreeding: the dioecious *Fragaria chiloensis* (L.) Duchn., widespread along the western coasts of the Americas, has reached the Hawaiian Islands with a monoclinous population (Staudt, 1968), and the same phenomenon has been observed in the dioecious *Coprosma pumila* Hoof. f. (Rubiaceae) from New Zealand which is represented on Macquarie Island by a monoecious form (Taylor, 1954).

For the Pteridophytes too there is evidence that oceanic islands are predominantly settled by isosporous forms with hermaphrodite and self-compatible gametophytes (e.g. in *Psilotum nudum* (L.) Beauv.). Klekowski (1972a,b) has shown that outbreeding in the fern *Pteridium aquilinum* (L.) Kuhn. is mostly due to the accumulation of sporophytic recessive lethals which prevent successful intragametophytic mating. While N. and S.American continental biotypes have an average of 44% of such lethal alleles, an average of 32% is found in Hawaiian and only 8% in Galapagos island biotypes.

In spite of all the evidence supporting the importance of autogamy (and apomixis) for island colonisation, one must not overlook that there are several cases where establishment of founder populations on oceanic islands was achieved by dioecious Angiosperms. Baker (1967) has critically reviewed the examples listed for Hawaii by Carlquist (1966d), but several overall dioecious taxa of Euphorbiaceae (*Antidesma, Drypetes*), Menispermaceae (*Cocculus*), Theaceae (*Eurya* sect. *Proteurya*) and Nyctaginaceae (*Pisonia umbellifera* Seem. ex Nad.) actually appear to parallel instances of animals where males and females have simultaneously and successfully embarked on long-distance dispersal.

Insular evolution: the breeding system

Founder populations of vascular plants on islands are relatively homozygous due to inbreeding. It appears that the escape from this homozygosity is an essential prerequisite for their subsequent radiation and diversification. Apart from crossing, hybridisation and recombination between genetically different and separately introduced biotypes there are several breeding strategies for such an escape from homozygosity.

Isosporous pteridophytes differ in their genetic system from seed plants in regard to selfing because fusion of eggs and sperms from a single haploid gametophyte ("infragametophytic mating") will always lead to absolutely homozygous daughter sporophytes, even if the mother sporophyte had been heterozygous (Klekowsky, 1972a). In contrast, selfing of a diploid seed plant sporophyte, heterozygous in n loci with 2 alleles, will result in only $0.5n \times 100\%$ homozygous offspring. Founder population of ferns originating from single spores therefore will be fully homozygous. Polyploid isosporous ferns counteract this homozygosity by homoeologous and heterogenic meiotic chromosome pairing between their different genomes and the resulting segregation of their progeny (Klekowski, 1976). Furthermore, outbreeding is enhanced by the accumulation of sporophytic recessive lethals already mentioned (p. 298), by the establishment of temporary or obligatory unisexuality of gametophytes etc. In spite of all this, evolutionary diversification on islands is clearly less active in ferns than in seed plants. This is evident from the increased rate of contemporary species over the number of probable immigrants for the floras of the Hawaiian Islands: ferns $= 1.5$, Angiosperms $= 5.5$ or for the Galapagos islands ferns $= 1.05$, Angiosperms $= 1.48$.

Angiosperms which have switched towards selfing during long-distance dispersal and the establishment of island founder populations are not known to have reestablished complex gametophytic or sporophytic S-gene systems, heterostyly etc. to inforce outbreeding. Instead, the genetically more simple way to dioecy as the most reliable outbreeding mechanism has often been developed during subsequent island diversification (Baker, 1967; Carlquist, 1974). Presumably 3·7% only of the original immigrants to the Hawaiian Islands have been dioecious, but today's flora contains 27·7% (and in addition 3% which are gyno- or polygamo-dioecious). This and the relatively high percentage of dioecism in other island floras (e.g. in New Zealand: 13·5%) as compared to continental floras (e.g. SW Australia 4·4%, California 2·6%) illustrate the general trend towards intensified outbreeding on islands. Further proof for this thesis can be obtained from quite a number of Angiosperm groups.

Baker (1966) has elegantly shown, how monomorphic and self-compatible derivatives of *Ameria maritima* in California have not returned to the original heterostyly (cf. p. 298) but have switched to gynodioecy (with hermaphrodite and female plants) under selective pressure for outbreeding. Similarly, incipient gynodioecy has been observed in self-fertile Pacific island species of *Cyrtandra* (Carlquist, 1974)!

The normally hermaphrodite New World-centred Onagraceae genus *Fuchsia* has extended with sect. *Skinnera* to islands of the South Pacific. According to Godley (1955) hermaphrodite individuals are self-fertile; *F. cyrtandroides* J. W. Moore from Tahiti appears to be monomorphic, but on New Zealand gynodioecy has originated in *F. excorticata* L.f. and *F. perscandens* Cock. & All., and *F. procumbens* Cunn. even has become "trioecious" (with male, female and hermaphrodite plants).

Within Compositae-Anthemideae the genus *Cotula* (Lloyd, 1972a,b) has attained a world-wide distribution (including many islands) with gynomonoecious self-fertile members of sect. *Cotula* and sect. *Strongylosperma*. With the latter one can link the S.Hemisphere- and New Zealand-centred sect. *Leptinella*. Its primitive members are monoecious and have heads with marginal flowers pistillate and disc flowers staminate; selfing is still possible. Abortion of female or male flowers in several evolutionary lines has led to subdioecy and finally dioecy in the more derived and purely outbreeding species of sect. *Leptinella*. A similar trend has been observed in Hawaiian species of the Compositae-Heliantheae genus *Bidens* (Carlquist, 1974).

After obvious island hopping from the north, Australian and New Zealand representatives of the Rubiaceae-Rubieae genus *Asperula* have become established as a distinct dioecious group in the S.Hemisphere (Shaw and Turill, 1928).

Carlquist (1974) has drawn attention to the secondary origin of gynodioecy and dioecy in a number of Hawaiian Angiosperm groups. *Styphelia* (Epacridaceae) subg. *Cyathodes* is centred in New Zealand and has reached an extensive area in the Pacific (van Steenis and Balgooy,

1966) with hermaphrodite biotypes; on the Hawaiian and Marquesas Islands it is represented by two endemic and gynodioecious species (Sleumer, 1963). The Hawaiian Amaranthaceous genus *Charpentiera* is on the verge from gynodioecy to dioecy, but related genera still have hermaphrodite flowers (Sohmer, 1972). The closely knit species of *Pittosporum* on Hawaii are all dioecious (Carlquist, 1974) and evidently related to W.Pacific members of the genus. Monoclinous taxa have reached some SE Polynesian islands, but among New Zealand and Australian species there is an obvious trend towards polygamy (Cooper, 1956). Within Rutaceae-Zanthoxyleae the dioecious genus *Pelea* has differentiated as a vicariant on the Hawaii and Marquesas Islands from predominantly hermaphrodite progenitors near to extant members of *Melicope* and *Evodia* in the W.Pacific.

Insular evolution: pollination and floral biology

When island populations start to expand geographically and are spreading into different ecological niches, isolation and disruptive selection become effective and often lead to adaptive radiation. As an example of floral biological radiation the endemic Hawaiian berry-fruited Lobeliaceae-Cyaneinae can be mentioned (Rock, 1919; Wimmer, 1943–1968; Carlquist, 1970, 1974). There are four closely related genera (*Delissea*, *Cyanea*, *Rollandia* and *Clermontia*), obviously monophyletic and derived from a single immigrant stock, but today represented by more than 100 species. Apart from great diversity in growth form and leaf structure (linked to differences in habitat: from rain forests to dry cliffs, from sea level to about 2300 m, and from terrestrial to epiphytic), and some variety in inflorescences, fruits and seeds, the group displays a bewildering array of floral differentiation. This affects corolla length (15–90 mm), breadth and division of tube, shape (straight to strongly bent or curved), colour, (white, yellowish, greenish, violet, blue, red to purple; uniform, striated or double coloured), consistency, indumentum, position of flowers (erect to pendent, loosely to densely arranged), and flowering periods. Though outbreeding of the hermaphrodite flowers is favoured by proterandry, pollen discharge through the style, and pollinator visits (nectar!), self-pollination is possible. It is deplorable that the floral biology of Hawaiian *Lobelia* species has not yet been studied in detail. Such studies will become more and more difficult because a growing number of the plant and pollinator species involved have become or soon will be extinct. Available data indicate that the flowers are visited by insects (*Brachypeplus*, small Carabidae and Nitidulidae beetles etc.), but more important, by birds

(Meliphagidae and particularly Drepanididae). The Drepanididae or honey-creepers are also limited to the Hawaiian islands and their adaptive radiation in terms of bill-shape and diet (with varying proportions of insects and nectar) is well known (see Carlquist, 1974 for references). There can be little doubt that the very marked differences in bill dimension, length and curving among species of *Loxops*, *Himatione*, *Drepanidis*, *Hemignathus* etc. are linked with more or less specialised food-plant preferences and have originated in the course of a certain co-evolution with the Hawaiian Lobeliaceae and other ornithophilous Angiosperms on the islands. For example, the endemic Malvaceae genera *Hibiscadelphus* and *Kokia* with typical and curved bird-flowers illustrate how local flower-birds can influence the evolution of insular plant immigrants.

The development of a closer symbiosis between bird–flowers and flower–birds can lead to critical situations when one of the partners becomes extinct. Such a situation may arise more easily on islands with their limited and more vulnerable plant and animal life. Examples from the Canary Islands are the local species of *Canarina* (Campanulaceae), *Isoplexis* (Scrophulariaceae) and the *Lotus berthelotii* group (Fabaceae) which are obviously adapted to bird-pollination. Their brilliant flower colours (orange, yellow etc.), shape, lack of odour and ample nectar production, all typical characters of the bird–flower syndrome, strongly suggest a former co-evolution with flower–birds (Vogel, 1954; Yeo, 1972). But while East African members of *Canarina* are actually pollinated by birds, such flower birds have disappeared from the Canary Islands. By what pollination mechanism the ornithophilous Canarian genera survive today still needs study, but it is a fact, that *Lotus berthelotii* is practically extinct on the islands by now. Other complex but also primitive pollination systems have been preserved intact on islands, e.g. the one between *Ceropegia* (Asclepiadaceae) imitating decaying organic matter and trapping Diptera (Melichidae) on the Canary Islands, or the high proportion of primitive Winteraceae (e.g. *Zygogynum*) with beetle pollination (*cantharophily*) on New Caledonia (evidently *not* an oceanic island).

Island floras are characterised by a relatively high proportion of species with inconspicuous and generalised flowers which can be pollinated by various smaller insects (Carlquist, 1974). This is obviously correlated with insular insect faunas which are less diverse and consist mostly of smaller-sized species. Furthermore, there is usually a much higher frequency of wind-pollinated plant species on islands than in comparable continental floras, e.g. 19·8% on Hawaii, 29% on New Zealand, and 34% on Juan Fernandez. One can largely ascribe this to the better pre-adaptation of anemophilous taxa to island establishment. But sometimes wind-pollination appears to have originated on islands as an escape from animal pollinator dependence, e.g. in the Compositae genus *Rhetinodendron* on Juan Fernandez, or within the otherwise predominantly zoophilous Rubiaceae in the endemic genera *Phyllis* and *Plocama* on the Canary Islands or in *Coprosma* on New Zealand etc.

Insular evolution: spore, seed and fruit biology

Much of the evolutionary radiation on islands can be described as adaptive shifts away from the original coastal or open pioneer and weedy habitats where most of the colonisers establish their populations. For this penetration into interior and more closed communities the original light, easily and widely dispersed propagules are of selective disadvantage. This is a general principle, well documented for many continental floras (Salisbury, 1942), and it is therefore not surprising to find it in island vascular plants too: Their propagules tend to loose mechanisms for long-distance dispersal and to become heavier and better equipped with nutrients for improved competition under crowded conditions. From the numerous relevant examples studied by Carlquist (1966b,c, 1974) a few should be considered in this context.

Within Pacific pteridophytes spore-size increases in Blechnaceae, *Athyrium, Rumohra, Pteris, Schizaea*, etc. from wide-spread to insular-endemic, and from dry and open to wet and closed forests.

Many Compositae are efficient colonisers with their small achenes and the calyces transformed into dispersal mechanisms. Among the species of *Bidens* (Heliantheae) the American *B. pilosa* group has become a wide-spread Pacific weed; it has relatively long and spreading calyx awns with retrorse barbs and hairs on the achene margins for epizoochorous dispersal. Endemic Pacific island species of *Bidens* illustrate various steps in the loss of barbs and hairs, the shortening or even elimination of calyx awns, increasing size, or the origin of aberrant flattened or even coiled shapes. Generally, these changes appear to be related to a shift from coastal to open interior habitats, to dry lowland and finally to wet upland forests. Similar trends have been demonstrated for the related genus *Fitschia* and the Hawaiian endemics *Dubautia – Wilkesia – Argyroxiphium*, representatives of the Californian-centred Compositae-Madiinae.

Some of the characteristic Pacific Island Leguminosae apparently mark the pathway which has led to a loss of floating capacities typical for sea-dispersed fruits and seeds: Among *Erythrina*, seeds and fruits of the widespread *E. variegata* L. float because cotyledons contain air-filled intercellular spaces and because ripe legumes remain closed around air chambers, but in the endemic *E. sandwichensis* (Hawaii) and *E. monosperma* Gaud. (Tahiti) the legumes open and the seeds have lost their buoyancy. A similar situation is found in the phyllodial *Acacia* species, probably of Australian origin, which occur on the Hawaiian Islands (*A. koa* A. Gray) and on Mauritius (*A. heterophylla* Willd.), while *A. simplicifolia* Druce from Samoa and Tonga still develops loment-like fruit segments with sufficient air inclusions to make them float. The S.Hemisphere *Sophora* sect. *Edwardsia* is centred in New Zealand but reaches Lord Howe, Chatham, Rapa, Hawaii, Easter I., Chile, Gough I., and Réunion; all stages from excellent to absence of capacity for floating are represented.

General, and sometimes manifold, increase in fruit and seed size (at the expense of number) has been documented by Carlquist for Pacific island representatives of *Alectryon* (Sapindaceae), *Fagara* (Rutaceae), and for *Tetraplasandra* (Araliaceae), endemic to Hawaii. Here again, the trend is usually linked to an invasion of forest habitats. One could speculate that such fruit and seed gigantism is tolerated because predators are often absent or rare on islands: in contrast, many continental species have to maintain a large number of smaller seeds as one of the possible strategies against more intensive predator pressure. Such animal–seed–plant relationships are obviously another wide open field for further research in island reproductive biology.

Conclusion

The data presented in this survey of reproductive biology in island plants illustrate and characterise several general aspects of island biology: the filtering by long-distance dispersal and the vicissitudes of founder population establishment, the problems and possibilities connected with the disharmonious constitution of island biota, the pre-adaptations to available niches and the adaptive radiations into not yet "saturated" biocoenoses, the erratic and bizarre developments under relieved selective pressure, and the delicately balanced, vulnerable nature of island ecosystems. In this way I hope to have shown how essential reproductive biology is for our understanding of island biology in general and for the urgent conservation of the much endangered island biota. Therefore, let us intensify our studies on the many open questions of island reproductive biology before it is too late!

REFERENCES

Baker, H. G. (1953a). Dimorphism and monomorphism in the *Plumbaginaceae*. II. Pollen and stigmata in the genus *Limonium*. *Ann. Bot.* N.S. **17**, 433–445

— (1953b). Dimorphism and monomorphism in the Plumbaginaceae. III. Correlation of geographical distribution patterns with dimorphism and monomorphism in *Limonium*. *Ann. Bot.* N.S. **17**, 615–627

— (1955). Self-compatibility and establishment after "long-distance" dispersal. *Evolution* **9**, 347–349

— (1959). The contribution of autecological and genecological studies to our knowledge of the past migrations in plants. *Amer. Naturalist* **93**, 255–272

— (1966). The evolution, functioning and breakdown of heteromorphic incompatibility systems. I. Plumbaginaceae. *Evolution* **20**, 349–368

— (1967). Support for Baker's law – as a rule. *Evolution* **21**, 853–856

Balgooy, M. M. J. van (1971). Plant geography of the Pacific. *Blumea* Suppl. **6**, 1–222

Bramwell, D. (1972). Endemism in the Flora of the Canary Islands. In *Taxonomy, Phytogeography and Evolution* (D. H. Valentine, ed.), 141–159. Academic Press, London and New York

Carlquist, S. (1965). *Island Life*. Amer. Mus. Nat. History, New York

— (1966a). The biota of long-distance dispersal. I. Principles of dispersal and evolution. *Q. Rev. Biol.* **41**, 247–270

— (1966b). The biota of long-distance dispersal. II. Loss of dispersibility in Pacific Compositae. *Evolution* **20**, 30–48

— (1966c). The biota of long-distance dispersal. III. Loss of dispersibility in the Hawaiian flora. *Brittonia* **18**, 310–335

— (1966d). The biota of long-distance dispersal. IV. Genetic systems in the floras of oceanic islands. *Evolution* **20**, 433–455

— (1967). The biota of long-distance dispersal. V. Plant dispersal to Pacific Islands. *Bull. Torrey Bot. Club* **94**, 129–162

— (1970). *Hawaii, a Natural History*. Natural History Press, New York

— (1974). *Island Biology*. Columbia University Press, New York and London

Cooper, R. C. (1956). The Australian and New Zealand species of *Pittosporum*. *Ann. Mo. Bot. Gdn* **43**, 87–188

Docters van Leeuwen, W. M. (1936). Krakatau, 1883–1933. *Ann. Jard. Bot. Buitenzorg* **46–47**, xii, 506 p.

Einarsson, E. (1967). The colonization of Surtsey, the new volcanic island, by vascular plants. *Aquilo*, ser. Bot. **6**, 172–182

Fosberg, F. R. (1963). Derivation of the flora of the Hawaiian Islands. In *Insects of Hawaii* (E. C. Zimmermann, ed.). Vol. 1, Introduction, 107–119. University of Hawaii Press, Honolulu

Godley, E. J. (1955). Breeding systems in New Zealand plants, I. *Fuchsia*. *Ann. Bot.* N.S. **19**, 549–559

Klekowski, E. J. (1972a). Genetical features of ferns as contrasted to seed plants. *Ann. Mo. Bot. Gdn* **59**, 138–151

— (1972b). Evidence against genetic self-incompatibility in the homosporous fern *Pteridium aquilinum*. *Evolution* **26**, 66–73

— (1976). Homoeologous chromosome pairing in ferns. In *Current Chromosome Research* (K. Jones and P. E. Brandham, eds.), 175–184. North Holland Publ. Co., Amsterdam, New York and Oxford

Lloyd, D. G. (1972a). A revision of the New Zealand, subantarctic and South American species of *Cotula*, section *Leptinella*. *N.Z.J. Bot.* **10**, 277–372

— (1972b). Breeding systems in *Cotula* L. (Compositae, Anthemideae), I-II. *New Phytol.* **71**, 1181–1194, 1195–1202

Moore, D. M. and Yates, B. (1974). *Armeria* L. in South America. *Bot. Notiser* **127**, 183–192

Nettancourt, D. de (1977). *Incompatibility in Angiosperms.* Monographs on Theoretical and Applied Genetics **3**. Springer Verlag, Berlin, Heidelberg and New York

Porter, D. M. (1976). Geography and dispersal of Galapagos Islands vascular plants. *Nature, Lond.* **264**, 745–746

Rick, Ch. M. (1966). Some plant-animal relations on the Galapagos Islands. In R. I. Bowman, *The Galapagos.* University of California Press, Berkeley and Los Angles

Rock, J. F. (1919). *A Monographic Study of the Hawaiian Species of the* Lobelioideae, *family* Campanulaceae. xvi, 394 pp. Publ. Bishop Museum, Honolulu

Salisbury, E. J. (1942). *The Reproductive Capacity of Plants.* Bell and Sons, London

Shaw, H. K. A. and Turrill, W. B. (1928). Asperulae australienses. *Kew Bull.* 1928, 81–105

Sleumer, H. (1963). Materials towards the knowledge of the Epacridaceae mainly in Asia, Malaysia and the Pacific. *Blumea* **12**, 145–171

Sohmer, S. H. (1972). Evolutionary trends in the genus *Charpentiera* (Amaranthaceae). *Brittonia* **24**, 283–312

Staudt, G. (1968). Die Genetik und Evolution der Heterözie in der Gattung *Fragaria*. III. Untersuchungen an hexa- und oktoploiden Arten. *Z. Pflanzenzücht.* **59**, 83–102

Steenis, C. G. G. J. van and Balgooy, M. M. J. van (1964). Pacific plant areas, Vol. 2. *Blumea* Suppl. **5**, 1–312

St. John, H. (1966). Monographs of *Cyrtandra* (Gesneriaceae) on Oahu, Hawaiian Islands. *Bishop Mus. Bull.* **229**, 1–465

Taylor, B. W. (1954). An example of long distance dispersal. *Ecology* **35**, 569–572

Vogel, St. (1954). *Blütenbiologische Typen als Elemente der Sippengliederung.* Botanische Studien 1. G. Fischer, Jena

Vuilleumier, B. S. (1967). The origin and evolutionary development of heterostyly in the angiosperms. *Evolution* **21**, 210–226

Wimmer, F. E., (1943, 1953, 1968). Campanulaceae-Lobelioideae, 1.-2. Teil, Suppl. und Campanulaceae-Cyphioideae. In *Das Pflanzenreich* (A. Engler and L. Diels, eds.), IV.276b,c, 1–1024

Yeo, P. F. (1972). Miscellaneous notes on pollination and pollinators. *J. Nat. Hist.* **6**, 667–686

15 Magnolioid Island Plants and Angiosperm Evolution

MICHEL GUÉDÈS   *Laboratoire de Phytomorphologie, Muséum d'Histoire Naturelle, Paris, France*

Desde hace tiempo, se ha venido observando que las islas, quizás por lo reducido de su presión selectiva, han supuesto un abrigo para organismos vivos que no han sobrevivido en ningún otro sitio. Estos organismos derivados de ancestores primitivos pueden haber conservado algunas peculiaridades arcaicas. Hay el peligro, sin embargo, de que interpretando las características de los organismos isleños, podamos confundir otras peculiaridades que han evolucionado "in situ" en el ambiente de la isla con estos rasgos primitivos.

Angiospermas supuestamente primitivas se conocen en Fiji, Nueva Guinea, Molucas, Juan Fernandez, Islas Salomon, Este de Australia, Tasmania, etc., y de estas plantas isleñas, las que presentan "leños sin vasos" son las que más han atraido la atención. Como este tipo de leño se supone que es primitivo, a menudo se ha pensado que la mayoría de las otras peculiaridades de estas plantas, tales como carpelos "conduplicados" y estambres aplastados son también caracteres relictuales. En este trabajo sin embargo, se argumenta que estos caracteres son en realidad peculiaridades mejoradas.

Es cuestionable que las Angiospermas nacieran en la región tropical del Pacifico, ya que el polen fosil atribuido a Angiospermas más antiguo está recogido lejos de esta supuesta "cuna de las Angiospermas" y normalmente en regiones que no estaban de hecho en latitudes tropicales en aquella época, como actualmente. Mas parece haber tenido un clima subtropical seco, soportando la teoría de Stebbins de que la diferenciación de géneros y taxa mayores está favorecida por los condiciones semi-áridas.

Las plantas "primitivas" de las islas del Pacifico parecen haber evolucionado en refugios casuales y no desde lejos de las Angiospermas realmente antiguas. El "primitivismo" de muchos de sus caracteres es objeto de cuestión. Estos no se asemejan a los fósiles de leño y hojas más viejas de las Angiospermas y caracteres tales como "leño sin vasos" pueden haber derivado secundariamente. Algunos ejemplos de tipos "primitivos" de polen han sido señalados para Angiospermas del Pacifico, pero no existe evidencia suficiente para soportar esto.

En conclusión, se llama la atención sobre el peligro de asumir las islas del Pacifico como la "cuna de las Angiospermas" y el autor sugiere que estas islas pueden albergar solo curiosas plantas insulares con engañosos caracteres pseudo-primitivos.

Introduction

Islands have attracted the attention of students of evolution since the time of Darwin (1859, 1872) and Wallace (1892). They were found to have fewer species but more endemics than similarly sized continental areas. These endemics may be palaeoendemics which survived in islands on account of lessened selective pressure, but neoendemics, however, are also abundant. Bizarre living forms are apt to appear on islands and to survive as a result of less intense competition (Carlquist, 1965). Such neoendemics may well evolve from palaeoendemics in which case they may harbour primitive features along with modern and erratic traits. In dealing with such organisms many difficulties will be encountered in deciphering which is primitive and which advanced.

Primitive Angiosperms, wood and the tropics

As long as palaeobotany was despaired of in looking for a solution to the "abominable mystery", recourse had to be made to comparative study of modern plants only. In that research, which remains of paramount importance, two trends, I believe, became unduly pervasive.

First, temperate plants were deemed too effete. They had been studied for too long. New tropical brooms would sweep cleaner, thence, sweeping statements to the effect that botany was lost without recourse to the tropics. I once heard an outstanding tropical phytogeographer say that a temperate botanist may or may not believe Angiosperms to have been born in the tropics, but once you have set foot in a tropical forest, then you *feel* they must have appeared there[1]. Having never set foot in the tropics, such a poetic appeal is alien to me.

Second, far too much reliance was probably put on wood. When Carlquist (1969) wrote his acrid and generally well-received paper, he exercised his caustic wit on everything but wood. Wood, on the contrary was the touchstone of all other theories. There is hardly any justification for this, except for Carlquist's own standing as a wood anatomist.

There were Angiosperms with vesselless wood. Gymnosperms have such wood. Vesselless Angiosperms then had to be primitive, the more so as they were tropical. By the same token, leafless Angiosperms also are primitive since leaves were lacking in the first land plants.

Vesselless Angiosperms belong to the ex-Ranales or Polycarpicae. Comparative morphology had indeed long drawn attention to the *typologically* primitive characters of the Ranales, and these soon came to be

---

[1]Takhtajan (1969, p. 159) also remarks that one is forced to such a conclusion "when one ... has visited some of these lands for oneself".

considered phylogenetically primitive as well. That conclusion in fact proved largely justified for these characters, from which it was implicitly admitted that such plants must be primitive in about all their features, and, most important, that they must be the *only* primitive group of Angiosperms.

Most of the allegedly very primitive Ranales are woody (although many other trees are robbed of their primitiveness despite very justified claims to it, see below), and are island plants which may well, however, have many neoendemic characters. It is the purpose of the present essay to suggest that in studying Angiosperm evolution we are under no compelling obligation to focus on the Ranales, the tropics or both, and that we must beware of island plants.

Brief census of alleged living fossils on islands

Reviews by Hutchinson (1964, 1969), Takhtajan (1969), Smith (1970, 1971) and Vink (1970, 1977) make it easy to sum up some phyto-geographical data on primitive Angiosperms as they now are seen by American and Russian botanists.

The Winteraceae are known from the Malay Archipelago, New Guinea, eastern Australia, Tasmania, Lord Howe Island, New Caledonia, New Zealand, Solomon Islands, Madagascar, and also Central and South America with the Juan Fernandez Islands. Among the 70 species (Hutchinson) or 120 (Takhtajan) only one or two *Drimys* appear to be American, i.e. continental.

The monospecific Degeneriaceae are endemic to the Fiji Islands.

The monogeneric Himantandraceae are found in the Moluccas, New Guinea, and northeast Australia.

The monogeneric Eupomatiaceae are known from eastern Australia and New Guinea.

The Austrobaileyaceae are comprised of two species from Australia.

The Amborellaceae is a single species from New Caledonia.

The Trochodendraceae now accommodate only *Trochodendron aralioides*, from South Korea, Japan and Taiwan. They are close to the Tetracentraceae, which are continental with the single species *Tetracentron sinense*, from China and upper Burma.

Among these families, the Winteraceae, Degeneriaceae, Amborellaceae, Trochodendraceae and Tetracentraceae are vesselless. So is *Sarcandra* of the Chloranthaceae, but it has hardly been considered primitive as a whole.

These families are members of the Takhtajan orders Magnoliales and Laurales whose bulk is by no means made up of island plants. Those of their members whose description now occupies so many pages in textbooks as living fossils, are however, prevailingly so. Most Magnoliales and Laurales cannot really be taken to mirror a truly ancestral state in the Angiosperms. Many of their flowers are partially with spiral phyllotaxis, but the carpels are highly specialised, and when in a spiral with a rather idiosyncratic ontogeny (Tucker, 1960). Floral vascularisation of these plants is often uniquely complex among Angiosperms. Turning to vegetative features, their leaves have often an extremely complicated vascularisation, highly peculiar stipules found elsewhere in advanced families, or no stipules at all. So although it is obvious that they have retained primitive features, as nearly all taxa have to some extent, there is no reason why, after having suffered so many specialisations, they could offer a reliable picture of primitive Angiosperms. It is not necessary to discuss the matter at much length, since anyway they are not offered as a whole as the most primitive Angiosperms. Their island relatives, however, are. They, too, may have arisen rather directly from ancestral stocks, but even less than their continental counterparts do they, in my opinion, afford a model of primitive Angiosperms, the more so as I hope to show that there is a definite *possibility* of their supposed remarkably primitive traits being advanced ones.

Before proceeding in that direction, it is proper to ask two questions: is there really some reason, besides poetry, why we should look towards the tropics in our search for primitive Angiosperms? And is there some reason, besides typology, i.e. comparative morphology and rational rather than historical sequencing of data, why we should then be so selectively attracted to the Magnoliales, Laurales and related orders?

No direct proof for the tropical origin of the Angiosperms

The fossil record is the only cornerstone of phylogenetic speculation, provided fossils can and are actually studied from a proper comparative point of view and, as far as Angiosperms are concerned, this fossil record is not so scant.

Among the most ancient reasonably authenticated remains of Angiosperms is pollen (Muller, 1970; Hughes, 1976). If *Clavatipollenites* is accepted as from an Angiosperm, as apparently it generally is, it is remarkable that it, the most ancient fossil of the class, appears as early as the Lias in Central Europe. Then it is found in the late Jurassic and early Cretaceous of Egypt and Canada. Afterwards, it occurs in the Barremian[1] of England and West Africa, and in the Aptian-Albian of Portugal, Central America, the Argentine and Canada.

If account is taken of data on continental drift (e.g. Barry *et al.*, 1973;

[1]In Hughes' view (1976) the oldest reliable record is from the Barremian of England.

Hughes, 1976), at the time *Clavatipollenites* was produced in Central Europe, this may have been at about lat. 30°N. The plants that gave it may thus have migrated later towards tropical countries, while colonising temperate and even colder zones in the Southern Hemisphere (Dettman, 1973). Angiospermous pollen indeed appears in eastern Australia as early as the late Middle Albian but these ancient Angiosperms do not seem to have arisen in the tropics of their time, nor in lands that are now tropical.

Clavatipollenites is already more advanced than our supposedly primitive Magnoliales in its sometimes irregularly distributed equatorial apertures. But monosulcate pollen of the *Magnolia* type unfortunately hardly fossilises, so the possibility remains that even older pollen of that type indeed was from tropical plants. If so, these then colonised temperate northern zones and further evolved there, but there is no evidence whatever for this.

In any case, definitely Angiospermian tricolpate pollen with psilate and reticulate sculpturing appears as soon as the lower Aptian, but it is in the Netherlands, already by then temperate. It becomes much more widespread in the Albian, but in Muller's words (1970), "no evidence has been found so far which would suggest an earlier occurrence in the tropics . . .. or in the Southern Hemisphere".

Interesting data may also be gained from fossil woods. A comprehensive survey in Boureau's *Traité de Paléobotanique* is eagerly awaited. In the meantime, one may draw on Boureau's list of 1957, with some additions (see also Wolfe *et al.*, 1975 for discussion of partly unpublished work). No unquestionable Angiosperm wood appears to be known before the Cretaceous. Some, given merely as from "the Cretaceous", belongs to the Aceraceae, Anacardiaceae, Celastraceae and Lauraceae (or Euphorbiaceae?), and was found in Madagascar (not tropical at the time), Libya, Russia and Arizona. Other records are from the upper Cretaceous and belong to the Cornaceae, Ebenaceae, Fagaceae, Juglandaceae, Lauraceae, Proteaceae, Sabiaceae (a family in the Ranunculales), and Saururaceae. They were found in Egypt, Germany, Japan, Patagonia and the neighbouring Antarctic continent, and Austria.

There are no Magnoliales among Cretaceous woods. It may be that a homoxylic wood from the Eocene of Greenland is near the Trochodendraceae, but it is not precisely tropical. Several mesozoic woods (*Sahnioxylon, Homoxylon*) sometimes attributed to the Angiosperms, may well have belonged to Bennettitales (Boureau, 1957). They are not tropical. Neither India and New Caledonia, nor the Ural, whence they come, were tropical at the time. Several upper Cretaceous woods may

L

belong to the Monimiaceae (Mädel, 1960 in Gothan and Weyland, 1973), but they are from South Africa.

Magnolia and *Liriodendron*, however, are known from leaves and a petal in the upper Cretaceous (Leppik, 1963; Gothan and Weyland, 1973) but these occur in Europe and North America, not the tropics. There is even a dubious pollen record from mid-Jurassic, but it is from Scotland. They must have been in existence as early as the upper Cretaceous. They surely occurred in the lower Eocene, but in Germany and Hungary. The Lauraceae are known in Cretaceous times, but in temperate countries. The Monimiaceae flourished in the Cretaceous, but in South Africa.

Many present day tropical plants are known as relatively very old fossils from locations that were not tropical, even if they were surely warmer than at present, e.g. *Dalbergia* is in the upper Cretaceous of Greenland and *Sterculia* in the same strata of Alaska.

Of other families, many of which are as old as or more ancient than "primitive" ones, very few are known from the Cretaceous tropics. The Nymphaeaceae are, however, an exception (Tchad).

It may of course be argued that tropical regions are less explored than temperate ones. Many remains, however, are known from such regions as Indochina, Java, Sumatra, the Philippines, but they date back to the Tertiary only. *Magnolia*, for instance appears in Java in the Tertiary. Why should we admit it is originally tropical and from southeast Asia? The Fiji islands did not exist before the Eocene, if they harbour primitive plants they surely did not arise there.

On the whole, direct evidence from either pollen, wood or gross remains points to Angiosperms having appeared in a temperate zone, probably in the Northern Hemisphere, only afterwards to reach the tropics.

These should thus rather be viewed as refugia than cradles, since primitive plants are indeed numerous in them (Sporne, 1970, 1973).

"Living fossils" *from the Magnoliales and Laurales not the sole and/or most primitive Angiosperms*

It will already be clear from the above that besides being found outside the tropics, most of the ancient remains do not belong to supposedly primitive families.

Be it from gross remains (Gothan and Weyland, 1973), pollen or wood it is a fact that among the most ancient Cretaceous families are the Palmae (Arecaceae), Fagaceae, Juglandaceae and Proteaceae.

Palynological data (Muller, 1970) reveal that other "advanced" families were in existence during the Cretaceous. They include the

Apocynaceae, Aquifoliaceae, Betulaceae, Bombacaceae, Buxaceae, Casuarinaceae, Caesalpiniaceae, Chloranthaceae, Hamamelidaceae, Lecythidaceae, Linaceae, Myrtaceae, Olacaceae, Polygonaceae, Sapotaceae, Symplocaceae and Tiliaceae. Among these, the Apocynaceae are also known from wood remains in the Eocene of Wyoming.

Palynological data are borne out by finds of gross remains of the following families in the Cretaceous: Apocynaceae, Betulaceae, Myrtaceae (?).

Gross remains support data from wood in establishing the existence of the following families in the Cretaceous: Aceraceae, Celastraceae (?), Ebenaceae and Lauraceae.

Finally, gross remains from the Cretaceous interestingly belong to the Gramineae, Malvaceae, Moraceae, Myricaceae (wood in the Eocene), Nymphaeaceae, Platanaceae, Potamogetonaceae, Rhamnaceae, Sterculiaceae and Vitaceae.

It is clear, then, that although the Lauraceae and Monimiaceae of the order Laurales are indisputably very old, they are but two among widely different and very ancient families. Some Magnoliales are known from the Cretaceous, but they belong to the Magnoliaceae (*Magnolia, Liriodendron*) and perhaps the Annonaceae, both of which are not considered as the most primitive of the order.

The celebrated Trochodendraceae and Winteraceae are not unknown as fossil pollen, but they appear respectively in the upper Eocene and Oligocene, along with such families as the Typhaceae and Loranthaceae (whose Eocene age is supported by macroscopic remains), and, incidentally, in Europe and New Zealand, not in the tropics (Krutsch, 1966; Couper, 1960, cited in Muller, 1970).

Takhtajan (1969) mentions fossil remains of *Drimys* from western North America, eastern Australia and Antarctica. He gives no reference and it comes as a surprise that speaking of cherished living fossils, he does not bother to indicate the age of their true fossils. I am aware of Tertiary remains only, quite in agreement with pollen records.

The Magnoliales and Laurales are thus ancient, but they are not the only or most ancient Angiosperms. It is improbable that they arose in the tropics. Among them, our "living fossils" may well be among their most *recent* families. There is no straightforward justification for placing the Magnoliales and Laurales at the origin of anything but themselves.

All this of course is sacrilege to present Russo-American credo, but is implied in Sporne's results from his detailed calculations of the advancement index[1]. This work with its mathematical nimbus, should

---

[1] See also the lucid comments on Angiosperm evolution by Puri (1967).

have attracted more attention on the part of modern phylogeneticists. Is it not numerical evolutionism? Now in Sporne's latest tables of 1969 and 1974 one notices that whereas the Magnoliaceae and related families are indeed primitive, so are the Betulaceae, Hamamelidaceae, Fagaceae, Myrtaceae and Platanaceae, all of which were quoted above as among the palaeontologically most ancient. There are others in Sporne's list for which no direct evidence is forthcoming, and his most primitive family, surprisingly, is the Rhizophoraceae. This, it is true, appears to be a little older than the Trochodendraceae (Germeraad *et al.*, 1968, in Muller, 1970) and is allied to the ancient Myrtaceae.

The danger, then, is increasingly looming that the whole story of the primitive tropical Magnoliales which should stand alone at the roots of any phylogenetic tree of the Angiosperms, is but a fallacy. Not too much reliance, however, should perhaps be put on direct but always fragmentary evidence. That wonderful story was told from protracted and admirable studies of present-day plants. How firm is this basis?

Present "living fossils" *probably often misinterpreted*

Wood   Nothing would be as it is without wood. Dickison (1975) says: "In no other vegetative tissue of plants are the trends of evolution as clearly defined". He adds that "there is not the slightest doubt that the absence of vessels in eleven genera of woody Dicotyledons represents the retention of a primitive feature", only to grant, some lines later, that of course vesselless Cactaceae are "clearly the result of extreme specialisation".

The concept that vesselless Angiosperm woods are the most ancient stems from the assumption that vesselless Gymnosperms are the ancestors of the Angiosperms. This of course is circular reasoning. We are searching for ancestors with means that imply we already know where they are. Such an assumption ignores that the most ancient Angiosperm woods had vessels, and that vessels have already appeared in the Pteridophytes. They are known to occur in *Pteridium, Marsilea, Equisetum, Selaginella* and perhaps *Woodsia* and *Cheilanthes* (White, 1961, 1963). Among these, *Selaginella* and *Equisetum* are recorded from the Carboniferous and Permian, although no vessels have been seen in their fossils.

A possibility thus exists that Angiosperm ancestors had vessels, and quite naturally gave rise to many vesselled families. Afterwards, in some instances, peculiar families such as the Cactaceae and the Winteraceae could have lost them.

But it would be reversing an evolutionary trend, since first land plants had no vessels. Is that possible? It is no more extraordinary than the loss of leaves.

A case in point, in wood science, is that of the Araucariaceae. At first sight, the punctuations of present genera are very like those of palaeozoic Cordaitales (*Dadoxylon*), which also have no wood parenchyma and few punctuations on ray cells. In modern Araucariaceae, such are also the features of most of the wood, but wood from the cone axis, root and first secondary ring has parenchyma and many punctuations on the ray cells. The organs with such wood may have some claim to being primitive. During the Mesozoic there were woods with analogous features throughout, and Jeffrey (1912) came to the conclusion that modern Araucariaceae only mimic Cordaitales in their wood, being derived from the more advanced Mesozoic ancestors and having reverted to a Cordaitalian-like state. More recent studies confirm this view (Grambast, 1961).

In the same way, relatively modern Angiosperms without vessels may well have lost them, even within the Magnoliales and Laurales, the most ancient of which do have vessels.

Scalariform punctuations are taken to be primitive in Angiosperms and indeed are found in plants older than Angiosperms. On the other hand, however, circular bordered pits date back to the Devonian (Beck, 1970). So we need not accept automatically that scalariform pits are the source of all rounded pits, although, as Beck observed, the derivation may have occurred in some lineages. Furthermore, the possibility should be seriously considered that scalariform pits, when found in some not very old Angiosperms, are derived from rounded ones and merely mimicking those of the Cycadophytes, which nobody can be sure belong to the ancestry of Angiosperms.

Still, it may well be that scalariform *perforation plates*, whencesoever they come (perhaps from fusion of circular perforations) are primitive in Angiosperms. Besides the Magnoliales and Laurales, they are found in more than 100 families, notably the Araliaceae, Cornaceae, Fagaceae, Juglandaceae, Platanaceae and Rhizophoraceae (Boureau, 1957) to quote some of the most ancient ones. The same must be true of the length of vessel members.

Heterogeneous rays also may be primitive. All this being granted, the so-called primitive Angiosperms, *among others*, have *some* primitive characters. But it must be remarked that heterogeneous rays also are seen in the Malvaceae (known from the Eocene), Juglandaceae (known from the Cretaceous) and Leguminosae, whereas they are lacking in the Annonaceae and Canellaceae. On the other hand, there are more bars to perforation plates of the Theaceae than the Magnoliaceae (the latter without heterogeneous rays), and about as many to those of the Magnoliaceae as to those of the Betulaceae and Platanaceae.

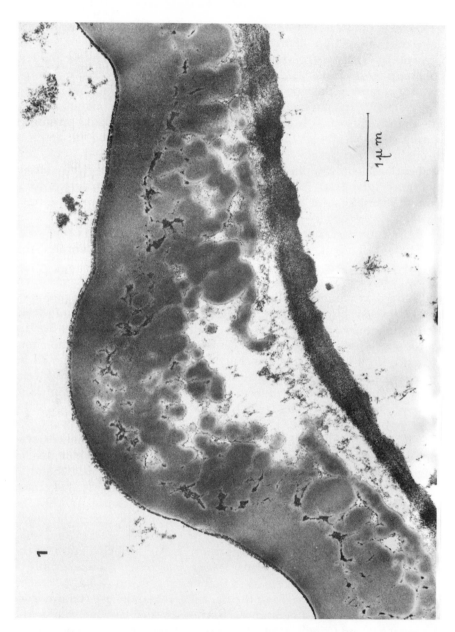

Fig. 1 Exine structure of three Annonaceae. (1) *Meiocarpidium lepidotum* (Oliv.) Engl. and Diels. (2) *Boutiquea platypetala* (Engl. and Diels) Le Thom. Massive exines with granular structure below a continuous tectum. Granules far less apparent in *Boutiquea*. (3) *Piptostigma calophyllum* Mildbr. and Diels. Intermediate state in granule distinctness. In A.

316

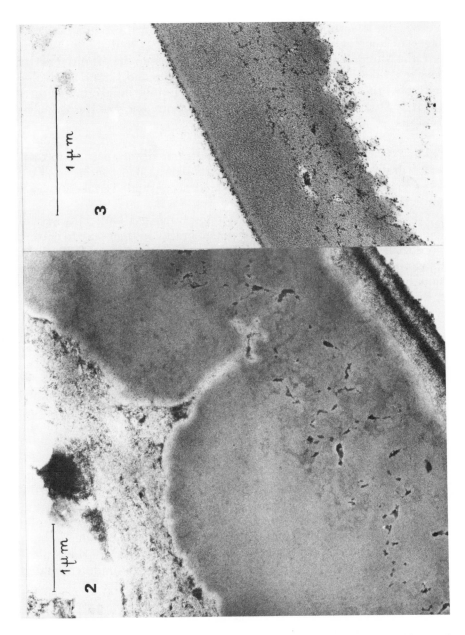

Le Thomas's opinion this structure is primitive, whereas 1 and 2 arose through fusion of previously discrete granules. It might however be considered to display still imperfectly merged former granules, being, as it were, 1 on its way to become 2. (All three photographs courtesy of Dr. A. Le Thomas)

317

Also, the length of vessel members is greater in the Euphorbiaceae, Fagaceae and Juglandaceae than in the Lauraceae, and about the same as in the Magnoliaceae. To one who has doubts as to the primitiveness of vesselless wood in Angiosperms, the Magnoliales and Laurales have no uniquely primitive wood. That it is not so primitive in its other features precisely strengthens my mistrust of the primitiveness of the vesselless condition of island "living fossils".

Pollen "Primitive" Angiosperms have but one distal aperture to their pollen grains. It may be a colpus (Magnoliaceae, Degeneriaceae) or a pore. (The Eupomatiaceae, Trochodendraceae and Tetracentraceae, however, have 2–3 distal furrows.)

This is of interest in so far as Gymnosperms also have but a distal aperture. We noted, however, that pollen grains on their way to getting more than one aperture (*Clavatipollenites*) were in existence before the appearance of any members of the Magnoliales and Laurales, even though the previous occurrence of the latter is a possibility. So it might be unwise to postulate that the Magnoliales or Laurales as we know them ever gave rise to more "modern" pollen.

Mono-aperturate grains are a feature of Monocotyledons, Piperaceae and Nymphaeaceae (excl. *Nelumbo*). Neither of these taxa is made to bear the whole of the phylogenetic tree of Angiosperms, although the Nymphaeaceae are known from the Cretaceous, and are vesselless.

Mono-aperturate Magnoliales and Laurales may indeed have retained that feature from their ancestors as the Monocots did. This is no indication that either of them originated any further taxon of the Dicotyledons.

Very interesting exine characters were lately discovered by Le Thomas and Lugardon (1974, 1976) and Walker (1976) with the electron microscope. The exine is massive and homogeneous in the Eupomatiaceae and Degeneriaceae. Rather than being *atectate*, in Walker's term, the grain may well be *holexinic*, i.e. with an exine undifferentiated into tectum, columellae, foot-layer and endexine, but incorporating the whole of them, in the same way as a ribbon-leaf incorporates a base, a petiole and a blade in an undifferentiated condition.

Various structures with "incipient" (or residual) columellae are found in the Magnoliaceae, Annonaceae (Fig. 1) and other families. They often demonstrate the deposition of sporopollenin in layers on membranes. This well-known feature of all developing pollen grains appears to be retained there in the adult state because the layers do not become merged into one another.

Holexinic (atectate) pollen grains also are known in the Gentianaceae (*Voyria*; Nilsson and Skvarla, 1969), as well as in the Flacourtiaceae and Cochlospermaceae (Keating, 1975) so they are not necessarily primitive. Fusion of exine components during evolution is easily envisaged. Columellae are known in fossil Gymnosperms (*Classopollis*, Pettitt and Chaloner, 1964). Cycadales have no columellae, but a honeycomb-like structure from which they may easily have evolved (Audran and Masure, 1976). We are thus certainly not compelled to view holexinic pollen as the most primitive in Angiosperms. We might grant that those of the Magnoliales and Laurales are so, coming from holexinic ancestors, but it would remain that there is no reason why columellate and tri-aperturate pollen of plants probably more ancient than them should nevertheless come from holexinic previous non-angiospermic states.

It may be that a granular structure below the tectum such as is found in Gymnosperms is a primitive feature of some Angiosperms. Besides many Magnolioid plants, where it and the holexinic structure intergrade (Fig. 1), this arrangement is interestingly found in the Betulaceae, Juglandaceae and Apocynaceae which were shown to be very old, as well as the Onagraceae, an advanced family by many criteria (Van Campo and Lugardon, 1973). It is questionable whether granular structures are basically different from columellar ones, and both seem to intergrade. It is also doubtful whether granular structures of Gymnosperms and Angiosperms are directly related. Those of Angiosperms may have arisen from columellar arrangements, or there may have been repeated inter-conversions of granular and columellar structures during evolution of Angiosperms, the oldest of which perhaps had Cycad-like or columellar exines.

Morphology

Habit   It is a fact that many of the first known Angiosperms belong to woody families, as do most other plants before them. The "living fossils" also are woody.

But it is a condition they share with many plants from other families as old as them or older, *viz*. Apocynaceae, Betulaceae, Buxaceae, Caesalpiniacae, Fagaceae, Juglandaceae, Myrtaceae. They are not at all extraordinary in this respect.

It is interesting that palms are amongst the oldest known monocots. Monocotyledonous Albian pollen (*Liliacidites*) may thus have belonged to some arborescent monocotyledon.

In view of such an early occurrence of palms, it cannot even be asserted that primitive Angiosperms had secondary wood. Furthermore, it should

L*

not be forgotten that many Angiosperm herbs already existed in the Aptian-Albian (Doyle and Hickey, 1976).

Vegetative morphology   This is generally highly advanced in "living fossils" and there is no way of deriving anything that belongs to other Angiosperms from it. *Austrobaileya*, however, has a leaf with a two-bundled midrib. This is widespread in cotyledons (Gravis, 1943), notably in the Fagaceae and monocotyledons. It may depend on the location of the mid-cotyledonary line between two stelar bundles instead of opposite one, or else, on the lack of fusion of the two wings of centrifugal wood of the "convergent" that, in the second case, makes up the median bundle. These wings, as a rule, fuse below cotyledonary petiole, but they may fuse somewhere along it, or higher up in the blade, or not at all. The situation is not yet understood in *Austrobaileya*. If it is a primitive character it was soon lost by very primitive Angiosperms, since the three-bundled condition was already in existence in *Ficophyllum* of the lower Albian (Wolfe *et al.*, 1975).

It would perhaps be proper to view that leaf character in *Austrobaileya* as an indication of neoteny, a cotyledon character being retained in the whole body. Neoteny is widespread among plants in New Caledonia, notably in the Apocynaceae (Boiteau, pers. comm.) It has been studied in *Parsonsia* of that family in New Zealand (Melville, 1976). Two-bundled midribs are also known in such families as the Labiatae and Solanaceae.

Degeneria and *Magnolia* have cotyledons with two-bundled midribs. But their leaves become extremely complicated with many divisions of the main bundles in the midrib, correlated with midrib thickening. Such leaves are much more specialised than the oldest known in a fossil state. The latter have a midrib with about three bundles only, and there is thus direct proof that such leaves as those of many of the Rosaceae (Guédès, 1972a; Rohweder and Ruthisauser, 1976) provide a far closer representation of what a primitive Angiospermian leaf was. Hickey and Wolfe (1975) were wise to feature the Magnoliales and the Laurales as two side-branches among others from the main line of their Magnoliidae. That main line led from *Ficophyllum* to the Ranunculidae and Rosidae *inter alia*.

There is no indication that primitive Angiosperms had stipules. If the lack of stipules is primitive, then the Winteraceae, Schizandraceae, Himantandraceae, Trochodendraceae, Annonaceae are primitive in this respect, as are many other "advanced" families. If however, the presence of stipules is primitive, our "living fossils" are advanced. So are the Magnoliaceae, for it is hardly feasible to consider their sheathing stipules as the source of other stipules. They are at least as complicated as those of the Fagaceae and the Platanaceae.

Flowers As a typologist, I rate highly of the strobilous theory of the flower. I am careful, however, not to mingle typology and phylogeny.

There are very few data on primitive flowers. From present-day plants, I believe it is firmly established that flowers are made up of fertile appendages (phyllomes) homologous with vegetative leaves, with or without homologous outer sterile ones (perianth). Furthermore, all flowers are mono-axial, i.e. all phyllomes are borne on one and the same floral axis (Guédès, 1972a; Guédès and Dupuy, 1977).

In view of such families as the Fagaceae, Salicaceae and Juglandaceae being so old, no one can be sure that primitive flowers were always bisexual. Judging from previous achievements among Gymnosperms, unisexual flowers might well be better candidates for being primitive (see also Dilcher, 1979). What is certain is that they did not become aggregated into multi-axial flowers as contemplated by Neumeyer, Emberger, Nozeran, Meeuse and Melville.

In any case, bisexual flowers soon appeared, with carpels above the stamens. Nobody knows whether these early bisexual flowers had many stamens and many carpels. They may well have had few stamens at first. Then in some lineages, these became numerous through extended production of independent phyllomes on the axis, whereas in other lineages, as in the very old Myrtaceae, the limited number of original stamens underwent intense splitting, originating a secondarily polyandrous androecium, with centripetal or centrifugal development of partial issuing stamens. The process is already under way in the Lauraceae, where the massive appendages of stamen filaments no doubt represent incipient stamens, the fertile stamen proper being formed from the median portion of the staminal primordium only.

There is no reason to believe that carpels were at first very numerous. If they were, *Degeneria* and *Drimys winteri*, with one carpel only, are especially advanced.

Also there is no evidence to show that sterile petals arose from stamens. What is known is that they are closely homologous. This is not surprising since petals are the phyllomes nearest to the stamens. Sometimes, there are intermediates between stamens and petals. Such staminodes occur in "primitive" Angiosperms, but also in the Sterculiaceae and Primulaceae. Their occurrence in the Nymphaeaceae might seem a strong argument for their primitiveness since that family is very old. It will soon become apparent that it is not so.

If highly polyandrous androecia are considered primitive, the "living fossils" are not *very* primitive. The Magnoliaceae would be more so were it not for the very complicated vascularisation of their flowers. In this respect it is the Ranunculaceae that would best mirror the primitive condition of the androecium on an elongated floral axis with straightforward vascularisation.

There is no reason to believe that stamens were primitively flat, even though they are definitely homologous with flat appendages. Long before the coming of Angiosperms, microsporangiate trusses or true stamens had been evolved in Gymnosperms. It is entirely possible that analogous trusses gave stamens without ever having been flattered. That flat stamens of "living fossils" (*Degeneria, Galbulimima*) are not primitive at all may be suspected since they are either introrse, the more common state, or extrorse (Degeneriaceae). This is easily understood if they are derived from a narrow structure which evolved in two directions.

Furthermore, in all Angiosperms, the stamen appears to be diplophyllous. It is an infolded phyllome with a solid filament and anther and fused ventral margins free only at the apex. On both sides, however, a deep longitudinal notch is formed so that two segments of margin appear free on each side. Each of them is hollowed out as a pollen sac. Pollen sacs are thus basically marginal (Baum and Leinfellner, 1952 etc.; see Guédès 1972a,b for references and further observations).

Such a structure becomes especially apparent when stamens are broadened normally or teratologically (petalisation) but is also obvious from normal ontogenesis. Since this structure was found in all families studied (Magnoliaceae, Liliaceae, Crassulaceae, Ranunculaceae, Scrophulariaceae, Apocynaceae, Rosaceae, Labiatae, Papaveraceae, Salicaceae, Violaceae) it must be a basic feature of all Angiosperms. When stamens in these families become broadened their diplophylly becomes obvious through extension of their four margins at anther level with their pollen sacs remaining marginal.

Primitive stamens must have been diplophyllous, for otherwise the feature should have been acquired independently in all lineages of Angiosperms. Since the supposedly primitive stamens are broadened, diplophylly should be obvious in them. It is not. All four pollen sacs are ventral or dorsal, and all seem to be laminar in location.

In my opinion (see also Leinfellner, 1956) their flattening is secondary to an ancestral diplophyllous state such as in other Angiosperms. Outgrowths develop dorsally to the dorsal sacs or ventrally to the ventral ones. In the first case, all four sacs become apparently ventral, in the second they seem dorsal, although in both, they remain essentially marginal.

These "living fossils", then, have as extremely advanced stamens as they have carpels (see below), also partly on account of outgrowths from the dorsal surface. Their stamens must be basically diplophylluous but their ontogeny and anatomy never appear to have been studied in this connection. Stamens of *Magnolia* and *Liriodendron*, which are thick rather than flattened show clear indications of diplophylly in their vascularisation, and so it is with stamens of *Nymphaea* (Leinfellner, 1956).

In the Nymphaeaceae, although Leinfellner (1956) has demonstrated the diplophylly of the stamen by studying its ontogeny and anatomy, it is not obvious in the normal petaloid stamens. All four sacs are in appearance on the ventral side. The same process as in flattened stamens of "living fossils" has been operative, to a lesser extent. All such stamens, flattened through outgrowths that obscure the basic marginal location of their pollen sacs, certainly are very advanced.

Carpels Besides wood structure, carpels are the most celebrated features in these island relics.

Ovules are said to be laminar in placentation. They are not. It has been shown (Tucker, 1959) that stigmatic crests are secondary outgrowths from the dorsal carpellary surface in the inrolling zone, with the ovular rows on the carpellary margin. Such proliferations occur in many (all?) other carpels, but are much smaller (Guédès, 1965; Padmanabhan, 1967; Rohweder, 1967).

These outgrowths of late protodermal origin, can hardly be considered primitive. Placentation is basically marginal and obscured through their development. In this way, carpels of e.g. the Ranunculaceae or Rosaceae are certainly more primitive. A carpel of *Drimys* or *Degeneria* is no more primitive than an Apocynaceous carpel. The latter has complicated stylar differentiations, but it has not these monstrous stigmatic crests. Both are deeply adapted to peculiar kinds of pollination, that of Apocynaceae is still unclear.

If the carpel cavity is supposed to have been ancestrally open all along the ventral line, carpels in the Winteraceae and Degeneriaceae are by no means the most primitive ones since their margins are congenitally fused below, i.e. they are peltate, or better, ascidiate. Carpels with completely free margins (although of course post-genitally appressed) are known elsewhere (Crassulaceae, Alismataceae). Furthermore, the fusion in our "living fossils" has often reached such an extent as is practically unknown in any other Angiosperms (except for the Potamogetonaceae, Zanichelliaceae and perhaps Berberidaceae). Carpels in several *Bubbia*, *Belliolum* , *Pseudowintera* and *Exospermum* have thus become erect funnels with narrowed horizontal rims below which the ovules are in a circle. Such carpels obviously lead nowhere. Their erratic morphology goes hand in hand with a bizarre modification in ovule irrigation. These become secondarily served by the median trace, a feature of minimal phylogenetic importance which also occurred in the Nymphaeaceae.

It may be that these carpels are primitive in lacking a stigma, but the way they are otherwise modified and the fact that they belong to relatively recent plants make it entirely possible that they arose from carpels with ordinary stigmas which later became lost.

Syncarpous gynoecia are a feature of the Trochodendraceae and Tetracentraceae, and are known in the Winteraceae. *Zygogynum* of New Caledonia has funnel-shaped carpels laterally fused congenitally, originating a plurilocular ovary. The flower axis is perhaps present in the middle (Leinfellner, 1966). In what was considered a *Bubbia* from Madagascar ("*B.*" *perrieri*, now *Takhtajania perrieri*), Leroy (1977) made the interesting discovery that the ovary is bicarpellate, syncarpous and unilocular with parietal apical placentation. The stigmas are well developed and folded down upon the backs of the carpels in a way reminiscent to those of *Papaver*. The genus is vesselless (Leroy, pers. comm.). Although the strange gynoecium of *Zygogynum* is clearly made up of Winteraceous carpels, I wonder whether with such a gynoecium as it has, *Takhtajania* may be retained in the Winteraceae. At any rate, each of them on its own island has originated a syncarpous ovary, the second of a very advanced kind (on the *Takhtajania* gynolcium, see also Vink, 1978).

Other troublesome specialisations in living fossils are the hood-like calyx of the Winteraceae and Himantandraceae, and especially the problematic calyptra of *Eupomatia*, as well as its turbinate receptacle, enclosing fused carpels. The detailed morphology of the gynoecium of this genus is still unclear, but has few primitive attributes.

In all these respects, "living fossils" are much more advanced than many unobtrusive plants from temperate countries, which better deserve these epithets since their families are older than those of our island plants.

Conclusion

Some 150 million years ago, plants began to differentiate that were to become Angiosperms. This occurred in temperate zones, probably in the Northern Hemisphere, which is no surprise since Stebbins (1972) found that speciation is more intense in semi-arid biota, and that apparently ancestral stocks of several genera and families are there.

Ten million years later some of our plants reached the temperate lands of the southern Pangaea. They had to cross the tropics, where they indeed have been found, but apparently they were not at first very successful there.

These plants were probably trees or shrubs. Nobody knows whether they had secondary wood or vessels. Their flowers might have been uni-or bisexual. They were soon to give rise to both types. Their pollen was monocolpate.

Seventy million years again elapsed, after which we find our plants having differentiated into palms, Juglandaceae, Proteaceae, Fagaceae etc. Among bisexual flowers, gamopetaly soon appeared and the Apocynaceae evolved, still with free carpels. Although the tropics were perhaps not yet very attractive, they may have become seriously colonised. Muller (1968) found numerous pollen grains of this age in Sarawak (Malaya). But were the latter then really tropical?

At this time the Magnoliaceae were in existence, but in temperate though warmer countries. Our "living fossils" were yet unborn.

It took a further 35 million years before a plant possibly allied to them (*Eupetelea*) appeared, and it was in northern Europe. Angiosperms were beginning to colonise the tropics massively, but at the cost of becoming polyploid. Pangaea was being disrupted. Ten million years later, one of the Winteraceae occurred in New Zealand.

Many Angiosperms thrived in the stable conditions of tropical rainforests. Under moderate environmental pressure they differentiated rather few species, but since the extinction rate was even lower, they at last became very numerous (Stebbins, 1972). Amongst the Magnoliales of large fragments of Pangaea the Magnoliaceae and Anonaceae like many other families became very advanced in several respects.

Some Angiosperms, on the other hand, became trapped on islands where they had come through the northern and southern halves of the disrupted Pangaea (Schuster, 1972), and then began evolving erratically. Some lost their vessels (as others did in peculiar conditions elsewhere on Pangaea). Their carpels became monstrously ascidiate, with disorganised vascularisation and remarkable submarginal outgrowths. Those which had retained free carpels sometimes lost all but one, or they fused them in bizarre ways.

After a further 35 million years, evolution had proceeded along various paths in the several lineages of Angiosperms. Despite the fact that many true primitive features were still obvious in temperate lands, Hallier (1912) postulated that Angiosperms must have been born "between Assam and Fiji". Bews (1927) postulated that the rainforests are ideal crucibles for Angiosperm production, more and more botanists came under the spell of the tropics, I. W. Bailey became interested in wood, and generations of students had to learn the twists and turns of deriving *Nothofagus* from *Drimys*.

REFERENCES

Audran, J. C. and Masure, E. (1976). Précisions sur l'infrastructure de l'exine chez les Cycadales. *Pollen Spores* **18**, 5–26

Beck, C. B. (1970). The appearance of gymnospermous structure. Addendum. *Biol. Rev.* **45**, 399–400

Bews, J. W. (1927). Studies in the ecological evolution of Angiosperms. *New Phytol.* Repr. No. 16

Boureau, E. (1957). *Anatomie Végétale*, Vol. 3. Presses Universitaires de France, Paris

Carlquist, S. (1965). *Island Life*. Nat. History Press, Garden City

— (1969). Toward acceptable evolutionary interpretations of floral anatomy. *Phytomorphology* **19**, 332–362

Cox, B. C., Healey, I. N. and Moore, P. D. (1973). *Biogeography*. Blackwell, Oxford

Cronquist, A. (1969). *The Evolution of Flowering Plants*. Nelson, London

Darwin, C. (1859–72). *On the Origin of Species* ... 1st and 6th edn., Murray, London

Dettmann, M. E. (1973). Angiospermous pollen from Albian to Turonian sediments of eastern Australia. *Publs. Geol. Soc. Austr.* **4**, 3–34

Dickison, W. C. (1975). The bases of Angiosperm phylogeny: vegetative anatomy. *Ann. Mo. Bot. Gdn* **62**, 590–620

Dilcher, D. L. (1979). Early angiosperm reproduction: an introductory report. *Rev. Palaeobot. Palynol.* **27**, 291–328

Doyle, J. A. and Hickey, L. J. (1976). Pollen and leaves from the mid-Cretaceous Potomac group ... In *The Origin and Early Evolution of Angiosperms* (C. B. Beck, ed.). Columbia University Press, New York

Gothan, W. and Weyland, H. (1973). *Lehrbuch der Paläobotanik*. BLV Verlagsgesellschaft, Munich

Grambast, L. (1960). Evolution des structures ligneuses chez les Coniférophytes. *Bull. Soc. Bot. Fr. Mém.*, 30–41

Gravis, A. (1943). Observations anatomiques sur les embryons et les plantules. *Lejeunia* **3**, 181p

Guédès, M. (1965). Remarques sur la notion de carpelle condupliqué. *Bull. Soc. Bot. Fr.* **112**, 54–68

— (1972a). Contribution à la morphologie du phyllome. *Mém. Mus. Hist. Nat. Paris B* **21**, 180p

— (1972b). Stamen-carpel homologies. Flora, Jena, 161, 184–208

— and Dupuy, P. (1977). Teratological modifications and the meaning of flower parts. *Vistas in Plant Science*

Hallier, H. (1912). Über frühere Landbrücken ... zwischen Australasien und Amerika. *Med. Rijksherb. Leiden* **13**

Hickey, L. J. and Wolfe, J. A. (1975). The bases of Angiosperm phylogeny: vegetative morphology. *Ann. Mo. Bot. Gdn* **62**, 538–589

Hughes, N. F. (1976). *Palaeobiology of Angiosperm Origins*. Cambridge University Press

Hutchinson, J. (1964). *The Genera of Flowering Plants*, Vol 1. Clarendon Press, Oxford

— (1969). *Evolution and Phylogeny of Flowering Plants. Dicotyledons*. Academic Press, London and New York

Jeffrey, E. C. (1912). The history, comparative anatomy and evolution of the *Araucarioxylon* type. *Proc. Amer. Acad. Arts Sci.* **48**, 531–571

Keating, R. C. (1975). Trends of specialization in pollen of Flacourtiaceae, with comparative observations of Cochlospermaceae and Bixaceae, *Grana* **15**, 29–49

Leinfellner, W. (1956). Die blattartig flachen Staubblätter . . . *Österr. Bot. Zeitschr.* **103**, 247–290

— (1966). Wie sind die Winteraceen-Karpelle tatsächlich gebaut? Ill. Die Karpelle von *Bubbia, Belliolum, Pseudowintera, Exospermum* und *Zygogynum. Österr. Bot. Z.* **113**, 245–264

Leppik, E. E. (1963). Reconstruction of a Cretaceous *Magnolia* flower. *Adv. Front. Plant Sc.* **4**, 79–94

Leroy, J.-F. (1977). A compound ovary with open carpels in Winteraceae. *Science* **196**, 977–978

Le Thomas, A. and Lugardon, B. (1974). Quelques types de structures grenues dans l'ectexine de pollens simples d'Annonaceae. *C. R. Ac. Sc. Paris*, Sér. D, **278**, 1187–1190

— and Lugardon, B. (1976). De la structure grenue à la structure columellaire dans le pollen des Annonacées. *Adansonia* **15**, 543–572

Melville, R. (1976). Neoteny, evolution and the New Zealand *Parsonsia* hybrids (Apocynaceae). *Bot. J. Linn. Soc.* **72**, 171–189

Muller, J. (1968). Palynology of the Pedawan and Plateau Sandstone formations in Sarawak, Malaysia. *Micropaleontology* **14**, 1–37

— (1970). Palynological evidence on early differentiation of Angiosperms. *Biol. Rev.* **45**, 417–450

Nilsson, S and Skvarla, J. J. (1969). Pollen morphology of saprophytic taxa in the Gentianaceae. *Ann. Mo. Bot. Gdn* **56**, 420–438

Padmanabhan, D. (1967). New aspects in the ontogeny of carpels in *Michelia champaca* L. *Proc. Indian Acad. Sc. B* **66**, 75–82

Pettitt, J. M. and Chaloner, W. G. (1964). The ultrastructure of the Mesozoic pollen *Classopollis. Pollen Spores* **6**, 611–620

Puri, V. (1967). The origin and evolution of Angiosperms. *J. Indian Bot. Soc.* **46**, 1–14

Rohweder, O. (1967). Karpellbau und Synkarpie bei Ranunculaceen. *Ber. Schweiz. Bot. Ges.* **77**, 376–432

— and Ruthisauser, R. (1976). Untersuchungen zur Architektur vegetativer Phyllome in der Gattung *Prunus. Beitr. Biol. Pflanzen* **52**, 127–161

Schuster, R. M. (1972). Continental movements, "Wallace's line" and indomalayan-australasian dispersal of land plants: some eclectic concepts. *Bot. Rev.* **38**, 3–86

Smith, A. C. (1970). The Pacific as a key to flowering plant history. H. L. Lyon Arbor. Lecture 1, 1–26. Honolulu

— (1971). An appraisal of the orders and families of primitive extant Angiosperms. *J. Indian Bot. Soc.* **50A**, 215–226

Sporne, K. R. (1969). The ovule as an indicator of evolutionary status in Angiosperms. *New Phytol.* **68**, 555–566

— (1970). The advancement index and tropical rain-forest. *New Phytol.* **69**, 1161–1166

— (1973). The survival of archaic Dicotyledons in tropical rain-forests. *New Phytol.* **72**, 1175–1184

— (1974). *Morphology of the Angiosperms*. Hutchinson, London

Stebbins, G. L. (1972). Ecological distribution of centers of major adaptive radiation in angiosperms. In *Taxonomy, Phytogeography and Evolution* (D. H. Valentine, ed.), 7–34. Academic Press, London and New York

Takhtajan, A. (1969). *Flowering Plants. Origin and Dispersal*. Oliver and Boyd, Edinburgh

Tucker, S. C. (1959). Ontogeny of the infloresence and the flower of *Drimys. winteri* var. *chilensis*. *Univ. Calif. Publ. Bot.* **30**, 257–336

— (1960). Ontogeny of the floral apex of *Michelia fuscata*. *Amer. J. Bot.* **47**, 266–277

Van Campo, M. and Lugardon, B. (1973) Structure grenue infratectale de l'exine des pollens de quelques Gymnospermes et Angiospermes. *Pollen Spores* **15**, 171–187

Vink, W. (1970). The Winteraceae of the Old World I. *Pseudowintera* and *Drimys*. *Blumea* **18**, 225–354

— (1977). The Winteraceae of the Old World II. *Zygogynum.Blumea* **23**, 219–250

— (1978). The Winteraceae of the Old World III. Notes on the ovary of *Takhtajania*. *Blumea* **24**, 521–525

Walker, J. W. (1976a). Comparative pollen morphology of the Ranalean complex. In *Origin and Early Evolution of Angiosperms* (C. B. Beck, ed.), 241–299. Columbia University Press, New York

— (1976b). Evolutionary significance of the exine in the pollen of primitive Angiosperms. In *The Evolutionary Significance of the Exine* (I. K. Ferguson and J. Muller, eds.), 251–308. Academic Press, London and New York

Wallace, A. R. (1892). *Island Life*, 2nd edn., Macmillan, London

White, R. A. (1961). Vessels in roots of *Marsilea*. *Science* **133**, 1073

— (1963). Tracheary elements of the ferns II. *Amer. J. Bot.* **50**, 514–522

Wolfe, J. A., Doyle, J. A. and Page, V. M. (1965). The bases of Angiosperm phylogeny: paieobotany. *Ann. Mo. Bot. Gdn* **62**, 801–824

16 Karyology of the Canarian Flora

LIV BORGEN   *Botanical Garden and Museum,*
University of Oslo, Norway

El número de cromosomas está conocido en 522 especies de plantas vasculares de origen canario. La frecuencia poliploide está calculada a un 28%. Solamente 151 especies (12%) de las no endémicas están investigadas y muestran un 36,4% de poliploide. Las notas registradas dan tanto como 360 especies endémicas (62%), 24,4% son poliploides.

La más baja frecuencia poliploide se ha encontrado entre las especies leñosas. Las anuales muestran frecuencias intermedias, mientras que las más altas frecuencias son encontradas entre las hierbas perennes.

El conocimiento de la cariología de la flora canaria es todavía incompleto, pero los datos sobre las especies endémicas permiten algunas reflexiones sobre la edad y origen de los elementos endémicos.

Existen tres notables peculiaridades referente a las plantas vasculares endémicas canarias:

1. Que constituyen una gran parte de la flora total de planta vascular.
2. Que están compuestas predominantemente de formas de vida leñosa.
3. Que están caracterizadas por un nivel extremadamente bajo de poliploide.

La cariología comparativa y otros principios de evidencia, indican que algunas especies endémicas son muy antiguas y que son palaeoendémicas, patroendémicas o antiguas schizoendémicas. La mayoría de estas endémicas antiguas muestran una afinidad mediterranea en consonancia con los registros de fósiles que datan del Terciario. Otras endémicas antiguas están relacionadas con floras más distantes del Este y Sur de Africa, Asia y América. Desestimando la posibilidad de dispersión a larga distancia, pueden retroceder a una época con conexiones de tierra entre los continentes. El predominio de formas de vida leñosas entre las especies endémicas antiguas mantienen el aspecto de que la leñosidad es un caracter primitivo. Los schizoendemicos constituyen el grupo principal de especies endémicas, y consisten mayormente en especies jóvenes o neoendémicas. Otras especies neoendémicas son apoendémicas. Estas especies jóvenes o neoendémicas son el resultado de una evolución intrinsular.

Tampoco está documentada la hibridización como de importancia. Los procesos principales reconocidos en el evolución de especies endémicas son radiaciones adaptativas y evolución vicariante.

Los factores importantes para el mantenimiento de los muchos relictos endémicos y el establecimiento de una diversidad de especies endémicas más recientes, han sido un clima favorable y estable, y una amplia distribución de habitats estables. Bajo tales condiciones ambientales, los poliploides han sido, aparentemente, de poco valor selectivo.

329

Introduction

Chromosome number reports on vascular plant material of Canarian origin date back to 1930 (Bleier, 1930). The first sporadic reports for Canarian endemic plants were mainly on cultivated material of uncertain origin.

The first extensive karyological investigation was made by Larsen (1958, 1960, 1962, 1963), most of his material having a known spontaneous origin. Later, Uhl (1961), Borgen (1969, 1970, 1974, 1975), Bramwell *et al.* (1971, 1972, 1976), and van Loon (1974) have made major contributions.

Karyological investigations have also been undertaken in connection with taxonomic revisions, for instance by Nordborg (1966) on different genera of Rosaceae, Roux and Boulos (1972) on *Sonchus*, and Humphries (1975) on *Argyranthemum*. Humphries' study on *Argyranthemum* included karyotype analysis and analysis of meiotic pairing, types of karyological data which are otherwise sparse for the Canarian flora.

Altogether about 525 species of vascular plants of Canarian origin have been investigated karyologically (Borgen, 1977), amounting to 28% of the total flora which comprises about 1860 species (Eriksson *et al.*, 1974).

Polyploidy spectrum of the Canarian vascular flora

The polyploidy frequencies of floras have attracted attention since Hagerup (1931) discussed their possible relationship to climate, ecology, and phylogeny. Larsen (1961), Borgen (1969), and Bramwell *et al.* (1972) have discussed the occurrence of polyploidy in the Canarian flora. Calculations based on recently published chromosome-number records (Borgen, 1977) show a total degree of 28% polyploidy.

Polyploidy and geographical area   Available data on polyploidy levels in floras of Europe and Africa are compiled in Table 1. Records from continental areas, islands, and mountains are compared.

Tischler (1934) drew attention to a gradient of polyploidy increasing from south to north in Europe. The hypothesis of polyploidy increasing with latitude seems still valid in Europe and Africa (Table 1) as well as in other continents (Löve and Löve, 1971).

The polyploidy frequency in the Canarian flora (28%) is at the same level as in the flora of Equatorial West Africa (26%, Morton, 1966) which is the lowest known (Löve and Löve, 1971).

TABLE I Polyploidy frequencies in floras of Africa and Europe

| Region | Latitude | Species studied (%) | Percentage of polyploidy | | | Reference |
			Liliatae	Magnoliatae	Total	
Continental areas						
Equatorial W. Africa	0–10°N	—	—	—	26	Morton (1966)
Timbuktu	17°N	—	67	27	31	Hagerup (1931)
N. Sahara	31°N	52	59.1	33.9	37.8	Reese (1957)
Roumania	44–48°N	—	—	—	43.5	Tarnavschi (1948)
Hungary	46–49°N	—	—	—	48.6	Tischler (1955)
Central Europe	46–55°N	—	—	—	50,7	Tischler (1955)
Pardubice (Czechoslovakia)	50°N	—	—	—	52.3	Löve and Löve (1949)
Schleswig-Holstein	54–55°N	86.4	72.4	48.1	54.5	Tischler (1955)
Denmark	54–58°N	90	70.2	47.4	53.5	Löve and Löve (1949)
Zealand, Denmark	55°N	—	—	—	53.2	Löve and Löve (1949)
Great Britain	50–61°N	—	—	—	50.6	Haskell (1952)
Sweden	55–69°N	87.3	74.8*	48.7	56.3	Tischler (1955)
Norway	58–71°N	86.5	76.1	49.8	57.6	Löve and Löve (1949)
Finland	60–70°N	85.5	77.2	48.9	57.3	Löve and Löve (1949)
Northern Sweden	64–67°N	—	—	—	59.2	Tischler 1955
Pité-Lappmark	66–67°N	—	—	—	63.2	Löve and Löve (1949)
Islands						
Canary Islands	28–29°N	28	41.1	26.3	28	Borgen
Cyclades	36–38°N	48.3	44.7	31.2	34.6	Tischler and Wulff (1953–63)
Sicily	36–39°N	37.6	51.5	32.8	37.0	Tischler 1934
Kolgouiev Islands	69°N	—	—	—	64	Sokolovskaja and Strelkova (1941)
Faroe Islands (Indigenous)	64°N	—	—	—	71	Löve and Löve (1957)
Iceland (Indigenous)	63–67°N	—	—	—	72.1	Löve and Löve (1957); Löve (1970)
Jan Mayen Island	71°N	—	—	—	70.3	Löve and Löve (1957)
Spitzbergen	77–80°N	—	—	—	79.7	Tischler and Wulff (1953–63)
Sassen-area (Spitzbergen)	78°N	—	—	—	76.7	Löve and Löve (1949)
Franz-Joseph Land	78°N	—	—	—	75	Löve and Löve (1957)
Mountains						
E. African Mts	0–10°N	68	74	41	49	Hedberg and Hedberg (1977)
Cameroon Mts	0–10°N	—	—	—	49	Morton (1966)
The Alps	46°N	—	—	—	52.7	Favarger (1954)
Tatra Mts	49°N	—	—	—	c.50	Skalinska (1964)
Hesse Alps	50°N	—	—	—	52.1	Knapp (1953)
Knutsho (Norway)	62°N	—	—	—	51	Gustafsson (1948)
Tröllaskagi (Iceland)	65°N	—	—	—	75	Löve (1953)

331

Within the area of Equatorial West Africa the high altitude flora of the Cameroon Mts has a much higher level, 49% polyploids according to Morton (1966). Polyploids are found to be more frequent at high altitudes in some areas, but if the mountains of Africa and Europe are compared individually, the degree of polyploidy does not increase with increasing latitude, except in the Tröllaskagi area, which is under Arctic influence.

Island floras show a latitudinal gradient of polyploidy increasing northwards from the equator. The polyploidy frequency of the Canarian flora is so far the lowest for any island flora; the other archipelagos investigated are, however, situated at much higher latitudes (Löve and Löve, 1971).

Factors correlated with latitude, and sometimes altitude, such as climate and range of habitats, are important in the discussion of polyploidy frequencies of whole floras. The history and composition of a flora are even more essential in this discussion.

Polyploidy and climate   Hagerup (1931) first proposed that polyploids are better adapted than their diploid progenitors to extreme climates. Increased chromosome numbers were thought to have a direct influence on hardiness and other tolerance factors of importance under extreme conditions. Although later studies have failed to confirm this hypothesis (Reese, 1957; Johnson *et al.*, 1965), it is assumed that polyploids have a distinct selective superiority when a flora is drastically reduced in number of taxa by environmental influences (Löve and Löve, 1971). The apparently wider tolerance limits of polyploids can be attributed to the increase in number of genes, this being an effective preadaption mechanism (Löve and Löve, 1971). The high frequency of polyploids in areas with cold and short summers may thus be interpreted as the result of preadapted gene-combinations allowing the occupation of and adaptation to increasingly less favourable conditions (Löve and Löve, 1975).

In the Canary Islands plants seem to have had little need of polyploidy as an adaptive mechanism, which may partly be due to a relatively stable climate throughout the floristic history. The same tendency is observed for other areas of stable climatic conditions, such as Equatorial West Africa.

Polyploidy and range of habitats   Packer's (1969) work in the Canadian Arctic archipelago showed a correlation between polyploidy and the degree of disturbance. The availability of new and unstable habitats seemed to be important for the establishment of polyploids, giving polyploids a superior selective value, at least under the influence of an extreme climate.

In the Canary Islands new habitats have been formed after the frequent volcanic eruptions. Rapid erosion has also produced habitat changes. Owing to stable climatic conditions, the formation of new habitats has apparently not promoted the establishment of polyploids.

It is difficult to deal with whole floras in the discussion of such correlations. There are great differences in polyploidy frequencies in plants of different families and in plants having different life-cycles and growth-habits, and the composition of a flora in this respect differs from one habitat to another.

Polyploidy and taxonomic groups   The occurrence of polyploidy varies from family to family, and also within the same family in different areas.

Polyploidy frequencies in some families of the Canarian flora are compared in Table 2. The families are not equally well investigated. The best known family is Asteraceae, with records on nearly half of its 265 species in the Canarian flora and a polyploidy frequency of 23%. This frequency is lower than that found in the West African and Afroalpine members of the family: 29% and 32% respectively (Morton, 1966; Hedberg and Hedberg, 1977). Boraginaceae and Apiaceae are the two families with fewest polyploids, the Apiaceae showing little polyploid differentiation all over the world (Moore, 1971). Crassulaceae, with c. 16%, and Lamiaceae, with c. 21% polyploids, are also predominantly diploid families in the Canary Islands. In contrast, Lamiaceae of West Africa shows 71% polyploidy (Morton, 1966). Rosaceae shows the highest rate, actually 100%, but only six of its 22 species in the Canaries have been

TABLE 2   Polyploidy frequencies in some families of the Canarian flora

Family	No. of species studied	Total no.(%)	Polyploids (%)
Boraginaceae	23	45.1	4.4
Apiaceae	12	26.7	8.3
Brassicaceae	28	35.0	10.7
Crassulaceae	51	44.7	15.7
Lamiaceae	19	19.2	21.1
Asteraceae	121	45.7	22.9
Poaceae	22	13.9	31.8
Fabaceae	43	25	39.6
Liliaceae	19	35.8	52.7
Scrophulariaceae	15	35.7	66.7
Rosaceae	6	27.3	100

TABLE 3 Polyploidy frequencies and growth habits of Canarian vascular plants

| | MAGNOLIOPHYTA | | | | PTERIDOPHYTA + PINOPHYTA | | TOTAL | |
| | Magnoliatae | | Liliatae | | | | | |
Growth habit	No. Species	Polyploidy (%)	No. Species	Polyploidy (%)	No. Species	Polyploidy (%)	No. Species	Polyploidy (%)
Woody life forms	304	21.1	8	12.5	2	0	31.4	20.7
Perennial herbs	45	44.4	37	48.7	5	40	87	46.0
Annuals + biennials	99	34.3	11	36.4	0	0	110	37.3
Total	448	26.3	56	41.1	7	28.6	511	28.0

investigated. Other families of the Magnoliatae showing high frequencies are Fabaceae and Scrophulariaceae. The Liliatae families Poaceae, with c. 32%, and Liliaceae, with c. 53%, are also rich in polyploids. The Afroalpine Poaceae, in comparison, has 74% polyploids (Hedberg and Hedberg, 1977), and the Liliaceae of West Africa 32% (Morton, 1966).

A comparison of polyploidy frequencies in Magnoliatae and Liliatae generally shows higher frequencies in the Liliatae (Table 1). In the Canary Islands 56 species of Liliatae have been investigated, and 448 species of Magnoliatae (Table 3). The Liliatae comprises only 15% of all Canarian flowering plants (cf. Eriksson *et al.*, 1974). Relatively, the two groups are therefore equally well investigated. The degree of polyploidy is higher in the Liliatae, 41% against 25% in the Magnoliatae, but the lower frequency of Liliatae species in the Canarian flora results in a low polyploidy frequency.

Polyploidy and life-forms   Lems (1961) constructed a life-form spectrum of Canarian vascular plants, based on the classification of Raunkiaer (1934). Using Lems' data, growth-habit spectra are shown in Fig. 1. The

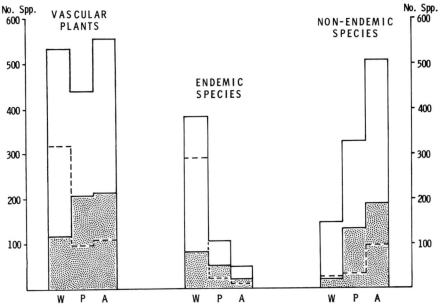

FIG. 1   The growth habit spectra of the Canarian vascular plants and the differences between the endemic and non-endemic element are shown. W, woody; P, perennial; A, annual. Within each group the chromosome number records are stippled, and the polyploidy estimates, based on the frequencies calculated, are hatched

phanerophytic and chamaephytic life-forms are included in the woody growth habit. Among the perennial herbs are included hemicrypto-phytes, geophytes, stem succulents, and lianas. A few biennial species are included among the annuals.

The polyploidy estimates, based on the frequencies calculated (Table 3, Fig. 1), show that the highest frequency of polyploids in the Canarian flora is found among the perennial herbs. This is in accordance with the polyploidy spectrum of the world's flora (cf. Stebbins, 1971). Perennials often have a device for vegetative propagation, which is essential during the establishment of a polyploid species.

Polyploids seem to be least frequent among the woody Canarian species. This does not coincide with what is known from elsewhere. In the world flora, polyploids are least frequent among annuals, whereas woody species show an intermediate position (Stebbins, 1971).

A comparison of endemic and non-endemic species shows that the two groups have opposite growth-habit spectra (Fig. 1). The actual number of polyploids found in different growth habits are, therefore, also different, but relatively the frequencies of polyploids are the same in the two groups: a low frequency of polyploid woody species, an intermediate frequency of polyploid annuals, and a comparatively high frequency of polyploid perennials.

The different groups are not equally well-investigated karyologically, as is indicated by the stippled lines in Fig. 1. The majority of species investigated are woody and endemic, the frequency found for this group being reliable. Few non-endemic species have been investigated, the polyploidy frequency calculated for the prominent annual non-endemic group being preliminary.

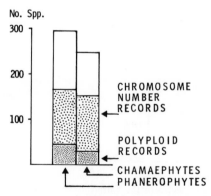

Fig. 2   The distribution of chamaephytes and phanerophytes among the woody species is shown. The total chromosome number records and the polyploid records are marked with stippling.

The Canarian flora has a low frequency of the predominantly polyploid perennials. Annuals and woody species, mostly diploids, are about equally frequent, and together constitute the major part of the flora, resulting in a low total degree of polyploidy.

In the Arctic areas where polyploids are frequent, the flora is mainly composed of cryptophytes (Löve and Löve, 1975): dwarf, spreading hemicryptophytes and chamaephytes. In the Canaries hemicryptophytes are comparatively less frequent, but among the woody species, chamaephytes and phanerophytes are nearly equally frequent and equally well-investigated karyologically (Fig. 2). Polyploids are somewhat less frequent among the chamaephytes, c. 16%, than among the phanerophytes, c. 25%. The extraordinarily low frequency of polyploids among the chamaephytes, and the high frequency of this life-form, is partly responsible for the low total degree of polyploidy.

Polyploidy and endemism According to recent estimates (Bramwell, 1976), about 470 species are endemic to the Canary Islands. One hundred and ten additional species are Macaronesian endemics. These 580 endemic species constitute nearly one-third of the Canarian flora.

As many as 360, 62%, of the endemic species have been studied karyologically. Only 24·4% have been shown to be polyploids (Table 4).

TABLE 4   Polyploidy frequencies and growth habits of endemic species

Growth habit	MAGNOLIATAE		LILIATAE		VASCULAR PLANTS (Incl. Pter. + Pin.)	
	No. Species	Polyploidy (%)	No. Species	Polyploidy (%)	No. Species	Polyploidy (%)
Woody	278	21.6	8	15.4	288	21.2
Perennial	37	51.4	11	18.2	52	44.2
Annual	19	21.1	1	0	20	35.0
Total	344	24.2	20	15.0	360	24.4

Of a total of about 1280 non-endemic species only 151, 12%, have been investigated karyologically (Table 5). Of these, 36·4% were found to be polyploids. More research on non-endemic species may, therefore, increase the percentage of polyploidy in the flora as a whole.

Among the endemic species an exceptionally low polyploidy frequency occurs. Polyploidy does not seem to have been a major force in the evolution of endemic species in the Canarian flora.

TABLE 5 Polyploidy frequencies and growth habits of non-endemic species

Growth habit	MAGNOLIATAE		LILIATAE		VASCULAR PLANTS (Incl. Pter. + Pin.)	
	No. Species	Polyploidy (%)	No. Species	Polyploidy (%)	No. Species	Polyploidy (%)
Woody	26	15.4	0	0	26	15.4
Perennial	8	12.5	26	61.5	35	48.6
Annual	80	37.5	10	40.0	90	37.8
Total	114	30.7	36	55.6	151	36.4

Karyology, endemism, and age of flora

Favarger and Contandriopoulos (1961) have proposed a system of classification of endemic species based on the ploidy level. They recognised four types of endemics: palaeoendemics, schizoendemics, patroendemics, and apoendemics. Within this system they distinguish between three groups of polyploids based on differences in age (Favarger 1961): palaeopolyploids, mesopolyploids, and neopolyploids. The classification has been provisionally applied to the Canarian flora by Bramwell *et al.* (1972) and Bramwell (1976).

In Tables 6–8 some taxa are grouped in the categories of endemics mentioned, but for most of the species and genera in question our knowledge is still too fragmentary to permit a proper classification. If not

TABLE 6 Examples of karyology, growth habit, and geographic affinity of probable Canarian palaeoendemics

Genus	Growth habit	Basic No. x	Ploidy levels 2x	4x	Geographic affinity
Gesnouinia	Woody	3	1		Mediterranean
Sanguisorba, sect. *Dendriopoterium*	Woody	7		1	Mediterranean
Neochamaelea	Woody	9		1	America, Mediterranean
Drusa	Annual	8	1		America
Tinguarra	Perennial	11	1		Mediterranean
Plocama	Woody	11		1	S. Africa
Cedronella	Perennial	10	1		America, E. Asia
Heywoodiella	Woody	3	1		
Sventenia	Woody	9	1		Mediterranean
Vieraea	Woody	8	1		
Babcockia	Woody	9	1		Mediterranean, Africa

Table 7 Examples of karyology, growth habit and geographic affinity of probable Canarian schizoendemics

Taxon	Growth habit	Basic No. x	2x	4x	6x	8x	Geographic affinity
Ocotea foetens		12	1				S. Africa
Persea indica		12	1				America, E. Asia
Crambe, sect. Dendrocambe		15	4				Mediterranean
Erysimum spp.		7		2			Mediterranean
Parolinia spp.	Woody	11	3				E. Africa
Greenovia spp.		18	3				E. Africa
Bencomia spp.		7		3			S. Africa
Dorycnium spp		7	2				Mediterranean
Teline spp.		12		3			Mediterranean
Todaroa spp.	Perennial	11	2				Mediterranean
Pterocephalus spp.		9		2			Mediterranean
Echium, endemic sects.		8	19				Mediterranean (Africa)
Isoplexis spp.		7				2	Mediterranean
Bystropogon spp.		7			2		America
Lavandula spp.		11	3				Mediterranean
Micromeria spp.		15	4				Mediterranean
Salvia spp.		11	2				S. Africa
Allagopappus spp.	Woody	10	2				Mediterranean
Argyranthemum spp.		9	17				Mediterranean
Gonospermum spp.		9	4				Mediterranean
Schizogyne spp.		9	2				E. Africa
Sonchus, subg. Dendrosonchus		9	16				Mediterranean, Africa
Taeckholmia spp.		9	3				Mediterranean
Tolpis spp.		9	3				Mediterranean

Table 8 Examples of Canarian apoendemics

Canarian apoendemic	Corresponding taxon or taxa
Limonium ovalifolium ssp. canariense, 2n = 24, 4x	L. pectinatum and L. papillatum, Canarian endemics, 2n = 12, 2x
Descurainia gonzalesi, 2n = 21, 3x	Descurainia, 4 Canarian endemic spp., 2n = 14, 2x
Tamus edulis, 2n = 96, 8x	T. communis, Mediterranean, 2n = 48, 4x
Asparagus pastorianus, 2n = 40, 4x	Asparagus, 6 Canarian endemic spp., 2n = 20, 2x A. albus, Mediterranean, 2n = 20, 2x

otherwise stated, references to the chromosome numbers cited below can be found in Borgen (1977).

Palaeoendemics According to the classification of Favarger and Contandriopoulos (1961), palaeoendemics *sensu stricto* are monotypic genera or sections with no corresponding taxa. They are either diploids or *palaeopolyploids*, which are polyploids without closely related diploids.

In my opinion, examples of diploid palaeoendemics in the Canarian flora are the monotypic genera *Gesnouinia, Drusa, Tinguarra Cedronella, Heywoodiella, Sventenia, Vieraea,* and *Babcockia* (Table 6).

Examples of palaeopolyploid palaeoendemics are three apparently tetraploid species: *Plocama pendula* Ait. and *Neochamaelea pulverulenta* (Vent.) Erdtm. of monotypic genera, and *Sanguisorba menendezii* (Svent.) Nordb., which is the single species of its section *Dendriopoterium* (Table 6).

Schizoendemics This is probably the most extensive of the four categories, and the one which is most difficult to circumscribe. It consists of diploid or polyploid taxa with corresponding taxa at the same ploidy level. The schizoendemics are of different ages. The polyploids are *mesopolyploids*, with ancestral diploid species in the same or a related genus.

According to Favarger (1972), schizoendemism is the main process in the endemism of the Alps. In my opinion, many of the Canarian endemics are to be interpreted as schizoendemics.

Schizoendemism is an active endemism, involving vicariant evolution and adaptive radiation. From a primitive taxon diversification has taken place. The formation of new taxa has been more or less simultaneous.

The result of these processes is the occurrence of endemic vicariant species in many genera found in different islands or in different ecological habitats in one island.

Some probable examples of schizoendemic groups and species are shown in Table 7. All species of some large genera, subgenera, or sections are at the same ploidy level, for instance 17 spp. of *Argyranthemum*, 16 spp. of *Sonchus* subgenus *Dendrosonchus*, and 19 spp. of different endemic sections of *Echium*.

The term "active epibiotics" has been used to describe such genera (Wulff 1950), and adaptive radiation has been well documented, for example in *Echium* by Bramwell (1975), *Sonchus* by Bramwell (1972), and *Argyranthemum* by Humphries (1976). In addition, a considerable amount of vicariant evolution is shown to have taken place.

Vicariant evolution without the stimulus of adaptive radiation is also sometimes in operation. An example is found in *Parolinia*, with *P.*

intermedia Svent. & Bramw. in Tenerife, *P. schizogynoides* Svent. in Gomera, and *P. ornata* Webb in Lanzarote, Fuerteventura, Gran Canaria, and Tenerife.

In California speciation without change in chromosome number is frequently met with, and the production of diploid endemics as a result of hybridisation is well documented (Lewis, 1972). In the Canary Islands this type of speciation has probably contributed to the diversity of endemic species. An example of a hybrid swarm between species of different sections of *Argyranthemum* is provided by Borgen (1976), indicating a hybrid origin of at least one of the species in this genus. Humphries (1975, 1976) has shown that in *Argyranthemum* no intrinsic barriers to gene exchange are in operation. Fertile hybrids are easily produced artificially, but they are rarely reported from nature.

Other groups than those presented in Table 7 are also mainly of the schizoendemic type, such as *Limonium* sect. *Nobiles*, *Senecio* subgenus *Pericallis*, *Aeonium*, *Ceropegia*, *Euphorbia* sect. *Pachycladae*, *Centaurea*, and *Asparagus*, but in these groups one or a few species show a deviating ploidy level.

That such a wide range of adaptive forms can exist within the Canary Islands depends probably on the presence of steep ecological gradients and a diversity of habitats which have remained stable over long periods of time.

Patroendemics Patroendemics are defined as old diploids whose corresponding taxa are polyploid. An example of an endemic taxon fitting this definition is the diploid *Viburnum tinus* L. ssp. *rigidum* (Vent.) P. Silva ($2n = 18$), which has its counterpart in the Mediterranean ssp. *tinus* ($2n = 36$, tetraploid, Egolf 1962) and ssp. *lucidum* Ait. ($2n = 72$, octoploid, Egolf 1962). Of the three taxa forming this polyploid complex, the diploid Canarian endemic is regarded as the oldest taxon.

The endemic *Laurus azorica* (Seub.) Franco apparently shows a lower polyploidy degree ($2n = 36$, 3x or 6x) than the corresponding Mediterranean taxon *L. nobilis* L. ($2n = 42$, aneuploid?, Battaglia 1947; and ($2n = 48$, 4x or 8x, Darlington and Wylie 1955). These two *Laurus* species are known from Tertiary deposits in the western Mediterranean region (Saporta, 1862–1874; Depape, 1922) and are regarded as relicts from the Tertiary subtropical laurel forests of the Mediterranean region. *L. azorica*, although polyploid itself, is probably to be regarded as a patroendemic and as older than its near relative *L. nobilis*, which has a higher polyploid number.

Apoendemics The apoendemics represent the inverse case of the patroendemics. Apoendemics are polyploid species whose corresponding taxa are diploid or at a lower polyploidy level. The apoendemic taxa are neopolyploids, and are younger than their corresponding taxa.

A few examples are given in Table 8. Endemic species that are at a higher ploidy level than their endemic relatives are, for instance, the tetraploids *Limonium ovalifolium* (Poir.) O. Kuntze ssp. *canariense* Pign. and *Asparagus pastorianus* Webb & Berth.; and the triploid *Descurainia gonzalezii* Svent.

The endemic *Tamus edulis* Lowe is octoploid; its corresponding Mediterranean relative *T. communis* L., tetraploid (Borgen, 1974).

Neopolyploids are more often chromosome races within a species. Such chromosome races are detected in the following endemic species: *Ceropegia fusca* Bolle, reported as diploid in Tenerife, tetraploid in Gran Canaria; *Lotus emeroides* Murr. as diploid and tetraploid in Gomera; *L. glaucus* Ait. as diploid in Tenerife and Gran Canaria, and tetraploid in Hierro; and *Reseda crystallina* Webb & Berth. as diploid in Lanzarote and diploid and tetraploid in Fuerteventura.

Polyploid races, apparently neopolyploids, are also known in some non-endemic species, *Silene cucubalus* Wib. being octoploid in the Canaries and tetraploid in Europe (Larsen, 1960), and *Asphodelus microcarpus* Salzm. & Viv. being dodecaploid in the Canaries and octoploid in Europe (Borgen, 1969). Intrainsular polyploid races are also reported in *Cardamine hirsuta* L., *Petrorhagia nanteuilii* (Burn). Ball & Heyw., *Erodium chium* (L.) Willd., *Avena barbata* Pott. ex Link, *Hordeum murinum* L., and *Cheilanthes catanensis* (Cos.) H. P. Fuchs.

Concluding remarks

Our knowledge of the karyology of the Canarian flora is incomplete. This is especially true for the non-endemic species. Karyological data for endemic species are more extensive and permit some reflections on the age and origin of the endemic elements.

There are three notable features concerning the endemic Canarian vascular plants:

1 they constitute a large part of the total vascular plant flora,
2 they are composed of predominantly woody life-forms,
3 they are characterised by an extremely low level of polyploidy.

Comparative karyology and other sources of evidence indicate that some endemic species are very old, being palaeoendemics, patroendemics, or old schizoendemics. Most of these old endemics show a Mediterranean affinity, and fossil records date back to the Tertiary. Other old endemics are related to more distant floras, of East and South

Africa, Asia, and America (Tables 6–8). Disregarding the posssibility of long-distance dispersal, they may date back to a time with land connections between the continents. The predominance of woody life-forms among the old endemic species supports the view that woodiness is a primitive character.

The schizoendemics constitute the main group of endemic species, and consist mainly of younger or neoendemic species. Other neoendemic species are apoendemics. These young or neoendemic species are the result of an intrainsular evolution.

Polyploid differentiation within the endemic flora is both of the palaeopolyploid, mesopolyploid, and neopolyploid type, but polyploidy has not been a main evolutionary pathway. Neither is hybridisation documented to be of great importance. The main processes recognised in the evolution of endemic species are adaptive radiation and vicariant evolution.

Important factors for the maintenance of the many relict endemics and for the establishment of a diversity of more recent endemic species have been a stable and favourable climate and a wide range of stable habitats. Under such environmental conditions polyploidy has apparently been of little selective value.

Summary

The polyploidy frequency of the Canarian vascular plant flora is calculated to 28%, based on studies of 28% of the species. The frequency is of one of the lowest recorded for any area and correlated with a low frequency of the predominantly polyploid perennials and Liliatae species, and a high frequency of woody, annual, and Magnoliatae species.

The polyploidy frequency is c. 24% for the endemic (62% recorded) and c. 36% for the non-endemic element (12% recorded). Polyploid differentiation is both of the palaeopolyploid, mesopolyploid, and neopolyploid type, but polyploidy has not been a main evolutionary trend.

The majority of endemic species are regarded as schizoendemics, but some palaeoendemics, patroendemics, and apoendemics are recognized. Important factors for the maintenance of the many relict endemics and the establishment of a diversity of more recent ones have been a stable and favourable climate and a wide range of habitats. Under these environmental conditions polyploidy has been of minor importance as an adaptive mechanism.

M

REFERENCES

Battaglia, E. (1947). La natura verosimilimente ibrida e poliploide del *Laurus nobilis* L. revelata dall'analise citogenetica. *Rend. Accad. Nazl. Linzei, Cl. Sci. Fis., Mat., Nat.* Ser. 8a, **2**, 463–467

Bleier, H. (1930). Experimentell-cytologische Untersuchungen. I. Einfluss abnormaler Temperatur auf die Reduktionsteilung. *Z. Zellf. Mikroskop. Anat.* **11**, 218–236

Borgen, L. (1969). Chromosome numbers of vascular plants from the Canary Islands, with special reference to the occurrence of polyploidy. *Nytt. Mag. Bot.* **16**, 81–121

— (1970). Chromosome numbers of Macaronesian flowering plants. *Nytt. Mag. Bot.* **17**, 145–161

— (1974). Chromosome numbers of Macaronesian flowering plants II. *Norw. J. Bot.* **21**, 195–210

— (1975). Chromosome numbers of vascular plants from Macaronesia. *Norw. J. Bot.* **22**, 71–76

— (1976). Analysis of a hybrid swarm between *Argyranthemum adauctum* and *A. filifolium* in the Canary Islands. *Norw. J. Bot.* **23**, 121–137

— (1977). *Check-list of Chromosome Numbers Counted in Macaronesian Vascular Plants.* Oslo (Mimeogr.)

Bramwell, D. (1972). Endemism in the flora of the Canary Islands. In *Taxonomy, Phytogeography and Evolution* (D. H. Valentine, ed.), 141–159. Academic Press, London and New York

— (1975). Some morphological aspects of the adaptive radiation of Canary Islands *Echium* species. *Anal. Inst. Bot. Cavanilles* **32**, 241–254

— (1976). The endemic flora of the Canary Islands. In *Biogeography and Ecology in the Canary Islands* (G. Kunkel, ed.). *Monogr. Biol.* **30**, Junk, The Hague

— Humphries, C. J., Murray, B. G. and Owens, S. J. (1971). Chromosome numbers in plants from the Canary Islands. *Bot. Not.* **124**, 376–382

— (1972). Chromosome studies in the flora of Macaronesia. *Bot. Not.* **125**, 139–152

— Perez de Paz, J. and Ortega, J. (1976). Studies in the flora of Macaronesia: Some chromosome numbers of flowering plants. *Bot. Macar.* **1**, 9–16

Darlington, C. D. and Wylie, A. P. (1955). *Chromosome Atlas of Flowering Plants.* George Allen and Unwin Ltd, London

Depape, G. (1922). Flore pliocène de la Vallée du Rhône. *Ann. Sci. Nat.* Sér. 10, **4**, 73–265

Egolf, D. R. (1962). A cytological study of the genus *Viburnum*. *J. Arn. Arb.* **43**, 132–172

Eriksson, O. Hansen, A. and Sunding, P. (1974). *Flora of Macaronesia. Check-List of Vascular Plants, 1974.* Umeå (Mimeogr.)

Favarger, C. (1954). Sur le pourcentage des polyploides dans la flore de l'étage nival des Alpes suisses. *VIII Congr. Int. Bot. Paris, Rapp. et Comm. déposés lors du Congrès, Sect. 9 et 10*, 51–56

— (1961). Sur l'emploi des nombres chromosomiques en géographie botanique. *Ber. Geobot. Forsch. Inst. Rübel* **32**, 119–146

— (1972). Endemism in the montane floras of Europe. In *Taxonomy, Phytogeography and Evolution* (D. H. Valentine, ed.), 191–204. Academic Press, London and New York

— and Contandriopoulos, J. (1961). Essai sur l'endémisme. *Ber. Schweiz. Bot. Ges.* **71**, 384–408

Gustafsson, Å. (1948). Polyploidy, life-form and vegetative reproduction. *Hereditas* **34**, 1–22

Hagerup, O. (1931). Über Polyploidie in Beziehung zu Klima, Ökologie, und Phylogenie. *Hereditas* **16**, 19–40

Haskell, G. (1952). Polyploidy, ecology and the British flora. *J. Ecol.* **40**, 265–282

Hedberg, I. and Hedberg, O. (1977). Chromosome numbers of afroalpine and afromontane angiosperms. *Bot. Not.* **130**, 1–24

Humphries, C. J. (1975). Cytological studies in the Macaronesian genus *Argyranthemum* Webb ex Schultz Bip. (Compositae–Anthemideae). *Bot. Not.* **128**, 239–255

— (1976). Evolution and endemism in *Argyranthemum* Webb ex Schultz Bip. (Compositae: Anthemideae). *Bot. Macar.* **1**, 25–50

Johnson, A. W., Packer, J. G. and Reese, G. (1965). Polyploidy, distribution and environment. *The Quaternary of the United States*, 497–507

Knapp, R. (1953). Über Zusammenhänge zwischen Polyploidie, Verbreitung, systematischer und soziologischer Stellung von Pflanzenarten in Mitteleuropa. *Z. Vererb. Lehre* **85**, 163–179

Larsen, K. (1958). Preliminary note on the cytology of the endemic Canarian element. *Sv. Bot. Tidsskr.* **54**, 167–169

— (1960). Cytological and experimental studies on the flowering plants of the Canary Islands. *Biol. Skr. Dan. Vid. Selsk.* **11** (3)

— (1962). Contribution to the cytology of the endemic Canarian element. *Bot. Not.* **115**, 196–202

— (1963). Contribution to the cytology of the endemic Canarian element. II. *Bot. Not.* **116**, 409–424

Lems, K. (1961). Botanical notes on the Canary Islands. III. The life form spectrum and its interpretation. *Ecology* **42**, 569–572

Lewis, H. (1972). The origin of endemics in the Californian flora. In *Taxonomy, Phytogeography and Evolution* (D. H. Valentine, ed.), 179–190. Academic Press, London and New York

Löve, A. (1953). Subarctic polyploidy. *Hereditas* **39**, 113–124

— (1970). *Islenzk Ferdaflóra*. Reykjavik

— and Löve, D. (1949). The geobotanical significance of polyploidy. I. Polyploidy and latitude. *Port. Acta Biol., Ser. A. R. B. Goldschmidt Jub. Vol.* 273–352

— (1957). Arctic polyploidy. *Proc. Genet. Soc. Can.* **2**, 23–27

— (1971). Polyploidie et géobotanique. *Natur. Can.* **98**, 469–494

— (1975). Cryophytes, polyploidy and continental drift. *Phytocoenologia* **2**, 54–65

Loon, J. C. van (1974). A cytological investigation of flowering plants from the Canary Islands. *Acta Bot. Neerl.* **23**, 113–124

Moore, D. M. (1971). Chromosome studies in the Umbelliferae. *Bot. J. Linn. Soc.* **64**, Suppl. 1, 233–256

Morton, J. K. (1966). The role of polyploidy in the evolution of a tropical flora. In *Chromosomes Today* (C. D. Darlington and K. K. Lewis, eds.), Vol. 1, 73–76

Nordborg, G. (1966). *Sanguisorba* L., *Sarcopoterium* Spach, and *Bencomia* Webb et Berth. Delimitation and subdivision of the genera. *Opera Bot.* **11** (2), 1–103

Packer, J. G. (1969). Polyploidy in the Canadian arctic archipelago. *Arctic and Alpine Res.* **1**, 15–28

Raunkiaer, C. (1934). *The Life Forms of Plants and Statistical Plant Geography.* Clarendon Press, Oxford

Reese, G. (1957). Über die Polyploidiespektren in der nordsaharischen Wüstenflora. *Flora (Jena)* **144**, 598–634

Roux, J. and Boulos, L. (1972). Révision systématique du genre *Sonchus* L. s. 1. II. Étude caryologique. *Bot. Not.* **125**, 306–309

Saporta, G. (1862–74). Etudes sur la Végétation du Sud-Est de la France à l'époque tertiaire. *Ann. Sci. Nat. Bot. Sér. 4*: 16, 309, 348; 17 191–311 (1862); 19, 5–124 (1863). *Sér. 5*: 3, 5–152 (1865); 8, 5–136 (1867); 9, 5–62 (1868); 15, 277–351 (1972); 17, 5–44 (1873); 18, 23–146 (1874)

Skalinska, M. (1964). Cytological studies in the flora of the Tatra Mountains. A synthetic review. *Acta Biol. Cracov., Ser. Bot.* **6**, 203–233

Sokolovskaja, A. P. and Strelkova, O. S. (1941). Karyological investigations of the alpine flora of the main Caucasus range and the problem of geographical distribution of polyploids. *Dokl. Akad. Nauk SSSR* **29**, 415–419

Stebbins, G. L. (1971). *Chromosomal Evolution in Higher Plants.* Edward Arnold, London

Tarnavschi, I. T. (1948). Die Chromosomenzahlen der Anthophyten-Flora von Rumänien mit einem Ausblick auf das Polyploidie-Problem. *Bul. Grád. Bot. Muz. Bot. Univ. Cluj* **28**, Suppl., 1–130

Tischler, G. (1934). Die Bedeutung der Polyploidie für die Verbreitung der Angiospermen, erläutert an den Arten Schleswig-Holsteins, mit Ausblicken auf andere Florengebiete. *Bot. Jahrb.* **67**, 1–36

— (1955). Der Grad der Polyploidie bei den Angiospermen in verschiedenen Grossarealen. *Cytologia* **20**, 101–118

Tischler, G. and Wulff, H. D. (1953–63). *Angewandte Pflanzenkaryologie.* Gebrüder Borntraeger, Berlin

Uhl, C. H. (1961). The chromosomes of the Sempervivoideae (Crassulaceae). *Amer. J. Bot.* **48**, 114–123

Wulff, E. V. (1950). *An Introduction to Historical Plant Geography.* Chronica Botanica Co., Waltham, Mass.

17 Palaeoendemism and Evolution in Macaronesian *Dryopteris*

MARY GIBBY   *Department of Botany, British Museum*
(Natural History), London, England

La flora de helechos en Macaronesia parece consistir en su mayor parte en especies antiguas que existieron en la flora Terciaria de Europa y que han sobrevivido desde entonces como reliquias. La mayoría de las especies son diploides, en contraste con el alto porcentaje de especies poliploides encontradas en la moderna flora de helechos tropicales, y en mucha menor extensión en una flora templada como ocurre en Bretaña, donde el 50% de especies de helechos son poliploides.

Las especies de *Dryopteris* son plantas de bosques que se encuentran en los bosques de Laurel en Macaronesia. En Macaronesia existen probablemente, nueve especies, seis de las cuales son endémicas, mientras que otras tres aparecen también en le continente europeo. *D. aitoniana* Pichi Serm. y *D. ologodonta* (Desv.) Pichi Serm. son diploides relictuales, en las que sus especies hermanas son desconocidas. *D. aitoniana* de Madeira tiene, probablemente, afinidades con el agregado *D. filix-mas*. *D. oligodonta* está confinado al Oeste de las islas Canarias y posiblemente aparece también en Cabo Verde. Sus afinidades son inciertas, pero pueden estar relacionadas a *D. inaequalis* (Schlecht.) O. Ktze. de Africa del Sur y Tropical. Otra especie *Dryopteris* diploide, similar en morfología a *D. oligodonta* o *D. guanchica*, existe en La Palma, pero esta especie requiere una investigación mas concienzuda.

D. azorica (Christ) Alston es una especie endémica diploide que crece en la mayor parte de las islas azóricas, estando muy cerca en morfología a otra endémica diploide de Madeira, *D. maderensis* Alston. De evidencias morfológicas, citológicas y fitoquímicas; estos dos diploides son muy cercanos a *D. intermedia* (Muhl.) A. Gray, una especie diploide del Este de Norteamérica.

D. aemula (Ait.) O. Ktze., *D. pseudomas* (Wollaston) Holub & Pouzar y *D. guanchica* Gibby & Jermy, se hallan en Macaronesia y Europa. *D. aemula,* un diploide, tiene una distribución atlántica y se ve en las islas Canarias, Madeira y Azores. *D. pseudomas* es una especie diploide apogamica en Macaronesia; en Europa ambos citotipos, diploide y triploide, aparecen, estando la especie muy extendida. *D. guanchica*, especie tetraploide, es solamente conocida en las islas Canarias, España y Portugal. Evidencias morfológicas y citológicas sugieren que sea una especie alotetraploide, basada en *D. aemula* y *D. maderensis*. *D. guanchica* es simpatrica con *D. aemula* en España y la isla de La Gomera, pero no crece junta con *D. maderensis*. Parece probable que *D. guanchica* surgió en el Continente europeo durante el Terciario, cuando *D. maderensis* estaba más extendida y subsecuentemente llegaron a las islas Canarias.

El tetrapolide *D. crispifolia* Rasbach, Reichtein & Vida ha sido hallado hasta el momento en tres islas de las Azores: Pico, Faial y Sao Miguel, donde crecen mezcladas con *D. aemula* y *D. azorica*. Se ha sugerido, ante una evidencia morfológica, que esta especie tetraploide ha surgido de *D. aemula* y *D. azorica* por hibridización y el consecuente doblamiento de cromosoma; pudiendo muy bien haber evolucionado en las Azores. La relación entre *D. crispifolia* y *D. guanchica* no es segura; aunque difieren en morfología y química, las dos pueden probar que son muy similares citológicamente si estos orígenes indicados son correctos.

Introduction

The fern flora of Macaronesia appears to be composed largely of species which existed in the Tertiary flora of Europe, and have since survived as relicts. *Woodwardia radicans* (L.)Sm., with a present distribution in Macaronesia, Portugal, Spain, Corsica, Italy and Crete (Jalas and Suominen, 1972), and *Adiantum reniforme* L., with a disjunct distribution in Macaronesia, Madagascar and Réunion (Bramwell, 1972), are known from Pliocene deposits in the Rhône valley (Tardieu-Blot, 1946).

At least 50% of fern species in Europe are polyploid (Vida, 1972), whereas the majority of ferns in Macaronesia, 60% or more, are diploids (Manton, 1950; Page, 1973). This difference is seen in the genus *Dryopteris*, which has eight species in Macaronesia, six of which are diploid with $2n = 82$, and two tetraploid with $2n = 164$; in Europe there are 17 *Dryopteris* species, eight diploids, and the remainder include triploids and tetraploids.

Description of Dryopteris *species*

Species of *Dryopteris* are reported from the Azores, Madeira, the five western islands of the Canaries and the Cape Verdes. They are found usually in woodland or in shaded damp areas, and are most abundant in the laurel forests. In the Azores and Madeira they occur also in the *Erica* zones, at higher altitudes, but are absent from this zone in the Canary Islands, probably owing to the lack of sufficient moisture. In the Cape Verdes *D. elongata* (Sw.) A. Chev. is recorded only from the higher islands, São Antao, São Nicolau and Fogo, at altitudes of 800–900 m (Chevalier, 1935) in the shrubby composite – labiate zone, where the climate is more Mediterranean-like than in other zones. *Dryopteris parasitica* (L.) O. Kuntze, *D. grunowii* (Bolle) A. Chev. and *D. crenata* (Forssk.) O. Kuntze, which are recorded from the Cape Verdes by Chevalier (1935), are no longer placed within *Dryopteris*; the first two are now in *Thelypteris* sens. lat. and *D. crenata* is more correctly named *Hypodematium crenatum* (Forssk.) Kuhn.

Dryopteris aitoniana Pichi Serm. is a diploid species ($n = 41$) (Widén *et al.*, 1971), which is endemic to Madeira, and it is a relictual diploid of which no close relatives are known. In its gross morphology and its spore ornamentation it shows similarities with the *D. filix-mas* (L.) Schott complex, and it was considered a subspecies of *D. filix-mas* by Christensen. It is distinct from *D. filix-mas*, however, in several characters; *D. aitoniana* has a triangular-shaped frond, as it does not narrow towards the base as does *D. filix-mas*; the fronds of *D. aitoniana* are thicker and more rigid; the scales on the stipe base are much thicker, and chestnut coloured with a dark central stripe; both lamina and indusia are profusely glandular. A chemical investigation of the phloroglucinols of *D. aitoniana* by Widén and colleagues (1971) has shown it to be different from *D. filix-mas* in lacking filixic acid, which is a major compound in *D. filix-mas*, and in containing large amounts of trisflavaspidic acid. In fact its chemistry seems to show closer affinities with the *D. villarii* (Bellardi) Woynar ex Schinz & Thell. complex in Europe, than with *D. filix-mas*.

D. oligodonta Pichi Serm. is a diploid species endemic to the Canary Islands and it occurs on Hierro, La Palma, Gomera, Tenerife and Gran Canaria, where it is a dominant species of the laurel forest (Gibby *et al.*, 1977). It is by far the largest and most abundant *Dryopteris* species in the Canaries. It may occur also in the Cape Verdes. Chevalier (1935) recorded *D.* "*elongata*" from three islands as a rare species, and *D. filix-mas* var *oligodonta* (Desv.) C Chr. is included by Chevalier in the synonymy of *D. elongata*. As with *D. aitoniana*, the affinities of *D. oligodonta* are uncertain. It has been called a variety of *D. filix-mas* by Christensen; Kuhn (1879) regarded it as belonging to the same species as *Aspidium inaequale* Schlecht. *Dryopteris inaequalis* (Schlecht.) O. Kuntze has a geographical distribution in tropical and South Africa, and in the East African islands. Pichi Sermolli (1951) believed the two species to be different. The phloroglucinol composition of *D. oligodonta* and tetraploid Kenya material of *D. inaequalis* was investigated by Widén and colleagues (1973), and *D. oligodonta* proved to be different from *D. inaequalis*, and from all the European *Dryopteris* material previously investigated. In morphology *D. oligodonta* is similar to *D. filix-mas*; the spore sculpturing is of the same type, but *D. oligodonta* is once more pinnate.

Herbarium material of possibly a further *Dryopteris* species, similar in morphology to *D. oligodonta*, was collected from west of Barlovento, La Palma by Dr C. N. Page, but this may be *D. guanchica* (see p. 352).

D. pseudomas (Wollaston) J. Holub & Pouzar is the only definite representative of the *D. filix-mas* complex which occurs in Macaronesia. It has been recorded from Madeira, from São Miguel, Terceira, Pico and Faial in the Azores and on Gomera in the Canaries; it is widespread in Europe, and reaches as far east as the Caucasus (Fig. 1). Two cytotypes

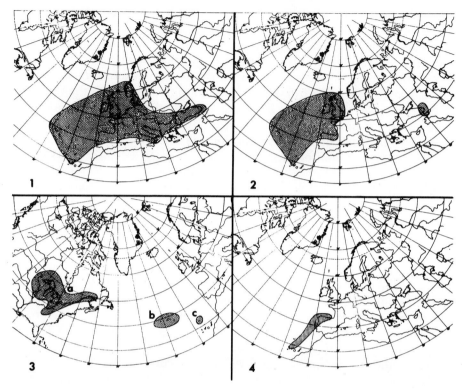

FIG. 1   Distribution map of *D. pseudomas* (2x, 3x, apogamous)
FIG. 2   Distribution map of *D. aemula* (2x)
FIG. 3   Distribution map of a. *D. intermedia* (2x), b. *D. azorica* (2x), c. *D. maderensis* (2x)
FIG. 4   Distribution map of *D. guanchica* (4x)

occur, one diploid and one triploid and both are apogamous; the triploid is by far the more common in Europe, but only the diploid cytotype has been found in Macaronesia. The absence of the triploid cytotype here may be explained by its probable origin from a hybrid of the diploid cytotype with the diploid *D. oreades* Fomin (=*D. abbreviata* (DC.) Newman). This is a closely related species of the *D. filix-mas* complex, and it is absent from Macaronesia but occurs in Europe. This origin of the triploid cytotype is supported by comparison of the phloroglucinols of the species (Widén *et al.*, 1971).

If *D. aitoniana* is indeed closely related to the *D. filix-mas* complex, then one might expect it to hybridise with *D. pseudomas* in Madeira, to form an apogamous triploid. There is no evidence of such an occurrence. Perhaps this means that *D. aitoniana* is not closely related to this complex.

The remaining five *Dryopteris* species from Macaronesia all belong to the *D. carthusiana* (Vill.) H. P. Fuchs complex. Three of these are diploid species and two are tetraploids.

D. aemula (Ait.) O. Kuntze (n = 41) has an Atlantic distribution and is found in Britain, Ireland, France, northwest Spain, the Azores, and Madeira and it has recently been found on Gomera in the Canaries (Fraser-Jenkins, 1974) (Fig. 2). This species occurs also in the Caucasus region, in Turkey and the USSR, where it was known as *D. liliana* Golicin. It has a distinctive appearance; the triangular frond is profusely glandular and smells of coumarin; the scales on the stipe are brown or greyish, concolourous and the stipe is purple-brown at the base.

D. azorica (Christ) Alston and *D. maderensis* Alston are endemic diploids to the Azores and Madeira respectively (Fig. 3) and they are fairly close in morphology. *D. azorica* has a less finely cut frond, in comparison with *D. maderensis*; it bears small scales on the pinna and pinnule margins on the underside of the frond, and the pinnae and pinnules of *D. azorica* may overlap (giving a blacker silhouette). The lowest basiscopic pinnule in both species is shorter than its neighbour; this is one of the distinguishing features, as in the tetraploid *D. austriaca* (Jacq.) Wåynar, from Europe, this pinnule is as long as, or slightly longer than, its neighbour. In the diploid species *D. assimilis* S. Walker, which is circumboreal in the Northern Hemisphere, this pinnule is often twice the length of its neighbour. *D. azorica* and *D. maderensis* can also be distinguished as they have a smaller spore size than *D. austriaca* and *D. assimilis*. *D. azorica* and *D. maderensis* are very closely related to another diploid species, *D. intermedia* (Muhl.) A. Gray, from North America (Fig. 3), which is similar in morphology, with the fairly fine cutting, small spore size and also the relatively short lower basiscopic pinnule. The American species can be distinguished as it is glandular, whilst the other two species are glabrous, and also *D. intermedia* can withstand frost, but the Macaronesian species are susceptible to it. All three species have been examined phytochemically (Widén *et al.*, 1975) and all show a similar phloroglucinol spectrum with large amounts of aspidin BB and aspidin AB, and with flavaspidic acid and "albaspidins-1" and "-2" present in smaller amounts. Cytological evidence, also, suggests that these three species are essentially conspecific. *D. austriaca* from Europe was demonstrated to be an allotetraploid species by Manton and Walker (1954), as an apogamously produced diploid *D. austriaca* plant showed complete failure of chromosome pairing at meiosis; the two genomes in *D. austriaca* are not homologous. These genomes were designated "C" and "D" by Walker (1955) and *D. austriaca* has then the genomic constitution "CCDD". *D. austriaca* hybridises with the diploid species *D. assimilis* in

M*

the wild in Europe, and under experimental conditions, to produce a triploid hybrid (Walker, 1955); this hybrid shows about 41 bivalents and 41 univalents at meiosis. Pairing is interpreted as being allosyndetic, between the *D. assimilis* genome and one genome of *D. austriaca*, and *D. assimilis* therefore represents a diploid parent of *D. austriaca*; it can be designated "DD". *D. austriaca* is not sympatric with any of *D. intermedia*, *D. azorica* or *D. maderensis*, but triploid hybrids have been synthesised between *D. austriaca* and each of the diploids (Walker, 1961; Gibby and Walker, 1977). Each of these triploid hybrids shows approximately 41 bivalents and 41 univalents, and so each diploid must represent a parent of *D. austriaca*. However, they do not represent the same parent as *D. assimilis* – they are not the "DD" genome (see Fig. 11) – since synthesised diploid hybrids of *D. assimilis* × *intermedia* and *D. assimilis* × *azorica* show almost complete failure of chromosome pairing at meiosis (Gibby and Walker, 1977). *D. intermedia*, *D. azorica* and *D. maderensis* all appear to represent the "CC" genome (see Fig. 11). Their geographical separation implies that they must have been isolated for a very long period of time, and they have since differentiated to a limited degree, in morphology and to a lesser extent in their phloroglucinol spectra. As may be expected, the diploid hybrids *D. assimilis* × *intermedia* and *D. assimilis* × *azorica*, which have the genomic constitution "CD", are very similar to *D. austriaca*, which is "CCDD", in both morphology (Gibby and Walker, 1977) and phloroglucinol spectra (Widén *et al.*, 1977).

   D. guanchica Gibby and Jermy (see Figs 5 and 6) and *D. crispifolia* Rasbach, Reichstein and Vida are two tetraploid species from Macaronesia which have been recognised only very recently (Gibby *et al.*, 1977). Both were previously confused with other *Dryopteris* species, in particular, *D. austriaca*, and records of *D. austriaca* and *D. carthusiana* for Macaronesia which have been made previously are now thought to be erroneous. *D. guanchica* has been found so far on Gomera and in Anaga, Tenerife, growing in the wetter parts of the laurel forest; more recently it has been found in Sintra, Portugal and in Galicia in northwest Spain (Fig. 4). This distribution is seen in other fern species; *Davallia canariensis* is known from Macaronesia, Spain and Portugal; *Asplenium hemionitis* is in Macaronesia, Sintra (Portugal) and southern Spain; *Woodwardia radicans* is in Macaronesia, Sintra, southern Spain, and in Corsica, southern Italy and Crete. *D. guanchica* is very similar in morphology to *D. austriaca* and where the two species are sympatric in Europe they can be difficult to differentiate. In *D. guanchica* the scales on the stipe base are usually brown and concolorous, but may have a slightly darker central stripe, whereas in *D. austriaca* the scales have a dark brown or black stripe; *D. guanchica* shows the lowermost apiscopic pinnule on the lowest pinnae to be distinctly

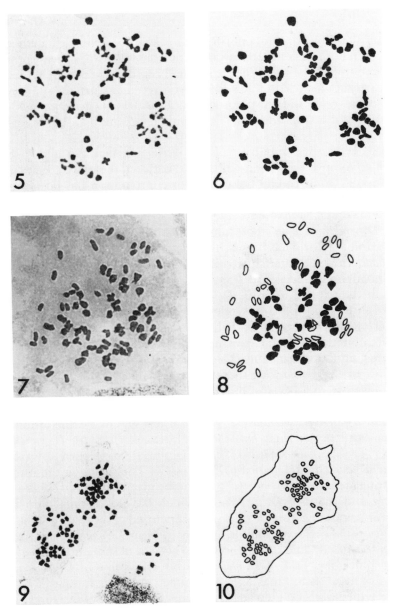

Fig. 5   Meiosis in *D. guanchica,* acetocarmine preparation, × 1000
Fig. 6   Explanatory diagram of Fig. 5, showing 82 bivalents (in solid black)
Fig. 7   Meiosis in *D. aemula* × *guanchica*, acetocarmine preparation, × 1000
Fig. 8   Explanatory diagram of Fig. 7, showing 41 bivalents (in solid black) and 41 univalents (outlined)
Fig. 9   Meiosis in *D. aemula* × *maderensis*, acetocarmine preparations, × 1000
Fig. 10 Explanatory diagram of Fig. 9, showing 82 univalents (outlined)

shorter than the adjacent one, or sometimes to be absent altogether. The two can readily be separated on spore morphology – the spores are similar in size but in *D. austriaca* they are densely spiny, whereas in *D. guanchica* they are rugulose, with a few spines or a reticulate ornamentation. The two species differ in their phloroglucinol spectra; *D. guanchica* lacks para-aspidin, and has in addition "albaspidins -2" and "-3" (Widén *et al.*, 1975).

D. guanchica is sympatric with *D. aemula* in Gomera and in Spain. Triploid hybrids have been synthesised between these two species, and in addition, a wild triploid hybrid of this combination has been found in Gomera by C. R. Fraser-Jenkins. Meiosis in the hybrid shows 41 bivalents and 41 univalents (Figs 7 and 8). Recently it has been shown that *D. guanchica* is an allotetraploid (Gibby *et al.*, 1978).

A triploid hybrid has been synthesised between *D. maderensis* (2 ×) and *D. guanchica* (4 ×). Again this triploid hybrid shows about 41 bivalents and 41 univalents at meiosis. If *D. guanchica* were autotetraploid, the pairing seen in the triploid hybrids, *D. aemula* × *guanchica* and *D. guanchica* × *maderensis* would be autosyndetic, and the diploids *D. aemula* and *D. maderensis* would be unrelated to *D. guanchica*. However, as *D. guanchica* is an allotetraploid, the pairing will be allosyndetic in the triploid hybrids, and *D. aemula* and *D. maderensis* must represent the two diploid parents of *D. guanchica*. Is there other evidence to show that these two diploids are the parents of *D. guanchica*? *D. guanchica* shares some characters with *D. aemula* – the dark purple-brown base to the stipe and the flat-topped crown and *D. guanchica* has glands on the lamina and indusia, but fewer than *D. aemula*. The frond shape of *D. guanchica* is similar to that of *D. maderensis*, and the pinnule teeth turn upwards in a manner very characteristic of *D. maderensis*. The scales on the stipe base are intermediate between the grey or brown concolorous scales of *D. aemula* and those of *D. maderensis*, which have a distinct dark brown central stripe. The frond of *D. aemula* is upcurled at the margins, that of *D. maderensis* has deflexed pinnule margins, whilst *D. guanchica* usually has a fairly flat frond. The spores show the rugosity of those of *D. aemula*, and bear spines like those of *D. maderensis* but the spines in *D. guanchica* are usually fused into anastomosing ridges. Chemical analysis of the phloroglucinols by Widén and colleagues (1975) shows *D. guanchica* to be very similar to *D. maderensis* but with the additional trace compounds phloropyrone and desaspidin, which could be contributed by *D. aemula*. The spectrum of *D. aemula* is characterised by large amounts of margaspidin and aemulin; if *D. aemula* is a parent of *D. guanchica* then the formation of these compounds must be suppressed in the tetraploid.

The synthesised diploid hybrid *D. aemula* × *maderensis*, which has the genomic constitution "CE" (giving *D. aemula* the genomic constitution "EE"), shows complete failure of chromosome pairing at meiosis as expected (Figs 9 and 10). If *D. guanchica* is "CCEE" (see Fig. 11) then these two should be very similar in morphology. They are indeed similar in the colour of the stipe, in the scales, the glandularity and in the relatively flat frond. However the frond of the hybrid is more triangular in shape and it does not have the short lowermost apiscopic pinnule on the lowest pinnae seen in *D. guanchica*. Recent analysis of the diploid hybrid *D. aemula* × *maderensis* (Gibby *et al.*, 1978) shows it to have a

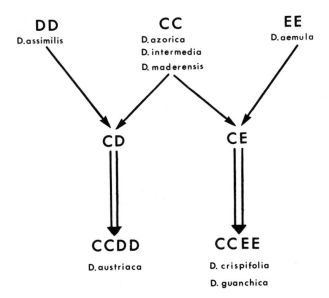

Fig. 11   Evolutionary relationships in some species of the *D. carthusiana* complex

similar phloroglucinol spectrum to *D. guanchica*. *D. maderensis* and *D. aemula* grow together in Madeira, and it is possible that *D. guanchica* arose here by hybridisation and subsequent chromosome doubling, then spread later to the Canaries and to Europe. *D. guanchica* has not been reported from Madeira, however, and it may well have had its origins elsewhere, perhaps in northern Spain, where *D. aemula* and *D. guanchica* are sympatric today (see Figs 2 and 4). *D. assimilis* is recorded from this area and if *D. maderensis* occurred here in the past, perhaps during the Tertiary period, it could have hybridised with *D. aemula* to give rise by chromosome doubling to *D. guanchica*, and with *D. assimilis* to give rise to the allotetraploid *D. austriaca* (see Fig. 11).

In their geographical ranges both tetraploids, *D. guanchica* and *D. austriaca*, appear to be found in areas intermediate between the present distribution of their putative diploid parents. The circumboreal *D. assimilis* is fairly widespread in Europe, like *D. austriaca*, but the diploid is by far the more common species of the two in the extreme north; for example, *D. austriaca* reaches only the southwesternmost tip of Finland, whereas *D. assimilis* is widespread in the country (Widén *et al.*, 1967). The range of *D. guanchica* (Fig. 4) lies in an intermediate position between that of *D. maderensis* in Madeira (Fig. 3), and the Atlantic distribution of *D. aemula* (Fig. 2).

Little is known about the newly discovered tetraploid species, *D. crispifolia*. It has been found so far from three islands of the Azores, Faial, Pico and São Miguel, where it grows together with *D. azorica* and *D. aemula* (Gibby *et al.*, 1977). It has the same phloroglucinol spectrum as *D. austriaca*, but it is very distinct from this species in the crisped appearance of the fronds. It is very glandular and smells of coumarin like *D. aemula*. The midribs of the pinnae and pinnules bear small lanceolate brown scales, as do those of *D. azorica*, and like *D. azorica* it is very foliose, with the pinnules and pinnae often overlapping. Since it shows these similarities with these diploids, and grows together with them, it seems likely that it may have evolved from them, by hybridisation and subsequent chromosome doubling. If this were the case it would have the genome constitution "CCEE" (Fig. 11), like that of *D. guanchica*. These two tetraploids are quite distinct however. *D. guanchica* has a flattened frond, no smell of coumarin, lacks the brown scales on the pinnae midribs, and the two differ in their pholroglucinol spectra (Widén *et al.*, 1975). However, both species have a flattened rhizome crown, purple-brown stipe base and the spores are similar in size and sculpturing. Perhaps, if *D. guanchica* has arisen from *D. aemula* and *D. maderensis*, and *D. crispifolia* had a separate origin from *D. aemula* and *D. azorica*, the differences between the two tetraploids are a reflection of the differences that are seen between *D. maderensis* and *D. azorica*. Both *D. azorica* and *D. crispifolia* have overlapping pinnules and pinnae, and bear small brown scales on the underside of the lamina, characters not seen in *D. guanchica* and *D. maderensis*. *D. azorica* and *D. maderensis* differ in their phloroglucinol spectra as *D. maderensis* has additionally the compounds "albaspidin − 2" and " − 3" present in large amounts; *D. azorica* lacks "albaspidin − 3" and "albaspidin − 2" occurs only as a trace amount. *D. guanchica* shows similarities with *D. maderensis* in having "albaspidin − 2" present in large amount and "albaspidin − 3" as a trace amount; *D. crispifolia* on the other hand lacks "albaspidins" (Widén *et al.*, 1975).

Summary

In summary, *D. aitoniana* and *D. oligodonta* are diploid palaeoendemic species in Macaronesia, with no known close relatives. The two diploids, *D. aemula* and *D. pseudomas* and tetraploid *D. guanchica* occur both in Macaronesia and in Europe. *D. azorica* and *D. maderensis* are diploid Macaronesian endemics whose sister species, *D. intermedia*, is in eastern North America. During the Cretaceous there must have occurred isolation from one original stock, giving American and European elements. The American element is now represented by *D. intermedia*; the Azores and Madeira were probably colonised at different times by the European element, and *D. azorica* and *D. maderensis* diverged subsequently, as a result of their isolation. The European element may have hybridised with *D. assimilis* and *D. aemula*, perhaps during the Tertiary period, to give rise by chromosome doubling to *D. austriaca* and *D. guanchica* respectively (Fig. 11). *D. crispifolia* is a tetraploid Azorean element which has probably evolved in the Azores from *D. aemula* and *D. azorica*.

Acknowledgements

I should like to express my thanks to the Cabildo Insular de Gran Canaria for financial assistance, and to Mr Peter York of the Photographic Studio at the British Museum (Natural History) who produced the figures.

REFERENCES

Bramwell, D. (1972). Endemism in the flora of the Canary Islands. In *Taxonomy, Phytogeography and Evolution* (D. H. Valentine, ed.), 141–159. Academic Press, London and New York

Chevalier, A. (1963). Les îles du Cap Vert. Flore de l'archipel. *Rev. Bot. App. Agric. Trop.* **15**, (170–171), 733–1090

Fraser-Jenkins, C. R. (1974). The distribution of *Dryopteris aemula* and its discovery in the Canaries and Turkey. *Fern Gaz.* **11**, 54

Gibby, M., Jermy, A. C., Rasbach, H., Rasbach, K., Reichstein, T. and Vida, G. (1977). The fern genus *Dryopteris* in the Canary Islands and Azores and the description of two tetraploid species. *Bot. J. Linn. Soc.* **74**, 251–277

— and Walker, S. (1977). Further cytogenetic studies and a reappraisal of the diploid ancestry in the *Dryopteris carthusiana* complex. *Fern Gaz.* **11**, 315–324

Gibby, M., Widén, C.-J. and Widén, H. K. (1978). Cytogenetic and phytochemical investigations in hybrids of Macaronesian *Dryopteris* (*Pteridophyta*: *Aspidiaceae*). *Pl. Syst. Evol.* **130**, 235–252

Jalas, J. and Suominen, J. (1972). *Atlas Florae Europaeae. I. Pteridophyta*.

Committee for mapping the Flora of Europe and Societas Biologica Fennica Vanama, Helsinki

Kuhn, M. (1879). Cryptogamae vasculares. In "Botanik von Ostafrika" in Cl. v.d. Decken's Reisen in Ostafrika, 3. Bd., 3. Leipzig and Heidelberg

Manton, I. (1950). *Problems of Cytology and Evolution in the Pteridophyta.* Cambridge University Press

— and Walker, S. (1954). Induced apogamy in *Dryopteris dilatata* (Hoffm.) A. Gray and *D. filix-mas* L. Schott emend. and its significance for the interpretation of the two species. *Ann. Bot.* N.S. **18**, 377–383

Page, C. N. (1973). Ferns, polyploids, and their bearing on the evolution of the Canarian Flora. In *Proceedings of the 1st International Congress pro Flora Macaronesica. Monographiae Biologicae Canarienses* No. 4, 83–88

Pichi Sermolli, R. E. G. (1951). On Desvaux's *Aspidium oliganthum* and *Aspidium oligodonton. Webbia* **8**, 147–154

Tardieu-Blot, M. L. (1946). Sur la flore pteridologique des îles atlantiques. *Mém. Soc. Biogéogr.* **8**, 325–347

Vida, (1972). Cytotaxonomy and genome analysis of the European ferns. In *Evolution in plants* (G. Vida, ed.). *Symp. Biol. Hung.* **12**, 51–60. Akadémiai; Kiadó, Budapest

Walker, S. (1955). Cytogenetic studies in the *Dryopteris spinulosa* complex I. *Watsonia* **3**, 193–209

— (1961). Cytogenetic studies in the *Dryopteris spinulosa* complex II. *Amer. J. Bot.* **48**, 607–614

Widén, C.-J., Faden, R. B., Lounasmaa, M., Vida, G., Euw, J. v. and Reichstein, T. (1973). Die Phloroglucide von neun *Dryopteris*-Arten aus Kenya sowie der *D. oligodonta* (Desv.) Pic. Serm. und *D. "dilatata"* von den Canarischen Inseln. *Helv. Chim. Acta* **56**, 2125–2151

— Lounasmaa, M., Vida, G. and Reichstein, T. (1975). Die Phloroglucide von drei *Dryopteris*-Arten von den Azoren sowie zwei Arten von Madeira und den Kanarischen Inseln zum Vergleich. *Helv. Chim. Acta* **58**, 880–904

— Sarvela, J. and Ahti, T. (1967). The *Dryopteris spinulosa* complex in Finland. *Acta Bot. Fenn.* **77**, 1–24

— Vida, G., Euw, J. v. and Reichstein, T. (1971). Die Phloroglucide von *Dryopteris villarii* (Bell.) Woynar und anderer Farne der Gattung *Dryopteris* sowie die mögliche Abstammung von *D. filix-mas* (L) Schott. *Helv. Chim. Acta* **54**, 2824–2850

— Widén, H. K. and Gibby, M. (1977). Chemotaxonomic studies of synthesised hybrids of the *Dryopteris carthusiana* complex. *Biochem. Syst. Ecol.* **6**, 5–9

SECTION FOUR
Conservation

18 Endangered Island Floras

R. MELVILLE   *Royal Botanic Gardens, Kew, England*

Las floras relictas de islas tales como Sta. Helena, las Azores, islas del Oceano Pacifico e Indico, son discutidas con relación a la deriva continental.

La supervivencia del modelo primitivo de la venacion de las hojas en las islas ha sido ya comunicada. Muchos taxones con venación "glosopteroide" se encuentranen las islas oceánicas, estando dichas plantas consideradas como relictas antiguas de gran importancia científica.

Muchas de estas están amenazadas de extinción y nombraremos la *Foetidia obliqua*, de Madagascar comó primer ejemplo.

La condición de la flora de las islas oceánicas varía desde casi una completa destrucción en Sta. Helena hasta un estado casi virgen en la isla de Henderson. La mayoría de las islas están de algún modo entre estos dos extremos con pocas e inadecuadas reservas naturales y con un aumento de las presiones debido a las actividades del hombre. La perspectiva para su supervivencia no es buena a menos que se tomen medidas en un inmediato futuro. Las medidas más apropiadas de conservación son la formación de las reservas del ecosistema y Parques Nacionales, pero para las especies amenazadas, el establecimiento y propagación en jardines botánicos puede ser la única posible esperanza para su supervivencia y estudio científico dejando abierta la posibilidad de una reintroducción dentro del habitat natural para cuando se creen (si se crean) reservas apropiadas.

Introduction

The floras of oceanic islands frequently include many endemic species that have evolved in isolation over very long periods of time. I refer to the floras of elevated islands, for low-lying islands and atolls generally have depauperate floras of little diversity, and share a common group of species dispersed mainly by oceanic currents. However there a few low-lying islands representing the last stages in the subsidence of former elevated islands that still retain diverse and interesting floras. The long isolation of these high islands, with the absence of herbivorous mammals, has allowed the survival of many species with primitive features that have been eliminated from the adjacent continents. On this account island floras are of the greatest scientific interest for floristic and evolutionary studies. By the nature of their situation, island endemics have limited distributions and are especially vulnerable to interference by Man and his domestic animals and by competition from introduced weeds and crop plants. The purpose of this chapter is to enquire into the origin of a selection of island floras and examine the impact of natural factors and human interference on island ecosystems.

Continental drift

One of the major factors affecting both the origin of the islands themselves and of their biota is continental drift. Over the last 20 years much information has accumulated concerning sea floor spreading and drift in the Atlantic region. The rift valley phase was passed through during the Jurassic and would have been accompanied by an upwarping of the crust probably of the order of 2 km. It is known that along the present Rift Valley in East Africa the surface has been raised by 1·5–2·0 km since the Miocene (Holmes, 1965). At the other end of the orogenic cycle, after drift has taken place, the ocean floor subsides by an amount of the order of 2 km as in the present Pacific (Menard, 1964). These earth movements have profound effects upon oceanic islands and upon the colonisation of islands and survival of any biota that may reach them. In the Atlantic region, about 110 million years ago in the lower Cretaceous, sea passages had broken through between Africa and South America and between North America and Europe. An approximation to the position of these continental blocks at that time can be visualised by bringing the margins of the continental shelves into contact with the mid-Atlantic ridge (Fig. 1). Any volcanic islands then developing would have been within flight range of birds from the mainland and the birds could have been vectors for plant propagules. The Cretaceous was a period for great diversification of birds, which were destined to play a major part in plant dispersal.

In the early stages of continental separation the narrow channel with a funnel shaped southern end must have been responsible for tidal surges which would not have been blocked around the northern end of South America as the Central American isthmus did not then exist. Under such conditions tree trunks and floating rafts of vegetation, so often invoked to explain some plant distributions, could have been carried 30 m or more above normal tide levels, where any propogules present would have a chance of survival. As the continents drifted further apart such tidal effect would dwindle until the importance of rafting for plant dispersal became insignificant.

It is evident that conditions for the dispersal and establishment of immigrant plant species on newly emerged islands must have been much more favourable in the early stages of drift than at later periods. The one exception to this is the group of strand plants having seeds capable of surviving long periods of floating on salt water and able to develop under

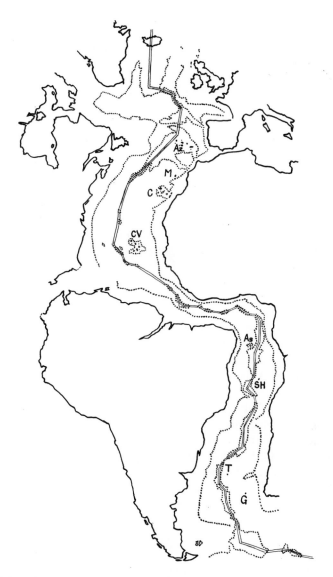

Fig. 1.   Map of the Atlantic with the foot of the continental shelves brought into contact with the mid-Atlantic ridge to simulate conditions at an early stage of continental drift. Az, Azores; M, Madeira; C, Canary I.; CV, Cape Verde I.; As, Ascension I.; SH, St. Helena; T, Tristan da Cunha; G, Gough I. (·· ···) – the 3000 m isobath

363

littoral conditions. The pantropical *Sophora tomentosa* L. is an example. A few years ago W. S. Sykes of The Botany Division, Christchurch, New Zealand picked up drift seeds of *S. microphylla* Ait. on the beach of Raoul Island (Sykes and Godley, 1968). These seeds germinated although they must have made the ocean voyage of 800 km from New Zealand the nearest possible source of seed. Seeds of this species must have been reaching the shores of Raoul for a large part of the Tertiary and yet it has never established itself there. The contrast between these two species underlines the importance of ecological factors and the necessity for seeds to be deposited where they can survive, before establishment can take place.

St. Helena

Turning now to individual islands, St. Helena has an interesting flora and history. When the island was discovered in 1502 it was densely clothed in vegetation. Goats were introduced in 1515 and by 1588 had increased to many thousands, with flocks up to 1.6 km long on an island that is only 16 km long. Unfortunately no extensive collections of the flora were made until W. J. Burchell resided on the island from 1805–1810. By this time cattle, sheep, horses, donkeys and pigs had been introduced and allowed to run wild. Only remnants of the former forests remained and severe erosion has set in. Burchell recorded 31 endemic Angiosperms and of these 11 are now extinct. It is impossible to say how many had been lost since the island was first discovered.

The relationships of the St. Helena flora are predominantly with Africa as exemplified by *Pelargonium*, *Hedyotis* and *Phylica* each with one endemic species. *Acalypha rubra* Roxb., now extinct, was most closely related to a Mascarene species, *A. reticulata* Muell. Arg. A similar transcontinental relationship exists in the Sterculiaceae between *Trochetia erythroxylon* Benth. and *T. melanoxylon* Benth. of St. Helena and *T. uniflora* DC., *T. parviflora* Boj, *T. blackburniana* Boj and *T. grandiflora*. Boj. in Mauritius. To turn to the *Compositae*, *Commidendron* with four species, one extinct and *Melanodendron* are endemic genera. *Psiadea rotundifolia* Hook.f., now extinct, was the only representative of a genus with a number of species in Africa and in the Mascarenes. *P. dracaenifolia* Humb. from Madagascar has the most primitive leaf architecture in the genus with flabellate primary veins and a dichotomo-reticulate reticulum. Slightly later evolutionary stages are represented by *P. coronopus* Benth. & Hook. of Rodriguez and *P. anchusaefolia* (Pior.) Cordem. of Mauritius, whereas all of the African species have relatively advanced leaf architecture.

These facts provide a clue to some of the gaps in the African flora and the survival of many relatively primitive relict species on islands. Close relatives or progenitors of the island relicts must have been present on the African continent in the Cretaceous, when the islands received their first colonists. This was followed in the Eocene and later Tertiary by a great diversification and multiplication of herbivorous mammals on the continent. That many of the early Angiosperms were extremely palatable to grazing mammals is borne out by field observations on island floras. There is selective feeding on the foliage of palatable species, seedlings are destroyed, and the thin bark of tree species is stripped and eaten by goats and cattle. On a visit to the Volcanoes National Park in Hawaii in 1971 I observed a marked contrast on either side of a goat-proof fence that enclosed the bird park. Inside the fence numerous seedlings were growing; outside the palatable bark was being stripped by goats from saplings and young trees of *Coprosma pubens* Gray causing complete destruction. Similarly, all of the tree Compositae of St. Helena, the *Trochetia* and the *Acalypha* had thin and vulnerable bark that was attacked by goats and cattle after their introduction by Man.

In 1970 a small expedition led by N. R. Kerr visited St. Helena to assess the present condition of the endemic flora and make recommendations for its conservation. A few specimens of the She-Cabbage-Tree *Senecio prenanthiflora* Benth. & Hook.f., which had not been seen for many years, were found struggling on the steep slope of the ridge against the introduced New Zealand Flax *Phormium tenax* Forst. A number of reserve areas were proposed and have since been established and the competing *Phormium* was weeded out from the vicinity of the *Senecio*. There is some hope now of preserving the last remnants of this island flora.

Ascension

About 1280 km north of St. Helena lies the island of Ascension. It is smaller than St. Helena, being only 11 km long and it lies a little to the west of the crest of the mid-Atlantic ridge, whereas St. Helena lies to the east of the ridge. A botanical survey was made recently by Duffey (1964) who expressed the opinion that the island might be no more than 10 000 years old. It is true that the greater part of the island is covered by rough and tumbled lava flows which appear to be of comparatively recent origin and are little weathered in the arid climate. On floral evidence such a late origin is highly improbable. In general, the only certain method of determining the age of an island is to bore down to bedrock and date the core. Usually the oldest islands are on or near the continental shelf and the youngest near the mid-oceanic ridge. On account of subsidence of the sea floor in the later stages of drift, periodic eruptions are necessary to maintain the island above sea level. The superficial rocks on volcanic islands on this account will be of geologically recent origin. If volcanic replenishment fails, the island sinks and becomes a seamount or guyot topped by a wave-cut platform.

The only naturally vegetated area on Ascension is situated high up on the flank of Green Mountain. This area I interpret as a Kipuka, an island of vegetation left behind undisturbed by the surrounding lava flows. The surviving indigenous flora was very sparse and included *Euphorbia origanoides* L., *Aristida adscensionis* L., *Sporobolus durus* Brongn., *Hedyotis adscensionis* DC. and *Wahlenbergia linifolia* ADC. The *Euphorbia* has its closest relative in West Africa (*E. trinervia* Schum. & Thonn). The *Hedyotis* is nearer to African species than to the St. Helenan *H. arborea* Roxb. The *Wahlenbergia* is also on St. Helena and of the ferns, *Asplenium ascensionis* Watson has recently been found by Kerr on St. Helena. Goats were placed on the island at an early stage, but the first human settlement was not made until 1815. J. D. Hooker visited the island in 1843 and recommended plants for acclimatisation on the island. Following his advice, numerous exotics were introduced about the middle of the century, to the detriment of the remnants of the flora.

In addition to the above records of the Ascension flora which are vouched for by herbarium specimens, there are two others that cannot be thus substantiated. Hooker (Hemsley, 1885) repeated a report by Burchell of about 1810 of the presence of *Commidendron rugosum*, which he said was then very scarce on Green Mountain and the principal food of the wild goats. There is no reason to doubt Burchell's ability to identify the plant, but it cannot have survived for very long afterwards. The other more doubtful report occurs in Dampier's account of his voyage of 1699–1701, from which he brought back the first known specimens of the Australian flora. On his return Dampier's ship, the *Roebuck*, sprang a leak off Ascension and all efforts to save it failed. The ship's company was marooned on the island for about six weeks, but they did not lack food for there were "plenty of turtle and an abundance of goats". At a point about two miles southeast of the spring on Green Mountain Dampier observed three or four shrubby trees on one of which was cut an anchor and cable and the year 1642. *Commidendron rugosum* does not reach the size necessary for this operation, but the tree might well have been *C. robustum*. In any event, no regeneration was possible in the presence of the goats and the trees could not have survived much after Dampier's time. If this is the correct interpretation, there must have been originally at least two tree Composites on Ascension.

The flora of Ascension clearly has some links with St. Helena but how did it acquire its original flora? Did *Commidendron rugosum* arrive from St. Helena or from the African mainland? It has the most primitive type of leaf venation of its genus and my examination revealed a thin cuticle and epidermis so that the leaf should make a tender morsel for a goat. This species, or its progenitor, is not likely to have survived the mammalian explosion of the Eocene in Africa. St. Helena is therefore the more likely source. It is possible that the two islands were united along the mid-Atlantic ridge before the general sinking of the central Atlantic floor in the latter half of the Tertiary. Birds may have been the vectors for the *Hedyotis* and the *Euphorbia* before the Atlantic had opened to its present extent.

From this discussion it appears that the indigenous flora of Ascension is probably only a small remnant of a much larger flora that had been almost completely overwhelmed by volcanic eruptions and latterly had been further depleted by human interference. I am not aware that any steps have been taken to preserve the remnants. It would be necessary to clear the exotics from a reserve area on the mountain and assist the establishment of the surviving species.

Macaronesian islands

Turning now to the islands of Macaronesia, I will deal only with a few points bearing on continental drift, the survival of relict species and the need for conservation. The map (Fig. 1) shows the Canary Islands close to the continental shelf with Fuerteventura and Lanzarote actually on the edge of it. These two islands consist partly of continental rocks and partly of volcanic deposits. The remaining islands of the group are entirely volcanic. These facts indicate an origin of the Canaries very early in the drift process. The outer islands may have been united with one another for part of the Tertiary, the present islands surviving the effects of subsidence and erosion by periodic eruptions. Madeira lies a little further off the edge of the continental shelf and the Azores are far out in the Atlantic. The Azores platform is linked upon the map with the continental shelf of Europe and Africa, a condition which continued until the Miocene. The general deepening and widening of the North Atlantic that then took place broadened and deepened the channels between Greenland and Iceland, between Iceland and the Faroes and between the Azores and Europe. Up till this period the islands were probably larger and there may have been additional islands forming stepping stones to the European mainland as well as a link between Madeira and the Canaries via the Selvagens. The sea passages would not then have been too great for migrant pigeons to cross. Pigeons feed on the fruits of the laurels and are the chief vectors of these trees. These birds were the link between the Miocene laurel forests of Europe and the Macaronesian islands. With increasing sea distances to traverse the island pigeon populations became isolated and they differentiated into species and subspecies. Thus we now have (Bannerman, 1922) two endemic pigeons on the Canaries (*Columba bollei* Godman, *C. junoniae* Hartert) and one (*C. trocaz* Heineken) on Madeira. There are separate rock dove (*C. livia* Gmelin) subspecies on the Canaries, Madeira and the Azores and a ring dove (*C. palumbus azorica* Hartert) on the Azores. It is significant also that *Columba bollei* which now occurs on Tenerife, Gomera and Palma, formerly lived in Gran Canaria, but died out in recent times following the destruction of the laurel forests. Pigeons are responsible for the dispersal of other seeds in addition to those of the laurels. Bannerman (1922) mentions the dispersal of *Erica*, *Juniperus* and *Myrica* by *Columba livia*. Smaller granivorous birds no doubt play a part in the dispersal of some genera.

A number of Canarian species have trans-African connections comparable with those of some St. Helena plants. The genus *Aeonium* is of special interest, with a considerable diversification of over 30 species in the Canaries and one species in the Atlas Mountains and another in Somalia on the northern mountain ranges. Both of the African species now survive on cliffs or precipitous rocks where they are out of reach of goats. Recent studies of the structure and ontogeny of the leaves of *Aeonium* suggest that it is a relict genus and so may have been among the first colonisers of the Canaries when the Atlantic opened. The leaves represent a rather early stage in the transformation of a leaf of the *Gangamopteris* type into a more modern Angiosperm type. The present distribution suggests that *Aeonium*, or its progenitors, must have been widespread in northern Africa but that grazing pressure and increasing aridity have brought it to the verge of extinction on the mainland. It is fortunate that such a wide range of species has found sanctuary on the Canaries, where some of these are now threatened.

There are many other Canarian species of great phytogeographical and taxonomic interest but as these will be discussed in other contributions I will pass on to conservation aspects of the flora. An assessment of the status of the endemic flora was made in 1972 and out of a total of 514 species and subspecies 75% were assigned to one or other of the conservation categories recognised by IUCN. This figure included 70 species (14%) actively endangered. At the other end of the scale was a total of only 81 species that were either frequent or common. This very serious state of affairs is due to a combination of factors, chief among which is the destruction of the laurel forests. Felling of the laurels has been going on for hundreds of years, but has increased in the present century. Regrowth laurel forest is worked on a coppice system to supply poles for supporting tomatoes, bananas and vines. The coppice tends to produce too dense a shade for most of the laurel associates and with each coppice cycle some of the laurel stools die and are replaced by *Erica*. There is thus a continuing degradation of the flora which is not helped by the collection of forest litter for mulching the crops at lower levels. In some localities laurels have been replaced by exotic conifers, which results in the complete destruction of the laurel ecosystem. The laurel forests occupy the cloud zone of the islands and assist in water catchment. Destruction of the forests is causing a lowering of the water table, with failure of springs, leading to increasing aridity. These processes are aggravated by the increasing water needs of a growing population and the great increase in the tourist trade. Thus there is an interaction of natural, economic and social factors that are combining to hasten the degradation of a most beautiful and scientifically very important flora. It is important that national parks and reserves should be established to preserve representative samples of the different ecosystems and their endemic species. Some reserves have already been established but more are needed to ensure the survival of the flora.

Indian Ocean islands

In the Indian ocean, as in the Atlantic, continental drift determined the time of origin and subsequent history of the island groups and the sources from which their floras could be derived. The first break in the ancient southern continent of Gondwanaland of the Carboniferous and Permian took place early in the Triassic according to palaeomagnetic evidence (Creer, 1964, 1970). This resulted in the separation of Africa plus South America and India from Australia plus Antarctica. The submerged continental fragments on which Kerguelen, the Crozets and Prince Edward and Marion Islands stand must have been separated at that time. With the separation of these islands, the progenitor of the unique relict *Pringlea antiscorbutica* R.Br. most primitive member of the Cruciferae, must have been isolated. *Pringlea* has retained a leaf architecture only slightly altered from its Permian forebears with leaves of the *Gangamopteris* type (Melville, 1969). There is palynological evidence that *Pringlea* survived the climate of the Pleistocene on these islands (Schalke and Van Zinderen-Bakker, 1967), which confirms that it is not a recent arrival. Although it is not in danger at present it should be kept under constant surveillance to ensure its survival.

Madagascar began to separate from Africa early in the Triassic but the sea passage along the rift valley was not completed until well into the Jurassic. India began its northward drift in the Jurassic and Australia with Antarctica resumed their eastward drift. These movements left behind the Seychelles as continental fragments and Réunion, Mauritius and possibly Rodriguez may also have begun as continental fragments later to be covered by volcanic deposits. The richness of their floras suggests this course of events. In the far north lie Socotra with Abdal Kuri cut off from the Arabian mainland when the Red Sea opened up about 10 million years ago. The Socotran flora is closely related to those of adjacent Somalia and southern Arabia, but includes 93 endemics a number of which have become extinct or very scarce since Balfour's visit in 1881 (Balfour, 1888). There are no primitive relicts, as might be anticipated from the late isolation of these islands, though *Dirachma socotrana* Schweinf. represents a monotypic family, now endangered and reduced to about 30 trees. With poor seed-set and in the presence of goats there is little hope of regeneration. Overgrazing by goats is the main cause of the decline in the flora and there are social and economic obstacles in the way of establishing effective reserves.

The tropical islands of the Indian Ocean have far flung phyto-geographical relationships. For example, there is a concentration of genera of Pittosporaceae in Western Australia. *Pittosporum* itself extends eastwards into New Zealand and westwards into India, Arabia and Africa. *P. wrightii* Hemsl. of the Seychelles is closely related to *P. senacia* Putterl. of Réunion and several other species occur in Madagascar. It is probable that *P. coriaceum* Ait. was transported by pigeons from Africa into Tenerife and Madeira before the end of the Miocene but by this time the Atlantic was an impassable barrier and *Pittosporum* failed to reach America. *Keraudrenia* with one species in Madagascar is linked to Australia with six and the baobabs, *Adansonia*, are represented by one species in Africa, 6 in Madagascar and 2 in Australia. These are but a few samples of such distributions, all of which point to the probability that progenitors of the modern species were already present in the Gondwanic fragments before their dispersal in the Jurassic.

Parallel evidence is provided by leaf architecture, for primitive venation patterns often survive on islands long after they have disappeared from the continents. Examples in *Psiadea* and *Pringlea* have been mentioned above. Bearing in mind that *Glossopteris* follows *Gangamopteris* in the fossil record, attention is drawn to a sequence in the Thymelaeaceae spanning the Indian Ocean. Very simple gangamopteroid leaves occur in South Africa in the genera *Struthiola* and *Lachnaea* (Melville, 1972). The leaves of *Gyrinops walla* Gaertn. have a structure very similar to that of a *Glossopteris*, but show the first stages in the development of pinnately arranged arcuate costae that are characteristic of so many Angiosperm leaves. The transformation into a curvipinnate leaf is completed in *Aquilaria* of which there are several species in Malaysia (Melville, 1970). The critical intermediate stage of evolution has survived only in Ceylon. Another comparable sequence is found in *Foetidia* (Lecythidaceae). The Madagascan species all have glossopteroid leaves with many primitive features, whereas *F. mauritiana* Lam., which is confined to Mauritius and Reunion, is much more advanced, having lost most of the glossopteroid characters (Melville, 1969). Such plants are ancient relics of the greatest scientific importance pointing, as they do, to the *Glossopteridae* as the progenitors of the Angiosperms and to the Jurassic origin of these island floras.

Nearly all of these relict species are now threatened to some extent. *Foetidia obliqua* Blume was formerly a common forest tree in Madagascar, but it is now heavily depleted. According to Perrier de la Bathie (1921) nine-tenths of the Madagascan forests had already been cut down by 1920 and the destruction has continued unabated. The other Madagascan species were more localised in their distributions, but up to date information on their status is lacking; they may now be endangered, in company with many other species.

Of the three Mascarene islands Rodriguez has suffered most at the hand of man. When Francois Leguat led the first attempt at colonisation in 1691 it was completely forested and he described it as a paradise on Earth. Now the forests have gone, to be replaced by cultivated crops, rough pasture, introduced weeds and eroded hills. No natural ecosystems have survived and few of the endemic species. Mauritius has suffered less severely: the lowland forests have been replaced by crops but ten reserves were declared in 1944 to protect representative ecosystems and their endemics. Increasing population pressure with the extension of cultivation and invasion of the reserves by aggressive alien weeds such as *Ligustrum walkeri* Decne. *Psidium cattleanum* and *Rubus* and *Ardisia* spp. are increasing the difficulties of conservation. Réunion is the least damaged of the three islands. The coastal forests have given way to sugar cane and other crops. Orchids were one of the groups that suffered most from the destruction of the forest. Out of a total of about 160 indigenous species three quarters have been lost by the destruction of their habitat. Much of the upland forest is still in good condition and it is hoped that some effective reserves can be established.

In common with other islands, the Seychelles have suffered by clearing for cultivation but much native vegetation remains on rough hills. A survey of the condition of the flora was made by Proctor and his recommendations for reserves were implemented by the government. Now that the islands have gained their independence it is to be hoped that the new administration will foster the reserves and take any measures necessary to prevent damage by the increasing tourist traffic. *Medusagyne oppositifolia* Baker, sole representative of the Medusagynaceae, was found again by Proctor, after it had not been seen for many years. The famous double coconut, *Lodoicea maldivica* Pers. is one of the endemics that will attract tourists and will need fencing to prevent damage to the roots.

Pacific Ocean islands

The problem of the origin of the floras of the major island groups of the Pacific has been much discussed and there has been a tendency to grossly underestimate the time since they originated. The geophysical evidence on this question, most of which has been revealed during the last 20 years is not yet widely known to biologists. Lower to mid-Cretaceous corals have been dredged from the Hess and Cape Johnson guyots on the Necker Ridge to the West of Hawaii at a depth of 1800 m and there is coral at 2000 m on another bank in that area. Borings made on Bikini revealed 1300 m of coral and on Kwajelein 2000 m before the basement rock was reached (Menard, 1964). Over much of the North Pacific basin the sea floor has sunk at least 2 km since the early Cretaceous. Large numbers of islands have been submerged and only those on which coral growth or volcanic activity has kept pace with the subsidence have survived. In the Hawaiian group there is a wave worn platform of Miocene age on the flank of Oahu at a depth of 500 m (Menard, 1964). If the 500 m isobath is followed it becomes evident that Oahu, Maui, Molokai and Hawaii must all have been united as one island in the Miocene about 15 million years ago. The channel between Oahu and Kauai is somewhat deeper, but the latter must also have been linked up in an earlier period. Such facts should be taken into account in any discussion of island floras.

In the South Pacific it is known that the Tuamotu ridge has sunk about 1000 m since the Eocene (Menard, 1964) and it is probable that neighbouring island groups such as the Marquesas have subsided at least as much. Bathymetric maps show that the Marquesas islands can be divided into a northern and a southern group at about 2000 m and there is some differentiation between the floras of the two halves. However, there is not sufficient evidence at present to follow this line of thought further.

Formerly the Marquesas Islands were almost entirely forested but they have suffered severely since human occupation and especially by the introduction of goats, cattle, horses and donkeys. The drier sides of some islands have been completely denuded of vegetation. The flora of the lower slopes has been disrupted by cultivation and grazing, aggravated by the introduction of numerous alien weeds. Feral cattle have caused great damage to the rainforest of the higher levels and the elimination of these low quality beasts and their replacement, under control, of high yielding stock is one of the necessary preliminaries for a conservation programme.

The Marquesas have their share of unique endemics among which may be mentioned *Lebronnecia kokioides* Fosberg a small tree of the Malvaceae formerly thought to have been reduced to a single tree on Tahuata, but a small colony has since been found on Hivaoa. It has been brought into cultivation by the Pacific Tropical Botanic Garden and distributed to other gardens. The endemic palm *Pelagodoxa henryana* Becc., formerly frequent, has now been reduced to a few semi-wild trees around villages, but it also has been brought into cultivation.

The composite genus *Oparanthus* is represented on the Marquesas by *O. albus* (F. Brown) Sherff and is now very rare and possibly endangered on Hivaoa. Elsewhere the genus occurs only on Rapa in the southern Austral Islands where there are three species. Of these *O. coriaceus* (F. Brown) Sherff has a very primitive type of leaf architecture with oblique, closely parallel (lirate) secondary veins and the minor venation dichotomo-reticulate. The most advanced species is *O. rapensis* (F. Brown) Sherff, with widely spaced pinnate secondaries and a polygonal reticulum. The other two species are intermediate. *Oparanthus* is confined to this part of the Pacific and the progenitors of the present species probably arrived on the islands soon after their formation in the late Cretaceous or Eocene. There is no possible mainland source for the genus at the present time.

The section *Campylotheca* of *Bidens* is distributed on many islands groups in the Pacific from the Marquesas in the South to Hawaii in the North. Typical *Bidens* has the achenes crowned with 2–4 barbed awns that are very effective for animal dispersal. In *Campylotheca* the awns are missing or very much reduced and the achenes appear to have lost their capability for animal dispersal as the result of long isolation in the absence of suitable vectors. Six species are recorded for the Marquesas all shrubs or small trees, two each on Hivaoa and Nukuhiva and one each on Uapou and Eiao. According to Sherff *B. uapensis* (F. Brown) Sherff of Uapou and *B. beckiana* (F. Brown) Sherff from Eiao are related to *B. cordifolia* Sch. Bp. of Nukuhiva. The northern group of species is more closely related to one another than to the two species of Hivaoa in the southern group, an example of the differentiation between the floras of the two halves of the archipelago referred to above.

The Marquesas are volcanic islands and show evidence of considerable erosion, only half or less of the original cones surviving on some of them. On Uapou about a dozen pinnacles project from the summit ridges, one having vertical sides about 600 m high. The pinnacles are capped by vegetation and some plants find a hold in crevices on the sides. Imagine Uapou sunken below the sea until only the pinnacles are exposed and the present condition of Marotiri would be reproduced. Marotiri consists of 9 stacks of basalt the tallest 100 m high situated about 74 km SE of Rapa. It was visited by St. John, Fosberg and Zimmerman in 1934 (Fosberg, 1962). Twelve vascular plants were discovered including several endemics the most interesting of which is *Bidens saint-johniana* Sherff. Zimmerman (1935) found a number of endemic insects and other Arthropods and it is significant that those found associated with the *Bidens* and *Portulaca fosbergii* v. Poell. var *major* v. Poell. belonged to genera normally found on trees and shrubs of the upland forests of other high islands. The facts all point to the origin of Marotiri as a former high island. It does not seem either practicable or necessary to take any action for the conservation of Marotiri, but it would be worth while to get the *Bidens* into cultivation so that its cytology, physiology and anatomy could be studied in relation to other members of the genus.

Another island in which vertical movements of the ocean floor have been involved is Henderson Island. It is a raised coral island 8 km long and 30 m high and lies 168 km NE of Pitcairn Island. Its flora is similar to those of high islands of the South Pacific and unlike those of low lying islands. The probable history of the island is that it began as part of the fringing reef of a large volcanic island, which was eroded away over a considerable period of time. As the parent island was eroded, isostatic readjustment raised the reef above sea level and allowed elements of the parent island flora to migrate onto the dried out reef. With the complete erosion of the parent island only part of the reef remained as a raised coral island. The present flora consists of 55 Angiosperms of which 10 are endemic, and 8 ferns. The endemics include *Bidens hendersonensis* Sherff, a member of the *Campylotheca* section, forming a small tree 3–4 m high. *Santalum hendersonensis* F. Brown, *Celtis paniculata* Planch. var. *viridis* F. Brown and *Myrsine hosakae* St. John also reach the stature of small trees. Henderson is the best surviving example of a raised coral island and its vegetation is almost undamaged. It was recommended for conservation under the "Islands for Science" scheme, but the proposal has not been implemented. Although it is comparatively safe for the time being, it is visited occasionally by Pitcairn islanders to collect wood for making souvenirs for the tourist trade. It is highly desirable that this practice should be stopped and the island declared a reserve.

No discussion of threatened island floras would be complete without mention of the rapid and complete destruction of forest now possible using modern machines. In general the islands I have considered are either too small or have too little forest left to justify financially the application of the most modern technology. Viti Levu in the Fiji group is a borderline case. Tracks are rapidly blazed by the aid of large bulldozers and great extraction vehicles haul out the logs. Good forestry practice for selective felling aimed at ensuring regeneration has been thrown to the winds. The forest is left smashed and broken and within a year is thickly covered with lianes so that any seedlings present have little chance of survival. Only remnants of the dryer forests now remain and exploitation of the rainforest is progressing. *Agathis vitiensis* (Seem.) Benth. & Hook.f. and the larger podocarps that formerly were important constituents in the forest are becoming scarce. *Degeneria vitiensis* Bailey & Sm. is a large tree providing a good timber. I saw small specimens in the Victoria National Park in 1962, but no grove of mature trees has been preserved and the possibility of such action being taken is receding. Many other endemics are becoming rare or endangered. In company with E. J. H. Berwick in 1971 I made an estimate of the numbers of the palm *Neoveitchia storckii* (Wendl.) Becc. It grows only in one valley that was logged many years ago and is now filled with secondary jungle above which about 100 emergent stems were counted. The Rhinoceros beetle had been introduced recently into Fiji and was defoliating coconut palms. We found that the beetle was also transferring its attention to the *Neoveitchia* and providing another hazard for this unfortunate species.

The most destructive of all the modern techniques of forest exploitation was introduced by the Japanese for the manufacture of chipboard. Everything is milled from large trees down to small shrubs of finger thickness. The ground is left bare and the ecosystem is completely destroyed. Severe erosion is liable to follow this kind of exploitation, which is now becoming widespread in Malaysia, the Philippines and Australia.

Conclusion

The condition of the floras of oceanic islands varies greatly from almost complete destruction as on St. Helena and Rodriguez to an almost virgin condition on Henderson. The majority of islands lie somewhere in between with few and often inadequate reserves and threats from land clearing, grazing and weed competition constantly increasing. Many species are already severely depleted and the outlook for them is gloomy unless effective conservation measures can be taken in the near future.

With the increasing tempo of destruction, the time is short and may not extend beyond the end of this century for many islands. Undoubtedly the most effective conservation technique lies in the preservation of complete ecosystems in reserves of adequate size. Financial, political, social and economic obstacles block the progress of conservation, but efforts must be redoubled to save something of our rich heritage of plant life for posterity. Many of the species mentioned in this paper are plants of special scientific interest, important for evolutionary and phytogeographic studies. What may be called "Fire Brigade action" should be taken for plants in this category. Propagating material should be obtained and established in botanic gardens where the species could be maintained and anatomical, cytological and other studies made upon them before it is too late. The possibility of restoring such rescued species to wild habitats when an opportunity presents itself should be kept under review.

REFERENCES

Balfour, I. B. (1888). Botany of Socotra. *Trans. Roy. Soc. Edin.* **31**, 1–446
Bannerman, D. A. (1922). *The Canary Islands, their history, natural history and scenery*. Gurney & Jackson, London
Creer, K. M. (1964). A reconstruction of the continents for the Upper Palaeozoic from palaeomagnetic data. *Nature, Lond.* **203**, 1115–20
— (1970). Review and interpretation of palaeomagnetic data from the Gondwana continents. *Proc. 2nd Gondwana Symp., C.S.I.R., S. Africa* 55–72
Duffy, E. (1964). The terrestial ecology of Ascension Island. *J. Appl. Ecol.* **1**, 219–251
Fosberg, F. R. (1962). Marotiri (Bass Rocks) Austral Islands. *Atoll Res. Bull.* **162**, 9–10
Hemsley, W. B. (1885). Report on the Botany of Bermuda and various other islands of the Atlantic and southern oceans. *Rep. Sci. Res. Voy.* Challenger, *Bot.* **1** (3)
Holmes, A. (1965). *Principles of Physical Geology*. Nelson, London
Melville, R. (1969). Leaf venation patterns and the origin of the Angiosperms. *Nature* **224**, 121–125
— (1970). Links between the *Glossopteridae* and the Angiosperms. *Proc. 2nd Gondwana Symp., C.S.I.R., S. Africa* 585–588
— (1972). On the nature of the bud scales in the *Cunoniaceae*. *Kew Bull.* **26**, 477–485
— and Jeffrey, C. (1970). Annotated list of the endemic flowering plants of the Seychelles, I.U.C.N., Red Data Book 5, Suppl.
Menard, H. W. (1964). *Marine Geology of the Pacific*. McGraw Hill, New York
Perrier de la Bathie, H. (1921). La vegetation Malgache. *Ann. Mus. Colon, Marseille* **9**, 1–268

Schalke, H. J. W. G. and Zinderen-Bakker, E. M. van (1967). A preliminary report on palynological research on Marion Islands. *S. Afr. J. Sci.* **63**, 254–9

Sykes, W. R. and Godley, E. J. (1968). Trans-oceanic dispersal in *Sophora* and other genera. *Nature* **218**, 495–6

Zimmerman, E. C. (1935). Entomology in Report of the Mangarevan Expedition. *Bishop Mus. Bull.* **133**, 68–71

19 Botanic Gardens and Island Plant Conservation

A. H. M. SYNGE   *IUCN Threatened Plants Committee,*
c/o Royal Botanic Gardens, Kew, England

El papel de los jardines botánicos en la conservación de las plantas se discute con especial referencia a la flora de las islas. Aunque generalmente se acepta que el método más adecuado es la conservación *in situ*, en reservas naturales, existen algunas especies silvestres tan criticamente amenazadas, que la única esperanza para su futuro es el cultivo en jardines botánicos. La experiencia hortícola del personal de jardines puede ser necesaria para asegurar su supervivencia.

Los jardines dedicados a la flora local son de especial interés para los turistas y pueden también jugar un importante papel en conservación, educación y promoción de endemismos locales en horticultura y jardinería para mantener una reserva de material en cultivo. Las investigaciones llevadas a cabo sobre la flora local en los jardines botánicos puede ser vital para el establecimiento de reservas naturales y los jardines deberían estar implicados en la dirección de tales reservas en el futuro.

El intercambio de material de propaganda e información sobre cultivo entre jardines botánicos es también extremadamente valuable y una reciente inspección de la Cycadaceae llevada a cabo en Kew ha permitido al CPA establecer cual de las especies en peligro está en cultivo y en que jardín botánico ocurre. Se espera poder extender este proyecto a otros grupos de plantas.

El endemismo canario *Lotus berthelotii* es un ejemplo de una especie criticamente amenazada que ha sido salvada gracias a su cultivo en jardines botánicos, particularmente en el Jardín Botánico "Viera y Clavijo".

Introduction

During the last ten years, there has been a great increase in concern over threatened plants and the dangers of massive extinctions throughout the plant kingdom. Botanic gardens have been at the forefront of this movement and it has been primarily through field word done by botanic gardens and their associated herbaria that the true facts are beginning to emerge about which species are threatened and where they still occur.

Just as the basis for this knowledge is work in the field rather than in the botanic garden, so too must be the solution. It is generally accepted that plants are best conserved in their native habitats and that the great priority must be the preservation of intact ecosystems, so ensuring not only the well-being and survival of the plant species they contain, but also

N*

the maintenance of the essential processes they support. In comparison, botanic gardens are a poor substitute, particularly since only a small proportion of the genetic diversity of a species can usually be held; with annuals and biennials genetic erosion is a constant problem. Perhaps even more intractable is the organisational problem of maintaining large numbers of species from different climates, in good condition and correctly labelled, over long, indeed infinite, periods of time. Jacobs (*Flora Malesiana Bulletin* **30**, 2880, 1977) cites how out of 14 botanic gardens and stations founded in the Malay Peninsula before 1910, 11 had been abolished by this date, with life-spans of only 4 to 14 years. This is clearly an extreme example, and one hopes it would no longer be valid, but the central problem remains. Another important factor is that energy costs alone may make it impossible for many temperate botanic gardens to grow more than a small selection of tropical plants.

Nevertheless there are some species so critically endangered in the wild that botanic gardens must surely become the holding grounds for the future. In some cases it may be felt that the chances of conserving these plants in the field are very low, especially in a "developing world" where human survival dictates precedence over plant species conservation. In some cases, threats may be reinforcing evolutionary trends already present, for example in the decline of many relict plants. However, once a decision has been made to try and maintain a species, bringing it into cultivation need not be an additional threat in itself, since in most cases seeds or cuttings can be taken without further jeopardising the wild population, provided of course that only a minimum of plant material is collected. Thus there is room for a "safety first" policy of maintaining such plants in a botanic garden, as well as attempting to conserve them *in situ*. This is of crucial importance, for decision-makers must not be allowed to see botanic gardens as an excuse for avoiding conservation of plants in their natural habitats, but rather as a necessary adjunct to such a policy, and an adjunct without which the policy is less likely to succeed.

The situation is similar for species whose populations are critically low, say below 10–100 individuals, but do not seem to be in any immediate danger from Man. An example of such a plant is *Bupleurum kakiskalae* Greuter, a monocarpic, partly woody species from some very inaccessible rocks in the White Mountains of Crete. It was discovered only in 1966, but it seems unlikely that the population was much larger in the recent past (Lucas and Synge, 1978). The only threat from Man is likely to be collecting by botanists. However, the species may be threatened by biological factors, since if the population drops below a certain critical level, the chance of cross-pollination is so heavily reduced that extinction becomes almost inevitable in a medium to long-term situation. Its monocarpic habit combined with a long sterile period make it particularly vulnerable in this respect. It is clearly important that reserve stocks of species such as this should be held in cultivation, so that a re-introduction can be attempted if it dies out in the wild.

In many cases a little help from Man may be needed to ensure survival in the wild. Consider the case of *Badula crassa* A.DC. which is only known from 3 individuals on the island of Réunion (Lucas and Synge, 1978). Hand-pollination, growing-on of the seedlings for establishment in the wild, hand-weeding around the seedlings – all may be necessary at this critical point in the life of the species to ensure survival in the wild as well as in cultivation. This is particularly true of island endemics, whose populations are often dangerously low. Botanic gardens, with their great horticultural expertise in growing difficult and unusual species, are in a unique position to carry out this type of horticultural field-work. General protection of the ecosystem, though vital in itself, will not necessarily ensure the survival of the endangered species for which it may have been undertaken. In some cases active management of the habitat may be required – Raven (1976) cites the example of the fen orchid, *Liparis loeselii* (L.) Rich., which became extinct in Britain's oldest nature reserve, Wicken Fen, due to the habitat not being maintained. The *Liparis* appears to be declining throughout Europe; it is classed as Vulnerable on the IUCN European List and Endangered in Britain (IUCN Threatened Plants Committee, 1977; Perring, 1977). In contrast, however, *Viola persicifolia* Schreber (*V. stagnina* Kit.), a nationally endangered species, has survived at Woodwalton Fen, Huntingdonshire, because its similar habitat of open peat, flooded in winter, has been maintained by active and successful interference (Walters, pers. comm.).

Rare and declining species

Botanic gardens also have a secondary but nevertheless fundamental role in the wider context of holding live material of species that although are not endangered are nevertheless rare in the wild or are declining. Again this must be seen to complement field conservation, especially since the aim is not necessarily long-term insurance although this is of course important, but for education and publicity on threatened plants, as well as to be able to provide propagating material on request for the needs of research and horticulture, so taking the collecting pressure off the remaining wild populations. Where such work is concentrated on the local flora, as with the Jardín Botánico "Viera y Clavijo", it can develop into a major attraction for the many visitors from other countries, enabling them to enjoy and appreciate far more of a remarkable flora than they would otherwise have seen during a brief visit to the islands. Perhaps more important is that colourful displays of native plants are an ideal way of interesting local people in their flora and in persuading them of the drastic need for conserving their plants, not only in strict reserves and National Parks, but in all areas where they grow and do not conflict with other land-uses. This appreciation of local flora will help people to realise that picking large bunches of the less common species, in particular ground orchids, is detrimental and that such plants should be cherished *in situ*. It is also very exciting to see how in many parts of the world, the main emphasis in landscape and amenity planting is moving onto the use of local species, partly because they are usually cheap and easy to grow, but partly because such plants will then emphasise the original character of the place.

In the great tropical land-masses of the world, a number of factors conspire to make the emphasis rather different for a botanic garden involved in conservation. This is perhaps most acute in areas where tropical rainforest is the dominant vegetation; the combination of fabulous abundance of species, very real difficulties of field-identification, and the very scattered distribution patterns of many species make a species-by-species approach to conservation almost an impossibility, especially now that whole ecosystems are coming under threat. The rate of change is so fast and the relative lack of information so pressing that we are unlikely to know which species are endangered before their whole habitat has been destroyed and they are likely to have become extinct. Immense problems of taxonomy, field identification and exploration remain. The sheer number of taxa in itself is very daunting; Raven (1976) estimates that "nearly two-thirds of the world's plant species appear to be tropical in distribution", with a "staggering figure of perhaps 90 000 species in South America". Inevitably a great many of these species will be lost before the century is out; large sample areas of rainforest protected in massive reserves and national parks may save a great many, but the number of species lost in the wild will undoubtedly be large.

It seems clear that it will be at the very least extremely difficult for botanic gardens in these areas to maintain permanent stocks of such species; the lack of pollinators alone in such predominantly out-breeding plants may be a crucial limiting factor for cultivation (Jacobs, Raven, *l.c.*), and it may only be possible to maintain stocks of some of the epiphytes in the botanic garden. Rather, a role is emerging that greatly emphasises the need for public education at all levels with the emphasis both on the economic and traditional values of the forest flora and on encouraging ecologically sound forms of land-use in which conservation and development can be reconciled. Detailed surveys and field-work will help to gather much needed information which can be used to help stimulate the setting up and careful maintenance of reserves and other protected areas. One idea, outlined by Jacobs (*l.c.*), is that of bringing the botanic garden to the plant rather than the plant to the garden, by establishing research areas in the forests and by opening up "the ecosystem . . . for study and education, with labelled plants and ample instruction, by word and picture, on how plants live, interact with animals, and maintain themselves as species".

As far as possible all these approaches should be seen as a shared problem, in which the sharing of resources between the gardens can greatly assist their sister organisations in another region, especially in matters of staff-training, plant identification and in the techniques of field and survey work.

Whether tropical or temperate, island or mainland, a concern for conservation may also prompt the adoption of different concepts over the selection of species to be grown in the botanic garden. As pointed out by Shaw (1976), many of the older botanic gardens, unable to expand in recent years, have found that the number of taxa they hold has stayed relatively constant, despite large numbers of accessions each year. For each species gained, another must have been lost. This has brought about a greater awareness of the need to develop clear criteria over the selection of plants to be grown. An example of such criteria is given by Shaw (1976) for the Royal Botanic Garden, Edinburgh, although clearly such criteria will greatly vary from one garden to another. A later paper by Walters (1977) discusses in some detail how the aim of growing plants of conservation importance can often be reconciled with the more traditional botanic garden tasks of growing plants for scientific research, for teaching purposes and education, and at the same time providing displays of plants to delight the eye in a pleasant and restful setting. He shows how each of these objectives can be brought together into a unified policy as has been done in the University Botanic Garden, Cambridge.

Scientific research

One of these tasks, scientific research, is just as vital for conservation as it is for botany, and indeed for the long-term survival of the institutions as botanic gardens rather than as public parks. Only when the taxonomy of a flora has been worked out, the distributions of the individual elements known and an extensive up-to-date field knowledge acquired, can the list of rare and threatened species for the area be made fully comprehensive.

Another prime research need for conservation is autecological studies on rare and threatened species – often a prerequisite before conservation measures can be formulated. Such studies concentrate on monitoring populations, studying pollination and breeding systems, and assessing the effect of external factors on the ecosystem such as grazing. The results are sometimes surprising; for example *Degenia velebitica* (Degen) Hayek, a monotypic and very rare Crucifer from Yugoslavia, appears to benefit rather than suffer from grazing by cattle. Its natural habitat of open mountain scree appears to have been considerably enlarged during heavy grazing in the nineteenth century. The lack of cattle in recent years is thought to be a major factor in its decline at its principal locality in the remote Velebit mountains. A textbook example of an autecological study on a threatened species is that carried out by Prentice on *Silene diclinis* (Lag.) M. Laínz, a Spanish endemic only known from one locality where it grows in a Man-made ecosystem of carob and olive groves. If the area is allowed to revert back to dense Mediterranean scrub or to forest, it appears unlikely the species would survive, according to the Red Data Book. *Degenia* and *S. diclinis* may not be typical examples, coming as they do from the Mediterranean flora which has been drastically altered by Man over the last five thousand years, but experience with conserving rare species in Britain, and data accumulated by the Threatened Plants Committee for many other areas, especially islands, does lead one to the view that each case of the threatened species is ecologically more difficult and complex than might have been expected and that if such studies are not carried out, conservation work in the field may not have a very high chance of success.

More research is also needed on the fast developing horticultural techniques of micro-propagation; this includes virus-cleansing and *in vitro* germination of seeds. Such practices are clearly very important when growing on very small and infinitely precious propagules of critically endangered species. We need to be more certain of success than we can be using nineteenth century techniques of horticulture. For long-term maintenance of cultivated material, such techniques may well prove essential to keep the plants free of pests and diseases, and in good condition. Another aspect of such work includes the facilities of the seed-bank, such as that of the Universidad Politécnica in Madrid, initiated by Gómez-Campo. There is a great need for an enlarged pro-gramme of research on which types of seeds can and cannot be stored and on finding optimal conditions, as well as for technical training of staff. The seed-bank in Madrid plays a key role in maintaining stocks of most of the numerous endemics of the Iberian Peninsula, not only for long-term insurance purposes but also so as to be able to provide plant material for research purposes.

These roles, and many of the technical problems involved, were explored in some depth at a conference entitled "The Functions of Living Plant Collections in Conservation and Conservation-Orientated Research and Public Education", held at the Royal Botanic Gardens, Kew, England in September 1975. The proceedings were published (Simmons *et al.*, 1976), and the resolutions are given as an appendix to this paper. Throughout the conference the idea strongly developed of institutions paying special attention to their own local floras, so benefitting from local knowledge of taxonomy, ecology and other disciplines. An equally important reason for this approach is that each garden is then in a position to offer from direct experience unique information and advice on how the plants in their area can best be conserved in the field. Botanic gardens are in a key position to help local and national conservation bodies; public education and private lobbying by institutions in such influential and well-established positions as botanic gardens may be of crucial significance in the years to come. Indeed it is hoped that some botanic gardens, particularly those in the tropics and subtropics, will feel able to go further and set up small habitat reserves within easy reach of the garden for research and other purposes. There is clearly a complete gradation between the acquisition and maintenance of strict reserves and the recreating of natural ecosystems in the botanic garden; all have their place, becoming a vital contribution to conservation of genetic resources and to education. Experience with creating native ecosystems within a garden may yield vital information on how such ecosystems can be restored in the wild and may be a way of demonstrating that the conservation of such areas is not necessarily incompatible with economic uses. Indeed it is a central tenet of conservation that in most cases the maintenance and utilisation of native ecosystems may prove more economically beneficial in the long term than their replacement by exotic species. The laurel forests of the Canaries, recreated in part in the "Viera y Clavijo" garden, are a classic example.

Information systems

How far each garden can go in the practical tasks of holding stocks of threatened species is obviously a matter for individual choice, but it is clear that no garden can either hold all the species already known to be rare or threatened, or more than a minute proportion of the vast range of tropical plants that might disappear in the next 25 years. The answer, as far as it is possible, lies not only in the sharing of resources, but also in the back-up information systems so that each garden can have at its disposal information on which species are rare or threatened, whether they are in cultivation, and if so, where they may be found.

As a result of the Kew Conference a working party was set up to explore how this collaboration and exchange of data could be brought about.

A preliminary survey was carried out at Kew on the Cycads, a group that are apparently well known, and in many cases very rare and threatened in the wild. They can be maintained successfully over long periods of time, and seem to be old favourites of botanic gardens. Due to the kindness of numerous institutions in answering our enquiries, we now know which species of the group are in cultivation and in which gardens they occur, so that any garden which wishes to acquire material of a particular species can be put in touch with a garden that holds material of it. The Conference Working Party has expanded the concept and an initial paper (Walters, 1977) has been circulated among European botanic gardens inviting collaboration in an initial data handling scheme. The response has been most encouraging, with the majority of countries being represented. A logical conclusion for such activity is (a) the circulation and regular updating of lists of threatened plants among botanic gardens so that they can receive lists for the countries and plant groups in which they are interested; and (b) the circulation of a regularly produced compilation listing which threatened species are in cultivation and from where stocks of known wild origin are available. It is hoped very much that an informal principle will develop whereby collecting of a threatened species not already in cultivation is made by the national garden concerned and that botanic gardens and individual research workers from other contries do not indiscriminately collect such taxa, but work through the local institution.

In all these considerations, the relatively few botanic gardens on islands become of crucial significance. For a start, islands tend to have a much higher percentage of species known to be endangered than other areas. Islands have always attracted botanists and for most areas information is available both on taxonomy and distribution, and on the conservation status in the wild of individual species. Island endemics clearly had very small distributions before the era of Man, and with the great pressures on limited amounts of land for agriculture, forestry and development, in addition to the often considerable problem of introduced plants and animals as with *Opuntia* in the Canary Islands, it is easy to see how such plants have become endangered. Two salutary examples may suffice: on the island of St. Helena, goats were introduced in 1513 and had formed herds 2 km long within 75 years. When the forests were explored botanically by Burchell in 1805–10, they had already been devastated, but nevertheless 31 endemic species were found. Of these, 11 are now extinct and the majority of the remainder are endangered, reduced to a handful of individuals surrounded by vigorous invasive exotics. There are reports that the goats have now been reduced in number, but the far more intractable problem of the introduced exotic plants still remains. Another example is the Hawaiian Islands, noted botanically for their remarkably high degree of endemism, estimated at c. 97% by St. John (1973). Fosberg and Herbst (1975) list 273 taxa as extinct and 800 as endangered; they emphasise that these are minimum figures and that the status of a large number is not yet known, due to the lack of information. To put these figures in perspective, the European List, recently published, includes only 108 endangered and extinct species *for the whole of Europe*; the great majority of the c. 2000 species listed are classified as rare (i.e. only known from relatively small populations and hence at risk, but not critically low and not believed to be declining).

The tragic situation of the floras of St. Helena and Hawaii is not dissimilar for many other islands, especially those on the Pacific and Indian Oceans. The Threatened Plants Committee is putting together information on endangered plants from islands wherever it can (see Lucas, chapter 22) and already information at list level is available from oceanic islands. As a result of work on the Canarian flora (Kunkel, 1975; Bramwell, pers. comm.), similar data will soon be available for the Canaries.

Conclusion

The high numbers of species known to be endangered and the scientific interest of most island floras indicate that island botanic gardens are of crucial importance, both in terms of undertaking rescue work and of giving technical advice and help to conservation bodies. On islands it is often possible to grow plants from a wide range of different climates and so botanic gardens may be able to hold stocks of rare and threatened species from other more tropical areas without the need for expensive oil-consuming glasshouses. This makes island botanic gardens doubly important in the world scene. The cultivation of plants such as the famous Canarian endemic, *Lotus berthelotii* Masferrer, is an example; although it is now believed extinct in the wild (Bramwell, pers. comm.), it is now flourishing in the Jardín Botánico "Viera y Clavijo" and in many other botanic gardens of the world. Such a plant is a botanic gardens' success story, contributing as it does not only to botany and conservation, but also to our sense of pleasure and well-being with the plant kingdom.

Acknowledgement

I would like to thank Mr. G. Lucas for help in preparing this paper.

REFERENCES

Fosberg, F. R. and Herbst, D. (1975). Rare and endangered species of Hawaiian vascular plants. *Allertonia* **1** (1)

Kunkel, G. (ed.) (1975). *Inventario de les recursos naturales renovables de la Provincia de Las Palmas.* Las Palmas de Gran Canaria

Perring, F. H. (1977). *British Red Data Book: 1, Vascular Plants.* Society for the Promotion of Nature Conservation, Lincoln

Prentice, H. C. (1976). A study in Endemism: *Silene diclinis. Biol. Conserv.* **10**, 15–30

Raven, P. H. (1976). Ethics and Attitudes. In *Conservation of Threatened Plants* (J. B. Simmons *et al.*, eds.), 155–179. Plenum Press, London and New York

St. John, H. (1973). *List and Summary of the Flowering Plants in the Hawaiian Islands.* Pacific Tropical Botanical Garden Memoir No. 1. Hawaii

Shaw, R. L. (1976). Future: Integrated International Policies. In *Conservation of Threatened Plants* (J. B. Simmons *et al.*, eds.), 39–47. Plenum Press, London and New York

Simmons, J. B., Beyer, R. I., Brandham, P. E., Lucas, G. Ll. and Parry, V. T. H. (eds.) (1976). *Conservation of Threatened Plants.* Plenum Press, London and New York

Walters, S. M. (1977). The rôle of European Botanic Gardens in the Conservation of rare and threatened plant species. *Gärtnerisch-Botanischer Brief* **51**. (English, German, French)

APPENDIX

Resolutions of the conference on "The Functions of Living Plant Collections in Conservation and Conservation-Orientated Research and Public Education", held at the Royal Botanic Gardens, Kew, England, 2–6 September 1975

1   This Conference, conscious that the rich tropical floras of the world are now in great hazard, (1) urges that a strong network of nature reserves and conservation-orientated gardens should be established throughout the tropics both through the strengthening and development of existing foundations and through the creation of new ones where the need exists; (2) recommends that institutions in temperate countries should offer all possible help in this programme through technical aid, training and the secondment of personnel; and (3) urges that this aim should be pursued through the International Union for Conservation of Nature and Natural Resources to ensure good co-ordination and proper understanding of the importance of the work for the tropical countries themselves and for the whole of mankind.

2   This Conference urges that special attention be given to the Conservation of Threatened Floras particularly of Islands and those parts of the world with

Mediterranean or similar climates since both are often inhabited by very large numbers of narrowly endemic species of plants endangered by human activities.

3   This Conference recommends that institutions maintaining plant collections (including seed collections) for conservation purposes should, in general, give priority to their local flora, so as (1) to benefit from local taxonomic ecological, physiological and other pertinent specialist knowledge; (2) to reduce the need to simulate remote climates with the attendant costs and dependence on Man-generated energy; (3) to be able to offer from direct experience information and advice concerning field conservation in the country of the institution, and (4) to provide a basis from which public interest and pride in the indigenous flora can be developed through display and education services

4   This Conference urges all governments to ratify the "Convention on International Trade in Endangered Species of Wild Fauna and Flora" as soon as possible.

5   This Conference recommends that, wherever possible, all living plant collections grown for conservation purposes should also be stored in the form of seeds under appropriate conditions for long-term conservation.

6   This Conference urges that the propagation of rare and endangered species, including research into appropriate techniques, should be actively pursued by Botanic Gardens and other bodies maintaining living plant collections, and that such activities should be financially supported where necessary by Conservation, or other appropriate Organisations. Special attention should be given to economic plants and their wild relatives and to plants which are or might be commercially used.

7   This Conference urges that whenever threatened plants are taken into cultivation, this be done by means of seed and/or cuttings whenever possible so as not to deplete the wild populations.

8   This Conference, aware of the urgent need for scientifically verified lists of threatened species on a world scale, calls for the full support for the work of the IUCN Threatened Plants Committee in compiling such lists, and urges the task of propagating stocks of species on institutions maintaining living plant collections.

9   This Conference calls for the widest publicity to its full deliberations to be given in all appropriate quarters, and urges that the resolutions should be made available separately for this purpose with the minimum delay.

10   This Conference, being acutely aware of the urgency and complexity of many problems which have been raised during the sessions, urges the desirability of continued study and exchange of information, and the setting up of working parties to continue the study of outstanding issues, e.g. (1) listing of collections, documentation and dissemination of information, (2) commercial use of wild species, (3) preparation of codes of practice, (4) publicity, (5) relationship between institutions maintaining living plant collections and organisations concerned with nature conservation, (6) compilation of a short list of rare and endangered plants of high scientific importance to be commended to botanic gardens to bring them into cultivation.

20 Conservation and Vegetation of the Galapagos Islands

H. VAN DER WERFF   *Instituut voor Systematische Plantkunde,*
Utrecht, The Netherlands

Las islas Galápagos muestran una sorprendente variación en los tipos de vegetación debido a las drásticas diferencias en clima y suelo entre las distintas islas, así como entre la costa y las partes interiores de la misma isla.

Desde que empezó la colonización, hace 140 años, el hombre ha alterado la vegetación nativa de varias formas:

(*a*) Las áreas húmedas con un terreno bien desarrollado han sido cultivadas. Los tipos de vegetación hallados en estas áreas están ahora reducidos a una fracción del terreno que alguna vez ocuparon y están en necesidad de conservación. Especialmente la vegetación de *Miconia* está en trance de desaparición.

(*b*) Especies de árboles introducidas (*Cinchona succirubra* y *Psidium guajava*) amenazan cambiar la estructura de los originalmente matorrales de *Miconia* y zonas de Pampa en Sta. Cruz. *Psidium guajava* ha cubierto casi completamente las tierras altas de San Cristobal; los informes indican que lo mismo ha sucedido en Floreana y Sierra Negra, Isabela.

(*c*) Los animales introducidos, especialmente cabras y cerdos, destrozan la vegetación nativa. Esto conduce ultimamente a una erosión del terreno como puede apreciarse en San Salvador. Es necesaria una acción inmediata para prevenir la destrucción de la mayor parte de la vegetación en esta isla.

Los esfuerzos de conservación empezaron no hace más de 15 años. Desde entonces, las cabras han sido desterradas de Plazas, Rábida, Santa Fé y Española, y existen esperanzas de que en unos pocos años, Pinta esté también libre de ellas. Se ha lanzado una campaña destinada a retirar de Santa Cruz los árboles introducidos de *Psidium guajava* y *Cinchona succirubra*.

Para una conservación más efectiva de la vegetación, se requieren conocimientos más detallados acerca de los tipos de vegetación y su distribución sobre el archipiélago.

The Galapagos Islands

The Galapagos Islands (Fig. 1) are a group of a dozen large islands and many smaller islands, islets and rocks, situated on the equator about 800 km west of Punta Arena, Ecuador, in the Pacific Ocean. The Archipelago is part of Ecuador and has a total land surface of 7800 km². All islands are of volcanic origin and usually consist of a single volcano or a mass of surfaced lava. Isabela is an exception, being formed by six

391

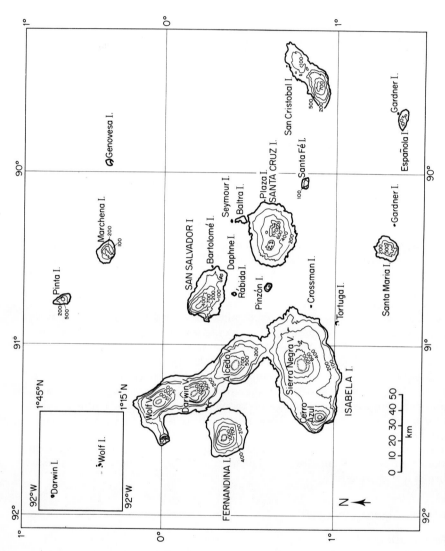

Fig. 1 The Galapagos Islands

392

volcanoes which are connected by extensive lava flows, making Isabela larger than all the other islands together. There is no geological evidence that the islands have ever been connected to the American continent.

Recently, rock samples from several islands have been dated. Two techniques have been used, magnetic studies (Cox and Dalrymple, 1966) and the Potassium-Argon method (Bailey, 1976). Both studies revealed comparable results and placed the age of the oldest islands at about 3 million years. According to Bailey, this is probably close to the maximum age of the islands, since studies of tholeiitic vulcanism in other islands indicate that this type of island-forming volcanic activity occurs rapidly (McDougall, 1972).

Not all islands are as old as 3 million years, however. Islands that are still volcanically active, such as Fernandina and Isabela, may not be older than 1 million years. These younger volcanoes generally have steep upper slopes and enormous, well-preserved calderas. The diameters of the calderas of Alcedo and Sierra Negra, two of the large volcanoes of Isabela, are approximately 8 km (Banfield *et al.*, 1956). On older islands such as Santa Cruz and San Cristobal, the calderas have disappeared due to erosion, and the upper slopes are less steep. Results from the age studies are in agreement with this. The oldest samples are from the central and eastern islands where distinct calderas are no longer found.

Soil types

The type of volcanism found in the Galapagos Islands is such that the upper slopes have a different soil than the lower ones, due to differences in the parent rock. Banfield *et al.* (1956) were the first to describe this phenomenon from the Galapagos. They observed that on the volcanoes of Isabela surface lava only occurred at lower elevations (on Cerro Azul below 600 m; on Sierra Negra below 150 m; on Wolf only lava below 600 m, lava and pyroclastic material between 600 and 800 m, and above 800 m, only pyroclastic deposits). The lava flows usually do not originate from the caldera, but from secondary craters and fissures on the lower slopes. These lateral lava flows build the gentle lower slopes and give the volcanoes their shield appearance. The steep upper slopes consist of pyroclastic deposits, such as cinders and ashes.

The division between gentle lower slopes consisting of lava flows and the steep upper slopes consisting of pyroclastic material has disappeared to a large extent on the older islands because of erosion. Laruelle (1966) described a soil sequence along an altitudinal transect on the southern slope of Santa Cruz. He distinguished 5 zones: the lower two zones had a lava bedrock, but differed in the degree of erosion; the third was formed by erosion products of lava and pyroclastic deposits; while the upper two had pyroclastic material as bedrock. Laruelle's findings agree favourably with those of Banfield *et al.* (1956).

Climate

The Galapagos Islands are small spots of land in the enormous Pacific Ocean. It is, therefore, not surprising that the climate is strongly influenced by the surrounding sea. Since the opening of the Charles Darwin Research Station, the scientific station on Santa Cruz, sea water temperatures have been measured every morning in Academy Bay. These data show a yearly cycle. Generally speaking, during the first five months of the year the sea water is several degrees centigrade warmer than during the remainder of the year; the highest monthly average being 27·6°C, April 1969 and the lowest 20·4°C, October 1975. It can be expected that the yearly fluctuation of the sea water temperatures is reflected in the climate. There are two seasons on the Galapagos Islands, a warm one and a cool one. The warm season coincides with the period of high sea water temperatures; the cool one with the low temperatures. The seasons have been called, respectively, the rainy and the dry season, but these terms are misleading since they are only correct for the coastal areas and do not apply to the interior parts. Therefore, the terms rainy and dry season should be replaced by warm and cool season. Precipitation has a stronger impact on the vegetation than the temperature, as is indicated by the observation that the resting periods of the plant life coincide with the season with the least rainfall (Table 1).

During the warm season, January to June, the rainfall pattern is irregular. Some years bring very little rain (1970), others bring a great deal (1969). Precipitation occurs as heavy local showers; otherwise skies are blue and evaporation is high, both in the coastal and interior parts.

During this season the coastal areas, where the vegetation is xerophytic with cacti, deciduous forests, and short-lived annuals, receive most of their annual rainfall and so appear quite green for a short period of time.

The interior of Santa Cruz, which is covered by evergreen forest rich in epiphytic mosses, ferns and orchids, requires a constant water supply which is not available during the warm season. In dry years cattle might even die because of lack of water and food when the vegetation goes into a resting stage.

During the cool season the situation is reversed: the coastal areas receive almost no rain and have a quite desolate, almost grey appearance, while the upper, southern slopes of the volcanoes enjoy a steady precipitation.

TABLE 1   Rainfall data from southern slope of Santa Cruz

Month	CDRS (6 m)		Caseta (200 m)		Devine's farm (315 m)		Media Luna (620 m)	
January	23·0	20·4	64·5	66·1	78·0	90·2	172·6	198·5
February	16·8	0·0	171·8	3·3	155·2	6·9	117·0	10·2
March	249·0	1,2	720·6	15·5	920·8	48·0	666·7	73·7
April	63·5	0·7	100·9	1·0	79·5	6·1	166·4	63·5
May	31·4	4·6	155·3	14·8	214·6	25·5	309·8	89·5
June	16·8	8·1	130·6	20·5	147·3	13·4	271·8	106·5
July	12·0	8·7	33·4	37·9	42·2	23·5	135·6	104·1
August	3·8	10·0	12·0	50·3	13·7	27·3	89·4	104·1
September	18·5	6·2	68·2	50·4	90·9	32·0	282·6	114·4
October	3·2	10·1	17·9	53·9	22·6	47·3	96·5	146·0
November	11·0	8·7	43·6	64·1	52·8	59·3	172·7	73·7
December	15·7	5·6	67·1	24·2	84·1	46·0	175·3	70·0
Total	469·7	84·3	1585·9	401·6	1901·7	425·5	2656·4	1154·4

Rainfall is measured in mm. The first column under every station is from 1969, the second from 1970.

The SE trade winds push moisture-laden air up against the volcanoes, causing increased condensation and rainfall at higher elevations. This condensation produces the drizzle or light rain that is locally called *garúa*. *Garúa* occurs mostly early in the morning and is a constant feature of the highlands during the cool season. This *garúa*, coupled with low evaporation due to frequent fog, is more important for the plant life than the heavy showers of the warm season. It is, therefore, in this period that the vegetation of the interior is lush and at its peak.

The northern slopes hardly collect any *garúa* and are much drier than the southern slopes. The same applies to the smaller, low islands where the mesic vegetation types are lacking. The climatic differences between the coast and the summit areas of Santa Cruz are drastic and provide an explanation for the equally drastic differences in vegetation.

The vegetation zones on southern Santa Cruz

As it is not desirable to discuss here all the vegetation types of the Galapagos Islands, the writer shall only present the altitudinal zonation of the vegetation found on the southern slope of Santa Cruz (see also Bowman, 1961 and Reeder and Riechert, 1975). This zonation reflects the influence of increasing amounts of *garúa* on the vegetation and is considered by the writer representative for the islands with human settlements. Though cultivation has destroyed the natural vegetation of some areas, the zonal vegetation types are better preserved here than on any other island the writer visited. On younger islands, as Fernandina and Isabela, the less-eroded cinder soils possess types of vegetation which are quite different from that found on older islands such as Santa Cruz.

In addition to the main climatic vegetation zones there are, of course, also a number of azonal vegetation types which result from local variation in soil, exposure, ground-water level etc. The azonal vegetation types sometimes differ from the zonal ones only in floristic composition or may possess a different structure as well (for instance, the vegetation of fresh water ponds). The litoral zone, as described by Wiggins and Porter (1971), consists of a number of structurally and floristically very different azonal vegetation types (for instance, mangrove forests, sand-dune vegetation and the vegetation of salt flats) and is, therefore, not accepted as a separate climatic zone.

Along an altitudinal gradient on the southern slope of Santa Cruz the following climatic zones are present from the coast to the summit:

(*a*) *The arid zone*. This zone is characterised by a deciduous forest in which *Bursera graveolens* (HBK) Trian. & Planch. is common or dominates. Tall cacti such as *Opuntia echios* Howell var. *gigantea* Howell and *Jasminocereus thouarsii* (Weber) Backbg. var. *delicatus* (Daws.) Anders. & Walkgtn. occur frequently. *Croton scouleri* Hook. fil. is the dominant shrub, though the shrub layer is not very dense. The herb layer is rather poorly developed and shows damage by feral goats. The only epiphytes found here are lichens.

(*b*) *The transition zone*. At an altitude of about 75 m *Bursera graveolens* and the tall cacti disappear or become rare. The forest remains deciduous and is dominated by *Pisonia floribunda* Hook. fil., *Piscidia carthagenensis* Jacq. and *Psidium galapageium* Hook. fil. The shrub layer changes drastically and turns into a dense tangle of weak, intertwining stems, mostly of *Tournefortia psilostachya* HBK. and *Clerodendrum molle* HBK. In the herb layer the number of perennial species increases. Some epiphytic bryophytes, ferns and an occasional orchid occur.

(*c*) *The* Scalesia *zone*. Above 180 m the forest becomes evergreen, has a closed canopy layer and consists almost exclusively of *Scalesia pedunculata* Hook. fil. The trunks of this tree are densely covered with epiphytes – mostly mosses and liverworts, but also ferns, orchids and some *Peperomia* species. The shrub layer is rather open and dense tangles as are found in the transition zone do not occur here. The herb layer is well developed and the number of terrestrial ferns has increased distinctly, compared with the transition zone. Much of the *Scalesia* forest on the southern slope of Santa Cruz is destroyed and the area is now used for cultivation.

(*d*) *The* Zanthoxylum *zone*. The *Zanthoxylum* zone is quite certainly the same as the Brown zone described by Bowman (1961), though in Wiggins and Porter (1971) it is not recognised as a main climatic zone. Very little of this vegetation zone remains on the southern slope of Santa Cruz. Fortunately, there is an almost untouched area on the northern slope very close to the summit. The distribution of the few remnants on the southern slope and their structural and floristic characteristics indicate that this forest type is the intermediate zone between the *Scalesia* and the *Miconia* Zones. Like the *Scalesia* forest the *Zanthoxylum* forest is evergreen and it is dominated by *Zanthoxylum fagara* (L.) Sarg., accompanied by *Tournefortia pubescens* Hook. fil. (tree) and *Acnistus ellipticus* Hook. fil. (small tree or shrub). The canopy layer is open and, especially where the canopy layer is interrupted, a very dense shrub layer is found. The number of epiphytes continues to be high and liverworts prevail. The herb layer is still fairly . well developed as ferns become more prominent.

(*e*) *The* Miconia *zone*. On the southern slope above 480 m a closed shrub vegetation consisting entirely of *Miconia robinsoniana* Cogn. is found. No native trees occur in this zone. Ferns dominate the herb layer. The biomass of epiphytes decreases, which is probably due to the lack of thick trunks and branches in this shrubby zone, although more species of liverworts seem to occur in this zone than in any other vegetation zone on the Galapagos Islands.

(*f*) *The Pampa zone*. This uppermost vegetation zone is characterised by the almost total absence of indigenous trees and shrubs. Only in sheltered places, such as in small craters or on the lee side of steep ridges, do small thickets of *Zanthoxylum fagara* or *Scalesia pedunculata* occur. The majority of vascular plant species found in the Pampa zone are ferns, grasses and sedges.

Conservation on the Galapagos Islands

The first law designated for the conservation of large areas of the Galapagos Islands dates from 1934; subsequent laws have reaffirmed and expanded that decision of the Ecuadorian Government. In 1959 the whole archipelago was declared a National Park with the exception of the areas that were cultivated or had been legally acquired by the colonists. This privately held land, usually areas with good soil and ample rainfall, includes a few important vegetation zones which are now without Park protection and subject to independent development.

Colonisation started more than a century ago on the Galapagos Islands and, as one might expect, Man's activity has changed the natural vegetation in sizeable areas. In many of these places we now find a stable, new vegetation which is maintained by Man. Where once there were forests, there are now fields. From point of view of a conservation-minded naturalist, such areas are lost. Much more important are those areas where changes in vegetation still take place. These changes may be due to human development or the rapid multiplication of introduced plants or animals. In the following section we will concentrate on the areas which are botanically important and where conservation measures, if taken soon, will have a beneficial effect. Only areas which the writer has visited in 1974 and 1975 will be discussed.

Vegetation types in need of conservation

Santa Cruz   (a)   *The* Zanthoxylum *zone.* The area once occupied by the *Zanthoxylum* forest on the southern slope is now cultivated. The whole area is privately owned and I have not seen any areas that are undisturbed and sufficiently large which would merit acquisition and inclusion in the National Park. The botanically interesting transitions from the *Scalesia* to the *Zanthoxylum* zone and from the *Zanthoxylum* to the *Miconia* zone can no longer be investigated. This is unfortunate since on several other islands the *Zanthoxylum* forest occupies large areas (i.e. Pinta) but where the *Scalesia* and *Miconia* zones are lacking.

A good *Zanthoxylum* stand is still present high on the northern slope near Cerro Precioso and forms part of the Park. Squatters had invaded this area but were evicted by Park officials a few years ago. A number of avocado and banana plants still remain there and should be destroyed as soon as possible.

(b)   *The* Miconia *zone.* Regrettably little of the *Miconia* zone is part of the National Park. Large areas are currently being cut and used for pasture land. During the last thirty years equally large areas have been burnt by Man and I expect that in 10 to 20 years from now the *Miconia* zone will have been destroyed.

A few isolated patches will remain of the once continuous belt of *Miconia* shrubs. This loss can only be prevented by the acquisition of large tracts of *Miconia* vegetation by the National Park Service.

(c)   *The Pampa zone.* This zone is almost entirely protected by the National Park Service but a number of introduced plants have become serious threats. Probably the worst of these is *Cinchona succirubra* Pav. ex Klotz., a tree introduced shortly after World War II. Mature trees now occur in the cultivated area below the Pampa zone and the seeds are spread by wind into the National Park land. Large numbers of young trees are now found in the Pampa and *Miconia* zones. If this invasion is not stopped, the originally treeless Pampa and *Miconia* zones will be changed into *Cinchona* forests and this drastic change in structure of these vegetation types will seriously affect the floristic composition.

The remedy is clear and difficult. Only the removal of the introduced tree species (*Psidium guajava* L. poses a similar problem) will help and the National Park Service has recently launched an eradication campaign against *Cinchona* and *Psidium*. All trees encountered in the Park area are to be cut and a herbicide applied to the trunks to prevent sprouting. This will help, but a definite solution also involves the removal of the source of seeds (the mature trees of *Cinchona succirubra* in the cultivated zone).

Another plant which is becoming a bad pest is the recently introduced *Digitaria decumbens* Stent, a forage grass which multiplies rapidly through runners. This grass has invaded the Pampa zone from the cultivated areas and tends to form pure stands, excluding the indigenous plant species. An attempt is being made to restrict the spread of *Digitaria decumbens* by manually removing the plants, but this is a time and labour-consuming task.

San Cristobal   San Cristobal, like Santa Cruz, is one of the older islands with a well-developed soil and an ample rainfall in the interior. Originally, this island probably displayed a similar vegetation zonation to Santa Cruz, but much of it is now destroyed. Colonisation started earlier here than on Santa Cruz and has seriously affected the interior of the island. During the writer's stay on San Cristobal, in 1975, he visited the southern and northwestern slopes and, unfortunately, found that none of the vegetation in the wetter parts appeared natural. The destruction has proceeded much farther than on Santa Cruz.

The original evergreen forest at middle elevations is replaced by an open *Psidium guajava* forest from which shrubs and tall ferns are removed to create a denser grass layer. Towards the top of the island this woodland gradually becomes lower, resulting in low, open *Psidium* shrubland. The reason *Psidium guajava* has overtaken the native vegetation so completely is that cattle raising is an important source of income on San Cristobal and that the farmers do not fence their lands (as is done on Santa Cruz), but rather let their cattle roam more or less freely. This makes it possible for the cattle to penetrate the natural vegetation, make trails and, since they eat *Psidium* fruits, spread the seeds along their way. It is only along the trails that the young *Psidium* plants receive the necessary amounts of light to grow; in closed *Miconia* shrubland for instance, one does not encounter *Psidium guajava*.

Nearly all of the upper slopes are privately owned and there is little the National Park Service can do towards their conservation. What can be done is the acquisition by the Park Service of carefully selected, smaller segments which, after removal of *Psidium guajava*, will display the various types of natural vegetation that originally were found in this area. A necessary prerequisite is that the farmers must fence their lands. As long as cattle can roam freely, there is little hope for the eradication of *Psidium guajava*. Equally serious problems with spreading *Psidium guajava*, combined with free roaming cattle, are reported from Floreana and Sierra Negra, Isabela island. On Santa Cruz, where the farmers keep their cattle under better control, *Psidium guajava* is not such a serious threat and can probably be eradicated. Seriously threatened vegetation zones on San Cristobal are the following:

(*a*) *Evergreen forest*. A *Scalesia pedunculata* forest has been reported from San Cristobal (Stewart, 1915), but this was probably never as extensive as that found on Santa Cruz. A serious effort should be made to localise and protect what is left of it.

(*b*) Miconia *zone*. *Miconia robinsoniana* occurs now as scattered bushes among the shrubby *Psidium guajava* in the highlands. It is only on the walls of stream beds that *Miconia* is more common, but even here cattle trails and invading *Psidium* shrubs are found. Probably much of the plateau around the summit was once covered by *Miconia* shrubs and the populations in the stream beds are remnants of this. Near Cerro San Joaquin a small area along a fresh water stream that provides Baquerizo Moreno with drinking water, has been fenced in to prevent the pollution of the water by cattle. There, one still finds a *Miconia* vegetation which is very similar to what is present on Santa Cruz.

No *Psidium guajava* grows inside the fenced part. It should be possible to repeat this on a larger scale – fencing in sizeable tracts of the summit area and removing the *Psidium guajava*. The damage done to the *Miconia* zone is particularly alarming since this zone occurs only on Santa Cruz and San Cristobal and is threatened seriously on both islands. If no action is taken soon, one can expect that only fragments of it will remain.

Cerro San Joaquin itself is a small, steep hill situated near the summit of the island. Its wind-exposed slopes were once covered with a dense tree fern brake and small, vertical *Sphagnum* bogs. These vegetation types are rare on the Galapagos Islands and only occur locally on steep, wet slopes. On Cerro San Joaquín cattle have severely damaged this vegetation, mostly by sliding down through it. Most tree ferns have been knocked over and *Psidium guajava* is increasing there too. Since the tree fern brakes are rare and the hill does not have much value as pasture land because of the steepness of its slopes, it should be possible for the National Park Service to acquire this area and give it the needed protection.

(*c*) *The Pampa zone*. Just as is the case with the evergreen forest and the *Miconia* zones, the Pampa zone is almost completely privately owned. Only the area around the El Junco crater lake, botanically very interesting, is included in the National Park. Free roaming cattle visit the Park area as frequently as their own pastures and, consequently, much of the El Junco area is covered with *Psidium guajava* shrub. Here the surrounding pastures should be fenced in before the National Park Service can start with the removal of *Psidium guajava*.

San Salvador In contrast to Santa Cruz and San Cristobal, San Salvador is presently not inhabited by Man. Several attempts at colonisation have been made in the past, but they were unsuccessful. Unfortunately however, domestic animals were introduced and goats and pigs, in particular, are now numerous and pose a severe threat to the native vegetation. As early as 1813, goats and sheep were introduced onto San Salvador (Slevin, 1959), but apparently this introduction was not successful as sheep have not been seen since and goats were not sighted again until 1926 (Vanderbilt, 1927). Pigs, rats and donkeys were reported during the second half of the nineteenth century from San Salvador. In a recent study L. Calvpiño and T. de Vries estimated the number of goats as more than 100 000 (pers. comm. T. de Vries). Such an enormous number of goats is bound to have a large effect on the vegetation. One notices in the first place a marked decrease in the number of species. Stewart, who visited the Galapagos Islands in 1905–06, published in 1915 his description of the vegetation types that he found on the various islands. He mentions several species, especially shrubs, from San Salvador that have now become very rare or are confined to inaccessible cliffs. (*Alternanthera echinocephala* (Hook. fil.) Christoph., *Lantana peduncularis* Anderss., *Waltheria ovata* Cav., *Scalesia atractyloides* Arn., *Dodonaea viscosa* Jacq. and *Macraea laricifolia* Hook. fil.). A few species (*Castela galapageia* Hook. fil. and *Vallesia glabra* (Car.) Link) are not eaten by goats and are now very common. These two, together with *Scutia pauciflora* (Hook. fil.) Weberb., form the shrub layer in the arid zone. The interior of the island is more severely affected. From Stewart's description it becomes clear that there was once an extensive *Scalesia pedunculata* forest; above that, a zone in which *Zanthoxylum fagara* dominated and a shrubby zone (though *Miconia robinsoniana* is absent from San Salvador) and probably also a Pampa zone. During the writer's visit in 1975 he found that the *Scalesia pedunculata* forest had nearly disappeared. This tree Composite has a short lifespan and when the young replacements are eaten by goats, a population soon disappears. In the *Scalesia* and *Zanthoxylum* forests the shrub and herb layers have been destroyed to a large extent. As a consequence, the soil is drying out and since most trees have a shallow root system, the trees are dying. The result of this is that large parts of the interior are covered by low, creeping herbs (e.g. *Elvira repens* (Hook. fil.) Robins.) and a few scattered *Zanthoxylum fagara* trees. Erosion gullies are becoming prominent on the steeper slopes. Since 1975 the situation has only deteriorated (pers. comm. from H. Adsersen, who visited this area in 1977). The situation here is critical. Not only the species diversity is greatly decreased, but also the soil is being destroyed. The destruction of the soil makes a future recovery of the vegetation very unlikely or even impossible.

The solution is obvious: removal of the introduced animals. Unfortunately, there is still not enough manpower and money available to the National Park Service to eliminate the animals by hunting. Other methods for goat control are under study, but are not yet in the executive stage.

An additional worry is that the goat population seems to increase rapidly. Though goats have been present on San Salvador since 1928, their population boom did not begin until 30 years ago or more likely, according to T. de Vries, not more than 20 years ago. Unless the goat population explosion can be stopped, in a few decades not much will be left of the natural vegetation on San Salvador.

Achievements in conservation

The first conservation efforts of the National Park Service have been directed at the endangered wildlife. Initially, they tried to prevent the extinction of individual species, but soon they realised that protection of the habitats is equally important. As a consequence, hunting programmes aimed at introduced animals were initiated.

Recently similar campaigns against introduced plants have also begun. However, campaigns specifically aimed at the conservation of vegetation types are lacking. This is due to the lack of information about the natural vegetation types. There are no published studies which describe and define the various types, nor do we possess reliable information about the distribution of the original vegetation over the archipelago. The available publications only contain observations made by collectors; of which those by Stewart (1915) are still the best. Until detailed studies are published, the National Park Service cannot do much besides the elimination of as many introduced plants and animals as is possible. This has been accomplished with some success of which the following are examples:

(a) *Plazas*. Two small islands (0·23 km²) just off the east side of Santa Cruz. Goats were eradicated from these islands about ten years ago. A result of this is that *Portulaca howelli* (Legr.) Eliass., rare on the large islands due to browsing by goats, is common here.

(b) *Rabida*, a somewhat larger island (4·9 km²) south of San Salvador. Goats were eradicated several years ago, reintroduced and hunted to extinction again last year.

(c) *Santa Fé*, (24 km²), situated southeast of Santa Cruz. Goats had lived here for at least a hundred years (Wolf, 1879) and had affected the vegetation strongly. Species as *Scalesia helleri* Robins. ssp. *helleri* only survived in small numbers on steep cliffs (Eliasson, 1974). The arid zone vegetation was reduced to an open parkland with scattered trees. The shrub and herb layers were greatly damaged. Since the elimination of the goats the vegetation has become denser and several species, including *Scalesia helleri* ssp. *helleri*, are increasing in numbers.

(d) *Española*, a medium-sized island (58 km²) in the southeastern part of the archipelago. Española is also covered with an arid zone vegetation. After an intensive campaign last year, the island is now believed to be free of goats. Realistically however, one can only be sure of this in a few years.

(e) *Pinta*, an island about the same size as Española (60 km²), situated in the northern part of the archipelago. Pinta is about 650 m high (Adsersen, 1976) and carries at the upper elevations an evergreen forest dominated by *Zanthoxylum fagara*. In 1959 goats were introduced here and, by 1970, large areas were already destroyed (Weber, 1971). By 1971 the situation on Pinta was probably as critical as it is now on San Salvador. The size of Pinta, however, is such that by hunting the number of goats can be drastically reduced. More than 38 000 goats have been killed since 1971 (Annual Report of the CDRS, 1975). The vegetation has responded quickly to this decrease in the goat population. In 1975 the small number of shrubs in the Transition zone was still noticeable; however, the vegetation in the *Zanthoxylum* forest was already similar to descriptions of the original condition (see also Adsersen, 1976). There is hope that within a few years goats will be eliminated altogether from Pinta. This success, together with the removal of goats on Española, will be two large steps towards the conservation of the Galapagos Islands.

Acknowledgements

I should like to express my thanks to Dr. R. Gradstein who read the manuscript critically and to Dr. D. M. Porter who also suggested improvements in the sections dealing with climate and soil. The field work in the Galapagos Islands was made possible through a grant from the Dutch Foundation for the Advancement of Tropical Research (WOTRO).

REFERENCES

Adsersen, H. (1976). A Botanist's notes on Pinta. *Not. de Galápagos* **24**, 26–28
Bailey, K. (1976). Potassium-Argon Ages from the Galapagos Islands. *Science* **192**, 465–466

Banfield, A. F., Behre, C. H. and St. Clair, D. (1956). Geology of Isabela Island, Archipelago de Colon (Galapagos). *Bull. Geol. Soc. Amer.* **67**, 215–234

Bowman, R. I. (1961). Morphological differentiation and adaptation in the Galapagos finches. *Univ. Calif. Publ. Zool.* **58**, 1–302

Calvopiña, L. H. and de Vries, T. (1975). Estructura de la poblacion de cabras salvajes (Capra hircus L.) y los daños causados en la vegetacion de la isla San Salvador, Galápagos. *Rev. de la Univ. Católica, Quito, Ecuador* **8**, 219–241

Cox, A. and Dalrymple, G. B. (1966). Palaeomagnetism and potassium argon ages of some volcanic rocks from the Galapagos Islands. *Nature,* **209**, 776–777

Eliasson, U. (1974). Studies in Galapagos plants 14. The Genus Scalesia. *Opera Bot.* **36**, 1–117

Laruelle, J. (1966). Study of a soil sequence on Indefatigable Island. In *The Galapagos* (R. I. Bowman, ed.). University of California Press, Berkeley and Los Angeles

McDougall, I. (1972). Potassium argon ages of lavas from the Hawaii and Pololu volcanic series Kohala volcano, Hawaii. *Bull. Geol. Soc. Amer.* **83**, 3731–3738

Palmer, C. E. and Pyle, R. L. (1966). The climatological setting of the Galapagos. In *The Galapagos* (R. I. Bowman, ed.) University of California Press, Berkeley and Los Angeles

Reeder, W. G. and Riechert, S. E. (1975). Vegetation change along an altitudinal gradient, Santa Cruz. *Biotropica* **7**, 162–175

Slevin, J. R. (1959). The Galapagos Islands. A history of their exploration. *Occas. Pap. Calif. Acad. Sci.* **25**, 1–150

Stewart, A. (1915). Some observations concerning the botanical conditions on the Galapagos Islands. *Trans. Wisc. Acad. Sci. Arts & Letters* **18**, 272–340

Vanderbilt, W. K. (1927). *To Galapagos on the Ara.* Privately printed, New York

Weber, D. (1971). Pinta, Galapagos: Une Île á sauver. *Biol. Conserv.* **4**, 8–12

Wiggins, I. L. and Porter, D. M. (1971). *Flora of the Galapagos Islands.* University Press, Stanford

Wolf, Th. (1879). Ein Besuch der Galapagos Inseln, mit drei Kaertchen. *Samml. Vortr. deutsches Volk* **1**, 259–300

21 Problems of Biological Conservation in Madagascar

WERNER RAUH   *Institute of Systematic Botany, University of Heidelberg, Germany*

Madagascar, una de las cuatro islas más grandes del mundo, tiene una flora única con un porcentaje muy alto de endemismos y siete familias de plantas se conocen solo para la isla. Muchas plantas y animales científicamente muy importantes han llegado a extinguirse en tiempos históricos, incluyendo lemures, ostras gigantes y tortugas de tierra.

Las principales communidades de plantas en la isla son señaladas y el autor insiste en la peligrosa situación de todos los tipos de vegetación. Las actividades del hombre que ha destruido ya alrededor del 80% de los primitivos bosques tropicales y el xerofítico terreno virgen. Los efectos de las prácticas agrícolas a base de incendios y otras, conocidas como cultivo "tavy" son discutidos y se explica el papel del ganado de Zebu en los rituales religiosos del pueblo malgache y en la destrucción de la vegetación natural.

Aunque durante la administración colonial francesa se creó una cadena de reservas naturales y parques naturales que cubren la mayoría de los tipos naturales de vegetación, estos no parecen haber sido bien mantenidos después de que la isla logró su independencia a pesar del número aparentemente importante de decretos gubernamentales. El autor recalca la necesidad de hacer grandes esfuerzos para la conservación, a nivél internacional, especialmente en términos de ayuda financiera, para salvar algunos remanentes de las curiosidades naturales de la "Grande Île".

Introduction

With a surface area of about 600 000 km², a length of approximately 1500 km and a maximum width of 500 km, Madagascar is one of the four largest islands of the world and is aptly known as "La Grande Île". In spite of its proximity to Africa, separated from the continent by the 400 km wide Mozambique Channel, Madagascar shows biologically relatively few affinities with Africa. The "Great Island" has been isolated from the continent since the Jurassic and its flora and fauna have, therefore, acquired a very pronounced individuality. This peculiar feature was recognised very early by biologists and the island has been generally considered as a separate microcontinent with a very high percentage of endemism. Today, we know about 10 000 Angiosperm species from Madagascar and more than 80% of these are endemic. Within these we

405

find very peculiar and very old phylogenetic groups so that Madagascar can be considered as a "museum of living fossils". The fauna of the island is also rich in peculiarities and endemic groups such as the lemurs, turtles and many others. I have mentioned about 10 000 as the known number of Angiosperms but this is surely only a small proportion of a much higher number of taxa which once covered the wide plains of Madagascar and of which we have no knowledge, for nearly 80% of the primary vegetation of the island has already been destroyed. Many species have disappeared as a result of the destruction of the plant biotopes and the fauna has also disappeared. The giant Malagasy Ostriches *Aepyornis* and *Mullerornis* became extinct centuries ago. We have little idea of the numbers of extinct plants and invertebrate animals; many will have disappeared before ever having been seen by scientists.

Physiognomy

Before discussing conservation problems in more detail it is necessary to present a brief survey of the geology, climatology and phytogeography of the "Great Island".

One of the main characteristics of the physical geography and geological structure is the asymmetry of Madagascar (Fig. 1) which can be divided into three large regions:

1   The eastern mountain range which extends from SW to NE with steep slopes to the Indian Ocean and a small, more or less sandy coastal plain. The mountain range is covered with tropical rainforest now mostly destroyed and replaced by secondary vegetation called *savoka*.

2   The central highlands (plateau central) with an altitude of 1500–2000 m surpassed by old volcanic massifs such as Tsaratanana in the north which is the highest point of the island reaching 2876 m and the Andringintra-massif in the centre with Pic Boby (2610 m). The whole eastern part of the island consists of old crystalline rocks, of granite and gneiss. Nowhere do the mountains reach 3000 m and there is, therefore, no permanent snow or glacier zone. The high plateau is a vast plain over which the old crystalline surface layers have been transformed into a red laterite soil which can be up to 30 m thick.

3   The western part of the island, separated from the high plateau by the Bonga-lava fracture, consists of Mesozoic, Tertiary and Quaternary sediment-layers, lime- and sandstones which are inclined in several terraces to the Mozambique channel. Southwards the high plateau peters out and merges into the Mahafaly and Antandroy limestone plains. Only in the extreme south near Fort Dauphin are there mountains which reach an altitude of about 1400–2000 m a short distance from the coast. In the north the Montagnes d'Ambres, with an elevation of up to 1400 m, cut off the Diego-Suarez region from the humid trade winds.

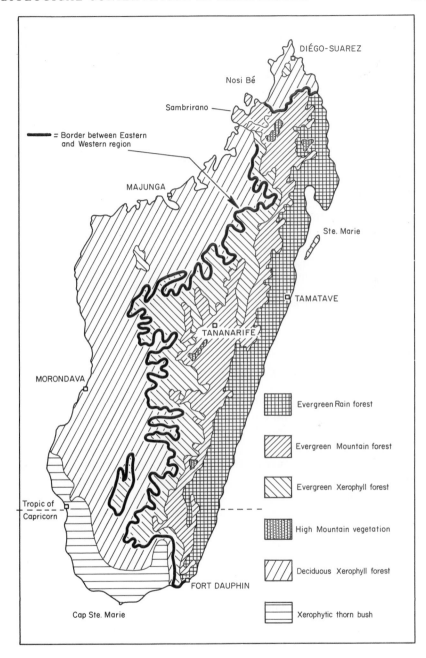

FIG. 1 The climax vegetation of Madagascar (modified after Humbert)

The climate of Madagascar

The asymmetrical relief of the island produces a consequent asymmetry in the climate. In principle there are two main seasons, the cold southern winter (April to October) and the warm summer (November to March). In winter the SE trade winds discharge most of their humidity on the steep slopes of the eastern mountain range and reach the plateau as dry winds, similar to the Föhn, only light rain or mist providing the highest mountains with moisture. Hoar-frosts on the mountains are not rare. The southern and southwest regions do not receive any humidity other than early-morning dew.

In summer rain falls over the whole island but the amount diminishes from north to south especially in the western region. Rainfall data can be summarised as follows:

	Region	Rainfall (mm)	Dry season
1	E. slopes of eastern mt. range	4000	No dry month
2	High plateau	1500	3–4 months
3	W. slopes of the plateau	1500	5–6 months
4	Middle and NW plains	700–1200	7–8 months
5	S. and SW region	300–500	Irregular, no wet month

Vegetation

Madagascar can be divided into very distinct phytogeographical regions, both in their vegetation and climate. (1) The eastern region (la région du vent), (2) the western region (la région sous le vent) and (3) the southern and southwestern region.

1   The eastern region includes the following areas, (*a*) the eastern part of the island which is characterised by high rainfall and humidity, high temperatures and a dense, evergreen, ombrophilous rainforest; (*b*) the high plateau including the centre of the island and those parts of the eastern region above 800 m and the high mountains. Rainfall is about 1500 mm mostly during the warm season and frequent mist is typical of higher altitudes. The climax vegetation is small-leaved, evergreen mountain-mist forest rich in tree-ferns epiphytes especially orchids, ferns and mosses; (*c*) the high mountains over 2000 m where the climax vegetation is mistforest with abundant epiphytes, mostly mosses and lichens. The upper border of this forest is formed by ericaceous bush (*Philippia*) and grassland; (*d*) the western slopes of the central plateau with rainfall below 1500 m falling only during the rainy season. The climax vegetation is a low forest of hard, evergreen sclerophyllous shrubs

(*Uapaca bojeri* Baill., Euphorbiaceae and members of the endemic family Sarcolaenaceae); (*e*) the Sambirano region of northwest Madagascar, a transition zone between the tropical rainforest of the east and the sclerophyllous forest of the western slopes of the central plateau.

2   The western region including the whole western side of the island has a rainfall of below 1500 mm and dry period of 6–8 months. The climax vegetation is rain-green, deciduous forest with a high percentage of interesting woody endemic succulents (*Adenia, Ampelocissus* etc.). This phytogeographical region includes also the northern Diego-Suarez region which is separated from Sambirano by the Montagnes d'Ambre.

3   The southern and southwestern region which is characterised by the aridity of the climate. The rainfall never exceeds 500 mm and is very irregular. There are years without any measurable rain and the vegetation is extremely xerophilous with many spiny plants. The substrate is poor with skeletal soils, limestones, red sandstones (sables roux) and sand-dunes near the coast.

The vegetation of the south has been defined by Perrier (1921) and Humbert (1927) as bush, a thicket in which the representatives of two families predominate, aphyllous *Euphorbia* species and the very thorny, endemic Didiereaceae (especially *Didierea* itself), which, in the Old World, show a striking convergence to the Cactaceae of the New World. The *Euphorbia-Didierea* bush looks, therefore, like the Caatinga of South America; the rosette life-form of the South American Bromeliads being replaced in Madagascar by several endemic *Aloe* species (Fig. 2a, b). The herb layer is generally absent or poorly developed with some dwarf succulent *Euphorbia*, Stapeliads (*Stapelianthus*), Cucurbits (*Seyrigea, Xerosicyos*) *Kalanchoe, Vellozia* etc., some poikilohydrous ferns and *Selaginella*, but very few Gramineae. This vegetation which is restricted to a small coastal region about 50 km wide is one of the most remarkable plant associations of Madagascar with the highest percentage of endemic plants and animals.

Changes in the vegetation of Madagascar

According to Humbert (1927) the climax plant communities of the island were undisturbed before the arrival of Man on Madagascar. In his opinion there was no natural area for the extensive grassland formation which today covers the greater part of the island. Only the swampy regions with *Raphia* and *Pandanus* swamps had a considerable covering of Gramineae and Cyperaceae.

A present-day distribution map of the vegetation shows that 80% of the primary vegetation described by Humbert no longer exists and has been

(b)

(a)

Fig. 2 Endangered natural vegetation and plant species of Madagascar; (a) rainforest, (b) Xerophytic *Didierea* bushland, (c) *Pachypodium lamerei*, (d) *Aloe suzannae*

replaced by secondary communities. The main reason for this alteration has been the activity of Man.

The total surface area of Madagascar is about 58 million hectares of which 53 million are occupied by some form of secondary vegetation which means that only 5 million hectares, including the southern bush, remain as natural vegetation. These include 2·5 million hectares of tropical rainforest, 1·5 million hectares of southern xerophytic bush and 1 million hectares of mountain sclerophyllous and deciduous forest of the plateau and west. The remaining 53 million hectares are divided between 6 million hectares of *savoka* and 47 million hectares of monotonous grassland which suffer tremendously from erosion in the rainy season when the rivers turn red with eroded material and the ocean is discoloured up to a distance of 50 km from the coast.

The deforestation has caused not only changes in the microclimate but has also destroyed the ecosystems of many endemic animals, thus causing the extinction, in the last few centuries, of all large animals, called in Madagascar "subfossil species", such as the large, running birds (ratites) *Aepyornis maximus*, *A. medius*, *A. hildebrandtii*, *Mullerornis*, the giant land-turtle *Testudo grandidieri* and the pygmy *Hippotamus lemerlii*. In addition, a considerable number of lemurs of the genera *Megaladapis* and *Palaeopropithecus* has also disappeared. In less than 200 years the green island of Madagascar has been transformed into a red island simply by the activity of Man!

The first immigrants, Palaeo-Indonesians, probably arrived about AD 500 and were the ancestors of the Sakalava tribe of the western region. There were probably further immigrations in the 9th–13th centuries, the Neo-Indonesians who were the forebearers of the highland Merina and northern Betsileo tribes and between the 8th and 18th centuries the west coast was settled by Africans and Arabs. These immigrants introduced Zebu cattle to the island and these still play an important rôle in the rituals of the Malagasy people and are one of the major factors in vegetation destruction.

The Palaeo-Indonesians practised shifting agriculture and had probably destroyed much of the natural forests when the later immigrants reached the central regions of the island. The Neo-Indonesians were rice farmers and continued with the destruction of the primary vegetation with their system of burning-agriculture.

The present population of the island is over 6 million people and their primitive agricultural systems are still in use thereby destroying even the small proportion of remaining natural vegetation. The recent introduction of Mohair goats for wool in the south and southwest has put further severe pressure on the Didiereaceae bush where the goats eat the young leaves of *Alluaudia* and *Didierea* despite their large, sharp thorns.

Shifting cultivation – "La practique des tavys"

This system of agriculture involves clearing of an area of rainforest and plantation with maize, dry-rice, manioc or batatas. Only a single crop is harvested and then a new "tavy" is cut down in a different area. The rains of the following season then erode and leach the soil to such an extent that only a degraded *savoka* can be re-established with undergrowth species such as *Ravenala madagascariensis* J. F. Gmel. (travellers-tree) (Fig. 3b), the bamboo *Ochlandra capitata* (Willd.) Camus, *Haronga madagascariensis* Choisy, an arborescent Hypericaceae and some introduced species such as *Solanum auriculatum* Aiton, *Rubus rosaefolium* Sm. and *R. mollucanus* L., "le vigne maronne". Particularly the *Rubus* species have become rampant weeds which invade and destroy the remaining primary forest ecosystems in the highlands, for example in Perinet.

The *savoka* is eventually replaced by grassland as fires further ravage the secondary communities.

European settlers have also destroyed the forest ecosystem by removing valuable timber trees such as *Diospyros perrieri* Jumelle and *Dalbergia* species.

Burning cultivation

Large areas of natural vegetation have been burned since the Palaeo-Indonesians invaded the island. The burning has been carried out in order to provide pasture-land for Zebu cattle. The number of grass species is very limited, *Aristida rufescens* Steud., *Hyparrhenia rufa* Stapf, *Heteropogon contortus* Beauv. ex R. & S. and *Imperata cylindrica* Beauv. which covers the poorest soils. Besides these only a few ephemeral or fire-resistant plants are able to survive, *Aloe macrocada* Baker, *Euphorbia* spp., ground orchids (*Habenaria, Liparis* etc.) and others. The palm savannas of the west and south (Isalo mountains) with *Hyphaene schatan* Boj., *Medemia noblis* Wehmer, *Borassus madagascariensis* Boj. and *Chrysolidocarpus decipiens* Becc. are also secondary formations as the palms or their seeds are fire-resistant. Several resistant endemics in Sarcolaenaceae and Compositae (*Dicoma incana* O. Hoffm.) are found in this formation as well as a few introduced species such as *Zizyphus mauritanicus* Lam.

The vast areas of grassland are burned year after year just before the start of the rainy season when the Zebu cattle no longer feed on the old, hard grass-leaves. When the rain comes, the burned grass-tufts rapidly develop fresh and tender young leaves which are excellent fodder for the cattle.

Most of the "Inselberge" of the plateau are not affected by the fires and

FIG. 3   (a) Sisal cultivation in the southern bush region, (b) Secondary vegetation of
Ravenala madagascariensis in former rainforest area of the southeast.

still harbour, therefore, relatively natural, extremely xerophytic communities with succulent *Pachypodium, Aloe, Kalanchoe, Cynanchum, Euphorbia* species, etc.

Zebu cattle

· Estimates place the number of Zebu on the island at over 10 million, somewhat larger than the human population, and Zebu cattle play a very important role in the lives of the Malagasy people, especially in their religious rituals.

The possession of a large herd (Fig. 4a) of male animals is considered a sign of wealth though, in fact, little profit is obtained from them and it is almost impossible to distinguish a rich from a poor man. The difference only becomes visible once he dies. The rich man is buried in a large tomb (Fig. 4b) which is paid for with Zebu and the actual burial ceremony is a major tribal festival when hundreds of cattle may be killed and eaten. The burial ceremony is one of the rare occasions when the Malagasy eat large quantities of meat. To signify the importance of the cattle tombs are decorated with "Alo-Alo", beautiful wood carvings which symbolically bear the figure of the Zebu and the tombs are also adorned with the horns of all the cattle eaten during the long burial ceremony.

These ritual burial ceremonies probably originated in Asia and are most predominant in the Mahafaly and Antandroy tribes and because death is expensive in terms of Zebu cattle people live and work only in order to obtain a large herd for their burial ceremony.

In the highlands the Merina and Betsileo tribes have different burial customs. They do not construct tombs individually, but have communal tribal tombs. Each year they celebrate the festival of "Retournement des morts" when they open the graves, take out the remains and wrap them in new clothes. This ceremony is a major festival and many Zebu are slaughtered. The Malagasy people have many ritual cult-ceremonies for which Zebu must be killed.

In order to maintain their vast herds of Zebu, the Malagasy have to burn the landscape. Aided by the wind, the fires rage over the country destroying the last remainders of the forest vegetation. The annual fires lead to a regressive evolution. As long as the soil is still rich in minerals, it is covered by a savanna with *Hyparrhenia rufa* and *Heteropogon contortus* but when all the minerals have been leached out only *Aristida multicaulis* Baker is able to survive and eventually the final stage of degeneration to bare earth and rock is reached.

There could, however, be a progressive improvement if fires were

(a)

(b)

FIG. 4   (a) Zebu herds in S. Madagascar, (b) Malagache tomb adorned with Zebu horns.

controlled. In spite of heavy grazing recolonisation by shrubs is possible but a true primary vegetation could never regenerate.

The grasslands are monotonous and poor in species, only about 1000 species are known from these areas whereas the 5 million hectares of primary forest harbour over 6000 species.

Forestry

In order to stop the process of erosion and also to provide timber for construction and fuel the forest service has made enormous efforts in afforestation, above all in the highlands. Indigenous species are generally slow growing so various species of *Eucalyptus* have been planted. Today these plantations cover 200 000 hectares and though *Eucalyptus* does prevent erosion to some extent it does not improve the quality of the soil as leaves do not rot quickly to form humus and also sterilise the soil inhibiting growth of other species below them. Several conifers such as *Pinus patula* Schiede & Deppe (Mexico), *P. khaysa* Royle ex Gord. (NE Asia) and *P. caribaea* Morelet have been introduced and *Acacia dealbata* Link was brought in for fuel and charcoal production. This species has, however, proved to be extremely invasive and a noxious weed in some parts of South America and South Africa.

The most intact plant formation in Madagascar is the southern *Euphorbia*-Didiereaceae bush. The reason being that the bush is relatively open and the plants grow in naked skeletal soil virtually without a herbaceous layer but in recent years the Mahafaly and Antandroy tribes have started rather unsuccessfully "tavy" cultivation for maize. European settlers have also destroyed parts of the southern bush, cutting down the largest specimens of *Alluaudia procera* Drake for making boards but fortunately this process seems to have been stopped. Many hectares of Didiereaceae bush have also been cut down in the Amboasary region for sisal (*Agave* spp.) plantations (Fig. 3a) and though the plantations proved to be economically inviable the sisal *Agave* plants remain and are, by means of their extremely effective vegetative reproduction, invading the margins of the natural communities and disturbing the delicate ecological balance.

In view of this pressure and also grazing by Zebu and Mohair goats Humbert (1927) predicted that the southern semi-arid bush region will eventually be transformed into a desert waste. In this region it is not only the endemic flora but also the rich fauna which is endangered. The lemur "Chi-fac" (*Propithecus verrauxii*) was formerly very frequent in the bush but both the Antandroy and Mahafaly hunt this beautiful animal for food and it is becoming consequently increasingly rare. The endemic star-turtle, *Testudo radiata*, is taboo for both the southern tribes and they will not eat it. It is, however, a favourite dish of the inhabitants of the island of Réunion and, therefore, the turtles are carried off in thousands from the Fort Dauphin region and exported by the boatload to Réunion. The situation has reached such a stage that only immediate drastic action will prevent the species being added to the list of extinct Madagascan fauna.

Conclusions

In conclusion it must be stated that the survival of the Madagascan flora and fauna is alarmingly endangered. We probably still only know a small percentage of the taxa, yet the clock shows 5 minutes to 12 o'clock. We have to attempt to mobilise all efforts in order to save what can be saved. French biologists such as Perrier de la Bathie, Humbert, Paulian and Millot, who have lived for many years on the island, have incessantly warned of the dangers but they also realised that the damage already done cannot be repaired. Too many species which could have given us information on the origin and evolution of the Madagascan flora and fauna have disappeared for ever. We are morally obliged in these circumstances to protect and conserve, with all our power, the last remains of this unique biotope and we have to ask, therefore, what can be done and how can the following proposals be acted upon?

1   An absolute prohibition of burning in those regions where the remaining primary vegetation could be destroyed. Grass-fires should only be permitted in areas where degradation has proceeded to such an extent that regeneration of even a bush-savanna would hardly be possible.

2   It is necessary to delimit grazing regions by means of fences and improve pasture-land with chemical fertilisers. Improved grass and legume races should be introduced. Given that water is available for the whole year this should be possible and is a question of providing adequate economic aid for the purpose.

3   The number of Zebu cattle should be reduced and replaced with more productive stock. Zebu are well adapted to the special conditions of Madagascar but in other tropical regions with a similar climate improved races of cattle are doing well. The growth-rate of Zebu is very slow and in 6–8 years they only achieve a body-weight of 330–420 kg and have a milk production of about 380 litres per year.

4   The "tavy" cultivation system should be prohibited and the nomadic tribes settled.

5   In the southern bush the villages could be removed from the intact bush to areas with better agricultural conditions. This would be difficult

because only a single water-hole, the famous well near the riverbed of the Linta south of Ampanihy, is available. This problem could be solved by digging more wells.

6 Water reservoirs should be created. Most rainfall is lost as run-off after the heavy storms and, using modern methods, the drier areas of the island could be irrigated.

The colonial French biologists saw the greatest chance for biological conservation in the creation of nature reserves and national parks and had already started their efforts as early as 1927. Over a period of 30 years 12 nature reserves and 2 National Parks were established. Unfortunately the status of one of the reserves, the Masoala Peninsula, was removed in 1964 by government decree. This reserve was originally of 27 682 hectares and had a very interesting flora and fauna.

The remaining reserves cover about 700 000 hectares and are so arranged that they reasonably cover the diversity and variability of the Madagascan flora and fauna. Besides the major reserves there are also a number of small zoological reserves for the protection of birds, turtles and lemurs.

With the aid of IUCN a special reserve on the small island of Nosy Mangabe in the Masoala bay was recently established especially for the protection of the "Aye-Aye" lemur *Daubentonia madagascariensis*. The "Aye-Aye" was brought from the "Great Island" to Nosy Mangabe and introduced into a similar biotope and it is hoped that it will be now protected from the attacks of Man.

The two National Parks can be visited by tourists with a special permit from the "service des Eaux et Forêts". These parks are in the Ambre mountains of the north near Diego-Suarez and the Isalo mountain-range in the south. Few tourists, however, visit these areas. Perhaps fortunately, Madagascar has not yet had the tourist invasion of other parts of Africa and the small number of tourists who do come to the "Great Island" visit only Tananarive, perhaps Antsirabé and Fort Dauphin or the island of Nosi Bé with its coconut-palm beaches. Madagascar has little to offer tourists who like grandiose landscapes and large mammals. It is a fascinating country only for biologists: a "museum of living fossils". If tourism is to be stimulated, it is essential to create special tourist areas where tourists can see, with the aid of trained guides, all the unique flora and fauna in their natural biotopes and in easily accessible reserves. A start has already been made with the zoological park of Tsimabzaza in Tananarive. The concept of nature reserves is an idealistic one. Projects in Africa and North America have shown that nature protection is possible if a large enough staff of trained wardens is available and if the mass of people, school children etc., have been educated in the importance of their local biological communities and if their interest in conservation is awakened. At the moment, little has been done in this sense in Madagascar. The government has, however, published a long decree concerning conservation and listing all the animals which cannot be hunted or caught without a special permit and hunting is forbidden during breeding seasons. There is also a special list of plant species, especially orchids with ornamental flowers of commercial value, which are completely protected.

We have to ask, however, if such a decree is of use for a population who cannot read or write? More than 50% of the older generations of Malagasy people have no formal education and there is no supervisory service to enforce the decree in the field.

In the period when Madagascar was a French colony the French government tried to reduce the numbers of Zebu by claiming a 5 franc tax for each head of cattle. The result was, however, that when tax-collectors appeared in the villages only a few taxable Zebu were found, the remainder had been driven out of sight into the bush away from the roads to be rounded up again later. The situation with the nature reserves is very similar. They look good and instructive on a map of Madagascar but the reality of the situation is quite different. Some of the reserves such as No. 8 near Namoraka which gives a cross-section of the western limestone biotopes, and Reserve No. 9, Tsingydu Bemaraha near Antsalova, which is tropical forest on limestone are not accessible by roads and so are very difficult to reach.

The reserve in the Tsaratanana mountains in the north of the island can only be reached by a difficult expedition and it is assumed that this protects it as it has not so far been destroyed by the indigenous people.

The author himself has visited several of the reserves. First, one needs a special permit from "Eaux et Forêts" to enter the reserve, second it is, on paper, strictly prohibited to collect plants even if one knows that some of them may be new and undescribed species. In practise, however, one enters the reserve by a gate with a few metres of fence on either side. The main parts of the reserve are unfenced so that Zebu can enter freely and graze. Few of the reserves appear to have full-time efficient wardens to enforce regulations.

According to Millot (1972) the reserves often serve as refuges for fugitives from justice and tax evaders who live there at the expense of the protected animals and even go so far as to practise shifting agriculture as areal surveys of the areas have shown. Elsewhere goats and cattle are allowed to graze and the Ankafaratsika Reserve is so neglected that nearly 70% of it has been burned in recent years.

We are conscious that the existing reserves offer very little protection for the flora and fauna at the moment. Millot (1972) says, however, that "what has been done in Kenya and South Africa would be perfectly possible in Madagascar if authorities from the Minister to village headmen were fully aware of the importance of the measures to be taken, and if they refused any concession, even partial, in these reserved areas to any commercial undertaking whatsoever. It is to be hoped that international pressure will succeed in convincing the government of Madagascar of the importance of these problems".

In comparison with reserves in Kenya or South Africa those of Madagascar, we must remember, do not generally attract tourists or bring money into the country, and this is essential in order to maintain the reserves. Madagascar is, in the economic sense, a poor country which must be supported by financial help from outside organisations. At the moment the primitive Malgache cannot understand the need for part of this aid to be used for the conservation of a biological paradise which is unique in the world. Immediate help is needed so that future generations will be able to see something of the curiosities of Madagascar.

REFERENCES

Humbert, G. (1927). La destruction d'une flore insulaire par le feu. *Mém. Acad. Malgache V*

Millot, J. (1972). In Conclusion. In *Biogeography and Ecology of Madagascar* (R. Battistini and G. Richard-Vindard, eds.) *Monographie Biologicae* **21**, Junk, The Hague

Perrier de la Bathie, H. (1921). La végetation Malagache. *Ann. Mus. Colon., Marseille* Ser. 3. **9**, 1–266

22 The Threatened Plants Committee of IUCN and Island Floras

G. Ll. LUCAS *Royal Botanic Gardens, Kew, England*

Dá la impresión de que las predicciones de antaño, que aseguraban que un 10% de las plantas del mundo estaban en peligro, están en la actualidad siendo mantenidas por la información recopilada por el Secretariado del Comité de Plantas Amenazadas (CPA). Esto parece particularmente cierto en las masas templadas continentales donde "conocemos" la flora razonablemente bien. Por ejemplo, en los E.U. aproximadamente 2100 especies están en peligro, o un 10.4% de las grandes plantas. En Europa, una cifra aproximada de 1500 especies están amenazadas, siendo exactamente menos de un 10% de la flora total.

Los peligros son muchos y diversos debido, en su mayoría a que la sociedad está basada en un engrosamiento de la economía y la necesidad general de producir más alimento para la gran población del mundo.

Está bastante claro de que el área disponible para todas las formas de "expansión" está limitada sobre cualquier isla y las presiones son más intensas – añádase a esto el alto grado de endemismos en la mayoría de los ecosistemas isleños y los resultados son números severamente más altos de especies amenazadas con un total de extinción. Un ejemplo del problema se muestra en Haway, donde 1088 especies y subespecies de una flora de c. 2200 especies, se encuentran en la lista de las amenazadas.

La primera tarea por consiguiente del Comité de Plantas Amenazadas IUCN, es obvia – recoger información de aquellos que saben, que son botánicos y todo aquel que trabaje en ese campo – de ustedes mismos, de manera que se asegure una exacta información que esté disponible para las personas encargadas de tomar las decisiones.

Esto es más facil decirlo que hacerlo – muchas áreas estarán perdidas, incluso antes de que la taxonomía básica sea llevado a cabo, y mucho antes de que empezemos a entender la biología de estas plantas. Sin embargo, debemos intentarlo ¡todos nosotros! Aquí debo decir que las islas tienen una dudosa ventaja en el contexto de conservación, porque con su flora limitada, es posible proveer datos exactos más facilmente que los bosques de lluvias tropicales.

La recogida de información es solo un punto de partida – Hay que dar el próximo paso vital.

La producción de prácticas medidas de conservación debe llevarse a efecto, no con esperanzas teóricas, pero si con sugerencias prácticas de cómo reservas o especies pueden jugar una parte en planes locales de desarrollo. La conservación en un vacio no es posible. Nosotros, como hombres de ciencias capaces de leer los factores como estudiamos nuestras regiones o grupos, tenemos una seria responsabilidad de comunicar nuestra ansiedad por las especies perdidas y lo que esto significa para el futuro, no ahora uno para con otro, sino para decidir hacerlo directamente y/o a través de IUCN CPA para asegurar la supervivencia de la diversidad de especies de plantas para un largo futuro. Debemos ser realistas y positivos con nuestras recomendaciones si hemos de tener éxito en esta nuestra más seria tarea.

Introduction

Islands were one of the first places where the results of Man's dramatic impact on natural ecosystems became apparent most forcefully, attracting early concern to endangered plants and threatened floras. The goats and other feral animals that devastated the floras of so many oceanic islands were introduced not over the last few decades but mostly between the 16th and 19th centuries. For example, in the case of St. Helena, the goats were first introduced in 1513 and damage was done before the island was thoroughly explored botanically. Hooker (in Melliss, 1875) estimated that there must have been over 100 endemic species in this "wonderfully curious little flora", but by 1805–10, when Burchell was on the island and made the first extensive collections, only small patches of the original forest remained; no more than 31 endemic species are known today. This familiar story is now being repeated in the rainforest floras of Amazonia and Central America. This concern at the high extinction rate in island floras over the last few centuries was a vital stimulus to the Survival Service Commission of IUCN when they set up the Threatened Plants Committee (TPC) in 1974; it has also led to the beginning of a world awareness of the problem, at least among botanists and conservationists, on which we have been able to build up the work of the TPC. Indeed, the high losses on islands provided the germ of an idea: to do for plants what had been done for animals, namely to find out precisely which species were rare and threatened, and above all to find out what were the threats to their survival. For it is perhaps on an understanding of the threats rather than of the species that effective conservation action will depend.

Threats to plants

The threats to plants are many and diverse, but most can be traced to two main causes: firstly, the concept of an expanding economy as the basis of our society, an idea still strongest in the most affluent countries, and secondly, the great pressure on vegetation by an expanding and hungry population in the developing world. The general need to produce more food, using the artificial and vulnerable ecosystems of modern agriculture rather than the more stable ones dependent on natural resources, can be seen as the strongest of all the threats to many plants.

In some regions, the pressure on vegetation for food and firewood production is leading not only to massive losses of species but also eventually to a breakdown in the food-producing capacity of the land, as brilliantly and tragically documented by Eckholm (1976). This catastrophic loss of agricultural potential has occurred over much of the Sahel area where humane but misdirected "improvements", particularly veterinary aid and well-drilling, resulted in a massive increase in livestock. Productivity was only maintained until the onset of the inevitable cycle of dry years, when the damage quickly accelerated and became non-recoverable. The human and ecological problems now faced in the ecologically unstable areas of the arid zone are perhaps more intractable, more complex and on a wider scale than any faced before on this planet. The political will to restore agricultural potential may exist, as the recent UNEP Desertification Conference showed so well, but the social and technical problems in any effective action are very formidable indeed. Restoration of vegetation, and hence of the plant species, is absolutely fundamental for the long-term survival of Man in such areas, and protecting threatened plants is one of the roots of the problem.

Clearly it is unrealistic to think that in such situations we as botanists can save such plants, although the scenario just outlined is perhaps the worst of them all. Nevertheless, for all areas, it is essential that the decision-makers planning the development of their country should have available the appropriate conservation data so that they can be aware of the consequences of their action in terms of species loss and the wider ecological consequences for the future. To do this we need a basic taxonomy for all regions, so that for each area of forest that is to be destroyed they know which species may be made extinct or put at risk. Such information provides forceful arguments with politicians, as they are likely to be far more responsive to arguments supported by information on individual species, unique to their country, for which they can feel a responsibility, than to arguments on general habitat approaches in which each area to be conserved is considered only on the various vegetation and phytosociological groupings.

In much of the tropics, the major threats can be given very simply: over-grazing; shifting cultivation; logging and chipping; and large scale destruction of native vegetation for conversion to prairie and plantation agriculture.

However on the continental land masses of the temperate zone, the situation is very different. The species threatened occupy only a small portion of the land area and a reserve development policy to include *all* threatened species is a possibility. Many of the threatened species are small herbs and the majority grow in areas that are of low agricultural potential. Conservation is appreciated as a means of enhancing the way of life and the future for the floras seems more assured. The threats are detailed below, in addition to those mentioned above: Changes in existing agriculture, in particular the use of chemical sprays and ploughing of old, herb-rich grasslands; forestry (e.g. changes in practice, drainage, monocultures of exotic species); regeneration of scrub (and lack of grazing); dam-construction and/or (associated) flooding of large areas; drainage of wetlands; water pollution; air pollution; industrialisation and urbanisation; road building; tourism and tourist developments – coastal and inland; mining and quarrying; pressure from introduced plants; lack of pollinators; critically low population (hence danger of breeding collapse); collecting for botany; collecting for horticulture; traditional rural uses; and natural causes.

How do these very general considerations affect island floras? All the evidence received by the TPC so far suggests that the threats to plants on islands are not dissimilar from those elsewhere, and that islands show very much a microcosm of world problems. There are island plants in danger from nearly all of the threats given above. However, due to the limited room for expansion on any island, the pressures become more intense and the threats more severe. Add to this the high degree of endemism in most island ecosystems and the small population sizes of most island endemics, and the threats become very severe indeed. A further danger is the fragility of island ecosystems, especially those which have been isolated for long periods of time, and the subsequent vulnerability of much of the endemic element to vigorous introduced plants and animals. The result is a considerably higher percentage of the flora that is threatened with total extinction. Whereas the early prediction of about 10% of the World's flora being dangerously rare or under severe threat is being borne out by the lists being completed for the main land-masses of the temperate zone, the percentage of threatened species is much higher. For example, the U.S.A. List (Smithsonian Institution, 1975) includes 2099 species, subspecies and varieties which represent 10·4% of the flora. The latest version of the TPC List for Europe also includes around 2000 species, but this represents a rather higher percentage of the European flora (IUCN Threatened Plants Committee, 1977). In contrast, for the Hawaiian Islands, Fosberg and Herbst (1975) list 1186 species, subspecies and varieties as Extinct, Endangered, Rare or Local, out of a flora of around 2200 species, and they emphasise that due to the lack of information on the status of many plants, these are minimum figures. And there is another difference as well: on temperate continental areas, only a small percentage of the species listed as rare and threatened are in the category Endangered, defined by IUCN as "in imminent danger of extinction", and used to include species whose populations are so drastically low that extinction may be more or less inevitable in the long term. Whereas for the whole of Europe only 108 species are at present listed as Endangered, many individual islands of the tropics and subtropics have lists of endangered endemics of comparable length. For example, there are believed to be over 80 such plants on the island of Socotra alone, out of an endemic element of about 214 species shared with the neighbouring island of Abd al Kuri. The status of the flora of the Mascarenes (Mauritius, Réunion and Rodriguez) may be even more drastic. Out of 50 families revised so far for the *Flore des Mascareignes*, at least 25 Angiosperm species endemic to Mauritius alone are Endangered or Extinct. A high degree of dioecism in the flora makes them doubly vulnerable. Many of the species are reduced to a handful of individuals, and their survival in the long term seems very doubtful. On the island of Rodriguez, out of 34 Angiosperm species recorded by Balfour (1879) as endemic to the island, all but two are Extinct or Endangered. This may be an extreme case, but it is dissimilar only in degree from the situation on most islands of the tropics.

Compilation of information

With situations like this coming to light, the first task of the IUCN Threatened Plants Committee became obvious. It is to gather and compile accurate information from the botanists and field workers, with the aim of finding out which species are rare and threatened, and where they still occur. This is easier said than done – the vegetation of many areas will be lost before even the basic alpha-taxonomy is carried out; large parts of South America are still unexplored botanically. One incredible fact highlighted from *Extinction Is Forever*, the basic source book for plant conservation in the Americas (Prance and Elias, 1977), is that after each fascicle of the *Flora of Panama* goes to press, about one new species in the group is found before the fascicle is formally in print (D'Arcy, 1977).

Islands, however, have one dubious advantage in such considerations. Island floras have always been of great interest to biologists, especially to those inclined to evolutionary speculation, and so in many cases the floras have been studied relatively thoroughly. With the exception, perhaps, of islands such as Madagascar, the numbers of species are relatively manageable and the small size of the island makes thorough botanical exploration a goal not too difficult to attain. The Threatened Plants

Committee Secretariat has been able to make good use not only of the basic research resulting in check-lists and floras, but also the field information of botanists working on the areas, assessing which species are particularly rare or under threat. The current work being undertaken by the "Viera y Clavijo" Botanic Garden, in Gran Canaria, is a good example of how this can be done; the taxonomy of the difficult groups is being studied, the basic lists are being prepared for the *Flora of Macaronesia*, and at the same time present field work is continuing to build up a very accurate knowledge on the distribution and abundance of each species, and a continual monitoring of the threats.

So how far have we got? In November 1977, the TPC had basic lists of endemic and threatened species for each of the following island groups:

Atlantic	Caribbean	Indian Ocean	Mediterranean	Pacific Ocean
Canary I.	Dominica	Mauritius	Balearic I.	Chatham I.
Falkland I.		Réunion	Corsica	Galapagos I.
St. Helena		Rodriguez	Crete	Guam
Tierra del Fuego		Seychelles	Malta	Hawaiian I.
Tristan da		Socotra	Sardinia	Juan Fernández I.
Cunha I.				Kermadec I.
				Lord Howe I.
				Ogasawara I.
				Philip I.

In each case the IUCN Red Data Categories, applied under tight guide-lines from the TPC, are used to show the degree of threat. Some of the lists are still very incomplete and in need of refining, but they do represent a beginning from which detailed conservation plans can be formulated and pursued with governments.

One result of this information is that detailed case-histories have been compiled on a selection of the species for the IUCN Plant Red Data Book. Out of the 250 sheets published in the 1978 edition, a relatively high proportion are on island plants, with the floras of most of the islands listed above being represented. Each sheet gives detailed information on the status, distribution and habitat of one species, with a section on its potential value and including a recommendation as to how best it can be conserved. The sheets are aimed not only at decision-makers in government both national and local, but at all those with an interest in plants, in particular science writers and horticulturists who should make use of the information and pass it on to the general public to make them more aware of the plight of plants and the underlying ecological and social implications.

Future Work and Conclusion

Once initial lists have been completed, the aim is to put together the basic information needed for each species listed as rare and threatened, though not revealing the exact localities. It is proposed that such data, compressed into concise paragraphs, one or two per species, will be issued as Red Data Bulletins. Each of these publications will cover the threatened and endemic flora of an island or island group; preceding the species paragraphs will be a general text on the flora, with the emphasis on the threats and conservation problems. The more detailed Red Data Sheets on the selected examples can be added as an Appendix. If necessary, information on localities and detailed recommendations for action can be put forward in confidence using the Bulletin as a baseline document, but such recommendations are likely to be more effective if first put forward by botanists on the islands or from the parent country, and then reinforced by support from IUCN and WWF. We appreciate that botanical research is an activity which can embrace all one's time and enthusiasm, and that good botanists are usually busy ones, but we do feel it is of the utmost importance that such men and women squeeze in time not only to provide the raw data from which detailed information can be put together enabling the conservation lobbies to get to work, but also to use their own, often influential positions to make governments aware of their concern and of the possibilities of massive species losses. Such efforts are far more likely to stimulate local action than those of the international bodies.

For information gathering is only a beginning – the vital next step must be undertaken. Above all practical suggestions must be put forward as to how reserves can be created, where they should be and how they should be managed. We must specify how conservation plans can play a part in local development plans. Conservation in a vacuum is not possible. We as scientists are able to see the facts as we study our regions or groups, and thus have a serious responsibility to communicate our anxiety over species loss and what this means for the future, not just to one another but to decision-makers, direct if possible but if not, through IUCN or TPC, with the aim of ensuring the survival of plant species diversity for the long-term future. We must be realistic and positive with our recommendations if we are to succeed in this most serious task.

REFERENCES

Balfour, I. B. (1879). Botany, in An Account of the Petrological, Botanical, and Zoological Collections made in Kerguelen's Land and Rodriguez . . . *Phil. Trans. Roy. Soc.* **168**, 302–387

D'Arcy, W. G. (1977). Endangered landscapes in Panama and Central America: The threat to plant species. In *Extinction Is Forever* (G. T. Prance and T. S. Elias, eds.), 89–104. New York Botanical Garden

Eckholm, E. P. (1976). *Losing Ground: Environmental Stress and World Food Prospects*. New York

Fosberg, F. R. and Herbst, D. (1975). Rare and endangered species of Hawaiian vascular plants. *Allertonia* **1** (1)

Heslop-Harrison, J. (1973). The plant kingdom: An exhaustible resource? *Trans. Bot. Soc. Edin.* **42**, 1–15

— (1974a). Postscript: The Threatened Plants Committee. In *Succulents in Peril* (D. R. Hunt, ed.), 30–32. (Suppl. to *Bull. Int. Org. Succ. Pl. Study* **3** (3))

— (1974b). Genetic resource conservation: the end and the means. *J. Roy. Soc. Arts, 1974*, 157–169

— (1975). Man and the endangered plant. *International Year Book 1975*, xii–xvi

Lucas, G. Ll. (1977). Conservation: Recent developments in international co-operation. In *Extinction Is Forever* (G. T. Prance and T. S. Elias, eds.), 356–359. New York Botanical Garden

— and Synge, A. H. M. (1977). The IUCN Threatened Plants Committee and its work throughout the world. *Envir. Conserv.* **4** (3), 179–187

IUCN Threatened Plants Committee (1977). *List of rare, threatened and endemic plants in Europe*. Nature and Environment Series No. 14. Council of Europe, Strasbourg. (Originally issued as Lucas, G. Ll. and Walters, S. M. (MS.), List of Rare, Threatened and Endemic Plants for the Countries of Europe. IUCN Threatened Plants Committee, Kew, U.K.)

Melliss, J. C. (1875). *St. Helena: a Physical, Historical and Topographical Description of the Island, including its Ecology, Fauna, Flora, and Meteorology*. London

Prance, G. T. and Elias, T. S. (eds.) (1977). *Extinction Is Forever*. vi, 437 p., illustr. New York Botanical Garden

Smithsonian Institution (1975). *Report on Endangered and Threatened Plant Species of the United States*. iv, 200 p. U.S. Government Printing Office, Washington, D.C.

23   The Future of Island Floras

V. H. HEYWOOD   *Department of Botany, University of Reading, England*

El hecho de que nuestro conocimiento de la flora insular de todo el mundo sea aún muy incompleto, ha sido destacado durante este Simposio y existe una clara necesidad de coordinar nuestros recursos limitados para mejorar esta situación.

El valor científico de la flora isleña es grandemente apreciado por los científicos, pero los no científicos, políticos y administradores tienen también que ser convencidos de la necesidad de la conservación.

El sistema más apropiado para la conservación es la creación de grandes reservas, pero los jardines botánicos tienen un importante papel que jugar, no solamente el de conservar especies raras, sino también educativo, investigación y supervisión de las actividades de conservación.

Debido al aumento de las presiones, nuestras remanentes áreas naturales continuarán siendo explotadas y destruidas; y el futuro de la flora de las islas dependerá grandemente de las decisiones Político-Sociológico-Económicos. El papel de los biólogos no está solamente en el campo o en los laboratorios, sino también organizar y comunicar sus conocimientos con el fin de influenciar estas decisiones.

Introduction

Island floras are regarded as fragile and vulnerable because of their special conditions as determined by the size, position, type, height, age, geology, soils and past biological history of the individual islands concerned, and because of their high percentage of endemics and the very fact that the populations are effectively isolated by the island condition from continental populations. The physical separation or isolation of the islands also leads in many cases to hydrological problems which can seriously affect the development and survival of species.

It is, of course, easier to talk about the future of island floras after the event – with the benefit of hindsight. In a sense one could predict the future of some island floras by extrapolating from our knowledge of past events and continuing processes. Much, too, depends on what we mean by the future although in this context I intend to consider the short and medium term which would therefore exclude, with rare exceptions, major climatic changes, earth movements and other natural phenomena.

Gradual and often progressive climatic changes (whatever their causes) will, of course, have their effect, causing the extinction of numerous species and favour the introduction and spread of others.

Then, as has been noted several times by authors in this book, there are various evolutionary mechanisms from which one can predict the future pattern of species in terms of population structure and composition, breeding system, changes in dispersal mechanism, radiation, ecotypic differentiation, etc.

Almost certainly the major factor affecting the future of island floras, within the parameters of ecological-climatic-biological change, is the action of Man. I think one has to be very clear about Man's role in the future of islands. It is not that this is a new rôle, rather that it has changed in quality and intensity.

We often tend to overlook the length of the period of intervention by Man in island (or other) vegetation. Unfortunately we do not have adequate historical evidence in most cases, but there is no reason to doubt that the progressively advancing phases of Man's evolution had corresponding effects on the vegetation of the areas he inhabited as natives or visited as colonisers or traders.

In the Canary Islands and in Macaronesia in general, deforestation has a long history. As the late Professor Ceballos wrote "The destruction of forests is fatally linked to the history of mankind". These islands were, almost certainly, densely covered with forest although perhaps not quite so extensive as the earlier chronicles suggested. Perhaps the first major attack on the forest vegetation was the result of the development by Man of cutting tools and axes leading him to hacking down trees as part of his learning process, gaining in the process a sense of power and enjoyment.

Again, referring to the Canary Islands, a special phenomenon which has a marked effect on the vegetation is the widespread terrace cultivation. Terracing is apparently a phenomenon of great antiquity and recent studies suggest that in some cases it dates back many centuries, serving not only as a means of soil build-up and protection but as a kind of territorial delimitation. Many of the terraces have now been abandoned, as has also happened in parts of the Mediterranean region, but little work seems to have been done on the consequential effects on the vegetation.

Fire is another major hazard which has contributed to the large scale devastation of the vegetation of several islands in Macaronesia such as Madeira as noted by Malato-Beliz (1976). Galloway (chapter 10) refers to the extensive burning of the pre-Polynesian forests of New Zealand which gave rise to the well-known plains of Otago. Ceballos (1953) believes that fire caused by Man was one of the factors which left its effect on the vegetation of the Macaronesian islands even before their occupation and conquest in the 15th century.

In Tenerife the first major deliberate deforestation occurred at the beginning of the 16th century with the introduction of the cultivation of sugar cane. Space was needed for growing the crop and wood was needed for fuel for distillation. The crop was first established in Madeira by 1419 and later in the Canary Islands, the Azores and the Cape Verde islands so presumably a similar pattern of deforestation took place in all these areas.

The effects of deforestation are well enough known. What is often difficult to appreciate or to communicate is the scale and the extent to which island floras have been ravaged by this process. When I described the Canary Islands as an ecological disaster area, I felt the description was an exact one considering the very reduced area of native forest still remaining on most islands and the widespread, often highly degraded secondary communities (as well as agriculture) that have replaced it.

The common pattern of events on older wooded islands in many parts of the world is (a) deforestation and fire giving rise to secondary vegetation, soil erosion, and increasing aridity; (b) introduction of goats, sheep, horses leading to excessive grazing (see the papers by Melville and van der Werff in this volume), even to the extent of animals eating strongly spiney plants, apparently oblivious of the damage caused to their mouths, and newspapers, as described by Malato-Beliz (1976); (c) cultivation of lower slopes; and (d) the introduction of weeds. Then there are the consequential climatic changes, reduction in rainfall, and the establishment and spread of new types of community – secondary forest, subseral communities, etc. and the opening up and invasion of marginal habitats by immigrant weeds. In addition there are several biological effects which then operate such as the breaking down of reproductive barriers, the spread of invasory/aggressive species and the adaptation of plant populations to the new conditions once established such as changes in the breeding system (e.g. escape from inbreeding by the evolution of dioecism, etc.), changes in or loss of dispersal mechanism (cf. Ehrendorfer, chapter 14).

The future of island floras is a complicated equation which has to take into account the aforementioned interrelated historical factors and biological processes. But in the last twenty to thirty years there has been a qualitative change in the effect of Man's role on native vegetation, to such an extent that, in many cases, the future of island floras depends on three or four principal factors: (a) the population pressure and changed living standards or expectations; (b) the plane loads of tourists; (c) political decisions, and perhaps (d) changes in agricultural practice which may be largely a consequence of the other factors.

The qualitative change is due, of course, to the development of Man the machine-operator. Man is no longer just a simple component of the ecosystem, as Malato-Beliz (1976) points out, no longer just an explorer, but is now a large-scale deliberate destroyer of ecosystems, largely due to ignorance of the effects and consequences (some of which may not become apparent for several years or in the area devastated as in the case of climatic changes evoked in neighbouring areas as a consequence of deforestation), ignorance of the degree of elasticity of ecosystems, and lack of perspective.

In addition to fires, felling, excessive grazing, intensive cultivation, soil erosion, use of chemical fertilisers and weedkillers, we have more recently witnessed the effects of the demographic explosion in many parts of the world leading to the consumption of large tracts of vegetation which are bulldozed away for new roads, urban settlements, airports, etc.

Largely due to our shortsightedness, few people thought to cry halt, let us consider what we were doing. We were too optimistic about the scale and extent of natural resources and their vulnerability in terms of regeneration or reversability, and perhaps even exaggerated what we thought had been achieved by biologists by way of ecological and taxonomic survey, assessment and description. Surely, it was believed, botanists and zoologists had done their basic work after two centuries of floristic and taxonomic research. Alas, it is only in recent years that we have come to realise just how incomplete is even the basic survey work on the flora of many parts of the world. There are vast areas, especially in the tropics, where no flora exists or is even realistically envisaged in the forseeable future. Ironically, it has largely been due to the tide of the resources and conservation movement that the inadequacy of our floristic/taxonomic knowledge has been revealed. Much conservation work is hampered (even assuming financial and manpower resources are available) by a lack of knowledge as to the floristic composition of areas at risk, which species are most endangered, etc. so that patterns of species diversity and distribution within communities are not known sufficiently well to allow even basic conservation strategies to be planned. The point cannot be emphasised too strongly that sound taxonomic/floristic knowledge is a necessary precondition for resource and conservation action. Failure to accept this fully is probably largely due to the fact that further effort in taxonomy and floristics is viewed as simply more of the same thing while conservation and resources studies have the benefit of being relatively new and exciting fields and consequently attractive to fund-givers, quite apart from the political, social and emotional overtones involved.

Future research

In considering areas for future research we should not fall into the trap of restricting our horizons to basic floristics and taxonomy, however necessary that is as discussed above. One area where there is a desperate need is that of floral and reproductive biology. It is, to quote an example already raised in this volume, faintly absurd to argue about the possibly relictual bird pollination of *Canarina, Isoplexis*, etc. in the Canary Islands when we do not possess adequate knowledge as to what happens to them today! Are they self-compatible? How far do they rely for survival and spread on vegetation reproduction or even longevity?

As Heslop-Harrison (1976) points out conservation requires positive management which will often demand special attention with regard to establishment and regeneration, not only of the dominant species but of the whole associated flora. It is, in fact, the whole reproductive physiology of plants that needs to be studied, embracing flowering, breeding systems, fruit and seed biology and dispersal. Most of our knowledge of these areas, with the exception of major crop species, has been obtained from plants of north temperate regions. We are, as Heslop-Harrison, says "lamentably ignorant of the reproductive systems of all but a tiny fraction of the Angiosperms, and for the tropics, where the problems are most urgent, the proportion is the least". Likewise most research on seed biology, viability, storage, germination and establishment has been concentrated on temperate species and the extent of our ignorance of even the most basic information about seed storage and viability in tropical plants is quite alarming. It is not, moreover, possible to extrapolate from our knowledge of temperate plants. Some aspects of this work must be carried out *in situ*, especially in cases where seed viability is limited through the absence of a dormancy mechanism, and cannot be entrusted to regional centres. Botanic gardens have a valuable rôle to play here as is discussed further below.

The need for this kind of information is, therefore, two-fold – firstly it is important to enlarge our understanding of reproductive physiology and biology which has been largely established on the basis of experiments and observations with temperate plants (wild or cultivated) and, secondly, it is essential for formulating conservation management policies and for the successful cultivation and propagation of material in botanic gardens and ultimately for economic or agricultural purposes.

Other areas where a case can be made for greatly expanded research are those of cytology and phytochemistry, the latter clearly being related to assessments of the potential economic value of island species which may be endangered today or in the short term. The work of Professor A. González and his school at the Instituto de Química in La Laguna is a model of what can be achieved.

Returning now to the essential survey work of taxonomic or floristic nature, there is clearly a need for a realistic appraisal of the threats to the flora and vegetation of the islands. In general it seems to be agreed that in world terms the greatest problems lie in the tropics, subtropics, island floras and those parts of the world with Mediterranean or similar climates. What conclusions can we draw from the various statistics and estimates that have been published and what do they mean in real terms when faced with the problem of planning remedial action?

It is, unfortunately, now widely recognised that the situation regarding the 150 000 or so species of flowering plants with a tropical distribution is such that our freedom of action is severely limited. Widespread devastation of habitats combined with an almost hopelessly inadequate knowledge of the taxonomy, distribution, ecology, and biology of the plants concerned, in effect means that there is not now available nor, for the majority, ever likely to become available an adequate basis for deciding which species are endangered and therefore deserving protective action whether *in situ* or by bringing them into cultivation with a view to preserving them. Raven (1976) suggests that at least a third of the tropical species will be threatened or extinct by the end of this century, with the first major wave of extinction in southeast Asia and New Guinea within the next ten years.

Considering specifically tropical island floras, we have to face the unpalatable fact that in some cases the situation is irretrievable as in Madagascar where 80% of the original vegetation has been destroyed (Rauh, chapter 21) by the action of Man – 47 million hectares out of a total of 58 million (Battistini and Richard-Vindard, 1972). Despite the establishment of a series of twelve (later reduced to eleven) nature reserves, covering some 545 000 hectares, agricultural practice and population pressures puts in serious doubt their long-term survival. It is worth quoting Bernardi's pungent comment on this situation (1974) "Il est juste et louable de se plaindre de la disparition des espèces rares, belles et faibles de la flore et faune malgaches. Cependant, même si 1000 ou 10 000 naturalistes réunis à Tananarive présentent des milliers de communications savantes et envoient des milliers de supplications à tous les présidents, rois, pape et marabouts de la planète, pas un arbre ou un lézard de la Grande Île ne sera épargné".

In Hawaii Wooliams (1976) calculates that almost 50% of the known flora is either under stress or facing extinction, the threats largely caused by depredation by feral goats, pigs and sheep and the rapid spread of introduced weeds. Valuable work is being done by Wooliams and others of the Waimea Arboretum, Hawaii in preserving through cultivation in botanical collections many of these endangered species and reintroducing them to the wild under scientific control.

O. and I. Degener (1975) give a striking set of estimates regarding the size of the Hawaiian flora. They suggest that it probably consisted of 50 000 well-recognisable species and varieties before the Polynesians arrived a few thousand years ago and that at the time of the rediscovery of the islands by Captain Cook in 1778 the flora was reduced to about 30 000 species and varieties. Today they consider only about 20 000 such taxa remain of which barely 3000 have been adequately described! There is clearly a major discrepancy between these figures and other current estimates of the Hawaiian flora but the Degeners make the valid point that for islands whose flora are incompletely known any list of endangered species could be unfortunate and "lull us into dangerous complacency".

Considering now the Macaronesian situation, it is sad to relate that much irreparable damage has already been caused. The felling and burning of the laurel forests, accelerated this century, the cultivation of vines and tomatoes, the terracing, the cultivation of the coastal areas for banana plantations and other crops, the effects of introduced crops and weeds on the native vegetation, lowering of the water table, increased aridity, urbanisation and roads, have all contributed to the heavily scarred and defaced landscape that we see today. While nothing can be done about reversing history, it is important when considering conservation and future action today to realise what a poor and depleted basis we are starting from. Very severe restrictions on further utilisation of the remaining natural or semi-natural vegetation is an urgent necessity as is the need for a soundly based masterplan, worked out by the local authorities in close collaboration with conservation organisations and knowledgeable scientists, for the rational exploitation of the natural resources of the islands. Fortunately the flora of the islands or island groups is reasonably well known and substantial studies have been made on the vegetation so that it should not prove too difficult, from a scientific point of view, to provide the basic information needed for such a plan.

Raven (1976) raises a pertinent point about the effectiveness of current legislation to protect the rich plant and animal life. He comments:

In such areas as islands and other regions with very high degrees of endemism, biologists would do well to consider whether the local laws provide adequate protection to their unique biota. The Canary Islands, for example, just such an area, are visited annually by hundreds of thousands of tourists, some of whom make extensive collections of plants or animals, including many which are endangered. The flora of the islands is already well represented in the herbaria at Kew, Paris and Florence, and one might well call into question the scientific value of additional, mostly random gatherings of these endemics. Would it not be preferable to allow collecting and the export of plants only under permit, still allowing scientific studies of all kinds when their need had been established? It certainly would seem far more important to attempt to provide future studies with living populations of these plants than with additional miscellaneous herbarium specimens.

A much more difficult subject is that of conservation management. Conservation strategies are difficult to establish and require detailed study. It has to be emphasised that they involve a different set of aims and procedures from simple forest management. The Macaronesian area is no different from other parts of the world where we may well know what we wish to preserve but do not yet have the necessary experience or expertise to know precisely how to achieve this. Questions such as the size of reserves, the effects of water-table changes due to drought, irrigation and other agricultural practices, grazing pressures, fencing and monitoring all require much further research. So too do such questions as establishing agroecosystems which best fit in with the overall land use plan. Finally the education of the public into the acceptance of ecological principles needs to be worked on unceasingly. Here the role of conservation bodies and of botanic gardens is fundamental.

A more open approach to conservation and resources management is needed. In some cases we can adopt strategies to encourage regeneration of secondary vegetation to produce a modified version of the original forest; in some cases we should aim for protection through the establishment of reserves; in some cases we should "sacrifice" certain areas of deforested secondary vegetation for the establishment of suitable artificial plantations or forms of agricultural development; finally in some cases we may simply have to accept that it is too late to do much other than assign the areas for urbanisation, roads, etc.

The word conservation has an unfortunate connotation. What we are concerned with is seeking the most satisfactory compromise between the, often conflicting, needs of Man – feeding expanding populations, use of agricultural land for trade to generate the wealth, without which conservation would be irrelevant if other basic needs were not met first, and from which the funds for conservation ultimately derive; provision of facilities for tourism, recreation, and amenities which improve the quality of life, etc.

Because of these numerous conflicting needs it is not the scientist's rôle to take decisions on priorities – his rôle is to inform with a view to influencing what are basically political, social and economic decisions.

Of course we are caught in a vicious circle – we do not in many cases have the necessary information to talk with authority. Emotional arguments are not sufficient to persuade administrators unless we can come up with hard facts. Even lists of endangered or threatened species are only a very preliminary step in the process of obtaining the necessary information about conservation procedures. Indeed there is the very serious risk that administrators may think that the work is accomplished when presented with such lists, instead of only just beginning. Unfortunately, as Heslop-Harrison (1975) wryly commented, conservation of non-agricultural species is largely funded like a charity.

We need financial resources to enable us to find the answers to justify conservation of particular species or ecosystems containing them. In the Canary Islands we are fortunate that the work of Professor González and his school has indicated the potential value in chemotherapy, pharmacognosy etc. of numerous native species although it has to be remembered that only a tiny percentage of these will ever pass through the various clinical trials necessary before they become acceptable, marketable drugs.

Conclusions

One of the themes that comes through repeatedly in this volume is the not surprising one that our floristic and faunistic knowledge is still very incomplete in some islands. This was noted for the Galapagos, the Indian Islands, Hawaii, parts of New Zealand and is true of many other islands in different parts of the world. But as Mabberley commented, who has the time? On the other hand much floristic effort is duplicated or wasted and there is clearly a need for better organisation and coordination of studies so that the limited manpower available is deployed more effectively.

We also have to be able to come up with the answers to some very awkward questions. Why are we concerned with the future of island floras? This is relatively easy to answer – because, as we have seen, they contain many interesting endemic plants. But who is interested? Which species are threatened? Does it matter and if so to whom? Why are we so concerned when apparently we do not appear capable of even identifying all of them? Are they of economic importance? It is easy to make a case for the preservation of dramatic species such as the Dragon tree (*Dracaena draco*) and other celebrated species, pachycauls or not. But many of them are in cultivation and how many people want to see them in the wild, indeed how many people other than botanists will ever have the opportunity to see some of them? Again, how do we justify attempts to preserve individual species when there are several related and quite similar ones available unthreatened? While it would be easy to convince

P*

our audience of botanists, they do not make the decisions. It is the general public, the voter, the taxpayer, the politician, the administrator who has to be persuaded, cajoled, convinced.

Preservation of large areas is generally a more profitable approach, because this is more natural and more embracing than attempting to conserve individual species. Moreover, reserves are more easily seen and appreciated because of their landscape effect and the pleasure they give. But as we have seen there are various technical difficulties to be overcome such as determining the appropriate size of reserves, management problems and finding out about the reproductive physiology and biology of the component species. Then there is the whole question, especially in developing countries, of finding acceptable ways of compensating them in return for their agreeing to maintain environmental quality.

The role of botanic gardens in the preservation and maintenance of individual species is bound to be a limited one although in many cases it will prove to be the only solution. Almost more important is the potential rôle of botanic gardens as centres of research, education and influence, and their supervision of conservation activities, including the establishment of satellite gardens and small reserves. The creation of international research and conservation centres in appropriate places such as the Jardín Botánico "Viera y Clavijo" in Gran Canaria, where many of the conservation and associated activities might be coordinated, should be explored.

The future, as I see it, will be one of mixed success. There will be substantial or even major losses, even of "primitive" or relictual species. There will be the creation of protected areas which will demand a high price or concessions such as the willingness to give up other areas for development.

Extensive travel, tourism, change of agricultural practices and crops to respond to economic and social needs will lead to an even greater introduction of exotic weeds with their consequential effect on marginal communities. There will inevitably be a greater tendency to uniformity and development of secondary, heavily modified vegetation.

Reforestation will provide a cosmetic covering of some of the devastated areas and help in soil stabilisation and climatic improvement rather than contributing to conservation as such. Grazing will come increasingly under control or even eliminated in many areas, with remarkable effects.

To summarise, the future of island floras will depend largely on political-sociological-economic planning decisions and the role of biologists is not just to work in the field and laboratory but to organise and communicate their knowledge so as to influence these decisions.

REFERENCES

Battistini, R. and Richard-Vindard, G. (1972). In *Biogeography and Ecology in Madagascar. Monographie Biologicae,* **21**, Junk, The Hague

Bernardi, L. (1974). Problèmes de conservation de la nature dans les îles de l'Océan Indien 1. Méditation à propos de Madagascar. *Saussurea* **5**, 37–47

Ceballos, L. (1953). Macaronesia Algunas consideraciones sobre la flora y vegetación forestal. *An. Inst. Sup. Agron. Lisboa* **20**, 79–108

Degener, O. and I. (1975). Silverswoods and the blue data book. *Notes Waimea Arbor.* **2**, 3–6

Heslop-Harrison, J. (1975). Man and the endangered plant. *International Year Book 1975*, xii–xvi

— (1976). Reproductive physiology. In *Conservation of Threatened Plants* J. B. Simmons *et al.*, eds.), 199. Plenum Press, New York and London

Malato-Beliz, J. (1975). Conservación de la naturaleza y recursos genéticos. *Bot. Macar.* **1**, 67–82

Raven, P. H. (1976). Ethics and attitudes. In *Conservation of Threatened Plants* (J. B. Simmons *et al.*, eds.), 155–179. Plenum Press, New York and London

Wooliams, K. (1976). The propagation of Hawaiian endangered species. In *Conservation of Threatened Plants* (J. B. Simmons *et al.*, eds.), 73–83. Plenum Press, New York and London

SUBJECT INDEX

INDEX OF ORGANISMS